studies in
AUSTRALIAN GEOGRAPHY

studies in
AUSTRALIAN GEOGRAPHY

edited by

G. H. DURY MA, PHD, FGS
McCaughey Professor of Geography The University of Sydney

M. I. LOGAN BA, PHD, DIP ED
Associate Professor of Geography The University of Wisconsin

HEINEMANN
EDUCATIONAL
BOOKS
H·E·B LONDON

HEINEMANN EDUCATIONAL BOOKS LTD
London   Melbourne   Toronto   Auckland
Singapore   Johannesburg   Hong Kong
Nairobi   Ibadan

SBN 435 34265 7

First Published 1968

Published by Heinemann Educational Books Ltd
48 Charles Street, London W.1
Printed in Australia by Halstead Press Sydney

Contents

Introduction

These studies are representative rather than comprehensive. In ranging through a number of topics they illustrate something of the substance of Australian geography: in applying geographical technique they exemplify the practice of geography in Australia.

We are aware that the coverage attained is less than full. Had it been possible, we should have included additional papers; but we have been constrained to some extent by the irregular development, to date, of geographical research on Australian subjects, and to a greater and far more serious extent by the prior commitment of certain authors whom we attempted to recruit. Nevertheless, although we are bound to regret a number of obvious omissions, we are not dissatisfied with the range actually achieved—the range, for instance, between terrain at one extreme and metropolitan industrial structure at the other, topics which we have ourselves chosen. We trust that this collection will serve, however modestly, to enhance the multiplier effect which is clearly apparent in the current vigorous development and expansion of geographical work in Australia today.

Our fellow-authors agreed to write, under titles of their own choosing, on themes suggested by us which corresponded to known special interests and expertise. Whatever the particular array of topics or of authors, it was inevitable that certain matters would persistently recur in any series of thematic treatments—the qualities of Australian terrain; the specialized character of Australian plant-assemblages; the frequently tight man-land-climate relationships in areas of farming settlement and of irrigation; the marked concentration of people in large towns on the continental periphery; migration of people, and immigration in particular; and intervention by government agencies, at all levels from Federal through State down to local. In all these respects Australian geography is in some way or other distinctive, as the following studies make plain.

We are grateful to our collaborators for joining with us, and are happy to be associated with them. We also owe them thanks for maintaining communication, during movements between country and country which, while this book has been in preparation, have involved most of them and both of us. They have been patient, forbearing, and co-operative towards us as editors.

Thanks are also due to our publishers, and in particular to Mr N. Barltrop, for help in sustaining contact between mobile editors on the one hand and mobile authors on the other, for relieving us of certain editorial tasks, and for considerable assistance in preparing the index.

G. H. Dury
M. I. Logan
Department of Geography, The University of Sydney
7 July 1967

An Introduction
to the Geomorphology of Australia

G. H. DURY

To consider the physique of Australia on the continental scale, and the extent to which it is known in detail, invites a comparison with Canada. The tripartite division of Australia into shield, interior sedimentary basins, and highland margin on the Pacific side is mirrored in Canada, even though contrasts between the two countries already appear on this coarse scale. Large areas of both have yet to be explored geologically beyond the reconnaissance stage; and far less is known of their geomorphology than of their geology.

This circumstance is not surprising. Canada, with a total population of some 18 million, records for its area of nearly 4 million square miles a mean density of 5 p.s.m. In actuality, its people are concentrated mainly on the national margins. Australia's 12 million people and 3 million square miles give a mean density of 4 p.s.m. But here again most live on the margins, occupying discrete patches of coastland. Exploration of the eastern half of the Australian continent, except for the immediate seaboards, dates from the historically very late period 1813 to 1872. That of the western half, the seaboards again excepted, dates mainly from 1870 onwards and cannot yet be called complete: some areas have still to be visited on the ground.

An alternative comparison is one between Australia and the conterminous U.S.A. However, this second comparison cannot be made to depend on the fact of near-identical extent, for the U.S. mainland is far more easily penetrable and habitable than is that of Australia. A population-total of 12 million had already been surpassed by the U.S. in 1830. The comparative reference is to the development of geomorphic thinking. Like the U.S.A., Australia has been fortunate in the attention paid by its great pioneering geologists to the form of the ground, particularly in arid parts, where some of the most outstanding pioneer efforts in each country were made. Furthermore, physiography as developed in the U.S.A. has greatly influenced physiographic thinking in Australia, even if not always for the best.

Nothing here said or implied about gaps in the knowledge of Australian geomorphology is meant to derogate the work which has actually been performed. Accounts of the physiography of individual States range from that of Murray in 1895 to that of Hills in 1940 [1, 2, 3, 4, 5, 6b, 7, 8a, 9]. Taylor summarized the physiography of eastern Australia in 1911 [10a] and of the continent in 1914 [10b]. David and Browne [11b] deal specifically with physiography at some length, partly on a regional basis, while Gentilli and Fairbridge [12] have produced a physiographic map of the continent, with accompanying regional notes. These several comprehensive accounts, moreover, are based not solely on work by the authors themselves, but also on that of their predecessors in the field. Reference lists prove remarkably voluminous. To take but one instance, Jutson [6c] cites no fewer than fifty-eight sources on the physiography of the Great Plateau of Western Australia.

Geomorphologists proper are, however, still few in this country, and fewer yet have been at work for more than a short term of years. In consequence, despite the great usefulness of physiographic accounts produced by geologists, the vigorous state of pedology in Australia, the lively activity of the land-research teams of C.S.I.R.O. and some conservation authorities, and the contributions to geomorphology made by hydrologists, cartographic agencies, and air photographers, it is not possible to advance far in certain directions beyond physiographic description. Future prospects, by contrast, are excellent. Australia seems by far the most likely of the southern continents to multiply its geomorphic workforce. It offers at least as much scope as do the other two for work on continental drift and the effects and implications of drift. It is also especially well suited to the study of arid landscapes, arid-humid transitions, climatic change, and the deep weathering which is more widely recorded here than anywhere else in the world. Nor do all prospects relate to the distant or the middle future. The first collection of essays on Australian geomorphology has recently come from the press [13].

In the meantime, and for immediate purposes, it is proposed to examine some of the results hitherto achieved by areal classification, then to summarize the gross distribution of relief and landform. There will not be space for anything but the briefest of references to tectonic development, even though these references will be confined to structures expressed in the existing surface. However, the highly planated condition of the Shield, the huge extent of sandridge country, the large-scale plan of the eastern Basins, and the tabular character of much of the Highland division, combine to ensure that treatment in some respects can be broad indeed. Against this the far-reaching implications, as opposed to physical characteristics, of certain types of landscape will require extended discussion.

Areal Classification

Since treatment of discrete areas of the Australian surface requires areal names, and since these names depend in part upon regional classification, it is appropriate to begin with a selective review of principles of classification already in use, and with a sample of the results obtained by their application. More than one scale of working, more than one principle of classification, and more than one range of criteria is evident in the literature. Much of what purports to be regional is in actuality largely systematic, with regional heads used to introduce specific topics. The relevant mode of treatment, perpetuated by Jutson [6a, 6b] and by David and Browne [11a] among others, may well owe something to Gregory [14].

Table 1 summarizes chosen aspects of the results obtained in areal classification by selected authors. There is a great range of size

Table 1 *Selected Data on the Practice of Subdivision*

Author	Coverage	Unit identified (Number of units in brackets)	Area (sq. mls.)			Ratio, max/min. area
			Maximum	Mean	Minimum	
Jutson [6a]	Western Australia	Physiographic division (9)	—	100,000	—	—
Gentilli and Fairbridge [12a, 12b]	Australia	Geomorphological Region (41)	450,000	72,000	2,500	180
	Australia	Subdivision of geomorphological region (110)	—	27,000	—	—
Fenner [8a]	South Australia	Physiographic subdivision (12)	—	32,000	—	—
Hills [9]	Victoria	Major part (6) Subdivision (19)	— —	14,500 4,500	— —	— —
Christian and Stewart [15]	Katherine-Darwin region	Land system (19)	6,890	1,400	42	164
Gibbons and Downes [16]	Southwest Victoria	Land system (21) Land unit (107)	600(a) 285	220(a) 42.5	9 1.1	67(a) 260

(a) See text also.

among the units severally distinguished, and not all of this range is due to varying complexity of terrain. The divisions of Jutson and the regions of Gentilli and Fairbridge are, on the average, of the same order of size as the whole State of Victoria (area, nearly 88,000 square miles). The subdivisions of Gentilli and Fairbridge and of Fenner probably belong with Hills's major parts, but thereafter comes a marked shift of scale into the remainder of the series listed. Some account ought probably to be taken of the extension of particular units beyond the limits of coverage, where this coverage is neither Australia-wide nor is limited, as with Christian and Stewart, to a clearly-defined and fairly sizeable part of the Australian landmass. On the other hand, the ratio of extent between largest and smallest units, as distinguished by the various authors, is perhaps sufficiently consistent to suggest general comparability of treatment, allowance being made for scale of working. The one exception concerns the land systems of Gibbons and Downes, whose survey, incidentally, is equivalent as an average to one acre p.s.m. of the whole of Australia. Elementary frequency-analysis of their data [17] shows that a more reasonable estimate of their maximum area for a land system is about 2350 square miles, the corresponding mean 1200 square miles, and the ratio of maximum to minimum area about 255. Thus corrected, the mean area for a land system with these two writers becomes very similar to the corresponding mean with Christian and Stewart. A complete assessment of Australia on the land-system plan would apparently require the identification of between 2000 and 2500 of such units.

Jutson's regional partition is specifically physiographic; it makes allowance for the form of the ground and for the character of the surface. Although the cartographic portion of the Gentilli and Fairbridge presentation emphasizes landform, the accompanying notes reveal that geologic distributions are relied on in the making of primary divisions. Where hypsographic considerations are introduced, these are related closely to structure and to lithology in the first instance, although climate is appealed to in relation to extent and severity of dissection when the regions are subdivided. Little attention is paid, in this scheme, to the effects of superficial deposition. Fenner and Hills, among others, also appear to be guided chiefly by geology and geological structure.

Christian and Stewart originated that practice of classification into land systems, which reappears in later publications of the C.S.I.R.O. and of certain other bodies. They define a land system as an area, or group of areas, through which there is a recurring pattern of topography, soils, and vegetation; boundaries, according to them, are set where this pattern changes. The characteristics of land systems are listed under the headings location, extent, topography, geology and geomorphology, soils, vegetation, natural water supply, accessibility, present land use, agricultural prospects, and pastoral prospects. The first eight sets of criteria have largely or entirely to do with physiography in the broader sense of the term, and the text [their p. 77] reveals that the primary breakdown is into geomorphic units. The scheme is perhaps open to challenge in that pattern, and change of pattern appears to be assessed in a subjective manner. The form of graphical and tabular presentation adopted by Christian and Stewart [their Figs. 5 to 22 inclusive] is, of course, that of the transect diagram.

Gibbons and Downes give transect diagrams and accompanying tabular summaries which are considerably more detailed and elaborate than those of Christian and Stewart, but which are demonstrably of the same family. However, the classificatory system of these two authors is elaborated by the firm use of hierarchical terms. They take the land-component as the smallest fundamental unit; their land-unit is normally distinguished by uniformity of one or more of climate, parent material of soil, and topography; their land-system is an area composed of land-units which have in common landforms, structural forms of vegetation, or some other significant characteristics; and their land-zones are primary subdivisions of very large areas of country, which contain land-systems of similar kind and are separated from adjacent land-zones by significant differences in one or more of climate, parent material of soils, and vegetation. The land-unit diagram of these authors is a transect diagram (with tabular summary) for a given land-unit. If there is a fundamental difference of approach, between

Christian and Stewart on the one hand, and Gibbons and Downes on the other, it resides in the emphasis placed by this second pair upon plant growth.

Whereas Gibbons and Downes, still more deliberately than do Christian and Stewart, arrange their classification in an ascending scale of ranking, the rest of the authors mentioned are engaged in the breakdown of large areas into smaller. Both sets of writers encounter the usual problems of areal division and subdivision, to which the following account in its turn offers no complete solution. It is hoped, however, that the emphasis here placed on single and overriding characteristics will justify the unity of landscape implied for particular areas, at least upon the selected scale of working. The practice adopted is the practice of breakdown, for one of the intentions is to provide a general introduction to the physique of the Australian continent; but this intention need not be construed to involve complete coverage, and such coverage will not be attempted.

Wherever possible, areal names used here are names already current. The subdivisional scheme employed is illustrated in Fig. 1 and listed in Table 2. Where the information offered upon topography, structure, or tectonic development is already generally known, references to source papers are omitted. Similarly, references to sources which are themselves synthetic, and which have been drawn on in making brief synthetic statements in the following text [e.g. *11, 2b, 18, 19, 20, 21*] are also omitted, unless what is said here amplifies, extends, or differs from the views of others.

West Australian Shield

This is by far the largest of the three major divisions of the continent. Its area of 1,765,000 square miles is nearly 60 per cent of the whole. The East Australian Basins, with something in excess of 727,500 square miles (25 per cent), are less than half as extensive, while the East Australian Highlands, with somewhat less than 482,500 square miles (about 15 per cent) are one-quarter as extensive.

Use of the term *shield* might seem to imply that the rocks of this division, superficial deposits of sand and of lake beds excepted, are almost entirely of pre-Cambrian age. This is

Table 2 *Scheme of Areal Subdivision Used in This Text*

1. West Australian Shield
  1a. *Blocks and shelves of the west and south*
    1a1. Yilgarn block
    1a2. Dissected S.W. margins
    1a3. Hamersley-Pilbara blocks
    1a4. Western littoral
    1a5. Nullarbor Plain
    1a6. Gawler block
  1b. *Ranges of the Centre*
    1b1. Musgrave, etc., Ranges
    1b2. Macdonnell, etc., Ranges
  1c. *Inland plateaus of the north*
    1c1. Antrim Tableland
    1c2. Barkly Tableland
    1c3. Arunta block (exposed part)
  1d. *Marginal blocks of the north and east*
    1d1. Kimberley block
    1d2. Arnhem block
    1d3. West Carpentaria lowlands
    1d4. Mt. Isa-Cloncurry district
    1d5. Flinders Range
    1d6. Barrier Range
    1d7. Mt. Lofty Range
  1e. *Sandridge country on the Shield*
    1e1. Gibson Desert
    1e2. Great Sandy Desert
    1e3. Tanami Desert
    1e4. Arunta Desert
    1e5. Victoria Desert

2. East Australian Basins
  2a. *Carpentaria Basin*
  2b. *Great Artesian Basin*
    2b1. Simpson Desert
    2b2. ⎫
    2b3. ⎬ Gibber Country
    2b4. Riverine country, Darling basin
  2c. *Murray Basin*
    2c1. Riverine country, Murray basin
    2c2. Mallee

3. East Australian Highlands
  3a. *North Queensland Highlands* (*include Atherton Tableland*)
  3b. *Central Queensland Coast Ranges*
  3c. *Central Queensland Highlands*
  3d. *Southeastern Highlands*
    3d1. Toowoomba basalt plateau
    3d2. Northern Tableland of N.S.W.
    3d3. Liverpool Range, etc.
    3d4. Central Tableland of N.S.W. (includes Blue Mountains)
    3d5. Snowy Mountains, etc.
    3d6. West Victoria lava plains
    3d7. Tasmania
  3e. *Southeastern Sunklands*
    3e1. Clarence basin
    3e2. Cumberland basin
  3f. *Western Slopes* (*of N.S.W.*)
  3g. *Cobar block*

not so. It is true that the combined extent of the main pre-Cambrian outcrops is about one million square miles, nearly three-fifths of the area of the Shield and one third of the area of the continent, and it is true that additional

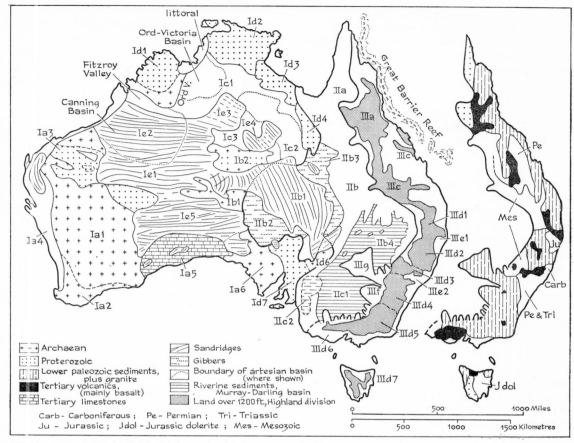

Fig. 1—Morphological subdivisions: for key to numbering see Table 2

exposures of pre-Cambrian occur in that 10 per cent of the Shield where lower Paleozoic and older outcrops are intermingled. But another 10 per cent of the Shield's surface truncates rocks entirely of lower Paleozoic age, while more than 20 per cent is underlain by sediments ranging from Carboniferous to Tertiary.

At least two orogenies took place during pre-Cambrian times in the area represented by the Shield, where, among the older of the rocks now exposed, granites, orthogneisses, paragneisses and metasediments are prominent. Planation also occurred, resulting in violent unconformity at the base of later, but still pre-Cambrian, deposits. These later materials are mainly sedimentary. They are powerfully lithified, but not greatly affected by metamorphism

except where they have been invaded by igneous bodies, or have been incorporated in belts of folding. They include the tillites which record a pre-Cambrian glaciation. The earlier and the later pre-Cambrian successions have long been distinguished from one another in geological writing, under the respective names *Archaean* and *Proterozoic*. Although the classification is now regarded as less than satisfactory, this is not the place to examine stratigraphic nomenclature; the two terms will, accordingly, be retained.

Proterozoic sedimentation was at first controlled by the Adelaidean Geosyncline and then by a shelf sea. The geosyncline ran northwards through the sites of the Mount Lofty Range, the Flinders Range, and Lake Eyre, swung westwards in the Centre, then crossing the line of the present northwest coast at the site of the Canning basin. The succeeding shelf sea covered a great northwestern segment of Australia, amounting to more than a third of the present land area. Tectonism in parts at least of the geosynclinal belt continued with little interruption from Proterozoic into Paleozoic times, but differed in intensity from area to area. Thus, whereas severe crumpling occurred in the Flinders and Barrier Ranges early in the Paleozoic, the Macdonnells underwent open folding.

Deposition in subsiding troughs which were less extensive than the geosyncline, and sedimentation on vast shelves, were repeated in some parts of the Shield up to Tertiary times inclusive. Remarkably extensive planation in the Tertiary, combined with lacustrine sedimentation and the formation of dunes in Tertiary or later times, have inclined to subdue the general relief and to minimize the physiographic significance of rock-type and of tectonic history; but that significance is not altogether lacking.

The main single outcrop of Archaean rocks occurs in the southwest of Australia, where it forms the Yilgarn block (Fig. 1). Strong folding has affected parts of the southern and southwestern margins, where the Darling Hills and the Stirling and Mount Barren Ranges have undergone marked dissection. Towards the northeast the Archaean rocks descend gently beneath the Proterozoic, except where they are uplifted in horsts, and faulting prolonged into the Tertiary is demonstrated by the inclusion of Tertiary sediments in the rifts of the Pilbara subdivision.

West of the sandridge country, which is treated separately below, the exposed area of shield is about 400,000 square miles. All is essentially plateau. Much is over 1200 ft. a.s.l., but little above 3000. The greatest heights, exceeding 4000 ft., are reached in the Pilbara subdivision in the Hamersley Ranges, where residuals carved from Proterozoic rocks stand above the widespread remnants of the deeply weathered Tertiary plane. Deep weathering is associated, as is normal throughout Australia, with duricrusting (see below). The duricrusted surface is the Old Plateau of Jutson [6d], while the New Plateau, in some areas no more than 25 to 75 feet lower, has been identified by Mabbutt [22] as an etchplain.

The Yilgarn block is noteworthy for its many playas. Some arrays of these seem to accord with Gregory's early view [23] that they are relics of former river systems disrupted or destroyed by oncoming aridity. The limited state of knowledge about possible modes of origin and development of playas, and in particular about their possible lateral migration, combine however with the markedly subdued relief of this subdivision to demand that interpretation of the playa systems be left for the time being in abeyance.

On the western and northwestern margins of the Shield occurs a narrow littoral belt. Patches of fixed dunes occur in this belt in the extreme northwest, but elsewhere come gently sloping outcrops of solid rocks of varying age, plus veneers of alluvium. The boundary between plateau and littoral on the western side corresponds chiefly to the Darling fault. Generally speaking, the western littoral coincides with artesian basins, but these are neither as yet fully assessed in detail nor intensively exploited.

The Nullarbor Plain, bordering the Great Australian Bight and extending over 75,000 square miles, also coincides with an artesian basin known as the Eucla Basin. Flat-lying and almost undisturbed Tertiary limestones here come to the surface. Elevations range from about 150 ft. a.s.l. at the top of the line of coastal cliffs, to about 650 ft. on the inland side. Large cave systems underground are believed to relate to pluvial episodes of the Pleistocene, although sea-level changes may have been influential in guiding cave development [24, 25, 26]. Outlying patches of sandridge occur on the Plain (Fig. 1) and playa systems are also present, forming in some parts reticulate patterns which appear to be controlled partly by the structures of the underlying limestone and partly by incipient dunes.

The Nullarbor country represents the effects of cratonic sedimentation, such as occurred still more widely in earlier than Tertiary times. Sedimentary rocks ranging back in age through the Cretaceous either to the Permian or to the Carboniferous are recorded beyond its northwestern limit, i.e. in the Great Victoria Desert. But the pre-Cambrian basement rises on the far side of this desert in the horsts of the Musgrave and neighbouring ranges, where Mt. Woodroffe approaches 5000 ft. a.s.l. Next north again, the Amadeus depression, containing the large ephemeral Lake Amadeus, is floored by Ordovician sediments. In the Macdonnells and neighbouring ranges, Lower Paleozoic rocks deposited in the central trough are folded on west-east lines. Archaean materials, also affected in this subdivision by folding, appear chiefly on the northern side. The whole sequence has been dissected into longitudinal ridges. Mabbutt [27] shows that the greatest elevations in the Macdonnells belong to one or more planated surfaces higher than, and pre-dating, the now-dissected surface upon which deep weathering and duricrusting operated. This writer demonstrates repeated alternation of planation and deposition with downcutting, and concludes that the alternation was climatically controlled. In some parts of the sequence he refers to conditions wetter than those of the present day, and considers that shifts between wetter and drier have been superimposed on a general trend of desiccation. The rivers of the Macdonnells are notably discordant with structure—a circumstance which Mabbutt takes as resulting from the direct inheritance of drainage-pattern from an erosional surface.

At the northwestern end of the ancient geosynclinal trough, sagging and sedimentation continued longer than in central Australia. A persistent sedimentary embayment, projecting inland across the line of the present coast, is represented by the mainly Devonian and Permian rocks of the Canning basin. Geological structure in this basin, largely overspread today by sandridges, is important chiefly as favouring the accumulation of artesian water.

Portions of the Shield reappear at the surface, beyond the central belt of tectonic depression, in the Kimberley block, the Arnhem block, and the extension of the latter into the low ground bordering part of the Gulf of Carpentaria. In the Kimberleys, Proterozoic rocks are rimmed by Archaean which, highly deformed and compressed, make up the King Leopold and Durack Ranges where some peaks exceed 3000 ft. On the outer side of these ranges come the deeply trenched Ord and Fitzroy valleys. Karst landforms are distinctively developed along the Fitzroy [28]. The Arnhem block is less elevated than the Kimberley country, standing mainly below 1000 ft.

a.s.l. Rectilinear valleys in parts of this block are guided by intersecting systems of very powerful and remarkably straight and long joints.

Next south from the Kimberleys and Arnhem blocks, the shield basement is variously overlain by sediments of Cambrian or later age, relics of sedimentation in shelf seas. The main exception concerns the extensive basalts (including pre-Cambrian basalts) of the Antrim district. These too, however, produce plateau country, combining large patches of duricrusted tableland with insets of lower ground. In considerable part, the Antrim district is co-extensive with the Ord-Victoria artesian basin.

Along the ill-defined eastern border of the Antrim district, where surface outcrops are of Cretaceous age, occurs a physiographic transition to the Barkly Tableland and its extensions. Here, the remains of Cambrian rocks—limestones, for the most part—overlie the basement. The tableland proper belongs to the old plateau and has undergone duricrusting and is bounded by erosional scarps. Its limits closely resemble those of the Barkly artesian basin. Southwestwards it merges into hill country developed on basement rocks, between the Arunta and Tanami Deserts.

Along the eastern edge of the Shield occur relics of ancient fold belts. In the Cloncurry-Mt. Isa district, tight folds with a general northerly trend have been eroded into parallel ridges. A crustal sag now separates this district from the Barrier Ranges, where exposures are chiefly of Archaean rocks, but where deformation has already been observed as continuing into the Paleozoic. The reconstructed arc of folding through Cloncurry-Mt. Isa and the Barrier Ranges comes together in the Mount Lofty Range with a more westerly arc represented by the Flinders Ranges. On the west side of the Flinders, the rigid foreland of this second arc is exposed in the Gawler block.

This southerly union of fold belts today constitutes a zone of rifting. The elevations of nearly 2500 ft. in the Mount Lofty Range and of nearly 4000 ft. in the Flinders result from differential uplift. In complementary fashion, Lake Torrens is contained in a graben, and Spencer and St. Vincent Gulfs also occupy down-rifted sites. This whole area may have experienced a very prolonged history of crustal

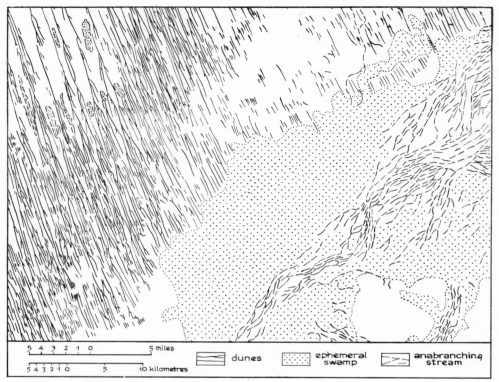

Fig. 2—Sandridge country and ephemeral drainage, Simpson Desert

disturbance, for it was possibly incorporated, at least in part, in the Tasman Geosyncline of eastern Australia (see below). Faulting is known to have occurred extensively during the Tertiary, and movement has probably not yet ceased.

Sandridge Country

Although sandridges are by no means confined to the Shield, this major division contains about three-quarters of the continent's total of sandridge country, and about one-third of its own extent is classified under this head. Although more is known of the Simpson Desert than of others, and although the Simpson Desert lies almost wholly off the Shield, it is nevertheless appropriate to discuss sandridge country in the context of the west.

Sandridge deserts, according to Madigan [*29, 30*], occupy 485,000 square miles of the Australian mainland; that is, about 16 per cent of the total area. David and Browne [*11c*] quote 523,000 square miles, or about 17 per

cent. Discussion of this matter is likely to be handicapped if the term *sandridge desert* is retained in full. It is probably better to write of *sandridge country*, in order to avoid for the time being the unwanted connotations of the term *desert*. Information about the distribution and extent of sandridge country, as collated in Fig. 1, suggests an area of at least 700,000 and possibly of 730,000 square miles which is nearly a quarter of the area of the whole continent. Parts of the blocks of sandridge are of course named as deserts, for example the Gibson, Great Sandy, Tanami, Arunta, and Victoria Deserts which are located on the Shield, and the Simpson Desert which is very largely confined to the Basin division. The arrays of sandridge within the Shield division amount to at least 500,000 square miles, while some 155,000 square miles of the Simpson Desert lie beyond the Shield's eastern edge. The balance of the total extent of sandridge is accounted for chiefly by outlying patches, including the Mallee.

All the named deserts are typified by dunes, and the characteristic dune form is the seif. Dunefields can be interrupted by ephemeral lakes, periodically flooded swamps, and rises of higher ground (cf. Fig. 2), while in some parts, particularly in the Victoria Desert, the dune pattern is confused. In general, however, the dunes tend markedly to run parallel to one another for great distances. Lengths as great as 200 miles have been reported for individual dunes, but a maximum of about 50 miles is probably a more truly representative figure.

Spacing of ridges varies with height. Madigan notes a range of spacing in the Simpson Desert from less than 100 yards to several miles, quoting five ridges per mile (equivalent to an average spacing of 1050 ft.) for the main part of this desert, and four ridges per mile (average spacing 1325 ft.) as ridge height increases. Fig. 2 suggests that one cause of increased spacing is the progressive convergence of ridges in a single direction. The same factor appears capable of explaining the association of increased bulk, and in consequence increased width and height, with increased spacing. Height of ridges in the Simpson Desert is reported to vary between 30 and 100 ft. Identical values apply in the deserts of Western Australia [6e], and are provided for the sand-ridge country generally by the air-photo interpretation included in current mapping programmes.

In the Simpson Desert, where the ridges run from a direction between south and east to one between north and west, the eastern side is steeper than the western. Madigan gives 15° as the average of the upper slope on the western side, and 25° for the corresponding eastern slope, ascribing the asymmetry to cross-winds. In mid-desert the sand is live for a width of 50 to 100 ft. on the ridge crests. In view of the general similarity of long seifs in one part of the sandridge country to those in another, it may not be unreasonable to compare this width of live sand with the total dune widths of 150 to 1500 ft. recorded for parts of Western Australia [6e]. The sandridges appear to be at least partly fixed, in large parts of the area occupied by them.

Dune convergences, such as are abundantly illustrated in Fig. 2, point downwind. Observations of sand movement along the length of the ridges led Madigan to conclude that the sand-driving wind is the prevailing wind [cf. 31a]. King [32a, 32b], holding cross-winds responsible for convergence, also finds a close correlation between ridge trends and the predominating strong-wind directions recorded at inland stations, even though the prevailing winds of the present day do not everywhere account for the sandridge pattern.

Convergences point eastward in those parts of the Victoria Desert which contain long seifs. The direction in the Simpson Desert is already swinging round to west of north, while north-westerly to westerly alignments appear in the Great Sandy and Gibson Deserts. The array resembles that of the circulation of wind around continental highs. However, an inference that the sandridges are associated with highs identical with those of today might be too facile. Very little is known of the date, or dates, when the dune systems came into being, although King is probably right in suggesting that they were formed in stages during repeated onsets of Quaternary aridity. Such onsets are abundantly demonstrated for other areas in generally similar geographic and climatic settings. [33a, 34].

There is, moreover, some evidence to suggest that the existing surface dunes are in places superimposed on older dunes of contrasted trend; and the surface trends are themselves capable of intersecting in some areas, particularly about 25°S and 129°E, as marked in Fig. 1. Confused patterns, and especially those of the Victoria Desert, are usually regarded as due to variable winds; but they could perhaps relate in part to a change in the direction of sand-driving, which failed to produce a revised alignment before the sand became fixed.

The sand of the ridges is fine-grained, mostly bright red, and composed mainly of quartz. Carroll [35] considers the red colouring to be produced by thin films of haematite. When red sand is remobilized it can turn yellow, as it has been reported to do in like circumstances in the Sahara; although Tricart [34] observes that dunes formed in the middle Niger valley during the pre-Flandrian were originally, and have remained, yellow and dates red dunes to an earlier interval of maximum dryness. Field observation during the wind-storms of 1965 on the border of northwestern New South Wales with Queensland showed that colour change does not set in immediately on remobilization. Some interval is presumably required for the haematite films to be abraded away.

Carroll's analysis of grain size demonstrates that sand from dune crests in the Simpson Desert is coarser than that from interdune areas. The crest sands, containing no grains larger than 1 mm. diameter, are concentrated in the range 0·24 to 0·12 mm. This, as a peak, is slightly finer than the peak range of 0·8 to 0·08 mm. reported by Bagnold for crest sand in the Libyan Desert. However, as Carroll points out, the peak frequency of interdune sands from the Simpson Desert, in the range 0·12 to 0·06 mm., means that the difference in grade between crests and interdune corridors is similar to that found in Libya.

Microscopic study of the quartz fraction in the Simpson Desert sand leads Carroll to infer an ultimate metamorphic parentage for this material. The inference is wholly compatible with the results of heavy-mineral analysis. However, the sand appears to have passed through more than one sedimentary cycle before being incorporated in the dunes. Crocker [36] considers that the sedimentary Eyre [Tertiary-lacustrine] Series was the main proximate source of supply for the Simpson Desert; and the map presented by David and Browne [11d] indicates that similar deposits of generally similar age were potential contributors to the supply of the eastern Victoria Desert. Too little is known of the lacustrine history of Western Australia for a comparable hypothesis to be applied there; but the possibility should not be dismissed out of hand, merely on account of the existing dryness of the western interior. Whitehouse's suggestion [37; cf. also 38] that ridge sand has a lateritic origin does not necessarily conflict with an origin in lake sediments, since these underwent duricrusting throughout large areas. But the breakdown of some at least of the siliceous variety of duricrust seems to produce gibber rather than sand (see below). Gentilli and Fairbridge [12] consider that a main source of supply of dune sand in the west was disintegrating sandstone of Proterozoic age.

In the direction of increasingly humid climate, the great arrays of seifs die away into scattered patches of fixed sandridge which in turn pass into sand sheets. Since it is not yet possible to map the respective distributions of sandsheet, fixed ridges, and ridges which are at least partly live, the Australian sandridge country cannot be discussed in the terms applied by Grove [39] and others to the fixed dunefields of Africa. Nevertheless, the outward succession of characteristics here signalized appears to be valid. Crocker suggests that the contrast between sandridges and sand sheets may result from a difference in grading, with the coarser sand occurring in the sheets. This idea obviously needs testing, but appears on the face of it to be improbable. The conspicuous absence of the silt fraction (0·02 to 0·002 mm. diameter) from the Simpson Desert sand doubtless means, as Crocker infers, that this fraction has been exported as loess. Loess export is still in progress. Red dust is frequently incorporated in the snows of Mt. Kosciusko, reddens the sun from time to time on the eastern mid-coast of Australia and is there brought down by rain, and occasionally reaches New Zealand. It seems at least possible that the next most easily exportable fraction is the fine-sand fraction, and that this is the most likely to build sand sheets. Bagnold [31b] states that some sheets at least may be composed of sand below a critical grade of size, e.g. about 0·3 mm. diameter, which, unless it is disturbed by something other than wind, is fine enough to resist erosion. Sand of this grade can be carried in suspension by strong winds, but drops when the strength of wind falls, forming even powdery sheets.

As was observed previously, dune patterns become confused in parts of the sandridge country, and it may be that one extreme of the seif range is represented in Australia by individual sandhills. Madigan recorded the opinion that a typical barchan is not to be found in the whole of the continent. Another type of dune, however, occurs on the lee sides of many lakes in dry areas. This is the lunette of Hills [40], which forms a crescentic ridge. Hills records the average height of lunettes as 20 to 30 ft., with windward slopes averaging about 4° and leeward slopes about 2°. Thus lunettes are more gently sloping than are seifs, and have properties of asymmetry opposite to those of the latter. Some lunettes are composed of silty clay, which may have been produced by the blowing of clay pellets or dust from the floors of drying lakes, and which may perhaps involve capture in flight by droplets of spray, but others consist mainly of sand [41].

Comparison with the maps drawn by Andrews and Maze [42] and by Marshall [43] shows that the blocks of sandridge country plotted in Fig. 1 occupy about the eastern two-thirds of the area currently classifiable as BWh on the Köppen scale, but that sandridges also extend eastward into the area of BShw and BSKw climates. This overlap aside, the 20 per cent of the continental area in sandridge country constitutes some 60 per cent of the area assessed by Marshall as climatic desert. Gentilli [44] arrives at a larger estimate than that of Marshall for the extent of arid climates at the present day, and draws boundaries for these climates which include almost all of the blocks of sandridge. Even so, these blocks account for 40 per cent of the arid areas.

However, the fixed or partly-fixed character of many dune systems, taken in conjunction with the degraded condition of the sandridges of the Mallee country, must inevitably be taken to mean that the Australian sandridge belts are as a whole less arid than they have been at some past time. The former increased aridity, and the former more pronounced activity of sand-driving, appear to apply not only to the sandridge country generally, but also specifically to its northern margins. There is considerable scope here for work on the alternative propositions, that at times of glacial maximum the equatorward margins of tropical deserts expanded, and that these margins contracted [33b, 45a, 45b, 46].

On the borders of the sandridge belts of Australia, perhaps more markedly than on most clima-morphological borders of the world, present conditions appear to be those of a dubious and easily-overset morphogenetic balance. There is no reason to suppose that conditions obtaining earlier in the Quaternary were dissimilar, allowance being made for spatial displacements. Dubious balance and wide frontier zones may be guaranteed by the extremely subdued relief of the continent as a whole, and particularly of the inland; and, in addition, by the fact that Australia generates many of its own air-masses. In turn, dubious balance implies that, in case of upset, pro-found morphogenetic changes become possible, disproportionate to the strength of the activating factors. The general history of the Pleistocene which emerges from recent and current work is one of superimposed change of a whole range of order. In the fairly short term, repeated but slight oscillations constitute the norm [45c, 45d] while similarly repeated oscillations of greater magnitude are recorded in the longer term [e.g., 47]. Slight climatic changes in the sandridge margins could conceivably mean the deep penetration of change into sandridge country, and might well be capable of promoting a great lateral displacement of morphogenetic activity. There is no a priori reason to suppose that the sandridges were brought into existence in a single, and geologically late, interval of dryness. On this count alone, it seems unfortunate that the term Australian Arid Period should be applied [48a, 48b, 48c, 49] to an interval which may eventually prove to represent no more than one of a whole series of climatic fluctuations in last-deglacial time.

The true fixes in the record are three: that still-uncertain interval of the Tertiary, when large portions of inland Australia were moist enough to sustain huge lakes; that presumably Quaternary time, or times, when the sandridges were constructed; and the present day, when many of the ridges are in part, or in whole, fixed.

East Australian Basins

In common with almost the whole of the Australian continent, the Basin division has been cratonic in post-Permian times. Although little is known of the basement structures concealed here beneath younger rocks, it seems highly likely that considerable portions of the east of the division were at one time incorporated in the Tasman Geosyncline. Similarly, Mesozoic basin sediments along parts of the western margin rest on deformed pre-Cambrian rocks, which reappear on the east in the Queensland section of the Eastern Highlands. It is possible, accordingly, that a considerable fraction of the Basin division once belonged to the Adelaide Geosyncline.

The Carpentaria subdivision, much of it today submerged in the Gulf, contains sediments of Cretaceous age. Along the present southeastern shore, the basement stands at 2500 to 3000 ft. below sea level. The Great Artesian Basin, which developed earliest and most widely, was the site of lacustrine deposition in Jurassic times. Jurassic sandstones outcropping on the eastern side provide some of the main intake beds, but those on the west, southeast of the Simpson Desert, come to the surface in a distinctly dry climate where increments of water to the artesian tables are infrequent. Cretaceous deposition, not all of it marine, supplied the chief aquifer of this subdivision, and also supplied the chief seal. Lakes persisted into Tertiary time, receiving deposits which have since undergone much dissection, and which are represented today mainly by tabular residuals. Later still, at least one vast lake was formed during the Quaternary, and lacustrine conditions of a sort obtain in the numerous occasionally-flooded playas of the present time.

The properties of the underground aquifers (explored by perhaps 20,000 bores of which some 4000 are artesian and 2000 still flowing [50]) are not closely relevant to the discussion of landform, except that the water has forced some natural outlets for itself, constructing at these the raised rims of mound springs.

Relief in the Great Artesian Basin is slight. Very little ground rises above 1000 ft. a.s.l., and the local amplitude of relief is very widely less than 500 ft. Almost the sole class of noticeable topographic break is provided by the steeply-eroded flanks of low mesas. In some central parts of this Basin, the basement lies more than 8500 ft. below sea level, and could go lower than 10,000 ft. Nevertheless, basement structures are expressed at the surface by the sags which contain internally-draining lakes, and by folding of the duricrust. It follows that deformation at depth continued well into Tertiary time.

The Murray basin, united in respect of surface hydrology with the basin of the Darling, is distinct therefrom in respect of geological development and artesian catchment. The principal sedimentation was here deferred until the Tertiary, overlapping in time with the deposition of the Nullarbor limestones, but involving lacustrine or paralic rocks in contrast to the marine sediments of the Nullarbor. The thickness of Tertiary sediments in the Murray basin reaches 1500 ft.

As pointed out above, and as indicated in Fig. 1, sandridge country overlaps from the Shield into the Basin division. Again, as has also been noticed, parts of the Shield are deeply weathered and duricrusted. But just as it was convenient to discuss sandridges in relation to the Shield, where they are most widely developed, so it is convenient to treat deep weathering and duricrusting in the context of the Basins, where they have been studied in most detail. In addition, drainage can reasonably be dealt with mainly in connection with the Basins, since its history involves particular attention to certain aspects of the fluvial and pluvial history of the Basin division.

Drainage

Although the Lake Eyre drainage basin includes a portion of the Shield, as a whole it belongs essentially to the Basin division. Similarly, the Murray-Darling catchment includes parts of the Eastern Highlands and their western slopes; but it also belongs with the great internal belt of structural depression. Most of what now follows will be concerned with the Lake Eyre and the Murray-Darling catchments.

Whereas Tasmania's drainage is wholly external, less than half of the mainland drains to the sea. How much less than half is difficult to ascertain. Those outer parts of the continent which, running from the southwest round through the north and to the southeast, are assessed as draining externally, amount to one-third of the total area. Some of this third ought probably to be classed as non-contributing, but the fraction may be accepted for purposes of discussion. The Bulloo-Bancannia basin, the Lake Eyre basin, and the Western Plateau where it lacks external drainage, account for more than 1·5 million square miles which is more than half of the mainland area. In addition, part of the topographic catchment of the Murray-Darling is non-contributing: this part includes the internally-drained Wimmera basin and the patch of uncoordinated drainage in the south, and, in addition, some northwestern districts where potential feeder streams scarcely ever reach the trunk channels. David and

Browne [*11e*] give data whereby 250,000 square miles of the Murray-Darling basin can be reckoned in the non-contributing class. If so, the totals become 1·15 million square miles (39 per cent) of the mainland with external drainage, and 1·8 million square miles (61 per cent) with internal or nil drainage.

Although records of stream-gauging are generally scant and in the main brief, it is nevertheless possible to obtain estimates of mean discharge for 185 catchments [*51*]. These, when cumulated, indicate a mean external run-off for the mainland which is equivalent to 1·8 inches of precipitation a year. When mean discharges for the individual catchments, expressed as precipitation-equivalents, are plotted on a map, the pattern which they suggest is not altogether orderly. When a somewhat arbitrary allowance is then made for the array of mean isohyets, the isopleths of mean

run-off become greatly simplified, as in Fig. 3. As a generalization, this map seems likely to be reasonable enough. It shows part of Tasmania as running-off more than 50 inches of precipitation a year, the Snowy Mountains and their immediate surroundings in the southeast mainland as running-off more than 10 inches, and a concentration of discharge on the Pacific coast of Queensland, in an area where mean annual rainfall rises above 150 inches, and mean annual discharge above 50. The isopleths of 10 or 20 inches of run-off lie on, or very close to, the remainder of the east coast.

From about long. 137° to about long. 124°, the 10-inch isopleth roughly follows the north coast. Values decline steeply west of long. 124°, with the 1-inch line at the coast where the tropic crosses. Only in the extreme southwest do values between 2 and 10 inches run-off reappear. The isopleth of 0·5 inches run-off

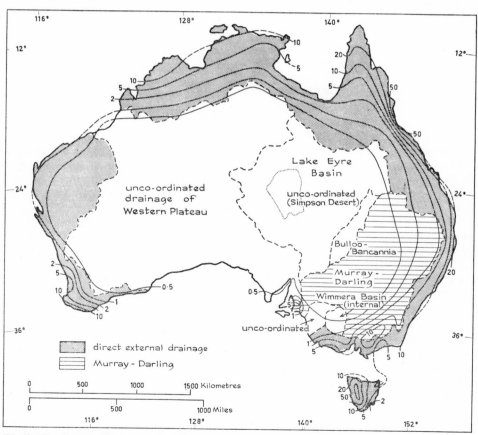

Fig. 3—Drainage divisions: mean annual runoff (inches)

runs close to the limits of external drainage, except in the northwest where data are particularly scanty. This same isopleth transects the Murray-Darling catchment, in general accord with the fact that discharge in this catchment is supplied mainly from the east. Indeed, were it not for the contributions of the headwater systems of the Murray, Murrumbidgee, and Lachlan, this whole basin might fail to achieve external discharge.

In parts of the catchments draining to the Gulf of Carpentaria, in parts of the Lake Eyre and Bulloo basins and the Australian northwest, and in much of the Murray-Darling catchment, downstream gradients ranging from 12 in./mile down to 3 in./mile (0·02 to 0·05 per cent) combine with highly irregular regimes of discharge to encourage the subdivision of stream channels. The phenomena in question differ from braiding; they concern not the internal splitting of a single channel by midstream bars, but larger-scale reticulation and anabranching. Whitehouse [52] associates reticulation with floodplains up to six miles in width, although the reticulated patterns mapped in Fig. 2 show that the width-limit should not be over-rigidly applied. Anabranching can take an offshoot more than 100 miles from the parent channel.

The combined extent of riverine deposits in the Murray-Darling basin is great. Those of the upper Darling system extend over more than 70,000 square miles (although part of this area may be interrupted by slightly higher ground), and those of the Murray and the lower Darling over more than 75,000 square miles. The total may possibly be 150,000 square miles, more than a third of the catchment, and equivalent to three-quarters of the area of France. Lesser patches of riverine sediment, e.g. on the Bulloo River, are omitted from the figure.

Reticulation and anabranching are cognate to the formation of distributaries on deltas. Indeed, the riverine sediments of the Murray-Darling can justly be regarded as vast alluvial fans, despite the very low downstream gradients of their surface. Since many or all of the trunk streams are levee-builders, or have been levee-builders in the past, the reunion of an anabranch with its parent channel can readily be deferred for very long distances. Levees con-

stitute the main exceptions to the negligible transverse gradients which, like gentle downstream gradients, favour channel subdivision.

In the riverine country, anabranches and lesser distributary systems were formerly much more densely developed than they are today [53a, 53c]. Discussion of the forms produced has regrettably been confused by the insistence of some authors [e.g. 53b, 54] that deposition is referable to arid phases, and by the attempts of at least one author [55] to make a verbal distinction between *prior streams* and *prior rivers*. The very much greater drainage-density of the prior stream system of former times, compared with the density of the existing network, and the greatly increased size of channel on the prior streams, can scarcely fail to point to increased discharge as the basic explanation of the facts observed. On this view, the record of prior streams in the riverine country accords with the demonstration of former pluvial conditions in the Lake Eyre basin (see below), and with the underfit conditions known to characterize certain Australian rivers [e.g. 56a, 56b]. All the signs are that surface drainage in the eastern half of Australia was formerly more abundant than it is today. This inference agrees precisely with that applied in the northern hemisphere to a great range of climatic settings [56c, 56d, 56e]. The general probability is that pluviation in Australia belonged to the glacial/interglacial shifts of world climate. But it is not yet known whether or not the interval from about 12,000 to 9000 years ago has the same significance here as in the northern hemisphere, where it produced the last general reduction of streams to underfitness.

The Paroo River does not always reach the Darling, dying away instead in swamps. Lake Bancannia, grouped with the Bulloo for convenience, is merely one of a series of playas in the northwest of New South Wales. Ephemeral swamps contained in a tectonic depression [57] receive the occasional farthest-flowing waters of the Bulloo River. Lake Eyre occupies the lowest part of a much larger tectonic depression, the topographic boundaries of which encompass an area of more than 440,000 square miles [51]. When they flow at all, streams in part of this basin head where the mean annual rainfall ranges up to 15 inches, but evaporation can dispose of much more than

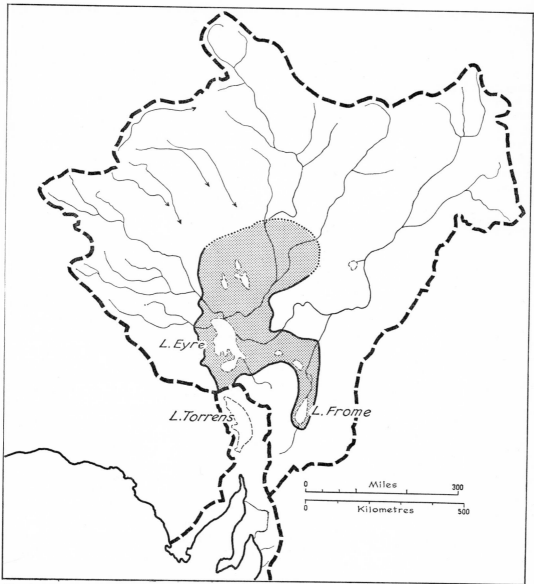

Fig. 4—The Lake Eyre basin, with pluvial Lake Dieri (stippled: mainly after David and Browne)

this. After the phenomenal floods of 1949 to 1950 which fed water into the lake, measured evaporation for the year 1951 was 94 inches, a value not seriously different from the computed value of 80 to 90 inches [58]. David and Browne [11f] identify an ancestor of Lake Eyre, Lake Dieri (Fig. 4), as having once stood at + 185 ft. a.s.l. The area which they quote for the lake at this stand, namely, 40,000 square miles, makes Lake Dieri at its maximum twice as extensive as pluvial Lake Bonneville in the U.S.A. Cordillera, and four times as extensive as pluvial Lake Lahontan [cf. 59a]. Lake Bonneville, however, is known to have possessed an outlet, and Lake Lahontan may also have done so. Whether or not Lake Dieri was connected with the sea during the 185 ft. stand is not yet certain.

The amount of water required to fill and maintain an enclosed lake is necessarily less than that required to supply an outlet in addition. Even so, the requirements of Lake Dieri may well have been greater than those implied by David and Browne. The area of 40,000 square miles seems to relate to the parts with known boundaries. Such hypsometric data as exist suggest that, at the 185 ft. stand, Lake Dieri probably covered at least one-tenth of the catchment (i.e., some 44,000 square miles) and that it may have been considerably larger, e.g. covering a seventh of the catchment with a surface of 63,000 square miles.

Rate of evaporation at Lake Eyre today resembles that at the sites of Lakes Bonneville and Lahontan [cf. 60]. If a climatic shift be assumed, similar to that inferred for the Great Basin between non-pluvial and pluvial times [59b], the former mean annual temperature for the Lake Eyre basin becomes about 53°F, and the former evaporation-rate about 45 in./year.

Wholly independent support for this assumed shift comes from the findings of Sparrow for the vertical range of lowering of the snowline in eastern Australia, at the time of the last glacial maximum [61; cf. also 62]. Now it is simple to compute the run-off which, added to precipitation on Lake Dieri itself, would maintain a water-surface of given area against a given rate of evaporation. Fig. 5 presents two graphs of precipitation/run-off requirements, one for a lake of 40,000 square miles and the other for a lake of 63,000 square miles.

Also in the diagram is inserted a curve of precipitation/run-off for a mean annual temperature of 53°F [63]. This intersects the other two graphs at points where requirements and relationships are identical, indicating that a mean rainfall of 22 in./yr. could maintain the smaller lake and one of 24·5 inches the larger.

These respective values are about 2 and 2·2 times as great as the present mean precipitation on the catchment [64]. Neither the values themselves nor the indicated ratios should be taken as other than rough. The manifold probabilities of imprecision, in the reasoning employed, are obvious. However, the indicated ratios between former and present precipitation are very close to those obtained by research into pluviation elsewhere [56c, 59c]. It can reasonably be inferred that pluvial Lake Dieri is explicable by

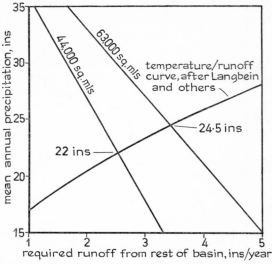

Fig. 5—Determination of runoff needed to sustain Lake Dieri: for method of construction see text

climatic shifts similar in sense and in magnitude to those responsible for Quaternary pluvial lakes in other dry regions.

Deep Weathering, Duricrusting, and Gibbers

An unknown but certainly large fraction of the surface of Australia exhibits the effect of deep weathering: and in some areas at least, deep weathering and duricrusting are associated with gibbers.

A complete deep-weathering profile includes an indurated zone at the surface, a mottled zone next below, and below that in turn a pallid zone, at the base of which a transition to unweathered bedrock is recognizable in places. The total depth of the profile can exceed 200 ft. [65a].

A pallid zone can be wholly kaolinized. It is fairly generally regarded as having formerly lain beneath the lowest seasonal level of a groundwater table. In many profiles the coloration of the mottled zone results from irregular kaolinization or less pronounced rotting, and from equally irregular blotching by sesquioxides. This zone is taken to represent the seasonal range of fluctuation of the water table. The indurated zone, which can be highly siliceous or highly ferruginous, is regarded as having formed above the water table, and to have experienced vadose and/or capillary action.

Suggestions that parts of the profile were deepened by lowering of the water table as a concomitant of dissection do not affect the general argument. Even if the indurated zone were deepened, and the mottled zone displaced downwards, the pallid zone might well gain at the base what it lost at the top. In consequence, the considerable thicknesses recorded for the pallid zone—up to 100 ft. or more—must be taken to indicate very deep weathering indeed. Ollier [66] has drawn attention to the problems involved in distinguishing between the effects of weathering and those of possible hydrothermal change in granitic areas, noting that some borings in the Snowy Mountains have gone as deep as 400 ft. in what is probably weathered granite plus corestones; but deep-weathering profiles in excess of 150 ft. deep are sufficiently well known from mesas of Tertiary sediments to validate the concept involved.

The indurated zone is usually equated with the duricrust of Woolnough [67a], although in some profiles the upper part of the mottled zone is better cemented than is the indurated zone proper.

The time of onset of deep weathering, and the time when it ceased to operate, as it did cease in huge areas of the continent, are imperfectly known. Nor has it yet been established whether or not more than one episode of deep weathering occurred. Stratigraphical evidence dates many of the relevant profiles to somewhere in the Tertiary, and a Miocene age is widely favoured. Difficulties arise from the uncertain age of some of the rocks which have been deeply weathered and duricrusted, from the assumption written into the early geological literature of Australia that the duricrust is part of a normal sedimentary sequence, and from the paucity of absolute dates from areas where deep weathering has affected, or has produced profiles overlain by, Tertiary igneous rocks [57]. One absolute date for a deep-weathering profile in southern Queensland gives a minimum age of about 23 million years [68a], placing the completion of the profile not later than early in the Miocene. Additional absolute dates are urgently needed—some are in prospect.

Dorman and Gill [69] demonstrate, by means of oxygen-isotope analysis of fossils, that temperatures in southeast Australia were,

during part of the Oligocene and in the early Miocene, some 10°F to 20°F higher than those of today [cf. 70a]. The data can be taken to suggest a decline in temperature, slow at first but gathering progressive pace, during the later Miocene and the beginning of the Pleistocene. The findings of Collins [71] appear to show that in the Pliocene and as late as the earliest Pleistocene, temperatures in the southeast of the continent were still somewhat above those of today. The inferred shifts are strikingly similar to those obtained by Wolstedt [72] for central Europe, both in value and in timing. Insofar as deep weathering in Australia requires greater than present heat, an interval no later than late Oligocene-early Miocene appears the most promising; but there is nothing in the temperature record as hitherto known to imply either a sudden onset or a sudden halt of the deep-weathering processes.

The inferred seasonal movement of the water table, the reconstructed record of temperature, and the powerful chemical changes produced by deep weathering, seem to call for the operation of a former climate of the Aw type, in inland areas parts of which are today classed as BWh. That is to say, a postulate of increased precipitation becomes necessary, in addition to the increase of temperature for which there exists independent confirmation [cf. 70b]. Gentilli, indeed, concludes from paleobotanical evidence [46] that the Eocene and early Oligocene climates of southern Australia were subtropical and very rainy, with areas which now receive 5 inches of rain a year then receiving at least 50, but he appears to dissociate this increased moistness from duricrusting, when he refers the crusting process to prolonged droughts. The fossil record of Tasmania requires increased temperatures, for instance, during the Oligocene and Miocene, and considerable increases of humidity during at least part of the Tertiary [70c]. The minimum climatic shift demonstrated by part of this record would raise July temperatures by 6°F; but the actual shift is likely to have been much greater, equivalent for example to the climatic difference between Tasmania and Cape York, since Tasmania also underwent deep weathering and duricrusting in the Tertiary.

In addition to the implication of climatic change, deep weathering implies the operation of the relevant processes on subdued plains. In large part these plains were erosional, although they may well have included lacustrine sediments in the Basin Division. Woolnough [67a, 67b] indeed concluded that a single continent-wide peneplain formerly existed, and that the duricrust formed upon it. What little is known of the shape of duricrusted surfaces, however, makes it likely that any erosional plain which they represent was a pediplain [cf. 57, 73a, 73b, 74]. It is by no means necessary to infer that the crusted pediplain was cut in arid or semiarid conditions.

With the record of paleotemperatures far too coarse to show sudden breaks, if any such occurred, and with nothing known of any changes in precipitation within the relevant interval of time, all that can be done is to assume that conditions of deep weathering set in and disappeared gradually. It would then appear to be no more than a coincidence that widespread residuals are crusted and deeply weathered, whereas lower and later-developed pediplain surfaces are not. Reports of weak laterization and of the formation of ortsteins below the level of crusting suggest that these effects were the maximum producible by the time that the new and lower surfaces had been cut.

As was pointed out to begin with, the crusts can be either highly siliceous or highly ferruginous. Where they are ferruginous they constitute laterite, except that where their aluminium content rises toward the threshold of commercial exploitation they are described under the name of bauxite [75]. Siliceous crusts are formed of silcrete. Unfortunately, many occurrences of silica crust have been recorded as laterite. The error seems to result from the tracing of crusts inland from the east, where they are typically lateritic, and from regarding silcrete as formed in the lower part of a ferricrete crust. This interpretation makes it necessary also to suppose that inland mesas, capped with silcrete as much as forty feet thick, have been completely denuded of a former ironstone cover.

But when the crust is traced in the opposite direction, from the inland towards the coast, a different interpretation emerges [68b]. Progressively towards the east, the following appear: red *silcrete* pisoliths overlying blocky silcrete; increasingly ferruginous pisoliths, also overlying silcrete which is represented in some exposures merely by sparse blocks; and well-defined laterite wherein ferruginous pisoliths overlie vermicular ironstone (Fig. 6). In some parts of the transitional area, the respective occurrence of silcrete or of ferricrete seems to depend on the nature of the bedrock; in other parts of the same area the indurated zone has been thoroughly stripped, leaving the summits of residuals capped with mottled-zone material. This effect may be ascribable to the original shallowness and weakness of a dominantly pisolitic indurated zone, and to the strong cementation of part at least of the mottled zone.

Exposures where deeply coloured pisoliths, whatever their composition, lie upon light-tinted silcrete blocks may well be responsible for the opinion that thick silcrete caps represent

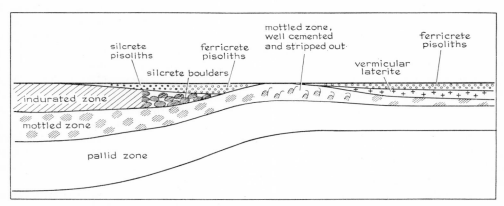

Fig. 6—Diagrammatic summary of passage from silcretic to lateritic crust

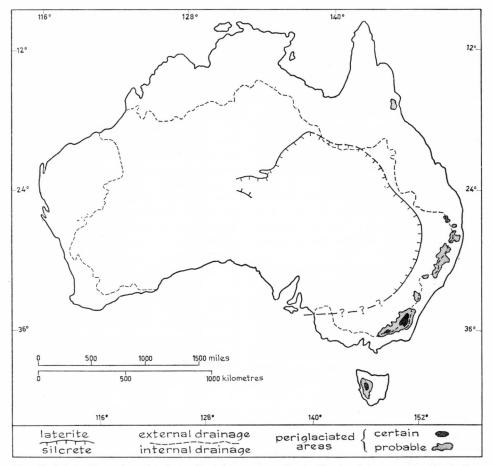

Fig. 7—The silcrete/laterite boundary in eastern Australia (various sources, including field investigation by author); areas of periglaciation, after Sparrow

merely the basal part of a former ferruginous crust: but, in the face of an identification of silcrete pisoliths, this opinion is no longer tenable. Furthermore, the relationships here cited demand reinspection of sites where laterite gravel has been stated to overlie silcrete [e.g., 65b]. If the gravel should prove merely to be reddened silcrete, then interpretation in terms of silicification followed by laterization may be no longer called for.

The spatial distinction between silcretic and lateritic crusts in eastern Australia, as so far defined, is presented in Fig. 7. Corresponding information for the west cannot be given, until crusted sites on the Western Plateau have been sampled anew. Laterite and siliceous caps are alike reported from that area, but identifications of laterite proper remain as dubious in the west as they once were in the east.

That part of the boundary between the two types of crust which is mapped in Fig. 7 roughly resembles, in some of its length, the boundary between external and internal drainage; but in the Centre which has been studied in considerable detail [76], the resemblance is mainly with the limits of the Lake Eyre catchment. In the Murray-Darling basin, where it has been reasonably well located on the ground [77], the boundary swings as much as 250 miles away from the divide between direct coastal and westward drainage, maintaining a fairly constant distance from the coast.

Hereabouts, it coincides approximately with the 20-inch annual isohyet and with the average limit of 0·5 to 1 inch of run-off a year.

Present-day conditions, however, may be poor guides to what happened in Oligo-Miocene times, particularly when the uplift of eastern Australia, dated by David and Browne to the Pliocene [11g], is taken into account. One crucial matter relates to the still-unknown conditions in which silica and sesquioxides can be mobilized, and to the conditions which could promote selective mobilization. Stephens [78] holds that the silica of the inland crusts has been transported by water from areas which were selectively enriched in sesquioxides: but the observation that silcreted residuals constitute remnants of a former pediplain militates against his conclusion.

King [79a, 79b] uses duricrust to correlate the affected surfaces with his Gondwana and Indian (pre-Cretaceous and Cretaceous to mid-Tertiary) surfaces. His contentions introduce continental drift. Now the general similarity between crusted surfaces in Australia and crusted surfaces in the southern part of Africa is beyond dispute. The two landmasses have experienced a similar, even if not necessarily a synchronous, geomorphic development. But allowance for continental drift demands still greater allowance for climate change independent of drift.

The reconstructions of King [79c] indicate an extreme poleward position for the centre of Australia at about 55°S in the late Permian, and thereafter a swift equatorward move in the Triassic and Jurassic. The poleward shift King regards as contributing powerfully to the well-documented Permian glaciation. Runcorn [80a, 80b], in a later review of paleomagnetic data, produces a more complex sequence of change for Australia, in the interval Carboniferous to Jurassic; and Opdyke's analysis of paleo-climatic information [80c] leads to inferences closely similar to those of Runcorn in the interval Silurian to Jurassic (cf. Fig. 8). Runcorn and Opdyke provide for a double move towards the pole, one approach in Carboniferous and one in Triassic times, against King's single approach during the Permian. Their data, being specific to the continent, may perhaps lead to more refined conclusions than does King's generalized reconstruction. On the

other hand, Blackett, Clegg, and Stubbs [81] indicate a single extreme poleward position in Triassic times (Fig. 8). Whether or not a double glaciation occurred in Australia during the Carbo-Permo-Triassic interval is not germane to the present discussion; the principal point is that, contrary to King's location of the centre of the continent at about 20°S in the Triassic, paleomagnetic data point to an equatorward shift during the last 100 million years, from a position near 60°S to that of the present time.

Unless this net displacement includes a greater northward movement than has yet been detected, plus a reversal to poleward shift during the last 25 to 40 million years, paleo-temperatures cannot be accounted for by drift alone. The paleomagnetic data, widely spaced in time though they be, do nothing to suggest that direction of displacement has been reversed; indeed, their tendency is to suggest the contrary. Similarly, the generalized tectonic relationship between the Australian landmass and the island arcs to the north also accords better with a persistent drive in the single direction than with its interruption. It becomes necessary, accordingly, to postulate changes in the global circulation of the atmosphere, sufficient not merely to offset the climatic effects of drift, but actually to overturn them, extending climates of the present-day tropical kind well beyond the tropic of part of the Tertiary. Only in this way, would it appear, can the paleontological record or the history of duricrusting be explained.

Gibbers

Approximate measurements on generalized soil maps of Australia indicate between 100,000 and 150,000 square miles as characterized by stony desert soils. In a loose sense, these soils can be regarded as co-extensive with gibbers. However, as will now be explained, the use of *gibbers* is normally more restricted than that of *stony desert soils*.

Originally, *gibber* was an aboriginal word for a single stone. By extension, it has come to be applied to the substance of a stony surface litter, and especially to such a litter in the dry inland. In this sense it constitutes a synonym of *gibber gravel*. A convergence of usage involves the formation of a singular from a

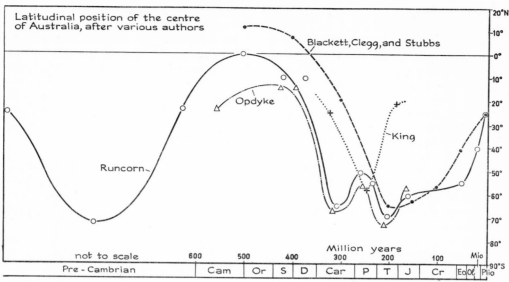

Latitudinal position of the centre of Australia, after various authors

Fig. 8

plural. Etymologically, the plural form *gibbers* is merely the equivalent of *stones*, but this form is replacing the older term *gibber plains*, while the derived singular *gibber* is coming to stand for a single stony expanse.

In addition, the term *gibber*, whether in the sense of fragment-strewn expanse or in the sense of the surface litter itself, is being increasingly limited in its application to cases where this litter is abundant. On those pediments which are cut below the level of the former duricrusted surface, and to which the wasting edges of duricrust caps supply copious loose material, the stony desert soils fall squarely into the gibber category. On the summits of residuals, however, the surfaces range from spreads of abundant loose fragments to outcrops of bouldery duricrust in place, where loose fragments are few or absent. Such outcrops are especially characteristic of districts where the crust is silcretic. Soil profiles vary correspondingly. Their whole range is united in pedological discussion under the heading *stony tableland soils*; but while those cases where the surface litter is abundant merit the title *gibber*, it is doubtful that this title would be applied to extensive outcrops of bouldery silcrete.

Again, by no means all gibbers, in the strict and limited sense of the term, are composed of the waste of duricrust. Quartz gibbers, composed of worn pebbles of vein quartz, are also widely known. These are provided by the breakdown of conglomerates, which may, but need not, have formed part of the indurated zone of a deep-weathering profile. Quartz and silcrete are well represented among the constituents of gibber; the full range of material has yet to be determined.

The total extent cited above for stony desert soils is contributed largely by three main, irregularly-shaped areas. One of these, amounting to less than a third of the total, occurs in the Gibson Desert; but sandridges are there sufficiently distinct, numerous, and close-set to have caused the relevant terrain to be already classed as sandridge country. The other two areas occur on the southwest and eastern sides, respectively, of the Simpson Desert. In the first of these, Mesozoic outcrops emerge westwards from beneath the sandridges; in the second, silcreted residuals, mainly of Tertiary lakebeds, rise above the level of the sandridge country. Gibbers are widely known from both of these areas, where they may be especially common; but they also occur in other parts of the dry inland, even if some of them are limited to the narrow exposed pediments between the flanks of residuals and the fills of desert basins or the incoming sandridges. A total extent for gibbers of 100,000 square miles is by no means unlikely, and could be a modest assessment.

The following discussion relates principally to work on gibbers which border, even if rather remotely, the Simpson Desert—i.e., to the best-known and best-studied areas of gibber. The range is in actuality one from the Centre, where the gibbers are located on part of the Shield, to the mid-part of the Basin division. In common with sandridges, gibbers require an overlap of treatment between Shield and Basins; but this overlap is partially overridden by the theme of duricrusting, since the gibbers which are here discussed are those composed of duricrust fragments.

Whereas some writers [e.g., 82a, 82b] describe the stone layer of gibbers as being but one particle deep, and look on it as a lag deposit in areas subject to deflation, others [e.g., 83] report stony soils up to sixty inches in depth, with stones concentrated at, but not confined to, the surface. Mabbutt [84] has drawn attention to a possible reason for the divergence of observation and of conclusion—namely, that, as has been remarked above, there is a contrast between the summits of residuals and the pediments developed at lower levels. He regards stone layers one particle deep as belonging to actively-developing piedmonts, whereas stones in deeper profiles occur on the tops of duricrusted tablelands. In the context of gibbers supplied by the breakdown of duricrust, this distinction requires an explanation of the origin of the fine-grained material which is widely associated with surface stones.

The chemical inertness of silcrete discourages the idea of reduction by rotting [cf. 82c], and the possibility of the complete breakdown of silcrete by fragmentation can probably be discounted [84]. Discussing the profiles of stony soils on the Wilyunpah Tableland of the Centre, Mabbutt finds lagging, truncation of a profile, and aeolian or alluvial import equally incapable of explaining the observed distributions of material, and in particular the occurrence and distribution of fines. He suggests, instead, that the existing profiles, with stones strongly concentrated at the surface, finer material below, and silcrete in place below again, represent residual profiles which have

been subject to prolonged pedogenesis, such as is indicated by heavy-mineral suites. Concentration of loose stones at the surface seems to be a response to alternate swelling and shrinking of the clay fraction [cf. 85]. This process is responsible for the surface patterns of gilgai [86a], which resemble in many ways the frost-soils developed in some cold climates [86b], but which are not confined to stony deserts or to stony tablelands.

It remains possible that fines can in the long term be transported, and deposited, in noticeable bulk. Notice is taken elsewhere in this essay of the occurrence of dust-storms and of the long-distance transport of fine-grained material. Moreover, many sites demonstrate that fines are by no means limited to the summits of residuals; they can equally occur on the flanks. They may of course have been derived, like those described by Mabbutt for tabular summits, from a soil profile overlying duricrust in place. But a distinction between stony soils on summits, which include a marked proportion of fines, and stony soils on lower slopes in which fines are minimal or nil, does not everywhere hold good.

Current work [87a, 87b] on the dimensional relationships of gibber stones to slope, concerned in part with downslope change in particle size, reveals a remarkably orderly reduction of size with increasing distance from the source of supply and with progressive reduction of slope angle. On some slopes at least, where the whole of the surface litter is supplied from above, diminution of median particle size corresponds precisely to reduction of slope: elsewhere, when fragments are also supplied by the sloping surface, the rate of reduction is less pronounced. But the general indication is that downslope comminution is nowhere sufficient to reduce the surface particles eventually below the sand grade. Here is an additional reason to look to some other process than comminution to account for the presence of fines.

East Australian Highlands

The title *Highlands* is preferable to *Cordillera* —a name sometimes applied to this division of the continent—for the latest episodes in a prolonged history of crustal disturbance have, in the main, been either epeirogenic or extrusive. Epeirogenesis has very broadly arched the extensive duricrusted surface which at one time truncated a very great deal of the total area; and although intermittent uplift has provoked intermittent onsets of dissection, large portions of tableland still remain sensibly intact. Extrusion, chiefly of basalt, has served to fill valleys or to flood whole landscapes. In addition, even where the terrain is well dissected, flat-lying sedimentary rocks in many parts have been carved into mesas which emphasize the tabular character of the division as a whole. As in Australia generally, many of the named ranges of the Highland Divisions are in actuality scarps, and not a few are erosional scarps. The ranges have been named from below, and their title is not uncommonly misleading. An obvious comparison is with the Drakensberg of South Africa.

Crustal elevations in the Highlands vary considerably. A height of more than 5000 ft. a.s.l. is reached south of Cairns in the Bellenden Ker Range, but little of the remainder of the division north of the latitude of Brisbane exceeds 2000 ft.—about half, in fact, is below 1000 ft. Heights increase to more than 5000 ft. in the New England tableland, vary between about 3500 and 4500 in the Blue Mountains, and then rise in the Snowy Mountains to culminate at about 7300 ft. in Mt. Kosciusko, the highest point of the continent. Parts of the so-called Australian Alps, which extend the high ground into Victoria, lie above 6000 ft., and summits above 5000 ft. occur in the detached Tasmanian portion of the Highlands, but little of the highest ground in western Victoria, where the division terminates at about 142°E, rises higher than 3000 ft.

The parting between easterly and westerly drainage in the Highland division is the Main Divide. The unsuitable term Great Dividing Range must be discarded, for the divide itself is singularly ill-marked in places. General considerations might seem to give the coastal rivers of the east great advantages over their westward-flowing competitors, and to favour westward displacement of the divide by repeated capture. But although the tributary-patterns of some coastal rivers are peculiar, conflict along the existing divide appears minimal. Despite the inferred captures listed by Gentilli and Fairbridge [12], little research in this matter has been done in recent years. Among the earlier relevant papers are those of Craft [88a, 88b, cf. also 11h]. What is probably the best-documented diversion of all belongs not in the Highland division, but in the Basins, where the course of the lower Murray has been influenced by the rise of the Cadell fault-block [89, 90].

For present purposes, the essential physiographic unity of the Highlands is most fortunate. The great total extent, and a record of deposition, vulcanicity, and erosion which includes lengthy geosynclinal development, provide for great structural and lithological complexity. It would be impossible, within the scope of this discussion, to attempt even the sketchiest outline of the whole. Attention will again be limited to selected principal matters, and particularly to those which have fairly wide implications.

Although the Eastern Highlands are here treated as distinct from the Shield, an exclusive distinction must be physiographic rather than structural. The Mt. Isa-Cloncurry element of the Shield is connected, at no great depth beneath the constriction of the Basin division, with pre-Cambrian outcrops in the northern part of the Highlands. On grounds of tectonic history, and possibly also on grounds of tectonic style, these respective outcrops may be separable from the outcrops representative of the Tasman Geosyncline. Alternatively, it could be that the western portions of the Tasman trough overlapped with, and incorporated, parts of the more ancient Adelaide Geosyncline.

Geosynclinal sedimentation in the Tasman belt began in lower Paleozoic times—very roughly in about the interval during which the Adelaide Geosyncline was becoming stabilized. According to locality, deposition continued up to or into the Permian. For instance, the abrupt sub-Permian unconformity in Tasmania marks the end of geosynclinal activity there, while the entire Australian continent has behaved cratonically since the end of the Permian, except for the Maryborough Basin in Queensland where geosynclinal depression and sedimentation endured longest of all.

Great thicknesses of sediment carried into the Tasman Geosyncline of eastern Australia, and deposited in huge complexes of unstable basins, now form shale, siltstone, greywacke, and sandstone. Times of principal compression were also times of batholithic invasion— notably, the Tabberabberan (Devonian) and Kanimblan (Carboniferous) orogenies. However, the total combined history of intrusion and of extrusion is long indeed. In the southeast of the continent, a major volcanic arc developed in the lower Paleozoic, with vulcanism accompanied by major granitic intrusion, while extrusive vulcanism was repeated in later Paleozoic times. Some sedimentation during the Permian, and much during post-Permian times, was controlled by large-scale crustal dimpling. This, in its turn, is presumably explicable by block-faulting in the basement. Permian rocks are preserved in great bulk in central Queensland, and sedimentation in some of the Queensland basins continued into the Cretaceous. Vulcanism and granitic intrusion were renewed in the Maryborough basin during the Jurassic. The [structural] Clarence basin is filled chiefly by Jurassic materials, and the [structural] Cumberland (Sydney) basin mainly by Trias which overlies a basement sagging in the centre of the basin as far as 2500 ft. below sea level. Much of the sediment fed into the marginal sunklands, during their period of development, was of sand grade. Thus, the Hawkesbury Sandstone of the Cumberland basin is a vast deltaic accumulation. Being generally resistant, it develops rugged landscapes under subaerial dissection.

Additional basins were initiated along the eastern margin of the Australian continent at about the end of the Jurassic. Lithological characteristics aside, the succession of orogeny by cratonism in the East Australian Highlands recalls the roughly synchronous and similar development in Britain, during Carboniferous to Jurassic times, of enclosed sedimentary basins with a tendency to persistent sagging. There is however a contrast in setting. The basins of eastern Australia belong, not only to a cratonic environment, but also to the zone of continental flexure. Although crustal dimpling makes this flexure in Australia far less simple than is sometimes represented, flexure nevertheless appears to be the mechanism · best capable of explaining the pronounced monoclinal deformation of parts of the eastern margins of the Highlands—capable of accounting both for the eastward descent of the duricrusted surface from the crestal Highland belt, and perhaps also for the Great Barrier Reef.

David and Browne [11] make numerous references to uplift of the Highland division towards the end of Miocene times, and again in the late Pliocene/early Pleistocene [see esp. 11g]. The movements in question long postdate the end of orogeny in this division. Their chronological significance will be mentioned below, in connection with the sculptural development of the coastland. Here, the main concern is their character. David and Browne call them epeirogenic, but King [91a] has no hesitation in calling them cymatogenic—that is, involving broad arching, with rifting and wedge uplift as possible minor attributes. King's model cymatogen [cf. his Fig. 242] appears to be identical with the type of macro-structure earlier presented by Cloos [92]. Although it could be objected that the Highlands apparently fail to display lengthy axial rifts, Tertiary faulting (including block-faulting) and Tertiary vulcanism are well in evidence. It is also true, as King shows [91b], that the gravity data of Marshall and Narain [93] can be reinterpreted to give closed negative anomalies, in areas of eastern Australia which appear to have undergone particularly marked uplifts in the Pliocene-Pleistocene interval.

Some parts of the Highland division record a very long history of vulcanism, while the division as a whole was volcanic during the Tertiary. Outbreaks continued in western Victoria and in eastern South Australia into Pleistocene and even into later times. Mts. Gambier and Schank were active as late as 5000 years ago. Central eruptions involved lavas mainly of the acid type, while extrusions of basalt from calderas or from fissures were, in total, strikingly extensive. In northern Queensland, forms produced by Tertiary vulcanism include scoria and shield volcanoes. Basaltic extrusions cover the Atherton Tableland, where crater lakes are known. A series of trachyte necks form the Glass House Mountains north of Brisbane, where the former piles have been so severely eroded that plugs rise 1000 ft. or more above their immediate surroundings. The Toowoomba district is broadly overspread by basalt, guided in its first flows along valleys but sheet-like in the mass, and erosional scarps up to 3000 ft. high terminate the basalt-capped plateau on the coastal side. This district includes the huge former Mt. Warning vent, of the caldera type.

In the New England block, Palaeozoic sediments and invasive granites are extensively covered by basalt. Some flows were early enough to have suffered deep weathering and duricrusting, while others overlie deep-weathering profiles and are not themselves much rotted. Absolute dates from this area should do much to elucidate the history of duricrusting. Meantime, the situation is rather confused, on account of the blanket reference of the duricrusted surface to the Miocene, and that of the next-succeeding, partially-developed plane to the Pliocene [cf. *11c, 94*]. It is indisputable that the main plateau, here as in other parts of the eastern seaboard, has been fretted and partly consumed by erosion working inland from the direction of the shore. Along all the major rivers, broad, widely-opened valleys cut below the main plateau level are bounded by steep edges and are separated from the uppermost valleys by waterfalls, and a still later renewal of erosion is required, to explain the deeply-trenched lowermost reaches of valley, which are incised below the floors of the middle valleys. But the precise relationship of the erosional sequence to the stratigraphic sequence remains incompletely known.

One question arising from the depth and extent of dissection in the coastal slopes is that of absolute speed of valley cutting. While extrapolation from short-term observations cannot possibly be reliable, and while, furthermore, present-day rates of deepening are likely to be far less than those of earlier more pluvial times, it is nevertheless worthy of record that Brittlebank [95] at the turn of the century attempted field measurements which anticipate those of the Vigil Network by more than two generations, arriving at a rate of profile lowering of 500 feet in about 1 million years. If the extrapolation has any value at all, it could mean that the compasses of Tertiary and post-Tertiary time, respectively since the (?)Miocene, (?)Pliocene, and (?)opening of Pleistocene, are adequate for the excavation of the observed sequence of coastal valleys.

Well-dissected volcanic rocks southeast of the New England block form the Liverpool and Nandewar Ranges and the Warrumbungle Mountains. In the last-named group, trachyte plugs are undergoing stripping. Although the process has not gone so far as in the Glass House Mountains, it has already revealed striking wall-like slabs of radiating dyke-rock.

The chief part of the Central Highlands of New South Wales consists of the Blue Mountains. These, with eastward-directed valleys cut through thick Triassic sandstone into underlying, equally thick shale, are characterized by a spectacular development of box canyons. Streams fall from the plateaus into the canyons, at most points by sheer drops which can exceed 1000 ft. Some of the Tertiary basalts of the Blue Mountains are today represented by residual mesas on the main plateau, while others, better-preserved, occupy the valleys which they originally plugged.

The western edge of the Blue Mountains proper is the west-facing, eastward-receding scarp of Triassic sandstone. Beyond this, draining in part to the east through gaps in the sandstone, rise further eminences; these are cut in Palaeozoic sediments and in granite, where beyond a somewhat ill-defined line of crest the terrain falls towards the inland basins. The western hill belt, interrupted in places by eroded folds and by volcanic masses, descends generally towards the plains. In respect both of its hilly character and of its width, this district contrasts with other districts comparably located on the western flank of the Highlands, and goes by the distinctive name of Western Slopes. Palaeozoic sedimentary outcrops and granite outcrops extend still farther than the slopes, into the pediplained Cobar block where the duricrusted surface is represented on the summits of low residuals [74].

South of the Blue Mountains, and separated from them by a kind of very large col, come the Snowy Mountains and their extensions. Structural graining on roughly north-south lines controls the coarse plan of relief in this part of the Highlands, where the types of outcrop noticed for the Western Slopes continue southward, but with granite becoming increasingly common. The generally increased height of the Snowy country is presumably due to additional uplift. Deep trenching by headwater streams can be related to a combination of uplift with copious run-off (cf. Fig. 3). Glaciation will be discussed below.

Craft [88a, 88b, 88c, 88d] has treated the landscapes of parts of the Blue and Snowy Mountains in considerable detail, distinguishing various erosional platforms and appealing in many specific contexts to faulting and differential movement, in order to account for relative heights. There can be no doubt that basement lineaments are reflected in some of the structures exposed at, and controlling part of, the present surface, nor is there any reason to suppose that these districts escaped Tertiary block-faulting of the kind proved in many other parts of the Highland division. However, opinion on faults postulated solely on physiographic evidence ought probably to be held in reserve.

Complex outcrops of granites and of ancient sediments, still with well-marked north-south alignments, continue from the Snowy district into the highlands of Victoria. Little need be added to the already-noted fact that elevations decrease westwards, except for the observation that crustal instability and vulcanism are especially well demonstrated in the western extremity of this portion of highland. The stratigraphic record of the Otway Hills, west of Melbourne, includes Pliocene deformation, while volcanic outbreaks of Pleistocene to Recent data occurred in Western Victoria. Some 100 vents are located here. Extensive flows of olivine basalt survive, but most vents were nevertheless of the central type. Forms produced include basalt cones, scoria cones, and explosion-craters. Minor features on the later flows are very well preserved [96].

After geosynclinal sedimentation and granitic invasion, and after its subsequent loss of crustal mobility, Tasmania underwent rifting from Permian times onward. Associated intrusive activity included the emplacement during the Jurassic of a great series of interconnected sheets of dolerite, chiefly in the eastern part of the island. Where the dolerite now outcrops, it distinctively influences the detail of relief. Rifting was especially marked in the Tertiary, when at least thirty basic vents fed lava into nearby valleys [97]. Davis [98: cf. also 99] holds rifting responsible for much at least of the vertical deparation of the erosional platforms which he

identifies, at heights ranging from 300 to 900 ft. up to 3000 to 4300 ft. a.s.l.

One leading interest in the Tasmanian landscape concerns glaciation, wherein it provides a standard of reference for the continent. Pleistocene glacial activity touched the Australian mainland but slightly. David and Browne [11j] claim to perceive evidence that the Mount Kosciusko district once bore an ice-cap 350 square miles in area, and that ice-tongues once reached down to about 4800 ft. a.s.l., 2500 ft. lower than the summit. The claim of three glacial phases is repeated by Browne and Vallance [100a], who also [100b] carry cirque glaciation down to a possible 5800 ft. and valley glaciers down to a possible 4500 ft. However, the surface forms of the Kosciusko country are, except for certain well-defined cirques, scarcely convincing as relics of glacial action. Ritchie and Jennings [101] have signalized the almost complete lack of similar relics in the neighbouring Grey Mare Range, while Galloway [102], reappraising the evidence from the Snowy Mountains, limits his identifications to thirteen cirques and to signs of an ice-cover extending over twenty square miles at maximum, as relics of a single (= Würm) glaciation (although he does not exclude initiation of the large cirques at some earlier time). He also specifies an orographic snowline at 6000 ft. a.s.l. at lowest, and a level of 5500 ft. for the lowest glacier terminus. Galloway points out that numbers of the features claimed as glacial in origin are more probably periglacial, while Costin and others [103], reporting evidence for nivation of Mount Twynam at the present day, remark that in areas such as the Snowy Mountains the relative importance of glacial and of nivational processes becomes difficult to evaluate.

Sparrow [61, 104], from whom the areas of known and probable former periglaciation in Fig. 7 are taken, considers that periglacial processes once affected the Kosciusko area down to about 1000 ft. a.s.l., that they operated in New England at heights above about 2500 ft., and that they also made themselves felt in the Mt. Bartle Frere district of Queensland. His estimate of level for the Snowy Mountains may however be too high, on account of the well-established eventual plunge of the snowline, and presumably of other associated climatic limits, towards high latitudes [59d].

In strong contrast to the mainland, Tasmania bears manifest signs of the work of ice; and the evidence for, and effects of glacial action there are summarized by Davis [98: see also 105, 106]. Despite earlier claims of three glacial phases, similar to those claimed for Mt. Kosciusko, there seems to have occurred but one phase unless the effects of earlier activity have been completely obliterated or concealed in later times. The formation of one main cap on the central plateau, about 1500 square miles in area, plus the formation of additional minor plateau glaciers, valley glaciers, and cirque glaciers accompanied the depression of the snowline by about 2000 ft., and the bringing of periglacial activity down to 2000 or even 1500 ft. a.s.l. All but one of the few radiocarbon determinations made so far [cf. 107] lie beyond dating age, but the exception—the date for wood fragments from a moraine—is a date of about 26,500 years. It appears certain that the one identified glacial of Tasmania correlates with the last glacial of the northern hemisphere.

Coasts, Mainly of the Highland Division

During the last several million years, Australia as a whole has proved much less unstable than other continents. Unlike the American cordilleras, its Highland division has escaped orogeny in Tertiary and post-Tertiary times. The entire continent is but slightly seismic. It possesses no active volcanoes and it is free from the kind of large-scale rifting which, in Africa, may be heralding the break-up of a continental mass. Furthermore, Australia has not experienced isostatic depression and rebound in the Pleistocene and Recent.

These circumstances, allied to the large-scale plans of many individual pieces of shore, favour coastal research on the macro-scale. It seems inevitable that the coastline will attract at least its just share of attention. Concentration of people in and near the coastlands includes concentration there of research establishments and of research workers. Although researchers with coastal interests are by no means confined to universities, university centres may be used to illustrate something of

the potential for study. Twelve such centres in the eastern half of the country are located in coastal towns. Ten of these twelve are situated in the Highland division, which also includes three additional centres less than 100 miles from the sea. The coastal universities range through 23° of latitude, on a coast where the general plan is simple, and where shoreline forms are dominantly influenced by Southern Ocean swell. Possibilities of comparative study are great indeed.

Much of the literature hitherto produced deals with this part of the continental margin. Expectably, it demonstrates that problems of coastal evolution in Australia resemble problems encountered elsewhere. The shores of the whole Australian continent have been affected by eustatic movements of the strandline; some are in a prograded, others in a retrograded condition; terraces in the valleys of externally-draining rivers invite correlations with old strandlines, and the general crustal stability does not exclude instability in certain areas. If the work already done has distinctive characteristics, these probably are, firstly the slight regard paid to high-standing erosional benches, and secondly the conversely great notice taken of shore platforms near sea level, the possibility of a Recent stand slightly above the present, and the effects of retrogradation or progradation. To some extent, these characteristics derive from the physical qualities of the coastal terrain.

Large areas of the eastern coastland are unpromising for work on high platforms. Where flat-lying sedimentary rocks crop out, as in the Cumberland structural basin, their topographic influence is strong; they make erosional platforms, if any, hard to identify. Then again, there may not have been sufficient time for the development of extensive platforms, whether eustatically or otherwise controlled. It has already been pointed out that the duricrusted surface in the Highland division is warped. In the crestal belt this surface can reach heights of 3000 or more ft. a.s.l., whereas along parts of the shore it comes down to sea level. If the crusting dates from Oligo-Miocene times, the warping cannot be earlier than middle or late Miocene. The broad-floored valleys cut through the duricrusted surface, usually taken as initiated in the Pliocene, are also regarded as having been uplifted since they were cut. The broad upheaval assigned by David and Browne [11g] to late Pliocene times is not presented as excluding further uplift in the Pleistocene. Although there is probably room for re-examination, both of the evidence for uplift and of the evidence of dating, the accepted view certainly implies that little time has been available for the cutting under eustatic control of platforms which have not later been deformed. Conditions here are different from those which elsewhere have produced hypotheses of long stability and of persistent eustatic control [cf. 108].

In any event, that attitude which might almost be styled a fixation on suites of high eustatic platforms has exerted little influence on coastal work in Australia. It is perhaps symptomatic that a committee of A.N.Z.A.A.S., established to investigate and correlate eustatic change, altered its purpose to the investigation of Quaternary strandline movements. Its 1956 report [109a, 109b] summarizes work accomplished or in progress up to 1955. It lists erosional platforms ranging up to 400 ft. on Kangaroo Island, South Australia [109c], and up to 800 ft. in Western Australia [109d], while Davies [110] has later described platforms in Tasmania as high as 4000 ft. Carrigy and Fairbridge [109e] identify nine submarine terraces off Western Australia at depths ranging from 60 ft. to 600 ft. But the total coverage is still minute, and trials of general correlation of high platforms have not yet occurred. Efforts to apply the Mediterranean sequence of Zeuner [111] have admittedly been made, but are concerned chiefly with levels not widely different from the present, and are moreover probably too few and too late to survive the growing criticism [cf. 112] of this particular scheme. Similarly, correlation with the findings of Fairbridge [113] have been attempted, but once again the concern is with levels close to the present. Moreover, as will presently be explained, the east coast is badly suited to the identification of close-set benches near to present sea level, such as Fairbridge reports from Western Australia.

Eastern rivers commonly enter the sea through low-standing deltas [cf. 114a], or by way of the rias drowned in the last great positive movement. Numbers of terraces occur at modest heights above the level of river or of floodplain. For instance, Paton [115] reports paired terraces in southern Queensland at 6, 13, and 21 ft. above normal river level. Rather surprisingly, in view of the debate on higher-than-present postglacial stands, investigation of low terraces has not yet progressed far. Among the best-known are those of an unstable coast in Victoria, where however the first radio-carbon datings serve to confuse rather than to illuminate [cf. 109f]. Terraces in the Sydney district have been mapped pedologically [116a], but ages offered for them are highly dubious. Later work, although refining classification, emphasizes the uncertainty of age [117].

Walker [116b] concludes that terraces of the Shoalhaven and neighbouring rivers relate to former sea levels at 20 to 25, 8 to 10, 5 to 10, and 5 to 6 ft. above the present, but regards eustatic control as operating only on coastal floodplains, immediately adjacent to the sea. The main bulk of terrace deposition he ascribes to climatic shift [cf. Mabbutt, 27, and this text, above]. Although he appeals to radiocarbon dates, Walker obtains correlations which appear unlikely. For instance, he cites 29,000 years B.P. for the beginning of pedogenesis on the terrace associated with the stand at 20 to 25 ft., but then correlates the episode with the Würm I/II interstadial. Now the climax of that interstadial can scarcely be placed later than about 50,000 years ago, even in schemes which assume a span of no more than about 275,000 or 300,000 years since the onset of the Gunz and corresponding glacials.

Again, temperatures during the Würm I/II interstadial, although higher than in Würm I or Würm II glacial times, were still well below those of the present day [118]; glacio-eustasy should in consequence have produced a stand well below the present. Fairbridge [113], working within the kind of time-limit just mentioned, shows sea level for 29,000 years ago at about—300 ft. In view of the discrepancy of age, Walker's correlation of the pedogenesis in question with the Würm I/II interstadial may be discounted; but the discrepancy of level is more serious. It cannot be explained unless the Shoalhaven country has experienced an uplift of some 300 ft. in the last 30,000 years; but there is no obvious sign of such an occurrence.

With specific difficulties of this kind left in

abeyance, it can be shown that the eustatic history of eastern Australia during the last deglaciation resembles that of other parts of the world. Hails [114b], plotting Australian age/depth data against Shepard's 1961 curve, finds agreement good. The Australian record is part of a general record of pronounced submergence as the sea rose from its last-glacial low stand, with the present level reached by 6000 or 5000 years ago.

What happened subsequently is by no means certain. The firmest claims that Australian evidence supports the hypothesis of Recent submergence beyond the sea level of today are those of Fairbridge [109g, 113], who asserts for instance that distinct emerged beaches on Rottnest Island, Western Australia, at about 15, 8, and 3 ft. above L.W.M., correspond most probably to platforms at 10, 5, and 2 ft., and offers dates in the range 6000 to 10,000 years B.P. for the submergences responsible. Jennings [119a, 119b] identifies a shore at 10 ft. a.s.l. on King Island, Bass Strait, referring it to the mid-Recent. However, the beach deposits of eastern Australia in some respects, and the coastal rock platforms of the east in their entirety, are badly adapted to record fluctuations of sea level within a narrow range.

The vertical range of deposits on many present beaches is greater than the 10 or 15 ft. between present sea level and higher levels postulated for last-postglacial times. Older beach deposits are represented mainly by certain of the barrier systems discussed below, but these, although indicating a stand in the 12 to 15 ft. range, date from before the last glacial.

Rock platforms at many east-coast headlands might seem, at first sight, to indicate a former high stand of the sea. But although their origin is far from being understood, the platforms are seldom interpreted in terms of eustatic shift. They differ from the extensive sloping abrasion-platforms of highly tidal shores in Western Europe, typically displaying little or no seaward slope: some, indeed, rise in ramparts at the seaward edge. Large expanses of platform lie above water level for a considerable fraction of total time in calm conditions, but are frequently washed over by moderate seas at high tide and by storm waves at most tides. Opinions that the platforms have been produced, and are still being developed,

by storm waves [120a, 120b] are countered by claims on behalf of weathering processes [121a, 121b, 122a, 122b, 122c, 123a, 123b, 124]. Among the agencies advocated from time to time, in addition to abrasion and quarrying, are alternate wetting and drying, dilatation, surface-tension phenomena, colloidal action, water-table control, spray erosion, solution, and crystallization of salt. Biotic attack is a further possibiilty. If some, or any, of these agencies can reduce the height of platforms, it follows that this height, as at present observed, must fail to indicate the level of strandline at which the platforms were initiated, supposing this level to differ from the level of today.

Beaches of the east Australian coast are typically sandy; shingle is rare. Sand has accumulated in many places in barrier systems, ranging from massive spits which enclose lagoons to multiple assemblages of beach ridge. Where extensive progradation has occurred [125a, 125b], numbers of parallel or concentric ridges can be preserved in former inlets. Two series of ridges are identifiable on the north coast of New South Wales, belonging respectively to the Inner and to the Outer Barrier systems, and between the systems a narrow lagoon may be present [126]. Radiocarbon dates place the formation of the Outer Barrier in the Recent. The Inner Barrier consists of the beach deposits previously mentioned as indicating a stand 12 to 15 ft. above the present [127a]. The few dates so far obtained set the formation of this Barrier earlier than the last glacial maximum; they invite preliminary correlation with the 10 to 15 ft. stand to which Fairbridge [113] allocates an age of 75,000 to 80,000 years. If this stand is authentic, it cannot fail to bring further difficulties into the interpretation of coastal platforms.

Erosion of some eastern shores has removed the Outer Barrier, if this formerly existed, and is attacking the Inner Barrier. Long extents of the low cliffs produced in this way are cut partly in sandrock, the dark-hued, cemented material widely present in Inner Barrier deposits but absent from the Outer Barrier. Sandrock is thought to be associated with former groundwater tables. Above it, the Inner Barrier sand is typically leached into whiteness.

The ridges of both barrier systems are liable

to masking by transgressive dunes, some of which bulk very large. Hails [114c] reports fixed transgressive dunes more than 500 ft. high. Blowout of transgressive sand produces parabolic dunes (U-dunes) where the tails point upwind.

Barrier systems and giant transgressive dunes alike require a copious supply of sand. Part of the supply may result from landward shepherding during rises of sea level. But since the present level was reached by 6000 or 5000 years B.P., and since parts of the Outer Barrier systems are younger than this, it becomes necessary to conclude that landward shift of sand is possible, independent of sea level change. The conclusion is not disturbed by the fact that retrogradation seems currently to dominate over progradation. Bird [125b, 125c], studying the coastal barriers of East Gippsland, uses wave-refraction diagrams for SW and SE swell to show that the latter is responsible for the outlines of Ninety Mile Beach and its parallel ridge-systems; and he points out that the SW swell, with wavelengths exceeding 600 ft., can be detected at depths of one wavelength and may carry sand inshore from depths approaching 250 ft.

Erosion on some parts of the New South Wales coast is exposing beach deposits unlike any of those yet described. In the first place, the deposits are of shingle, and secondly, they rise well above present sea level. One beach at 20 ft., and another at 60 ft., are well defined. There may also be an intermediate beach at 40 to 50 ft., while some evidence exists for a possible stand in the range 80 to 100 ft. [127a, 127b]. The 60 ft. beach has been traced laterally for more than 200 miles, throughout which distance it remains horizontal. Whether it can yet be classed as eustatic, or alternatively, what minimum length of horizontal beach would suffice to demonstrate a eustatic origin, is difficult to say.

If the 20 ft. beach predates the stand at 12 to 15 ft., it is of considerable antiquity. Fair-

bridge [113] cites the interval 95,000 to 90,000 years B.P. for beach formation and benching at 20 to 25 ft. and a date of about 100,000 B.P. for similar action at the 60 ft. level. In his scheme, both stands are contained in the Riss/Würm interglacial; but his 100 ft. stand, with an age of about 130,000 years, is placed in the late Mindel/Riss. However, this is not the place to debate Pleistocene chronology. The foregoing comments are intended merely to suggest that, if long-distance correlations of eustatic levels become generally acceptable, work now in progress on the shores of eastern Australia is likely to bring the local evidence into relationship with a general scheme.

Meanwhile, it seems justifiable to maintain that the observations collected to date are compatible with an intermittent eustatic descent of the east Australian strandline, from 60 ft. a.s.l. (and possibly from 100 ft. a.s.l.) down to 12 to 15 ft. The general principle that earlier beaches are likely to be destroyed in later submergences suggests that age of beach increases with height. Something by way of confirmation emerges from a comparison of the deposits of the scantily-exposed possible beach at 40 to 50 ft. with the deposits of the 60 ft. beach [128]. The higher series is distinctly more weathered than is the lower.

Conclusion

This introduction to the geomorphology of Australia has perforce been summary and selective. As implied at the outset, it deals with future prospects, just as much as with work already accomplished, and in this respect it forms a statement of immediate geomorphological tasks. But some of the qualities of Australia's surface are so clearly and widely expressed, and so different from those of terrains where the science of geomorphology has been chiefly developed, that future work of the exploratory and descriptive kind seems bound itself to assume a special character.

REFERENCES

1. MURRAY, R. A. F. (1895) *The Geology and Physical Geography of Victoria.* Government Printer, Melbourne.

2. ANDREWS, E. C. (1905) *An Introduction to the Physiography of New South Wales.* Brooks, Sydney.

3. HOWCHIN, W. (1913) The Evolution of the Physiographic Features of South Australia. *Austr.Assoc.Adv.Sci., 14,* 148–177.

4. HOWCHIN, W. (1929) (2 ed.) *The Geology of South Australia.* Author, Adelaide.

5. SUSSMILCH, C. A. (1914) *An Introduction to the Geology of New South Wales.* Angus and Robertson, Sydney.

6a. JUTSON, J. T. (1914) *An Outline of the Physiographical Geology of Western Australia.* Geol. Surv. W.A., Bull. *61.* Government Printer, Perth.

6b. JUTSON, J. T. (1934) (2 ed.) *The Physiography of Western Australia.* Geol. Surv. W.A., Bull. *95.* Government Printer, Perth.

6c. *Ibid.,* 182–195.

6d. *Ibid.,* 5–6, and subsequently.

6e. *Ibid.,* 121–122.

7. BRYAN, W. H. (1930) The Physiography of Queensland, in BRYAN, W. H., LONGMAN, H. A., & REID, J. F. F. (eds.) *Queensland Handbook, Austr.Assoc.Adv.Sci.,* 17–22. Government Printer, Brisbane.

8a. FENNER, C. (1930) The Major Structural and Physiographic Features of South Australia. *Trans.Roy.Soc.S.Australia, 54,* 1–36.

8b. FENNER, C. (1931) *South Australia.* Whitcombe and Tombs, Melbourne and Sydney.

9. HILLS, E. S. (1940) *The Physiography of Victoria.* Whitcombe and Tombs, Melbourne.

10a. TAYLOR, T. G. (1911) *The Physiography of Eastern Australia.* Bull. *8,* Cmnwlth Met. Bureau.

10b. TAYLOR, T. G. (1914) The Physical and General Geography of Australia, in KNIBBS, G. H. (ed.) *Federal Handbook, Brit.Assoc.Adv.Sci.,* 86–121. Commonwealth Government, Melbourne.

11a. DAVID, SIR T. EDGEWORTH & BROWNE, W. R. (1950) *The Geology of the Commonwealth of Australia* (3 vols.). Edward Arnold, London.

11b. *Ibid.,* (2), 3–141.

11c. *Ibid.,* (1), 633–635.

11d. *Ibid.,* (1), Fig. 155.

11e. *Ibid.,* (2), 11.

11f. *Ibid.,* (1), 616–618.

11g. *Ibid.,* (1), 586.

11h. *Ibid.,* (2), 8–10.

11i. *Ibid.,* (2), 79.

11j. *Ibid.,* (1), 628–629.

12. GENTILLI, J. & FAIRBRIDGE, R. W. (1951) *Physiographic Diagram of Australia.* Geographical Press, Columbia University, New York.

13. JENNINGS, J. N. & MABBUTT, J. A. (eds.) (1967) *Essays in Australian Geomorphology.* A.N.U. Press, Canberra.

14. GREGORY, J. W. (1903) *The Geography of Victoria.* Whitcombe and Tombs, Melbourne.

15. CHRISTIAN, C. S. & STEWART, G. A. (1953) *General Report on Survey of the Katherine-Darwin Region, 1946.* Land Res. Ser., *1.* C.S.I.R.O., Melbourne.

16. GIBBONS, F. R. & DOWNES, R. G. (1964) *A Study of the Land in South-western Victoria.* Soil Conservation Authority Victoria, Melbourne.

17. AUTHOR This analysis uses frequency-graphing. When the areas of the land systems of Christian and Stewart are plotted against ranking order, they produce a semilogarithmic scatter. The corresponding graph for the Gibbons and Downes data shows that rate of increase of area with rise on the ranking scale decreases sharply, at about the point where land systems which extend beyond the survey boundaries come in. Extrapolation of the lower limb of the graph supplies the corrected values.

18. BUREAU MIN. RESOURCES (1962) *Tectonic Map of Australia, with Geological Notes.* Canberra.

19. HILL, D. (ed.) (1960) The Geology of Queensland. *Journ.Geol.Soc.Austr., 7.*

20. SPRY, A. & BANKS, M. R. (eds.) (1962) The Geology of Tasmania. *Ibid., 9.*

21. BROWN, D. A. (ed.) (1965) The Geology of South Australia. *Ibid., 12.*

22. MABBUTT, J. A. (1961) A Stripped Land Surface in Western Australia. *Trans.and Papers,Inst.Brit.Geog., 29,* 101–114.

23. GREGORY, J. W. (1914) The Lake Systems of Westralia. *Geog.Journ., 43,* 656–664.

24. KING, D. (1949) Geological Notes on the Nullarbor Cavernous Limestones. *Trans. Roy.Soc.S.Australia, 73,* 52–58.

25. JENNINGS, J. N. The Limestone Geomorphology of the Nullarbor Plains (Aus-

tralia). *Deuxième Congr.Internat.de Spéléologie,Actes, 1*, sect. 1, 371–396.

26. JENNINGS, J. N. (1963) Some Geomorphological Problems of the Nullarbor Plain. *Trans.Roy.Soc.S.Australia, 87*, 41–62.

27. MABBUTT, J. A. (1966) Landforms of the Western Macdonnell Ranges. in DURY, G. H. (ed.) *Essays in Geomorphology*, 83–119. Heinemann, London.

28. JENNINGS, J. N. & SWEETING, M. M. (1963) The Limestone Ranges of the Fitzroy Basin, Western Australia. *Bonn.Geog.Abh., 32*.

29. MADIGAN, C. T. (1936) The Australian Sand-ridge Deserts. *Geog.Review, 26*, 205–227.

30. MADIGAN, C. T. (1946) The Simpson Desert Expedition, 1939, Scientific Reports No. 6, Geology—The Sand Formations. *Trans. Roy.Soc.S.Australia, 70*, 45–63.

31a. BAGNOLD, R. A. (1951) Sand Formations in Southern Arabia. *Geog.Journ., 40*, 78–85.

31b. BAGNOLD, R. A. (1941) *The Physics of Blown Sand and Desert Dunes*. Methuen, London.

32a. KING, D. (1956) The Quaternary Stratigraphic Record at Lake Eyre North and the Evolution of Existing Topographic Forms. *Trans.Roy.Soc.S.Australia, 79*, 93–103.

32b. KING, D. (1960) The Sand Ridges of South Australia and Related Aeolian Landforms of the Quaternary Arid Cycles. *Ibid., 83*, 93–108.

33a. BÜDEL, J. K. (1956-57) The Ice Age in the Tropics. *Universitas, 1*, 183–191.

33b. BÜDEL, J. K. (1952) Bericht über klimamorphologische und Eiszeit-forschungen in Nieder-Afrika. *Erdkunde, 6*, 104–132.

34 TRICART, J. (1959) Géomorphologie dynamique de la moyenne vallée du Niger (Soudan). *Ann.de Géog., 68*, 333–342.

35. CARROLL, D. (1944) The Simpson Desert Expedition, 1939, Scientific Reports No. 2, Geology. *Trans.Roy.Soc.S.Australia, 68*, 49–59.

36. CROCKER, R. L. (1946) The Simpson Desert Expedition, 1939, Scientific Reports No. 8, The Soils and Vegetation of the Simpson Desert and its Borders. *Ibid., 70*, 235–238.

37. WHITEHOUSE, F. W. (1940) Studies in the Late Geological History of Queensland. *Papers, Dept. of Geol., U. of Qld.*, new ser., *2*, 1–74.

38. HALLSWORTH, E. G., GIBBONS, F. R. & DARLEY, W. E. (1951) Desert Soil Formations of Australia. *Austr.J.Sci., 13*, 110–111.

39. GROVE, A. T. (1958) The Ancient Erg of Hausaland, and Similar Formations on the South Side of the Sahara, *Geog.Journ., 124*, 528–533.

40. HILLS, E. S. (1940) The Lunette, a New Land Form of Aeolian Origin. *Austr.Geog., 3*, 15–21.

41. STEPHENS, C. G. & CROCKER, R. L. (1946) Composition and Genesis of Lunettes. *Trans.Roy.Soc.S.Australia, 70*, 302–312.

42. ANDREWS, J. & MAZE, W. H. (1933) Some Climatological Aspects of Aridity in their Application to Australia. *Proc.Linn.Soc. N.S.W., 58*, 105–120.

43. MARSHALL, A. (1948) The Size of the Australian Desert, *Austr.Geog., 5*, 168–175.

44. GENTILLI, J. (undated) Australian Climates (map). Nedlands, W.A.

45a. BUTZER, K. W. (1957) Mediterranean Pluvials and the General Circulation of the Pleistocene. *Geog.Annaler, 39*, 48–53.

45b. BUTZER, K. W. (1957) The Recent Climatic Fluctuation in Lower Latitudes and the General Circulation of the Pleistocene. *Ibid., 39*, 105–113.

45c. BUTZER, K. W. (1957) Late Glacial and Postglacial Climatic Variation in the Near East. *Erdkunde, 11*, 21–35.

45d. BUTZER, K. W. (1959) Some Recent Geological Deposits in the Nile Valley. *Geog. Journ., 125*, 75–79.

46. GENTILLI, J. (1961) Quaternary Climates of the Australian Region. *Ann.N.Y.Acad. Sci., 95*, 465–501.

47. EARDLEY, A. J. & GVODETSKY, V. (1960) Analysis of Pleistocene Cores from Great Salt Lake, Utah. *Bull.Geol.Soc.Amer., 71*, 1323–1344.

48a. CROCKER, R. L. (1941) Notes on the Geology and Physiography of South-east Australia with Reference to Late Climatic History. *Trans.Roy.Soc.S.Australia, 65*, 103–107.

48b. CROCKER, R. L. (1946) Post-Miocene Climatic and Geologic History and its Significance in Relation to the Genesis of Major Soil Types of South Australia. *C.S.I.R. (Austr.) Bull., 193*.

48c. CROCKER, R. L. & COTTON, B. C. (1946) Some Raised Beaches of the Lower Southeast of South Australia and their Significance. *Trans.Roy.Soc.S.Australia, 70*, 64–82.

49. GILL, E. D. (1955) The Australian Arid Period. *Austr.J.Sci., 17*, 204–206.

50. HAHN, G. W. & FISHER, N. H. (1964) Review of Available Groundwater Data on the

Great Artesian Basin, in *Water Resources Use and Management* (Proc. 1963 Canberra Symposium), 167–187. Melbourne U.P., Melbourne.

51. AUSTRALIAN WATER RESOURCES COUNCIL (1965) *Review of Australia's Water Resources*. Dept. Natl. Develpt., Canberra.

52. WHITEHOUSE, F. W. (1944) The Natural Drainage of some Very Flat Monsoonal Lands (the Plains of Western Queensland). *Austr.Geog.*, 4, 183–196.

53a. BUTLER, B. E. (1950) A Theory of Prior Streams as a Causal Factor of Soil Occurrence in the Riverine Plains of South-eastern Australia. *Austr.J.Agric.Research*, 1, 231–252.

53b. BUTLER, B. E. (1958) Depositional Systems of the Riverine Plain in Relation to Soils. *C.S.I.R.O.Austr.Soil Pubn.*, 10.

53c. LANGFORD-SMITH, T. (1960) The Dead River Systems of the Murrumbidgee. *Geog. Review*, 50, 368–389.

54. HAWKINS, C. A. & WALKER, P. H. (1956) A Study of Layered Sedimentary Materials on the Riverine Plain, New South Wales. *J. Roy.Soc.N.S.W.*, 90, 110–127.

55. PELS, S. (1964) The Present and Ancestral Murray System. *Austr.Geog.Studies*, 2, 111–119.

56a. DURY, G. H. (1966) Incised Valley Meanders on the Lower Colo River, New South Wales. *Austr.Geog.*, 10, 17–25.

56b. DURY, G. H. (in preparation) Seismic Exploration of a Cutoff Valley Meander on the Colo River, New South Wales.

56c. DURY, G. H. (1964) *Principles of Underfit Streams*. U.S.Geol.Surv.Profl.Paper 452-A. Washington, D.C.

56d. DURY, G. H. (1964) *Subsurface Exploration and Chronology of Underfit Streams. Ibid.*, 452-B. Washington, D.C.

56e. DURY, G. H. (1965) *Theoretical Implications of Underfit Streams. Ibid.*, 452-C. Washington, D.C.

57. LANGFORD-SMITH, T. & DURY, G. H. (1965) Distribution, Character, and Attitude of the Duricrust in the North-west of New South Wales and the Adjacent Areas of Queensland. *Amer.J.Sci.*, 263, 170–190.

58. BONYTHON, C. W. & MASON, B. (1953) The Filling and Drying of Lake Eyre. *Geog. Journ.*, 119, 321–330.

59a. FLINT, R. F. (1957) *Glacial and Pleistocene Geology*, 226–232. Wiley, New York.

59b. *Ibid.*, 226.

59c. *Ibid.*, 225.

59d. *Ibid.*, 49.

60. LINSLEY, R. K., KOHLER, M. A. & PAULHUS, J. L. H. (1949) *Applied Hydrology*, Figs. 8–8 and 8–9, 180. McGraw-Hill, New York, Toronto, and London.

61. SPARROW, G. W. A. (1964) Pleistocene Periglacial Landforms in the Southern Hemisphere. *S.Afr.J.Sci.*, 60, 143–146. The reduction of temperature for the Bonneville-Lahontan basins is about 8°C. The range of snowline displacement cited by Sparrow corresponds to a temperature-reduction of about 10°C; but, as pointed out in the text, this author may not have allowed sufficiently for the poleward plunge of the snowline towards high latitudes, and may in consequence have arrived at too great a reduction of temperature.

62. SPRIGG, R. C. (1959) Stranded Sea Beaches and Associated Sand Accumulations of the Upper South-east. *Trans.Roy.Soc.S.Australia*, 82, 183–193. This author finds that strong westerlies which now affect Tasmania extended 4° to 5° lat. farther north during the Pleistocene. However, this displacement is clearly a minimum, and is not incompatible with shifts of the order recorded by Flint for N. America.

63. This curve is derived, by interpolation, from Fig. 2 in LANGBEIN, W. B. AND OTHERS (1949). Annual Runoff in the United States. *U.S.Geol.Surv.Circular*, 52.

64. Present-day weighted mean precipitation for the catchment has been determined, by planimetry, at about 11 in./year.

65a. WOPFNER, H. (1960) On some Structural Development in the Central Part of the Great Australian Artesian Basin. *Trans. Roy.Soc.S.Australia*, 83, 179–193.

65b. WOPFNER, H. (1961) The Occurrence of a Shallow Groundwater Horizon and its Natural Outlets in Northeasternmost South Australia. *Ibid.*, 85, 13–18.

66. OLLIER, C. D. (1965) Some Features of Granite Weathering in Australia. *Zeitschr. für Geomorph.*, N.F. 9, 285–304.

67a. WOOLNOUGH, W. G. (1927) The Duricrust of Australia. *J.Proc.Roy.Soc.N.S.W.*, 61, 24–53.

67b. WOOLNOUGH, W. G. (1918) The Physiographic Significance of Laterite in Western Australia. *Geol.Mag.*, dec. vi, 5, 385–393.

68a. LANGFORD-SMITH, T., DURY, G. H., & MCDOUGALL, I. (1966) Dating the Duricrust in Southern Queensland. *Austr.J.Sci.*, 29, 79–80.

68b. LANGFORD-SMITH, T. & DURY, G. H. Unpublished results of 1965 field campaign.

69. DORMAN, F. H. & GILL, E. D. (1959) Oxygen Isotope Palaeotemperature Measurements on Australian Fossils. *Proc.Roy.Soc.Victoria*, *71*, 73–98.

70a. GILL, E. D. (1961) Cainozoic Climates of Australia. *Ann.N.Y.Acad.Sci.*, *95*, 461–464.

70b. GILL, E. D. (1964) Rocks Contiguous with the Basaltic Cuirass of Western Victoria. *Proc.Roy.Soc.Victoria*, *77*, 331–355.

70c. GILL, E. D. Cainozoic Climates (of Tasmania) in entry [*20*], *above*, 250–253.

71. COLLINS, A. C. (1953) Pleistocene Foraminifera from Port Fairy, Western Victoria. *Mem.Nat.Mus.Vict.,Melbourne*, *18*, 95–103.

72. WOLSTEDT, P. (1954) Die Klimakurve des Tertiärs und Quartärs in Mitteleuropa. *Eiszeitalter u. Gegenwart*, *4*, 5–9.

73a. DURY, G. H. & LANGFORD-SMITH, T. (1964) The Use of the Term Peneplain in Descriptions of Australian Landscapes. *Austr.J.Sci.*, *27*, 171–175.

73b. DURY, G. H. & LANGFORD-SMITH, T. (1966) Reply to the Letter . . . on Peneplains and Pediments in Australia . . . , *ibid.*, *28*, 291.

74. DURY, G. H. (1966) Duricrusted Residuals on the Barrier and Cobar Pediplains of New South Wales. *J.Geol.Soc.Austr.*, *13*, 299-307.

75. OWEN, H. B. (1954) Bauxite in Australia. *Austr. Bureau Min. Resources, Geol. and Geophys. Bull.*, *24*.

76. MABBUTT, J. A. (1965) The Weathered Land Surface in Central Australia. *Zeitschr. für Geomorph.*, N.F., *9*, 82–114.

77. DURY, G. H. Field records in part unpublished.

78. STEPHENS, C. G. (1964) Silcretes of Central Australia. *Nature*, *203*, 1407.

79a. KING, L. C. (1950) The Study of the World's Plainlands: a New Approach in Geomorphology. *Quart.J.Geol.Soc.Lond.*, *106*, 101–131.

79b. KING, L. C. (1959) Denudational and Tectonic Relief in South-eastern Australia. *Trans.Geol.Soc.S.Afr.*, *58*, 113-138.

79c. KING, L. C. (1958) Basic Palaeogeography of Gondwanaland during the Late Palaeozoic and Mesozoic Eras. *Quart.J.Geol.Soc. Lond.*, *114*, 47–70; esp. Pl. IV and associated text.

80a. RUNCORN, S. K. (ed.) (1962) *Continental Drift*. Academic Press, New York and London.

80b. RUNCORN, S. K. Palaeomagnetic Evidence for Continental Drift and its Geophysical Cause, in entry [*80a*], 1–40, and esp. Fig. 22.

80c. OPDYKE, N. D. Palaeoclimatology and Continental Drift, in entry [*80a*], 41–65, and esp. Figs. 4 to 9, Fig. 11.

81. BLACKETT, P. M. S., CLEGG, J. A. & STUBBS, P. H. S. (1960) An Analysis of Rock Magnetic Data. *Proc.Roy.Soc.Lond.* Ser. A. *256*, 291–322; esp. Table 8 and text on p. 311.

82a. OLLIER, C. D. (1961) Lag deposits at Coober Pedy, South Australia. *Austr.J.Sci.*, *24*, 64–65.

82b. OLLIER, C. D. & TUDDENHAM, W. G. (1962) Slope Development at Coober Pedy, South Australia. *J.Geol.Soc.Austr.*, *9*, 91–106.

82c. OLLIER, C. D. (1963) Insolation Weathering. Examples from Central Australia. *Amer.J. Sci.*, *261*, 376–381.

83. JESSUP, R. W. (1960) The Stony Tableland Soils of the South-eastern Portion of the Australian Arid Zone and their Evolutionary History. *J.Soil Sci.*, *11*, 188–196.

84. MABBUTT, J. A. (1965) Stone Distribution in a Stony Tableland Soil. *Austr.J.Soil Research*, *3*, 131–142.

85. SPRINGER, M. E. (1958) Desert Pavement and Vesicular Layer of Some Soils of the Lahontan Basin, Nevada. *Proc.Soil Soc. Amer.*, *22*, 63–66.

86a. HALLSWORTH, E. G., ROBINSON, G. K. & GIBBONS, F. R. (1955) Studies in Pedogenesis in New South Wales, vii—The 'Gilgai' Soils. *J. Soil Sci.*, *6*, 1–31.

86b. COSTIN, A. B. (1955) A Note on Gilgaies and Frost-Soils *ibid.*, *6*, 32–34.

87a. DURY, G. H. (1966) Pediment Slope and Particle Size at Middle Pinnacle, near Broken Hill, New South Wales. *Austr.Geog. Studies*, *4*, 1–17.

87b. DURY, G. H. (in preparation) Dimensional Analysis of Gibber at Mt. Sturt, New South Wales.

88a. CRAFT, F. A. (1928) The Physiography of the Wollondilly River Basin. *Proc.Linn. Soc.N.S.W.*, *53*, 618–650.

88b. CRAFT, F. A. (1933) The Surface History of Monaro, N.S.W. *Ibid.*, *58*, 229–244.

88c. CRAFT, F. A. (1928) The Physiography of the Cox River Basin. *Ibid.*, *53*, 207–254.

88d. CRAFT, F. A. (1933) The Coastal Tablelands and Streams of New South Wales. *Ibid.*, *58*, 437–460.

89. HARRIS, W. J. (1938) The Physiography of the Echuca District. *Proc.Roy.Soc.Victoria*, new ser., *51*, 45–60.

90. JOHNSTON, E. J. (1953) Pedology of the Deniboota Irrigation District, New South Wales. *C.S.I.R.O.Austr.Soil Pubn.*, *1*.

91a. KING, L. C. (1962) *Morphology of the Earth*, 345–352. Oliver and Boyd, Edinburgh and London.

91b. *Ibid.*, 638–642.

92. CLOOS, H. (1939) Hebung-spaltung-Vulkanismus. *Geol.Rundschau, 30,* Zwischenheft 4A.

93. MARSHALL, C. E. & NARAIN, H. (1954) Regional Gravity Investigations in Eastern and Central Commonwealth. *Univ.Sydney Dept.Geol.Mem.,* 2.

94. VOISEY, A. H. (1956) Erosion Surfaces around Armidale, New South Wales. *J.Roy.Soc.N.S.W., 90,* 128–133.

95. BRITTLEBANK, C. C. (1900) The Rate of Erosion of Some River Valleys. *Geol.Mag.,* new ser., dec. iv, 7, 320–322.

96. OLLIER, C. D. & JOYCE, E. B. (1964) Volcanic Physiography of the Western Plains of Victoria. *Proc.Roy.Soc.Victoria, 77,* 357–376.

97. SOLOMON, M. (1962) The Tectonic History of Tasmania, in entry [20], 311–339.

98. DAVIES, J. L. (1962) Geomorphology and Glaciation (of Tasmania). *Ibid.,* 243–248.

99. NICHOLLS, K. D. (1960) Erosion Surfaces, River Terraces, and River Capture in the Launceston Tertiary Basin (Tasmania). *Proc.Roy.Soc.Tas., 94,* 1–12.

100a. BROWNE, W. R. & VALLANCE, T. G. (1957) Notes on some Evidences of Glaciation in the Kosciusko Region. *Proc.Linn.Soc.N.S.W., 82,* 125–143.

100b. BROWNE, W. R. & VALLANCE, T. G. (1963) Further Notes on Glaciation in the Kosciusko Region. *Ibid., 88,* 112–119.

101. RITCHIE, A. S. & JENNINGS, J. N. (1955) Pleistocene Glaciation and the Grey Mare Range. *J.Roy.Soc.N.S.W., 89,* 127–130.

102. GALLOWAY, R. W. (1963) Glaciation in the Snowy Mountains: A Reappraisal. *Proc.Linn.Soc.N.S.W., 88,* 180–198.

103. COSTIN, A. B., JENNINGS, J. N., BLACK, H. P. & THOM, B. G. (1964) Snow Action on Mount Twynam, Snowy Mountains, Australia. *J.Glaciology, 5,* 219–228.

104. SPARROW, G. W. A. (1961) The Granitic Relief of Southern New England. *Austr.Geog., 8,* 132–137.

105. JENNINGS, J. N. & AHMAD, N. (1957) The Legacy of an Ice Cap. *Ibid.,* 7, 62–75.

106. DERBYSHIRE, E. (1963) Glaciation of the Lake St. Clair District, West-central Tasmania. *Ibid., 9,* 97–110.

107. DURY, G. H. (1964) Australian Geochronology: Checklist 1. *Austr.J.Sci., 27,* 103–

109; items 49–51, and references appended thereto.

108. BROWN, E. H. (1960) *The Relief and Drainage of Wales.* U. of Wales Press, Cardiff. Esp. ch. 6, incl. tabular summary, 169–170.

109a. GILL, E. D. (ed.) (1956) Australian and New Zealand Research in Eustasy—Part I. *Austr.J.Sci., 19,* 17–23.

109b. GILL, E. D. (ed.) Australian and New Zealand Research in Eustasy—Part II. *Ibid.,* 54–58.

109c. Report of F. H. Bauer's findings, by TINDALE, N. B. *Ibid.,* 56.

109d. Summary by FAIRBRIDGE, R. W. of the findings of E. de C. Clarke and H. T. Phillips. *Ibid.,* 58.

109e. Summary by FAIRBRIDGE, R. W. *Loc.cit.*

109f. GILL, E. D. entry [*109b*], 55.

109g. FAIRBRIDGE, R. W. *Ibid.,* 57.

110. DAVIES, J. L. (1959) High Level Erosion Surfaces and Landscape Development in Tasmania. *Austr.Geog., 7,* 193–203.

111. ZEUNER, F. E. (1952) (3 ed.) *Dating the Past.* Methuen, London.

112. COTTON, C. A. (1963) The Question of High Pleistocene Shorelines. *Trans.Roy.Soc.N.Z., 2,* 51–62.

113. FAIRBRIDGE, R. W. (1961) Eustatic Changes in Sea Level. *Phys. and Chem. of the Earth, 4,* 99–185.

114a. HAILS, J. R. (1965) The Geomorphological History of the Macleay Deltaic Plain. *Austr.J.Sci., 27,* 214–215.

114b. HAILS, J. R. (1965) A Critical Review of Sea-level Changes in Eastern Australia. *Austr.Geog.Studies, 3,* 63–78.

114c. HAILS, J. R. (1964) The Coastal Depositional Features of South-eastern Queensland. *Austr.Geog., 9,* 207–217.

115. PATON, T. R. (1965) The Valley Fills of South-eastern Queensland. *Austr.J.Sci., 28,* 129–131.

116a. WALKER, P. H. (1960) A Soil Survey of the County of Cumberland. *N.S.W.Dept.Agric. Soil Survey Unit,* Bull., 2.

116b. WALKER, P. H. (1962) Terrace Chronology and Soil Formation on the South Coast of New South Wales. *J.Soil Sci., 13,* 178–186.

117. BELL, A. D. M. Personal communication.

118. EMILIANI, C. (1955) Pleistocene Temperatures. *J.Geol., 63,* 538–578.

119a. JENNINGS, J. N. (1957) Coastal Dune Lakes as exemplified from King Island, Tasmania. *Geog.Journ., 123,* 59–70.

119b. JENNINGS, J. N. (1959) The Coastal Geomorphology of King Island, Bass Strait, in relation to Changes in the Relative Level of Land and Sea. *Rec.Q.Victoria Mus.,Launceston,* new ser., *11,* 1–39.

120a. EDWARDS, A. B. (1941) Storm-wave Platforms. *J.Geomorph.,* *4,* 223–236.

120b. EDWARDS, A. B. (1951) Wave Action in Shore Platform Formation. *Geol.Mag.,* *88,* 41-49.

121a. BARTRUM, J. A. (1936) Honeycomb Weathering of Rocks near the Shoreline. *N.Z.J.Sci.Tech.,* *18,* 593-600.

121b. BARTRUM, J. A. (1938) Shore Platforms. *J.Geomorph.,* *1,* 266–268.

122a. WENTWORTH, C. K. (1938) Marine Bench-forming Processes I: Water-level Weathering. *Ibid.,* *1,* 6–32.

122b. WENTWORTH, C. K. (1939) Marine Bench-forming Processes II: Solution Benching. *Ibid.,* *2,* 3–25.

122c. WENTWORTH, C. K. (1944) Potholes, Pits, and Pans; Subaerial and Marine. *J.Geol.,* *52,* 117–130.

123a. JUTSON, J. T. (1939) Shore Platforms near Sydney. *J.Geomorph.,* *2,* 237–250.

123b. JUTSON, J. T. (1950) On the Terminology and Classification of Shore Platforms. *Proc.Roy.Soc.Victoria,* *62,* 71–78.

124. HILLS, E. S. (1949) Shore Platforms. *Geol. Mag.,* *86,* 137–152.

125a. BIRD, E. C. F. (1964) *Coastal Landforms: An Introduction to Coastal Geomorphology with Australian Examples.* A.N.U. Press, Canberra.

125b. BIRD, E. C. F. (1961) The Coastal Barriers of East Gippsland, Australia. *Geog.Journ.,* *127,* 460–468.

125c. BIRD, E. C. F. (1963) The Physiography of the Gippsland Lakes, Australia. *Zeitschr. für Geomorph.,* N.F. 7, 232–245.

126. LANGFORD-SMITH, T. & THOM, B. G. (in press) New South Wales Coastal Morphology. *J.Geol.Soc.Austr.*

127a. LANGFORD-SMITH, T. & HAILS, J. R. (1964) in GILL, E. D. AND OTHERS, A.N.Z.A.A.S. Quaternary Shorelines Committee 1964 Report, 389–390. *Austr.J.Sci.,* *26,* 388–391.

127b. LANGFORD-SMITH, T. & HAILS, J. R. (1966) New Evidence of Quaternary Sea Levels from the North Coast of New South Wales. *Austr.J.Sci.,* *28,* 352–353.

128. DURY, G. H. & LANGFORD-SMITH, T. Unpublished observations on the north coast of New South Wales.

Biogeography
With Australian Applications

G. ROSS COCHRANE

Introduction

Biogeography, the geography of living organisms, is concerned with the extremely varied and complex interrelationships of the phenomena of the biosphere. It investigates the origin, distribution, characteristics (adaptation to the environment), and association or interrelationships of plants and animals within areas.

Vegetation (the arrangement of the flora into discernible communities) is a geographical phenomenon of fundamental importance and is basic to human existence. Green plants, with their ability to convert light energy into bound chemical energy (photosynthesis), are fundamental to all life on earth. In addition to providing, both directly and indirectly, the food requirements of all animals (including man), plants provide fuel, materials for shelter, and many industrial raw materials for man.

Plant distributions are significant geographical elements in the visible landscape. After landforms, vegetation is the most widespread of all the readily visible phenomena of the earth's land surfaces. Frequently, it is more obvious than landforms as relief features are often masked by the vegetation cover. The universal character of vegetation is clearly expressed by Küchler [1, p. 434]: 'vegetation spreads its meaningful cover over the continents and islands and extends far out into the sea'.

Animal distributions are less obvious. Animals can migrate and need not adapt so much as plants to fixed environments. Nevertheless, animals also contribute to areal differences on the earth's surface [2, 3, 4, 5, 6].

Biotic communities exist more or less in harmony with their environment; hence they indicate conditions of the environment. All the individuals present, from the tallest tree or largest animal to the smallest micro-organism, compete for the resources of the environment, as they must adapt, migrate, or succumb. Each individual organism meets its requirements for space, food, shelter, and reproduction by various means. Morphological characteristics of plants are usually adaptive responses to environmental conditions. The structural and floristic differences of the four main land biochores (forest, savannah, grassland, desert) are an obvious expression of marked environmental differences (Fig. 1). Flag-form trees [7] and prostrate and wind-shorn coastal scrub are epharmonic responses to severe, sustained, largely unidirectional winds and strong, prevailing, salt-laden winds respectively.

Many species develop a wide tolerance. Thus *Eucalyptus radiata* (narrow-leaf peppermint) occurs over a much wider range of habitats than *E. regnans* (mountain ash). The latter is a good indicator of a rather narrow range of environmental conditions. Others escape unfavourable conditions by hibernation, by being deciduous, or by lying dormant as seed or spore. Activity and growth recommence with renewal of favourable conditions. This special aspect of tolerance is known as *avoidance*. It is characteristic of the numerous desert annuals frequently forming dense though short-lived herbage following heavy winter rains in Central Australia. Completion of the life-cycle takes only three to six weeks. *E. confertiflora*, *E. foelscheana*, *E. alba* and *E. tectifolia* become deciduous during the drought period of tropical Northern Australia's savannah climate.

A biotic community reflects climate and itself influences and modifies local and micro-climate, weathering, and erosional processes within, and at times beyond, the community habitat. The relationships of the ecosystem [8, 9, 10, 11], namely that of the community with its habitat (a surface area with its climate), are obvious in plant-physiographic patterns. Changes in altitude, slope, and aspect are faithfully recorded in the communities (Figs. 9, 10, 12, 14). Biogeography demonstrates the dynamic relationships among vegetation, soils, the abundance of micro-organisms, and animal populations. A community clearly indicates the degree of interference by man [12, 13].

Economic, social and cultural patterns can be equal in importance to factors of the physical and biotic environment. Malaria is a human disease caused by amoeboid pathogenic *Plasmodium* spp. introduced into man's bloodstream through the bite of an insect vector (various species of female *Anopheles* mosquito). Accumulating evidence shows that low standards of living, poor housing, lack of education, dietary nutritional deficiencies, lack of finance, primitive subsistence economies and low levels of technological achievement are important contributory causes of the disease in malarial areas. Temperature conditions, rainfall regime, nature of the surface soil, wind, humidity, and shelter afforded by vegetation and water directly influence the incidence of malaria. Historical factors are frequently important also. There is, for example, a close correlation in time and distribution between European trading and the spread of European malarial insect vectors to Asia.

If the dynamic character of communities is not appreciated, modification of one factor can lead to results far removed from those anticipated. Thus, in China, the removal of predators (sparrows) allowed a rapid increase of leaf-eating insect larvae to plague proportions. Resultant crop damage was enormous and far in excess of losses due to sparrows in previous years. The relationship between destruction of birds and army grub plagues on cereal crops in Victoria is a similar case. Where, then, does biogeography cease and do agricultural geography and human geography begin?

Biogeography can contribute much of value to policy planning. Its utilitarian value has been largely overlooked by many geographers, but biogeographical principles have long been appreciated elsewhere. Workers in various applied fields, in regional planning, in agronomy, in forestry, in commercial fishing, in wildlife management, in range management, in conservation, in public health, and in water catchment employ techniques of biogeography for the solution of many of their problems. One of Australia's most urgent problems is that of water, of water catchment, and of maximum economic utilization of water consistent with sound conservation practices. Repeated and eloquent pleas for the recognition of the complexity and dynamic nature of catchment area ecosystems [14, 15, 16, 17] are important first steps in long range planning in this context.

Thus, from a purely utilitarian point of view, biogeography has indisputable claims for closer study by geographers. The need for world plant inventories is obvious. An evaluation and reassessment of the intimate vegetation-soil-climate interrelationships is vital in view of the world's rapidly increasing population and technological advances. The urgency of these problems has been recognized; an International Biological Programme began, in 1965, investigating 'the biological basis of productivity and human welfare' [18].

Classification and Description in Plant Geography

In Australia, one of three main methods of the classification and description of vegetation seems to have been emphasized at a given time. The three methods are those of:

1. Floristic plant geography (the definition of floristic composition of vegetation, based on presence of individual species).

2. Ecological plant geography (the study of plant-habitat relationships).

3. Physiognomic plant geography (the study of the form or structure of plant communities).

Raup [19], Dansereau [20], and Küchler [1] give concise summaries of the aims and methods of such vegetation description.

Broadly speaking, floristics were most important until about thirty-five years ago when ecological studies increased. Structural studies have received attention during the last fifteen years. Blake [21], Wood [22, 23],

Crocker and Wood [24], Beadle and Costin [25], Christian and Perry [26], Costin [14], Williams [27], Christian [28], Webb [29, 30], Wood and Williams [31], Schweinfurth [32], and Cochrane [33] discuss aspects of these methods with reference to Australian vegetation. Phytosociological studies have received scant attention in Australia [34]. More recently, Goodall's objective statistical description of vegetation [35, 36, 37] has profoundly influenced world thought, but interpretation of method promotes some difficulty [38].

Each of these classifications has merits, each has its limitations. For a full and complete study of vegetation something of all approches is required—the complexities of ecosystems cannot be described by one method alone.

Environmental Dimensions

Because all organisms must exist in some habitat, many orders of magnitude of the environment are implied. A distinct hierarchy of units can be recognized, limited at each level of integration by the influences of the environment. The unit of greatest magnitude, the BIOSPHERE, comprises the earth's crust (lithosphere and hydrosphere) and the surrounding atmosphere, wherever living organisms occur or can exist (Fig. 1). The three divisions of the biosphere are the land, salt water, and fresh water BIOCYCLES. The first two generally occupy large contiguous areas, whereas the last is both localized and very diffuse in space. Density of the environment is the basis for differentiation into land and water biocycles and this, plus chemical composition, separates the water biocycles. Consequently, morphology of aquatic and terrestrial organisms reflect their adjustments to vastly different environments. Marine plankton must maintain a density near that of the surrounding water. This effect is achieved by obtaining a large surface-to-volume ratio, i.e. reduction to minimum size, by shape, giving 'form-resistance', by using the least and lightest structural materials, and by the inclusion of gas bubbles or oil globules. Terrestrial vegetation, characterized by higher plants than those of the water biocycles, commonly has complex specialized tissues. Rigidity and maximum size are often advantageous to land plants.

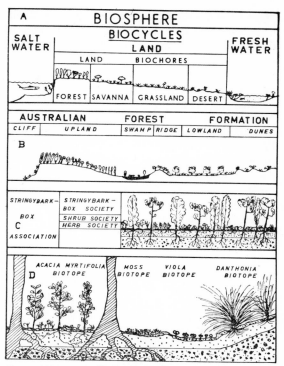

Fig. 1—Environmental dimensions, adapted from Dansereau [39]. A–The biosphere is made up of three biocycles in which the land biocycle is subdivided into four biochores. B–A formation within the forest biochore showing several habitats determined by topography. C–A single upland association with its three layers. D–The shrub and forest floor layers of the box-stringybark association with their ultimate divisions, the biotopes

Subsequent subdivisions of the water biocycles are chiefly related to depth, particularly to the depth of light penetration.

Within the land biocycle, the vegetation-soil-climate complex is clearly indicated in the four main BIOCHORES: forest, savannah, grassland, and desert (Fig. 1B). Each is characterized by a major type of vegetation the distribution of which is primarily, though by no means exclusively, a function of a meteorological gradient, *effective precipitation*. In addition to the purely climatic factors of precipitation (total, incidence, intensity, form and variability), and evaporation (temperature, wind and cloud), other factors (lithology, relief, slope, soil characteristics—e.g. depth and porosity—and vegetation cover)—all exert an important, interacting influence upon available moisture for plant growth. Responses to variations in light, heat, and moisture are obvious in the different dominant life-forms (trees, shrubs, herbs, grasses, lianas, forbs, epiphytes, succulents, palms, tree ferns, cushion plants and so on) present in the four biochores.

One or more plant FORMATIONS may be present within a biochore. A formation is defined on the basis of the physiognomy or life-form of the dominants. Within forests the dominant is considered as the tallest emergent tree, the main tree of the upper canopy. This need not necessarily be the numerically dominant species. Within Australia the forest biochore forms a narrow, peripheral and discontinuous band along the southeast and east of the continent from the dry and wet sclerophyll forests through areas of temperate rainforest to discontinuous pockets of tropical rainforest in the northeast. Rainforest is present in Arnhem Land, and dry and wet sclerophyll forest formations reappear in the extreme southwest. Temperate rainforest and dry and

wet sclerophyll forests are all present in Tasmania. In contradistinction, the savannah biochore forms a broad irregular crescent with a gap only at the Nullarbor Plains [33].

Within any of these formations there are one or more ASSOCIATIONS. These are usually climax vegetation (the most advanced vegetation type possible under prevailing conditions of the region). Associations within a formation are structurally similar but are recognizably distinct by the floristic composition of the dominants. Thus within the dry sclerophyll forest formation (the evergreen hardwood forest formation-type of Schimper [40]) the main structural characteristics are fairly homogeneous throughout southern Australia and Tasmania, but the floristic composition is widely variable. *Eucalyptus obliqua* (messmate) associations are common components of such formations in Victoria, Tasmania, New South Wales and South Australia, but are absent in Western Australia. *E. marginata* (jarrah) association is found in Western Australia. Even within quite small areas several distinct climax associations can be present. Four discrete associations (*E. obliqua, E. baxteri, E. rubida,* and *E. fasciculosa*) occur within an area of thirty-five square miles of dry sclerophyll forest in the Adelaide Hills (Fig. 2). Seven associations (*E. obliqua, E. radiata, E. elaeophora, E. macrorrhyncha, E. goniocalyx, E. baxteri,* and *E. viminalis*) are present in a similar formation in the Dandenong Range (Fig. 3).

Within any area, topography influences the number of habitats present. Each habitat in turn influences the nature of its ecosystem and the nature of the vegetation that develops. A HABITAT is an area of surface with its minerals, climate, light, heat, and moisture, where exchanges occur between organisms and the resources of the environment. Deeply-dissected areas with variable slopes and relative relief, complex lithology and pedology will have many habitats unlike undulating, well-drained areas of simple lithology and uniform soils which have relatively few. Commonly, many habitats are present even within 'uniform' areas of climax vegetation, e.g. the proportion of a region occupied by an ecosystem supporting the climatic climax formation (dry sclerophyll forest in Figs. 1-3) will depend upon the amount of well-drained areas.

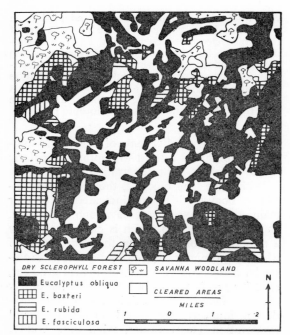

Fig. 2—Distribution of savannah woodlands, cleared areas, and *Eucalyptus obliqua,* E. *baxteri,* E. *rubida,* and E. *fasciculosa* associations in dry sclerophyll forest in the Mount Lofty Ranges, South Australia

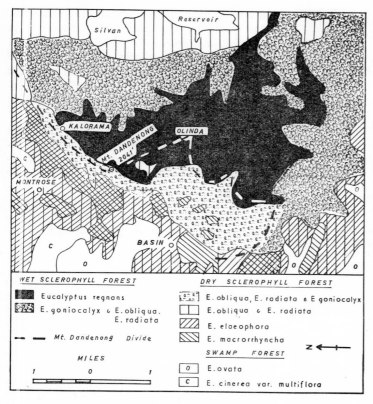

Fig. 3—The distribution of 'wet' and 'dry' sclerophyll forest in the Dandenong Range, Victoria, is found to the east and to the west of the mountain divide respectively. *Eucalyptus goniocalyx* occurs in both wet sclerophyll forest, and at the humid margins of dry sclerophyll forest (see Fig. 12): *E. regnans* occurs only in wet sclerophyll forest. The other associations shown all occur within the small area of dry sclerophyll forest mapped. This reappears on the low areas to the east beyond the lee of the range

Each habitat favours a particular ecosystem which consists of one or more communities. A COMMUNITY is a group of organisms living together, having mutual relationships among themselves and with the habitat, which they either alter or maintain. An ECOTONE is a zone between two adjacent communities where their elements mingle. This term is usually associated with CLIMAX VEGETATION, i.e. communities in harmony with their existing environment, and capable of reproducing themselves. A changeover stage in succession where elements of the incoming community mingle with those of the one being superseded is a MICTIUM (Fig. 13).

Communities, in turn, can be further subdivided. Many plant communities, particularly those with varying life-forms, are often structurally complex with layering or stratification present. The members of a community similar in growth form, with comparable habitat requirements, and occupying a horizontal layer of definite depth form a SYNUSIA, or layer

society. Dry sclerophyll forest communities have a tree, low shrub, and dwarf shrub and/or herb layer (Fig. 4). A fourth stratum, the tall shrub-low-tree layer, frequently occurs in moister habitats, but coverage is not extensive [41]. Tropical rainforests commonly have several different tree synusiae [42]. A more specialized, somewhat restricted definition of structural layers in equatorial rainforests has been advanced recently [43].

Any synusia, in turn, may be made up of several BIOTOPES occupying micro-habitats, the ultimate divisions of the habitat. Within a biotope (named according to its dominant plants) plant species utilize relatively little space and exist under even more restricted conditions than the synusia as a whole (Fig. 1D). Some plants have a very narrow range of tolerance and are therefore restricted to a limited range of habitats. Thus, certain epiphytic filmy ferns and non-vascular epiphytes (algae, lichens, mosses and hepatics) growing on the rough bark of *Acacia melanoxylon* (blackwood) or on

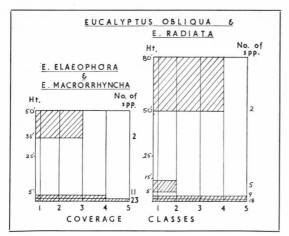

Fig. 4—Coverage-stratification diagrams comparing two different dry sclerophyll forest associations, Dandenong Range. Number and height of strata are graphically shown as well as the coverage class and the number of species involved in each stratum. Coverage classes: 1—under 5%; 2—5-25%; 3—26-50%; 4—51-75%; 5—76-100%

the fibrous trunks of tree ferns, *Dicksonia antarctica* and *Cyathea australis,* in the wet sclerophyll forest of the Otway Ranges, are good indicators of the specific biotope where they live.

Fig. 1 shows the progressive environmental control upon vegetation as the smallest biocenotic unit, the biotope, is approached. The whole evergreen hardwood forest formation, of which the Australian wet and dry sclerophyll forest formation is part, is a section of the land forest biochore. It is conditioned by climatic conditions of cool moist winters and warm to hot drier summers. In the Australian case, leached podzolic soils of low nutrient status are also an important influence. Within the appropriate climatic zone, the areal extent of Australian sclerophyll forest formation is further restricted by topography. Even within the formation, habitat conditions, particularly local climate (aspect) and edaphic factors (depth, texture, and moisture retentivity) influence the distribution of a specific association. Again, the forest-floor layer (dwarf shrub-herb synusia), a subordinate stratum within the forest association, reflects groundlevel microclimatic conditions within the forest vegetation. Finally the culmination of all of these environmental influences plus micro-climatic, micro-edaphic,

and biological conditions within the forest-floor synusia confines the small herb micro-society, e.g. *Viola hederacea* (ivy-leaf violet) to its particular niche. Thus, this ultimate unit, the *Viola hederacea* biotope, occurring in a specific site, is the final result of many varied interactions between environmental controls and vegetation.

These interactions between the environment and vegetation demonstrate a constant relationship or law—the law of geoecological distribution. Boyko [44] has shown that the specific micro-distribution of an ecotypic plant or of a plant community is controlled by the same ecological amplitudes that govern its broader geographical distribution, or macro-distribution.

Environmental Factors

We have seen that plant communities result from the interaction of the many factors of the environment. Four main groups of ecological factors can be recognized — climatic, physiographic, edaphic, and biotic. Some authors group together the closely-interacting physiographic and edaphic factors, others give pyric (fire) factors separate discussion. Fire factors result from lightning (climatic) or from man (biotic). Biotic factors are sometimes divided into biotic (plant and animal) and societal (man). Change in any one factor can set off a whole series of actions and interactions, each of which further modifies the environment. In turn these modifications induce functional responses by the vegetation. The visible expressions of these interactions are the complex patterns and forms of the world's vegetation.

Although environmental interactions are complex and often but poorly understood, the immediate agents of influence are largely limited to light, heat, moisture, and food. These are all affected, either directly or indirectly, by variations in the four chief groups of ecological factors.

Macro-climate is the chief controlling factor in plant distributions. World regional patterns of vegetation reflect the importance of the main factors of climate — latitude, juxtaposition of continents and oceans, physiography, pressure 'belts', and marine currents. Quantitative meteorological records for an area (e.g. 15 in. an. av. rainfall, 65° F an. av. temperature) rarely show a close parallel to vegetation distribution, because they fail to record interactions between climatic elements and living organisms. Nevertheless there is a close linkage among the distribution patterns of climate, of vegetation, and of soils. This relationship is demonstrated schematically by Thornthwaite and Blumenstock [45] using the climatic indices of P-E and T-E. It is important to remember that the major role of climate is a limiting one—it restricts the types of vegetation that can be present in an area. However, the actual communities occupying a specific habitat are a reflection not only of climate but also of other factors. In Australia, edaphic factors are of considerable importance [22, 46, 47, 48].

Climatic Factors

Of the various elements comprising climate, probably the most obvious in their influence upon vegetation are light, heat, precipitation, wind, and also humidity and evaporation which amount to combinations of the preceding three. Combinations of respective incidence produce differing types of regional climate, each with its own particular rhythms—diurnal, seasonal, and periodic. Seasonal rhythms are responsible for striking aspect dominance displayed by various undershrub species in the dry sclerophyll forests of South Australia and Victoria, e.g. the late hibernal-prevernal (i.e. late winter-before spring) aspect dominance of *Leptospermum myrsinoides* (tea tree), the early vernal aspect dominance of *Acacia myrtifolia* (myrtle wattle), and the late vernal aspect dominance of *Pultenaea daphnoides* (native broom or large-leaf bush pea) in the southern Mount Lofty Ranges in South Australia. A similar sequence is displayed in the Dandenong Range of Victoria by *Platylobium formosum* (handsome flat-pea), *Kennedya prostrata* (scarlet coral-pea), *Acacia myrtifolia* and *Pultenaea scabra* (rough bush-pea).

Those variations within regional climates which are produced by topography result in local climates, and, on a smaller scale, in micro-climates. Thus, distinct local climates occur on the steep northern and southern hill slopes in the Otway Ranges of Southern Victoria. *Eucalyptus obliqua* (messmate) and *E. goniocalyx* (mountain grey gum) associations found on the northern slopes are replaced by *E. globulus* (blue gum) and *E. viminalis* (manna gum) associations on the cooler, moister southern slopes (Figs. 5, 12a). In the Dandenong Range, the northern and western slopes are characterized by dry sclerophyll forest, chiefly of *E. elaeophora* (long-leaf box), *E. radiata* (narrow-leaf peppermint), *E. obliqua*, *E. baxteri* (brown stringybark), and *E. macrorrhyncha* (red stringybark) associations. In direct contrast the eastern and southeastern flanks, which receive less insolation, are characterized by wet sclerophyll forest dominated by *E. goniocalyx* and *E. regnans* (mountain ash) associations (Figs. 3, 12b).

Within a forest community, variations in canopy cover, number and density of vegetation tiers, and the protection from wind and insolation afforded by rock outcrops result in numerous micro-climates, each supporting its specific microsociety. Within an *E. macrorrhyncha-E. elaeophora* association on the north-western flank of the Dandenong Range, micro-climatic differences result in the occurrence on the forest floor of four different biotopes on adjacent sites and within a small area. These are the *Danthonia semi-annularis* (wallaby grass), *Kennedya prostrata* (a prostrate trailing plant), *Viola hederacea* (a creeping perennial herb), and *Ceratodon purpureus* (moss) biotopes. Thus, because climate largely prescribes vegetation types, some brief consideration of the main climatic elements is warranted. For a fuller discussion the reader is referred to Daubenmire [49] and Klages [50].

Light

Solar energy is vital to plant life because photosynthesis cannot occur without light. The duration, distribution, intensity, and quality of insolation vary enormously from place to place, and even within a stand of vegetation. The various synusiae within a forest have light-climates which differ even to the composition of the spectrum at successive levels. Light conditions vary with latitude, altitude, aspect, cloudiness, whether in the open, on the outside of a plant canopy, or on a forest floor. Furthermore, suitable light-climates for plant growth may have their effective period restricted by heat, cold, flood, drought, or similar excess, or by deficiency or fluctuation in some other interacting environmental factor.

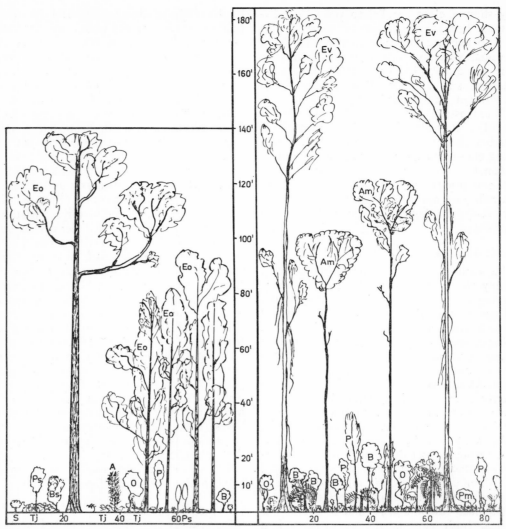

Fig. 5—Profile diagrams of *Eucalyptus obliqua* (left) and of *E. viminalis* (right) associations in the Otways show the influence of local climates upon structure and floristic composition. The former community occurs chiefly on north-facing slopes, the latter on south-facing slopes. Key to symbols: A, *Acacia verticillata;* Am, *Acacia melanoxylon;* B, *Bedfordia salicifolia;* Bs, *Bursaria spinosa;* Eo, *Eucalyptus obliqua;* Ev, *Eucalyptus viminalis;* O, *Olearia* spp.; P, *Pomaderris;* Pm, *Prostanthera melissifolia;* Ps, *Phebalium squameum;* Tj, *Tetrarrhena juncea*

Light Intensity. Not all plants increase photosynthesis with an increase in light intensity. Light-loving or light-tolerant plants (heliophytes) achieve maximum growth rate in full sunlight and with an increase in light. Examples are the cosmopolitan *Pteridium esculentum* (bracken fern), the provincial sclerophyllous porcupine grass, *Triodia irritans,* and the regionally distributed shrub

Goodenia ovata (hop Goodenia) and grass *Danthonia* (*Notodanthonia*) *semi-annularis*. Sciophilous (shade-tolerant) species such as tree ferns (*Cyathea cunninghamii, Alsophila australis, Dicksonia antarctica* and *Todea barbara*), ground ferns (*Blechnum* spp.), epiphytic filmy ferns (*Mecodium flabellatum* and *Hymenophyllum cupressiforme*), and forest-floor herbs utilize only a small percentage of

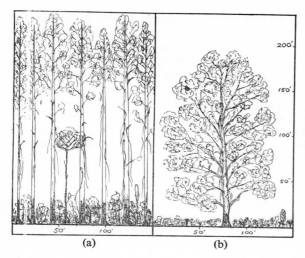

(a)   (b)

Fig. 6—Eucalyptus regnans of the same age and in the same locality. In conditions of restricted light, elongation is favoured and lateral growth is restricted. In the open, maximum light has retarded apical dominance and favoured lateral growth

full light intensity. These shade-loving plants exhibit an early check in their rate of carbon assimilation and do not increase photosynthetic processes with increasing sunlight above about one-tenth maximum light intensity.

Light intensity, which is so important for photosynthesis, also influences growth by inhibiting apical dominance. Thus, in the open, elongation of *Eucalyptus regnans* is retarded and lateral development favoured. In more closed conditions, for example in stands in forests, tree form is much taller, narrower, and pole-like (Figs. 6a, 6b).

Light Duration. Light duration is important for reproductive processes. Some plants require long days for flowering (longidiurns); others, require short day lengths (brevidiurns). The distribution of such plants corresponds to latitudinal insolation patterns so the brevidiurns are found in low latitudes and longidiurns in high latitudes.

Light and Germination

Light conditions for germination differ widely. Some forest dominants require the shade conditions provided by secondary forest or nursery scrub for successful germination, others require full light. *Leptospermum* spp. (tea tree) seedlings germinate in full sunlight and soon form a canopy which casts shade and prevents germination of new seeds nearby, thus effectively reducing competition. Sciophilous species later become established beneath the *Leptosper-*

mum. The exotic weeds *Cytisus canariensis* (cape broom) and *Ulex europaeus* (gorse) require full light for germination. The denuding of scrub and the defoliation of trees by bushfires in the Adelaide Hills provided more favourable conditions for vigorous germination of such seeds, than for many partly or fully shade-loving indigenous scrub species [41].

Table 1

Surface	Albedo (% reflectivity)
Fresh snow	87
Long dry grass	32
Vegetation (average value)	25
Oak leaves	25
Desert	25
Dry sand	18
Forest	15
Oak and pine forest	15
Moist bare ground	10
Wet sand	9
Water (angle of sun 60°)	6

Consequently these exotic weeds spread rapidly after bushfires, particularly where the ecological balance has been disturbed by man. Within three months of the severe January 1962 bushfire, the eastern flanks of the Dandenong Range were almost completely covered by a dense growth of *Pteridium esculentum* two to five feet high. The pronounced spreading of the twice or thrice pinnate fronds of this heliophilous plant to catch the maximum light produced a dense shade, and underneath a markedly milder micro-climate favourable for the germination of numerous sciophilous shrubs and herbs. Many of these have subsequently overtopped the bracken, in some cases killing it by their shade.

Phototropism. Another adaptation to light is the tendency of certain plants to grow away from or towards light (phototropism). Many *Eucalyptus* spp. demonstrate negative phototropism by orienting their leaves vertically, exposing the minimum surface to the light. Certain *Compositae* (daisy family) are positively phototropic. Some animals also exhibit strong positive phototropism, for example, kelp flies, moths, and other night insects.

Ecological Amplitude or Valence

The apparent preferences or adaptations of species to particular environmental factors demonstrate their range of tolerance, i.e. their ECOLOGICAL AMPLITUDE or VALENCE. Thus, sciophilous plants favour shady habitats, and heliophilous plants prefer sunny sites. Similar standard nomenclature is applied to plants normally existing where one environmental factor is dominant. For example, the basophilous are 'salt-tolerant', the xerophilous 'drought-resistant', and so on.

The ecological amplitude may be narrow (steno-) or wide (eury-). Euryvalent species have a broad ecological amplitude, stenovalent species a narrow one. Common heliophilous plants are *Goodenia ovata,* the composite, *Helichrysum scorpioides* (curled everlasting) and *Pteridium esculentum.* The former two are stenophotic, for they cannot tolerate shading, the latter is euryphotic. Bracken exists through a broad range of light conditions from semi-shade to full light, although it still remains at one end of the light-climate. In contrast, the euryphotic sciophilous undershrubs, *Indigofera australis* (austral indigo) and *Goodia lotifolia* (golden-tip) remain at the opposite end of the light range. Sciophilous plants with a narrow range, such as the stenophotic king fern (*Todea barbara*) and the river-fringe fern *Adiantum formosum,* are tolerant only of full shade conditions.

Temperature

Temperature is a very important climatic element affecting the rates of chemical reactions and of living processes. Under humid conditions, chemical reactions in temperate and tropic areas are 3 and 10 times faster respectively than in microthermal or polar areas. The broad vegetation regions of the world clearly reflect temperature distribution. Altitudinal vegetation zonation demonstrates a clear relationship with temperature and its influence upon plant physiological processes. Even man (particularly his comfort, his incentive and his ability to work) is affected by temperature, though probably not as categorically 'controlled' as Huntington [51] postulated.

Extreme temperatures limit plant growth, but there is a wide variance between both limiting and optimum temperature for different groups of plants. Indeed, there are but few places that are naturally either too cold or too hot for any plant life. Marked local temperature differences result from different albedo of receiving surfaces for insolation (Table 1). Similarly, soil colour, texture, and moisture content influence local temperatures, often resulting in significant vegetation differences.

The most widely used climatic classification, that of Köppen, both in its pure and modified versions, is primarily based upon temperature-vegetation relationships. Quantitative climatic indices are fitted to thermal vegetation regions recognized by the botanist de Candolle [52] in the late nineteenth century.

Plant-temperature Categories. Recognition of plant adaptations to temperature conditions is seen in the convenient classification of plants into the following groups:

MEGATHERMS, plants tolerant of warm to hot habitats (porcupine grasses, *Triodia* spp.; mulga, *Acacia aneura*; fan palm, *Livingstona humilis*; screw pine, *Pandanus spiralis*; Cycad palm, *Cycas media*; Mitchell grasses, *Astrebla* spp.).

MESOTHERMS, medium-temperature plants, intermediate between megatherms and microtherms (golden bush-pea, *Pultenaea gunnii*; common apple-berry, *Billardiera scandens*; *Eucalyptus radiata*).

MICROTHERMS, plants favouring cold conditions (snow gum, *E. niphophila*; alpine filmy-fern, *Hymenophyllum peltatum*; silver daisy, *Celmisia longifolia*; myrtle beech, *Notho-*

fagus cunninghamii; crag Wallaby-grass, *Danthonia alpicola*; *D. robusta*).

HEKISTOTHERMS, alpine and tundra plants, not important in Australia (giant wallaby grass, *Danthonia frigida*; anemone buttercup, *Ranunculus anemoneus*; *Plantago muelleri*; *Montia australasica*).

The parallel between these plant groups and Köppen's A, C, D, and E-type climates is obvious; the relationships with BS and BW climates is less apparent but is still present.

STENOTHERMS (*Ranunculus anemoneus, Danthonia frigida*) and EURYTHERMS (*Themeda australis* or kangaroo grass) are recognized, but the terms are not widely used.

Although vegetation is the single best reflection of climate, a close relationship between recorded meteorological values and the vegetation of an area is often not readily evident. This fact results from the obvious limitations of quantitative climatic averages (usually taken at one level only, restricted number of stations, and so on), and their failure to show effects of extremes, of interactions with soil, or of internal (physiological) and external (ecological and sociological) biotic factors.

Moisture

Moisture, as precipitation, as atmospheric water-vapour (measured using relative humidity), and as soil water, is vital for plant processes. Even under identical climatic, physiographic, and edaphic conditions, moisture requirements vary among plant species according to genetic makeup. Wide variations in ecological tolerance are shown by the great number of anatomical and morphological adaptations displayed by plants, from xerophytes (plants of dry areas) to hydrophytes (plants living in largely submerged conditions). Furthermore, moisture requirements of an individual plant can change at various stages in its life-cycle. Thus, established *Atriplex* (saltbush) plants exist through drought conditions. Seedlings do not germinate unless there is sufficiently heavy rainfall to dissolve salt in the seed capsule, and at the same time to moisten the soil so that there will be a reasonable chance for successful seedling establishment.

Acacia aneura (mulga) seeds may germinate with light rain, but will not continue growing unless there is a series of wet seasons. The deeper-rooted mature shrubs are untroubled by dry conditions that will kill young seedlings. The unusually wet winter and spring of 1964 in Victoria favoured luxuriant and profuse flowering of the irregularly-flowering Mallee Eucalypts, *Eucalyptus calycogona* (red Mallee) and *E. oleosa* (oil Mallee).

Moisture Availability. Moisture availability implies more than precipitation in its various forms (rain, snow, hail, sleet, fog, dew, etc.); it involves interactions with many other environmental factors. Vegetation reflects the effective precipitation of an area. It is obviously related to the amount, form, type (frontal, convective, orographic), intensity, and seasonal incidence of precipitation, and also to temperature. High totals of precipitation favour tree growth, particularly if precipitation is relatively evenly distributed. Moisture from snow thaw favours the herbfields and the tall, tussock grasslands of Australia's alpine High Plains. Dew is an important source of moisture for many desert plants in the continent's arid interior. The clear atmosphere, and the large diurnal temperature range resulting from heating by intense incoming short-wave, solar radiation during the day, and from cooling by outgoing terrestrial long-wave radiation at night, suit the formation of dew. The distribution of vicariant species of *Eucalyptus* with altitude clearly reflects orographic precipitation (Fig. 11). Much water is lost by surface run-off from high-intensity, short-duration, convective rain in the sparsely vegetated, semi-arid and arid areas of Australia. The high rates of evaporation resulting from the prevailing high temperatures, low relative humidities, and general windiness associated with lack of protective trees, further reduce the amount of water available for plant growth. The regimen of alternating hot dry summers and cool moist winters favours the growth of small and leathery-leaved (sclerophyllous) undershrubs in the southern sclerophyll forests.

Physiographic factors influence moisture availability. Slopes affect surface run-off and drainage. Evaporation is greatest on slopes exposed to wind and insolation. The vegetation on northeastern slopes is commonly more mesic than that found on the northwestern slopes exposed to the warmer afternoon sun (Fig. 10). Marked differences in water availability exist between windward and leeward (rainshadow) slopes.

Lithology and soil characteristics such as depth, texture (gravel to sand to clay), porosity, structure (crumb, columnar, compact . . .), depth of ground water level and whether relatively static or markedly fluctuating seasonally, humus content and moisture retentivity status —all constitute important factors in water availability for plant growth.

The local vegetation largely corresponds to the available water. It can be seen that water deficiency may result from climatic, edaphic, or physiographic factors, or from combinations of these. With decreasing rainfall, unless offset by some very favourable combination of factors, available moisture declines and plants adapt by becoming increasingly drought-resistant. Xeromorphic adaptations generally involve reducing moisture loss of the plant. Moisture loss is minimized by a reduction of surface area, such as with microphylly, rolled leaves, substitution of spines for leaves; by protection of leaf surfaces with epidermal hairs or wax; by succulence; by reduction of stomata, or by having these on the underside; and by various other morphological or anatomical modifications. In keeping with its reputation as the world's driest continent, Australia records a high percentage of its flora as exhibiting xeromorphic features.

Plant-moisture Categories. Plants can be classified according to their moisture requirements. The following categories are recognized:

HYDROPHYTES are species living more or less permanently submerged in water, such as the water lily, *Nymphaea gigantea*; the free-floating pondweed, *Pistia stradiodes*; the submerged *Ceratophyllum demersum*; and in shallow water, *Polygonum* spp., and sedges of *Cyperus* spp. and *Eleocharis* spp. Some authorities distinguish between Aquatics, which are permanently immersed species such as the examples above, and Amphibians, species that alternate between land and water biocycles. Examples of Amphibians are the mangroves, *Rhizophora*

mucronata and *Avicennia marina* var. *resinifera*, rushes (*Scirpus* spp.), sedges (*Eleocharis* spp.), and certain grasses such as *Oryza fatua* (wild rice), *Phragmites karka*, and the almost cosmopolitan *P. communis* (common reed.).

HYGROPHYTES are moisture-loving plants that generally require a saturated medium. Many ferns and epiphytic mosses, *Eucalyptus camaldulensis* (river red gum), *E. ovata* (swamp gum), *Pandanus aquaticus*, some *Melaleuca* species, especially varieties of *M. leucadendra* (paperbark tree), and *M. ericifolia* (swamp paperbark), the cord-rushes (*Restio* spp.), *Plantago muelleri*, and forest wire-grass (*Tetrarrhena juncea*), are all hygrophilous species. Most of these favour heavy damp soils and many flank swamps or bogs.

MESOPHYTES, intermediate between hygrophytes and xerophytes, are species growing where moisture is readily available. Normally, neither water excesses nor deficiencies occur. Many forest trees, shrubs, and herbs are mesophilous.

XEROPHYTES are species living in habitats where water is scarce. Arenarian grasses, such as *Zygochloa paradoxa* (sandhill cane-grass) of desert dunes, the sand-binding *Spinifex hirsutus* (hairy spinifex) and *S. longifolius* of southern and northern coastal dunes respectively; and *Triodia* spp. and *Plectrachne* spp. of sandy and stony areas are all tolerant of high temperatures and extended drought. The dune convolvulus, *Ipomoea pes-caprae*, is another. The spiny needle-bushes and needle-trees (*Hakea* spp.), the desert shrubs and small trees, *Acacia aneura*, *A. cambegei* (gidgea), *A. sowdenni*, *A. pendula* (myall), and *Casuarina* spp.; the semi-succulent, chenopodiaceous bushes of *Atriplex* spp. and *Rhagodia* spp. (saltbush), and *Kochia* spp. (bluebush), are also characteristic Australian xerophytes.

STENOHYGRIC plants (most forest ferns, e.g. *Adiantum formosum* (maidenhair fern), *Athyrium australe* (Austral lady-fern)) show very little tolerance to extremes. These two hygrophilous ferns occur only in very damp habitats and in addition, both are also stenophotic sciophilous species, growing only in deep shade. In contrast, the EURYHYGRIC species have a wide tolerance of moisture conditions. *Eucalyptus camaldulensis*, an hygrophilous tree, can withstand prolonged flooding (up to seven months), or very much longer periods of near-drought conditions. Various rushes and sedges, notably *Scirpus* and *Eleocharis*, display similar wide tolerances, as do also the succulent chenopods, *Salicornia* and *Arthrocnemum* (glassworts). *Glinus lotoides* (hairy carpet-weed) has been observed growing through the whole range of conditions from dry soils under drought conditions to complete submergence under shallow water—that is, from xeric to hydric.

Evaporation. The rate of water loss from plants, soils, free water surfaces, snow, and ice, obviously depends upon precipitation. Normally, evaporation increases with rising temperatures, exposure, and increasing wind velocities. Conversely, it decreases with increasing cloudiness and increasing humidity. Below 1650 ft. a.s.l. in the Otway Ranges, *Eucalyptus regnans* is restricted to moist sheltered valleys. Its more common occurrence over a wider range of topography above this altitude corresponds closely to the prevalence of the cloud base at this same elevation. The cloud blanket effectively reduces insolation, lowers temperatures and evaporation, and reduces temperature and humidity ranges. The lower temperatures and high relative humidity of the clouds (fogs or mists) further enhance the effectiveness of the relatively high orographic precipitation, thereby creating favourable conditions for mountain ash (*E. regnans*) forest.

The evaporating power of the atmosphere directly affects plant transpiration (the uptake of water, its use in plant metabolism, and its subsequent 'evaporation' from stomata into the atmosphere). The varying degrees of xeromorphy displayed by plants where water is scarce are attempts to reduce transpiration. The relative humidity of the atmosphere (the actual water-vapour content as a percentage of the total possible at a particular temperature) gives an approximate measure of evaporation potential. The saturation deficit of the atmosphere (the amount of water-vapour required to saturate the atmosphere) takes temperature into account, and therefore shows a much closer relationship to potential evaporation or plant transpiration than that of relative humidity. The direct relationship between saturation deficit and evaporation only holds if both the air and the evaporating surface are at the same temperature. As temperatures vary within vegetation communities, and even from different parts of the plant, relative humidity or saturation deficit figures for a particular station are wholly inadequate to explain plant distributions, even in relatively close proximity to the recording station, other than on the broadest basis.

Most available measurements of evaporation are taken on the free water surface of dish evaporimeters. Taking no account of soil moisture conditions, they contribute little to the interpretation of plant community composition and distribution. Atmometer readings, based

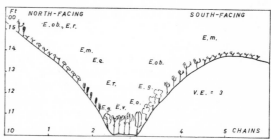

Fig. 9—Cross-section, with vegetation communities, of a valley in the Dandenong Range. Due to marked topographic relief, distinct local climates, with their resultant vegetation, are present not only on different aspects, but also on the valley floor, valley slopes, and ridge crests. Because of the steep valley sides, direct sun rarely reaches the valley floor where moist conditions favour tall stands of *Eucalyptus viminalis* (E.v.). *E. ovata* (E.o.) or swamp gum flanks the stream in the southern lee only. *E. goniocalyx* (E.g.) grows at higher altitudes on the shady southern slope than on its northern counterpart. It is replaced by *E. obliqua* (E.ob.) at about 1200 ft. on the south side, which does not appear on the northern slope until 1500 ft. where higher orographic precipitation offsets the greater insolation of the northern aspect. Decreasing protection from wind and insolation from the south-facing hill results in the successive replacement, on the north-facing slope, of *E. goniocalyx*, *E. radiata* (E.r.), *E. elaeophora* (E.e.) and *E. macrorrhyncha* (E.m.). The latter is also present on the hill crest where maximum exposure occurs. As already noted, with more precipitation from increasing elevation, *E. obliqua* (and *E. radiata*) replace *E. macrorrhyncha*

on evaporation from a porous sphere or cup linked to a reservoir and set in the ground, relate much more closely to transpiration rates of adjacent plants, but such readings are, as yet, few.

Wind

Wind is important in many ways, particularly its ability to increase the evaporation rate of exposed surfaces; as a dispersal agent; in its effects upon the distribution of plant communities reflecting a wide range of wind-tolerance; and in its sheer physical force, uprooting trees (Fig. 7), modifying plant form (Fig. 8), and increasing the heat intensity (radiant heat) of a forest fire.

No one meteorological factor is a good criterion of ecological conditions. Attempts have been made (usually involving various ratios of temperature, precipitation and evaporation) to identify a single comprehensive climatic value as a close influence on plant distribution [53, 54, 55, 56]. Some of the results (e.g. length of growing season) are encouraging, but detailed application is restricted by lack of widespread meteorological data. Also, any of these attempts merely emphasize that vegetation is not only a reflection of complex interactions between climate and plants, but also among these and topography, soils, and biotic factors.

Physiographic Factors

Altitude

Some interrelationships among topography, climate, and vegetation have already been noted viz. marked topographic relief produces local climates and associated different vegetation (Fig. 9); micro-relief influences the distribution of biotypes; relative humidity tends to increase whereas temperatures decrease with increase in altitude. Increasing windiness, exposure, and intensity of heat-radiation with altitude is reflected in the zonal sequence of vegetation from forest, through sub-alpine shrubs, to alpine tussock grasslands and fell-fields in the higher mountains of southern New South Wales, of Victoria, and of Tasmania [14, 57, 32].

Also associated with the change in life-form of communities from tree, to shrub, to grami-noid (grass-like herb) and forb (broadleaf herb) produced by increasing altitude, there is generally a reduction in the numbers of species present. This is even more marked at elevations above those found in Australia [34, 58, 59]. In the New Zealand Alps, which rise to a maximum height of over 5000 ft. more than Mount Kosciusko (7328 ft.), over 270 different species are found at 3000 ft., but only 22 occur above 5000 ft. [60].

The tree-limit or timberline varies with latitude. It is 5000 ft. in the southern highlands of New South Wales, 4500 ft. in Victoria, and 3000 ft. in Tasmania. Local variations also result from important topographic effects such as aspect and exposure. The tree line is noticeably higher on south-facing than on north-facing slopes on account of the greater insolation which produces warmer and drier conditions on the latter. Because of the warmth of the afternoon sun, western slopes are considerably warmer than eastern ones. This can mean quite different vegetation communities on the two sides of a mountain, a valley, or even of a spur. Numerous examples of such close juxtaposition of vegetation, correlated with aspect differences, occur in the Dandenong Range, not only among the forest dominants (Figs. 3, 9) but also among the sub-dominants of the sclerophyll scrub synusia [61] (Fig. 10).

Commonly in Australia, several species belonging to the genus *Eucalyptus* replace one another successively with increasing altitude. This substitution of vicariant species results from changes in local climate engendered by topography. From the river flats to the high plains up to a maximum of 6000 ft. the species listed in Fig. 11 replace one another, although in any transect one or more may be absent, or others present, because of habitat conditions. Also there can be substantial overlap, for example, between *Eucalyptus goniocalyx*, *E. regnans*, and *E. gigantea* (red mountain ash).

The important effects of aspect upon the sequence of vicariant species, up to 2000 ft. in the Dandenong Range and the Otway Ranges, are demonstrated in Fig. 12.

Lithology and Slope

In the Adelaide Hills, steep angular landforms supporting xeric plant communities on shallow

Fig. 7—A *Eucalyptus obliqua* uprooted by wind-throw. Strong winds, following heavy winter rains, uprooted many *E. obliqua* growing on shallow, saturated soils on exposed ridges in the Otways in 1964

Fig. 8—Wind epharmone of *Leptospermum*. Strong salt-laden winds have shorn the tree to a shrub form and growth occurs only in the protection of its own lee. The adjacent *Leptospermum*, sheltered behind the large, wind-resistant, and cyclic salt-tolerant *Metrosideros* have grown upright to 60 feet

Fig. 10(a)—An *Acacia myrtifolia* socies growing on the northwest slope of a spur in the Dandenong Range

Fig. 10(b)—A *Pultenaea scabra* socies found on the northeast slope of the same spur within a few yards of the *A. myrti-folia* community

Fig. 17—Yacca (*Xanthorrhoea australis*), *Astroloma conostephioides*, *Daviesia corym-bosa*, *Platylobium obtusangulum*, *Tetratheca pilosa*, *Epacris impressa*, and other subordinate species of dry sclerophyll forest growing under the canopy of *Eucalyptus baxteri*

Common Name	Eucalyptus Species (a)	Common Range in Elevation (ft)	Average Height of Tree (ft)
River red gum	E. camaldulensis	0–1000	80–150
Narrow leaf peppermint	E. radiata	400–1500	50–150
Manna gum	E. viminalis	500–2000	50–200
Messmate	E. obliqua	700–2000	80–250
Mountain grey gum	E. goniocalyx	1000–2000	200–250
Mountain ash	E. regnans	1500–3500 absolute range in Victoria (500–4400)	200–300
Red mountain ash	E. gigantea	2000–3000	100–250
Silvertop	E. sieberiana	1000–5000	80–150
Cider gum	E. gunnii	2000–5000	20–30
Dargo gum	E. perriniana	4000–5000	15–30
Snow gum	E. niphophila	4000–6000	15

Fig. 11—Vicariant species. The proteiform Eucalypts have a member in each tier or level of vegetation from lowland to sub-alpine

(a) Nomenclature of the Eucalypts used throughout this chapter as in BLAKELY, W. F., (1955), *A Key to the Eucalypts.*

skeletal soils develop on quartzite parent rock. These contrast strikingly with the deep soils supporting more mesic forest communities on the gentler-sloping, rounded hills derived from phyllites and shales [62].

Similar striking contrasts in lithology, slope, soils, and vegetation occur between the open grassy plains and the wooded hills of the Western Plains of Victoria [63]. The extensive olivine basalt flows and associated basalt and scoria cones, maars, and compound volcanoes of the Western Plains [64] are largely treeless [65]. The flanking areas of Palaeozoic sediments are deeply dissected, tree-covered, and support a numerically richer flora.

Lithological differences between Old Tertiary basalts and Silurian mudstones are accentuated by vegetation and by man's use of such areas in the Dandenongs [84].

The frequent and sudden changes of plant communities in the Mallee of South Australia and Victoria (often erroneously called 'monotonous uniform Mallee', although, floristically among the richest of Victoria's vegetation formations) faithfully reflect the topographic differences related usually to underlying lithological differences [66, 46, 67, 68].

Recognition of the close relationship among lithology, topography, soils, and vegetation is widely employed in broad land use surveys conducted by the C.S.I.R.O. Land Research Unit [69] and by Soil Conservation Authorities [70, 68, 71]. Each 'Land System' indicates potential land use, in addition to showing 'natural' vegetation patterns.

Lithology and geomorphic processes such as weathering, mass wasting, fluvial erosion and deposition, aeolian deposition and removal, and geodynamic processes, (e.g. vulcanism) markedly influence vegetation. Areas of rapid topographic change, such as sea cliffs, coastal dunes, mountain scree, river shingle banks, silting marshes, and river deltas are commonly associated with dynamic vegetation processes.

Edaphic Factors

Soils are particularly significant in biogeography. They are a natural complex of minerals (derived from weathering of the earth's crust), living and non-living organisms, air, and water, that is suited to plant growth. Soils provide habitats for vast numbers of microbiota (microflora and microfauna) such as soil bacteria, fungi, soil algae, and protozoa; for smaller numbers of mesobiota (small worms, small insect larvae, and soil mites or microarthropods); and for numbers of macrobiota, such as burrowing vertebrates, larger insects, earthworms, and roots. Soils are also the medium in which most terrestrial plants grow and to

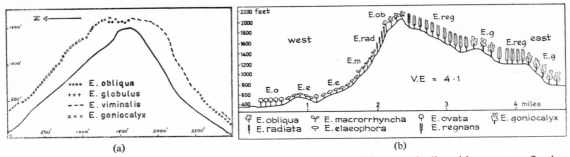

(a)   (b)

Fig. 12—The sequence of vicariant species at similar elevations differs markedly with aspect, reflecting the variations in local climates present. (a) shows the pattern on northern and southern sides of a ridge in the Otway Ranges; (b) shows the pattern present on western and eastern slopes of the Dandenong Range.

which they are attached. About one-third by bulk of land plants are in the soil layers. Soil minerals and soil water are essential for plant life processes. The relationship between soils and vegetation is a dynamic one. Vegetation contributes to soil formation, providing humus (decayed organic matter), and is itself engendered by soil conditions. Edaphic factors are important in plant succession.

Edaphic factors dependent upon the soil ingredients (minerals, living and non-living organic matter, air, and water) are of considerable importance in plant geography. Whereas climate influences the general character of vegetation over extensive areas, local modifications within a climatic region often reflect soil factors.

Vegetation and Soils

Natural plant-soil relationships provide valuable guides for planning potential land use, whether for pastoral, agricultural, horticultural, silvicultural, or other purposes. Indeed, most reconnaissance soil surveys, particularly in Australia, are based upon a plant community's preference for, or tolerance of, a specific set of soil conditions [72]. Australian horticultural irrigation districts provide good examples of the early ignorance and the later knowledge of complex plant-soil interrelationships. Indiscriminate use of water spoiled vast areas of initially productive land in early irrigation settlements [73, 74, 75, 76]. Detailed soil surveys [77, 78, 79, 80, 81] resulting in the planting of crops on soils best suited to their growth requirements minimized similar problems in later irrigation settlements [82, 83].

The close parallel between soils and vegetation is not confined to natural plant communities; the cultural landscape affords many similar examples. In the Woori Yallock Basin of Victoria, the neat patchwork of small, intensive, horticultural holdings on red loam soils is in vivid contrast to the larger grazing lands and uncleared areas on the immediately adjacent grey podzol soils [84].

Soils differ widely with structure, type of rock, and slope, even under similar climatic conditions. Prevailing weather conditions affect weathering processes, and relative rates of chemical and physical weathering of rocks vary with every difference in climate and rock type. Soils vary in depth, texture, structure, physical composition, chemical constitution, organic content, micro-organisms, and air-moisture content [85, 86, 87, 88, 89]. Biota (plant and/or animal communities) exhibit close links with soil variations. Although many different classifications of soils have been recognized, it is not intended to discuss these here. Robinson [90] gives a useful summary of these. Hallsworth and Costin [91] and Prescott [92] also provide useful references.

Residual and Transported Soils. Two widely recognized, very broad categories of soils are residual and transported. Climax vegetation is more frequently associated with the former and seral vegetation with the latter. Residual soils are those that are developed *in situ* on the parent rock. Transported soils are particularly significant, because they are usually sufficiently different from residual soils to produce distinct vegetational changes. Alluvial, colluvial, aeolian, and glacial soils are moved by water, gravity, wind, and ice respectively. Glacio-fluvial soils are transported soils where two agents, ice and water, have both been active.

Soil Morphology. One of the geographer's chief interests in soil is its morphology, or profile. Soil profile characteristics provide a useful key for mapping distributions and are also good indicators of environmental interrelationships. Soil morphology reflects particularly the interplay of climate, vegetation, organisms, topography, and time upon the parent rock in the complex process of soil formation or pedogenesis [89, 92, 93, 94, 95, 96, 97, 98, 99]. The following definition of soil by Joffe [100] emphasizes these points:

The soil is a natural body, differentiated into horizons of mineral and organic constituents, usually unconsolidated, of variable depth, which differs from the parent material below in morphology, physical properties and constitution, chemical properties and composition, and biological characteristics.

The climate-induced pedogenic processes of podzolization, laterization, calcification, solonization, and salinization, are clearly reflected in soil morphology [96]. Distinctive plant communities are commonly associated with such soil processes [22, 25, 14]; for example, Mallee occurs on greyish brown to reddish brown

solonized (salinized? [101]) sandy soils, saltbush communities (*Atriplex* spp.) on salinized soils, and dry sclerophyll forest (*Eucalyptus* spp.) on podzolized soils. To an even greater degree the ecological amplitude of individual species shows a close parallel to soil conditions (Fig. 13).

Chemical Factors

The chemical composition of soils, particularly an excess or a deficiency of certain minerals, clearly demonstrates the close relationship between soils and vegetation [72]. Alkaline tolerant (basophilous) plants such as *Spinifex hirsutus* and *Atriplex cinereum* are initial colonizers of southern coastal foredunes (Fig. 14). *Salicornia australis, Arthrocnemum halocnemoides,* and *A. arbuscula* perform a parallel function on estuarine mud flats (Fig. 15), while *Pachycornia triandra* is found on many Mallee salt lakes. All these plants tolerate excess alkalinity that is toxic to most other plants. Examples of acid-tolerant (acidophilous) plants are tiny sundews (*Drosera* spp.) growing on acid soils low in organic content, and *Restio* spp. found in bog soils high in acid organic content.

The dynamic relationship of plant-soil changes is demonstrated in plant succession

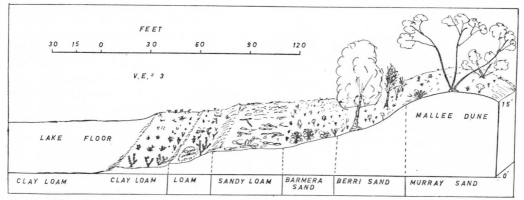

Fig. 13—Plant zonation, governed largely by soil conditions, fringing a salt lake in the Kulkyne State Forest, Victoria. At one extreme *Arthrocnemum halcnemoides* var. *pergranulatum* is restricted to the heavy clay loams subject to periodic flooding on the lake floor. At the other extreme, Mallee is confined to sand dune crests. Intermediate between *A. halcnemoides* var. *pergranulatum* and a *Mesembryanthemum australe* band on higher, better drained sandy loam an *A. halcnemoides* var. *pergranulatum—M. australe* mictium occurs with the latter species found only on the numerous small mounds a few inches above the general level. With increasing sandiness, a grass-herb zone (*Stipa, Danthonia, Ajuga australis*), a tree zone (*Hakea leucoptera, Heterodendron oleifolium*), and a Mallee zone (*Eucalyptus viridis, E. incrassata, E. oleosa*) replace each other in rapid sequence

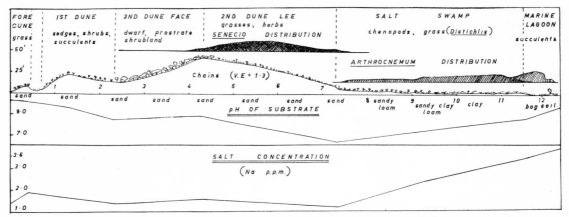

Fig. 14—Plant succession and soil relationships on coastal dunes, South Australia.

(Figs. 13-15). Soils restrict the species that can grow on a particular site, but the vegetation modifies the physical, chemical and organic composition of the soil as well as the depth of the layer utilized by plants. This in turn frequently favours growth of different species and seral stages (succession) of vegetation replace the initial plants. Such a process usually results in an improvement in soil structure and drainage, and a moderation of initial excess acidity or alkalinity, if present.

The addition of certain trace elements (particularly Cu, Zn and Bo) that were deficient in the soils of South Australia's Ninety Mile Desert, and in the adjacent Little and Big Deserts in Victoria, was necessary before these areas could be converted from deserts of stunted *Eucalyptus baxteri, E. fasciculosa*, Mallee broombush, and Mallee heath into productive pastures and cereal-growing farms. Closely adjacent areas on soils not lacking in trace elements supported vastly different natural vegetation, and when cleared presented no farming problems of the type in question [*102, 103, 104, 47*]. Many plant diseases in horticultural districts on calcareous Mallee sands can be prevented by the use of these and other trace elements such as Mg, Mn, and Mo [*105*]. In areas of cobalt-deficient soils, the deficiency is not apparent in the producers (grasses), but markedly affects the herbivore consumers of the ecosystem. Livestock grazed on the pastures soon sicken and die if the deficiency is not rectified.

Biotic Factors

A convenient division of ecosystems recognizes four groups:

1. the *abiotic environment*; 2. autotrophic organisms or *producers* (most green plants) which are capable of converting simple organic substances into complex food; 3. heterotrophic organisms or *consumers* (animals); 4. heterotrophic organisms or *decomposers* (microorganisms, chiefly bacteria and fungi) that break down complex compounds and release simple substances for use by the producers. Within any ecosystem, organisms and the abiotic environment interact. Also, most organisms within a community are part of the environment of all other organisms present. Thus, plants and animals, particularly man, are important biotic factors influencing any community [*106, 12*]. Unfortunately, man's ability to modify and change ecosystems is often ahead of his appreciation of the results of his actions. All too frequently within Australia, areas of depleted vegetation, severe gullying, sheetwash, and wind erosion, and fire-scarred forest bear mute but incontrovertible witness to man's detrimental interference with ecosystems [*107, 108, 109, 15, 41, 61*].

Man's interference is not, however, always detrimental to his interests because sometimes his technology has facilitated change from relatively unproductive ecosystems into economically productive areas. For example, in South Australia, infertile Mallee desert was

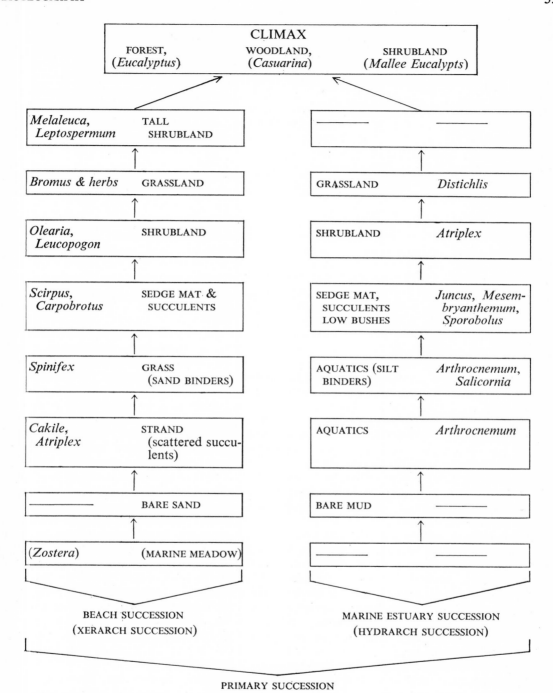

Fig. 15—A diagram of the trends of two primary seres in coastal succession. Specific species vary for different localities and trends progress at different rates but the pattern is representative of beach and marine estuary succession in southern Australia

converted into fertile horticultural oases by irrigation [*82, 83*], the Ninety Mile Desert into the Coonalpyn Downs pastoral and cereal area using trace elements [*110*], and the South East Swamps into productive pastures by drainage [*111*].

Since changes in biotic communities are concomitant with changes in environment, some of the complexities of biotic factors can be conveniently demonstrated through the study of communities. Plant community characteristics (particularly structure, composition, and succession) illustrate the dynamic role of biotic factors in ecosystems.

Plant Communities

Plant communities can be recognized either as essentially stable (CLIMAX) or as dynamic (SERAL). No vegetation is strictly static or stable. Small cyclic changes occur constantly within climax vegetation, although they may be barely discernible even over a long period of time. Seral vegetation will be replaced ultimately by a different community. Climax vegetation is more permanent because it is essentially in harmony with its existing environment. Furthermore, it is capable of reproducing itself, and is the last stage in succession in a given area.

Climax vegetation is characterized by uniformity of life-form, and frequently by uniformity of genera. Desert grassland climax communities throughout most of Australia are characterized by the *Triodia* genus. Similarly, the genus *Eucalyptus* is a dominant in most sclerophyll forest climaxes in Australia.

Some workers, notably Tansley [*10*], have claimed that the Monoclimax system was inadequate in explaining plant community distributions. Certainly the limiting of 'climax' only to climatic climax communities has proved unsatisfactory in Australia. Relief, drainage, and soil differences (especially mineral deficiencies) resulting from elements of past geological [*112*] and climatic history [*113, 114, 24, 22, 115, 116, 48, 117*] contribute markedly to divergences from a general pattern of climatic climax vegetation. Similarly, variable physiological tolerance of different species results in many anomalous areas that do not fit freely into the Monoclimax system [*118, 62, 46, 47, 104, 119, 120, 103*].

Tansley's Polyclimax system recognizes that succession is halted by climate, topography, soil, animal agency, or fire. However, unlike Clements [*121, 122*] he regards all mature communities as true climax vegetation, recognizing climatic, physiographic, edaphic, biotic, and pyric climaxes. The Polyclimax system has proved the most workable for Australian conditions [*123*].

Phytosociology

Not all ecologists concede the importance of climax vegetation. The Continental system of the Zurich-Montpellier School [*34*] is not directly concerned whether vegetation is climax or seral, placing emphasis primarily upon the community, which is studied by phytosociological methods. These methods are of two kinds: 1. analytical, involving measurements of abundance, coverage, dominance, sociability, vitality, and frequence; 2. synthetic, using criteria of comparative features such as constancy and fidelity. Phytosociology attempts to find an hierarchy of plant groupings based on the relative frequency and fidelity of taxonomic units. Virtually no advanced plant-sociological techniques have yet been tried in Australia.

Some workers query the whole idea of the climax, preferring to recognize vegetation as patterns of overlapping populations (continuum) distributed along some gradient—of temperature, of water, or the like [*124, 125, 126*]. No sharp divisions between populations or combinations of populations are recognized in a continuum. However, sharp changes in habitat do produce natural discontinuities. These are not fully explained by the continuum. Also, the concept that the end-result of succession is a stable (climax) community is theoretically sound: it is moreover based on observation. The climax concept has proved valuable; it is widely used in vegetation analysis.

Ecological succession

Plant succession is the process wherein communities are replaced by others which are induced by environmental change in a given area. Typically, the original plant communities engender changes in the habitat, thus favouring their replacement by a different community. This process is AUTOGENIC succession. Where replacement of communities results chiefly from substratum changes independent of the plants, such as shoreline changes, the process is ALLOGENIC succession (Fig. 14). Normally the succession of communities is relatively transitory, but it varies enormously with different communities and habitats. Thus, one seral stage may replace another within months [127], other replacements may take years [41]. Such changes are predictable for a given climatic area paralleling environmental changes and proceed from pioneer stages through more mature, though transitory communities, to the final mature community of the climax.

Although biotic factors are important in autogenic succession, a third type known as BIOTIC succession is distinguished as being particularly important in a great number of communities. Biotic succession results from many situations where intervention occurs by man [128, 129, 130], by a plant disease such as *Endothia parasitica* or chestnut blight, by an insect pest such as Sirex wasp, or by grazing animals [131, 132, 133]. With autogenic and allogenic succession, seral changes are mostly progressive, leading to more stable communities. Biotic succession can often involve regressive seral change and when such is the case, natural succession is halted. Regression can lead to reinstatement of pioneer conditions. Deflections and the establishment of disclimaxes (communities that owe their structure and composition to man's repeated interference) result [135].

Within any of the three types of succession (autogenic, allogenic or biotic), two kinds of succession may occur—primary and secondary.

Primary Succession occurs when an initially bare area, completely devoid of any vegetation, is colonized by plants. It is found when vegetation colonizes volcanic materials such as new lava, ash shower deposits, cinder, scoria and composite cones, and new islands; on new alluvium (fans, deltas, silt and shingle beds, meander scars, floodplain deposits, etc.); on colluvium (scree or shingle slides or steep talus); on aeolian deposits of dunes and loess; on newly-dried lake floors and stream beds; on bare faces exposed through processes of mass movement; on new moraines; and on other similarly bare habitats.

The initial habitat is subject to the maximum range of climatic extremes for the area. Buffering by plants is absent. Consequently, the initial colonizers must be hardy species adapted to tolerate extremes. Plant growth may have to await soil formation, and the subsequent rate of succession is largely governed by the rate of soil development.

Moisture availability is very important. On rocks, the initial colonizers are commonly the lowly lichens and mosses which can grow when water is available to them, and remain virtually dormant during long drought periods. Succession is termed HYDRARCH if the habitat is very moist (hydric); MESARCH if intermediate (mesic); and XERARCH if very dry (xeric). As was noted earlier, (p. 54), regardless of the condition of the initial habitat, interaction with vegetation makes it more suited for plants and improves soil and moisture conditions. Fig. 15 shows that hydric and xeric habitats alike become more mesic as succession progresses.

Secondary Succession results from disturbance of any vegetation and it may be seral or climax. Disruption may be by fire, milling, clearing, cultivation, draining, flooding, grazing, windthrow, pests, disease, or other similar agents that destroy or modify a community. Secondary succession is slow after severe fire, but it may be rapid after timber felling if numerous elements of the community remain [136]. Late stages in primary and secondary succession are similar, though early stages may differ widely. Since few areas of the world's vegetation have escaped at least partial modification by man, secondary successions are more widespread than primary.

Most problems of applied biogeography (e.g. conservation, silviculture) involve secondary succession. For example, insufficient attention is being paid to the dynamics of seral vegetation in milled areas of the Otway Ranges, where Victoria's best stands of mature *Eucalyptus regnans* are found. The result is a tremendous potential loss of a vital renewable resource, namely mountain ash forests for the future. Forest areas are milled first for *E. regnans*. Felling and logging open areas of forest to light, allowing the light-demanding *E. regnans* seedlings to become established. A second cutting-over for *E. viminalis* and

C

Fig. 16—Biocenotic relationships. An Australian dry sclerophyll forest showing eight different situations. A—COMPETITION: The dominant trees (from left to right *Eucalyptus macrorrhyncha, E. obliqua, E. radiata, E. viminalis, E. obliqua* and *E. baxteri*). B—COMMENSALISM: (B1), *E. macrorrhyncha, Acacia stricta,* and *Danthonia semi-annularis.* (B2), Eucalypts, *Acacia, Cassinia, A. myrtifolia, Pultenaea, Themeda, Kennedya, Platylobium,* and *Viola.* C—PARASITISM: (C1), *Loranthus* on *Eucalyptus,* (C2) *Choracartha* in *Eucalyptus,* (C3), *Cassytha* on *Acacia,* (C4), woodboring grubs (Cerambyciadae) in *Eucalyptus,* (C5), jewel beetle (Burrestidae) in *Acacia,* (C6), sawflies, *Perga bella,* on *Eucalyptus,* (C7), *Exocarpus* on *Eucalyptus.* D—SAPROPHYTISM: (D1), bacteria on wallaby faeces, (D2), fungi on rotting wood, (D3), soil bacteria on dead litter. E—EPIPHYTISM: (E1), *Microsorium* on *Acacia.* F—SYMBIOSIS: (F1), lichen (alga and fungus), (F2), *Micorrhizae* on *Eucalyptus* roots. G—PHYTOPHAGY: (G1), Christmas beetle (adult) on *Eucalyptus* leaves, (G2), wallaby on *Danthonia,* (G3), lava (Cossidae) on *Acacia* leaves, (G4), *Paropsis* on *Eucalyptus* leaves, (G5), lava (Hepalidae) on *Acacia,* (G6), koala on *E. viminalis* leaves. H—PREDATION: (H1), kookaburra (*Dacelo novae-guineae*) and snake and lizard, (H2), snake and lizard, (H3), lizard and fly, (H4), Echidna (*Tachyglossus aculeatus*) and ants

E. goniocalyx, and a third for *E. obliqua*, often however destroy most of the regenerating mountain ash seedlings. Destruction of seedlings, depletion of available seed reservoir through logging operations, plus competition from aggressive, light-demanding scrub vegetation, contribute importantly to the failure of these areas to regenerate mountain ash. One comprehensive milling for all timber trees followed by a light burning (considered by Ashton [137] as a necessary part of mountain ash regeneration) would be applying principles of succession in order to ensure continuity of these valuable mountain ash forests.

Biocenotic Relationships

The interaction of organisms within a habitat, with each and all participating in the resources of the environment, is known as BIOCENOSIS, e.g. the koala-manna gum biocenosis. Biocenotic integration is an important biotic factor: it demonstrates the dynamic reaction among organisms within an ecosystem. In a community, all organisms partaking of environmental resources (food, space, light, moisture, shelter, etc.) either share or compete for these. Eight different situations are common and some or all may occur within a single habitat (Fig. 16).

1. *Competition.* Organisms sharing the same habitat compete for the resources of their habitat, particularly for light, soil water and nutrients, space, and shelter. Competition occurs at all stages from seedlings to adults, and throughout all seral stages: it is also present within and between all synusiae in layered vegetation. Transgressive species experience a variety of competition from other plants of each layer.

In wet sclerophyll forest in the Otway Ranges, *Eucalyptus viminalis, E. goniocalyx,* and *E. obliqua* compete with one another in the upper canopy (180 to 250 ft.). Below these, in a second tier at 80 to 120 ft. *Acacia melanoxylon* compete. Similarly, active competition among several different species (*Bedfordia, Pomaderris, Olearia*) occurs in the third layer, the low tree synusia (20 to 35 ft.). Major breaks in the upper canopies, allowing direct light to reach the forest floor, promotes vigorous competition near ground level of such heliophilous plants as *Urtica* and *Tetrarrhena juncea* (Fig. 5).

2. *Commensalism.* In an ecosystem where organisms of different species live together as a community, their requirements must be similar. To some extent they must also be complementary (Fig. 17). Thus, in the Otway forests the lower layers are increasingly sciophilous, benefiting from shade cast by the higher synusiae (Fig. 5). Forest floor herbs, ferns, shrubs, low trees, and taller tress utilize successively deeper horizons of the soil. In some dry sclerophyll forests in Victoria commensal relations exist among the trees *Eucalyptus elaeophora, E. obliqua,* and *E. radiata,* the undershrubs *Acacia myrtifolia* and *Pultenaea scabra,* and the prostrate, forest-floor creepers *Kennedya prostrata* and *Platylobium formosum* (Figs. 1, 10). Within each of these layers the species present compete with one another—*K. prostrata* with *P. formosum* and *A. myrtifolia* with *Pultenaea scabra.*

3. *Parasitism.* This occurs when, in order to survive, an organism lives in or upon another organism (its host) and obtains nutrient directly from it. Parasites are economically important when they are pathogenic. Tremendous variety is present in parasitic adaptation. Some fungi are restricted to a single host species, such as *Gummosis* on apricots and *Oidium* on grape vines [82, 138]. Others undergo separate phases of their life cycle on different hosts; wheat rust (*Puccinia graminus*) on wheat and barberry is a classic example [139].

Entire families of some higher plants are parasites, for instance the Australian mistletoe (*Loranthaceae*) on Eucalypts. *Cassytha* is widespread in Victoria. Attaching itself by numerous haustoria, through which it obtains its nutrients, it forms dense tangles over its host (Fig. 16).

Animal parasites are innumerable: some are restricted to one host, others undergo different phases of their life cycle on different hosts (*Plasmodium* with stages in female *Anopheles* mosquitoes and in man and other mammals). Saw flies and moth larvae on *Eucalyptus* and *Acacia* cause considerable damage. Mulga 'berries', an important item of diet of some Northern Territory aborigines, are larval galls on *Acacia anuera.* The Sirex wasp lava is causing concern to State and Commonwealth foresters because of its potential danger to exotic softwood plantations. In the cool, wet forest areas of southern Victoria and Tasmania, leeches (animal ectoparasites) readily attach themselves to animals that brush past and they can cause discomfort to humans. Bush wallabies are often thickly infested.

Exocarpus cupressiformis (native cherry) is a secondary parasite (hemiparasite). Its roots are attached to the roots of its *Eucalyptus* host, but it produces its own chlorophyll (green leaf colouring) for carbon assimilation. Native mistletoes are also hemiparasites.

Two parasites useful in the biological control of pests or weeds are the German wasp (for the control of blowflies), and the *Cactoblastis cactorum* larva. The former lays its eggs in the eggs or larvae of blowflies. When hatched, the wasp larvae feed upon and eventually kill their host. Control has greatly reduced economic loss from 'blowfly strike' in sheep in New Zealand. The *Cactoblastis* moth larvae brought about the control, and later the destruction, of prickly pear (*Opuntia inermis, O. stricta*). These vigorous, rapidly-spreading weeds rendered useless over 60,000,000 acres of land in Queensland and northern New South Wales in the brief period between their introduction in about 1860 and the year 1925. Dodd [140] gives a full account of this remarkable success in biological control.

4. *Saprophytism*. This is the existence of organisms on decomposing organic tissues. Fungi on rotting logs, like many soil fungi and bacteria, are saprophytic. Carcinogenic bacteria associated with the excreta of pigeons, and certain lichens (caprophiles) which require high nitrogen concentrations, are saprophytes. Caprophiles are often initial colonizers on ground fouled by bird droppings (shag rookeries).

Scavenger animals, such as crows and magpies (*Gymnorhina tibicen*), could partly belong to this class.

5. *Epiphytism*. Epiphytes are plants that grow upon other plants, and in some cases on animals or inorganic objects (power poles and lines), but use them only as supports; the host is not used as a nutritive medium. Many ferns, mosses, lichens, bromeliads, and tropical orchids are epiphytic on trunks and branches of trees. In wet habitats in the Otways, the mosses *Ptychomnion aciculare* and *Cyathophorum bulbosum* cover limbs, branches and rocks. *Microsorium diversifolium, Mecodium* spp., *Ctenopteris heterophylla,* and *Hymenophyllum cupressiforme* are common epiphytic ferns in Victorian forests. In the Otways, although common on fallen logs, tree ferns, and rocks, they are most plentiful on mossy trunks of *Acacia melanoxylon*. The lichen *Sticta billardieri* is common on the shady sides of third-storey trees at altitudes above 1500 ft. in the same area. The presence of epiphytes normally indicates a moist habitat with high relative humidity.

6. *Symbiosis*. This involves a mutually advantageous association through contact between species. One of the best examples is the lichen, where the algae produce food and the fungi provide the protection; neither the fungus nor the alga can exist independently in nature. Nitrogen-fixing bacteria in root nodules of legumes, and micorrhizae (fungal mycelia) associated with the roots of certain forest trees (*Pinus, Eucalyptus regnans, E. obliqua*), are other examples of symbiosis. The micorrhizae take soluble food from root secretions, but the symbiotic system can extract soil minerals more efficiently than can roots without the micorrhizae. In many cases, trees are unable to become established without root micorrhizae, particularly in acid soils low in plant nutrients.

7. *Phytophagy*. This is the consumption of living plant materials by animals (herbivores) and most insects. Some herbivores are very specific in their food habits: for instance, the koala 'bear' (*Phascolarctos cinereus*) feeds on the leaves and young bark of about 12 species of *Eucalyptus*, but particularly of *E. viminalis*. When placed under protection in reserves on Kangaroo Island and French Island, the koalas had to be shifted periodically if they were not to destroy themselves by starvation. With increased numbers under protection, their highly selective feeding habits were killing out their food source [141, 142]. Other animals are less discriminating, e.g. possums (*Phalangeridae*) consume a variety of leaves, berries, bark and sap; wallabies (*Macropodidae*) prefer grass, but also browse on leaves, shoots, bark,

and roots [143]; introduced rabbits (*Oryctolagus cuniculus*) eat grasses, herbs, bark, buds, leaves, and roots of a great number of plants; galahs (*Kakatoe roseicapilla*) consume seeds of many semi-arid and desert plants.

8. *Predation*. This is the hunting and consuming alive of one animal by another. Predators that hunt as individuals (kingfisher, python, kookaburra), or in groups (dolphins, killer whales, wolves) are present in all classes of animals.

Food habits differ enormously. Many predator-prey relationships, aside from their ecological aspects, may also have widespread economic implications. Before the advent of European livestock in the Kimberleys, kangaroo and wallaby populations were kept in check by aboriginal and dingo predators. Numbers increased when these controls diminished. Now, in the virtual absence of their natural predators, kangaroos, and particularly the sand wallaby, *Macropus agilis*, have become major pests. Remarkable increase in numbers has resulted in severe denudation of vegetation and substantial reduction in stock-carrying capacity [144, 145, 146].

Man as a Biotic Factor

Man's activities result in many direct and indirect influences upon his environment [12, 147, 148, 149]. Broadly, six successive phases of man's influence on the environment can be recognized, i.e. economies associated with gathering, hunting and fishing, grazing, cultivation, industry, and urbanization. Within any area, these may occur concurrently or successively. Jones and Darkenwald [150], recognizing that each of these indicates an increasing measure of man's control as an ecological agent, have used this scheme as the basis of a study of economic geography.

Initially, man as a gatherer is a component of an ecosystem, and of no greater importance than other animals that are his commensals. Thus, the primitive Neolithic gathering economy of the recently-discovered desert Bindibu aborigines of tropical Western Australia causes no notable disturbance to their environment [151]. In such circumstances, modification by man is negligible.

Progressively, with advancing technology, man's influence upon the environment increases, through hunting and fishing, herding and agriculture, until in the last two stages of industrialization and urbanization, it is a controlling influence resulting in the substitution of completely new environments. Primeval Australian aborigines undoubtedly used fire in their hunting [152]. The use, whether intentional or accidental, contributed to quite substantial modification of plant cover. Man's ability to change extensive areas of his environment often follows rapidly upon his introduction of domesticated animals to new areas [153, 154, 155, 156, 157, 158, 159, 160]. European introduction of domestic and feral grazing animals into Australia resulted in widespread invasions of areas by alien animals and plants [132, 140, 133, 134]. Indigenous plant species were replaced by exotics, firing was widely practised, and over-grazing became commonplace [107, 108, 98]. Deterioration of plant communities and soil erosion frequently followed [161].

Man's disturbance of delicately adjusted ecosystems in areas with uncertain climatic fluctuation can bring on him economic repercussions. As a direct result of over-grazing, thousands of introduced wild water buffalo died between Alice Springs and Darwin during the 1965 drought. At the same time, many hundreds of camels (offspring from camels released years ago in Alice Springs by Afghan teamsters) died of thirst. Considerable damage resulted when many additional hundreds of frantic, thirst-crazy, wild camels rampaged across the arid interior of Australia, smashing fences and destroying water bores in their search for water. The tremendous losses of millions of head of livestock, the destruction of vegetation on an enormous scale, and severe soil erosion involving the aeolian removal of millions of tons of soil in dust storms during this same period, vividly reflect man's impact.

Competition between indigenes and exotics results in many modifications. Interference often results in artificially-maintained aliens [162] and when man's protection is removed, indigenous species replace the alien invaders. For example, exotic pastures rapidly revert to weeds and indigenous scrub, when left without strict grazing and artificial fertilizers [163]. Ultimately, the native vegetation will regain its former position (through succession) when interference by man ceases completely [109, 164].

Man's technological achievements find dynamic expression in agriculture. Frequently he creates considerable change in pre-existing environments, and may even substitute new ecosystems for his agricultural crops. Change is often greater in detail, although less extensive, than with grazing. Agricultural crops commonly run counter to regeneration to the climax, and man is constantly fighting the regeneration tendencies by weed control [165, 166, 167, 168, 169, 170]. Man's interference with existing ecosystems, the resultant biotic reaction, and subsequent economic repercussions, are illustrated in the early historical geography of New South Wales [171]. Apart from man's technological skills, cultural heritage may exert an important influence [172].

Common methods used to establish agricultural environments include felling and clearing of forests, burning [173], cultivation [166, 169, 174], drainage [111, 175], irrigation, introduction of new crops [176, 177, 178] such as subterranean clover, plant breeding (Wimmera rye), use of fertilizers and trace elements [104, 179], and transport [180]. Dune stabilization, soil conservation [181, 182], and flood control [183] are often closely related to agricultural activities. Numerous references to man's role in ecosystem dynamics have been made earlier. Lumbering, afforestation and silviculture can be considered as special cases of 'agriculture' with the same general principles applying.

Among the many tools, fire is a tremendously important ecological factor because of man's ability to 'control' it more easily than he can control other limiting factors of the environment. In few parts of forested Australia is it possible to find large areas not affected by fire during the last 50 to 100 years. Fires do occur naturally, but within Australia most result from man's carelessness, so that productive environments are annually destroyed. Controlled firing can however be advantageous with intelligent use [173, 184]. Pine forests (disclimax) are maintained in United States and southwestern France through the regular use of fire. Many workers consider savannah a pyric (fire) climax [185]. However, much

research is necessary to understand the full significance of pyric factors in biogeography [186]. 'Certainly there is no more fascinating and important field for ecological research' [11, p. 139].

Although some new ecosystems are substituted for existing ones in agriculture, modification of 'natural' environment is more general in man's industrial activities. At the industrial stage, man's increasing mastery over his environment is apparent. Waste deposits from mines and industry, plus discharge of industrial effluent into streams [187], and discharge of gas fumes, soot and ash into the atmosphere, create entirely new sets of conditions for living organisms. At Mount Lyell in western Tasmania, such processes are detrimental to plant growth. Mining leaves a very characteristic imprint upon the landscape [188, 189, 190, 191, 192, 193].

The typical assemblage of large buildings, heavy machinery and equipment, large storage areas, transport facilities and discharging fumes of oil refineries [194], of iron and steel mills [195], and of non-ferrous smelting and refining works [196] are essentially parts of man-made environments. Their occurrence in areas initially so ecologically different as Geelong, Kwinana, Port Kembla, Whyalla, Port Pirie, and Mount Lyell emphasize the man-made character.

The building of dams in the Snowy River scheme [197], along the River Murray [198] and the Ord River creates new water levels alien to the normal climatic and drainage patterns [127].

In the final stage of urbanization, completely new environments result [199, 200, 201]. Natural features such as soil, vegetation, and animals are largely replaced by man-made ones such as houses, roads, sewerage, heat, light, water supply, transport, and working and recreational conditions [202, 203, 204, 205, 206]. A completely new set of habitats presents many new problems [207, 208].

With the replacement of many natural elements, suppression of most other members of any possible biocenosis results. Exceptions, often unwanted and, ironically, largely beyond man's control, are domesticated elements (dogs, cats), naturalized species (sparrows, starlings, pigeons, minahs), the inquilines (flies, rats, cockroaches), and parasites (fleas, lice). Man has so modified the urban environment that he is no longer an influent, but the master.

Conclusion

Land-use patterns result essentially from man's use (and abuse) of geomorphic and bioclimatic elements of the environment. This is an important study on its own, long recognized by geographers, and one that links human and physical geography (in their broadest sense). In most cases, land-use studies involve the recognition of ecosystems, natural, modified, or man-created.

Biogeography recognizes that the reciprocal interaction between organisms and habitat produces changes in the composition, structure, and areal extent of communities or ecosystems [209]. It demonstrates on the one hand the biotic response to the ambient resources, and on the other hand the specific pattern of land use, indicating the degree of cultural (man-made) modification of primeval biocenoses or biotic communities. Such communities reflect environmental complexes. They are an important key—one might say an essential key—to the understanding of the geographic character of areas.

REFERENCES

1. KUCHLER, A. W. (1954) Plant Geography in JAMES, P. E. & JONES, C. F. (eds.). *American Geography: Inventory and Prospect*, 428–441. New York.

2. HESSE, R., ALLEE, W. C. & SCHMIDT, K. P. (1951) (2 ed.) *Ecological Animal Geography*. Wiley, New York.

3. DARLINGTON, P. J. JR. (1957) *Zoogeography: the geographical distribution of animals*. Wiley, New York.

4. DAVIES, J. (1958) *The Pinnepedia*: an essay in zoogeography. *Geogr.Rev.*, 48, 474–493.

5. DAVIES, J. (1961) Aim and method in zoogeography. *Geogr.Rev.*, 51, 412–417.

6. MATHIESON, R. S. (1958) The Japanese salmon fisheries: an economic appraisal. *Econ.Geogr.*, 34, 352–361.

7. LAWRENCE, D. B. (1939) Some features of the vegetation of the Columbia River Gorge with special reference to asymmetry in trees. *Ecol.Monog.*, 9, 217–257.

8. TANSLEY, A. G. (1920) The classification of vegetation and the concept of development. *Journ.Ecol.*, 8, 118–144.

9. TANSLEY, A. G. (1929) Succession: the concept and its values. *Proc.Intern.Congress Plant Sciences,* 677–686.

10. TANSLEY, A. G. (1935) The use and abuse of vegetational terms. *Ecology*, 16, 284–301.

11. ODUM, E. P. (1955) (2 ed.) *Fundamentals of Ecology*. Saunders, Phil. & London.

12. THOMAS, W. L. (ed.) (1956) *Man's role in changing the face of the Earth*. Chicago.

13. YARNELL, R. A. (1963) Reciprocity in cultural ecology. *Econ.Bot.*, 17, 333–337.

14. COSTIN, A. B. (1954) *A study of the ecosystems of the Monaro region of New South Wales*. Govt. Printer, Sydney.

15. COSTIN, A. B. (1957) *High mountain catchments in Victoria in relation to land use*. Govt. Printer, Melbourne.

16. COSTIN, A. B. (1958) The grazing factor and the maintenance of catchment values in the Australian Alps. *C.S.I.R.O.Aust.Div. Plant.Ind.Tech.Pap. 10.*

17. AUSTRALIAN ACADEMY OF SCIENCE (1957) *A report on the conditions of the high mountain catchments of New South Wales and Victoria*. Canberra.

18. NEWBOULD, P. J. (1964) Production ecology and the international biological programme. *Geography*, 49 (2), 98–104.

19. RAUP, H. M. (1942) Trends in the development of geographic botany. *Annls.Assoc. Amer.Geogr.*, 32, 319–354.

20. DANSEREAU, P. (1951) Description and Recording of Vegetation on a Structural Basis. *Ecology*, 32, 172–229.

21. BLAKE, S. T. (1938) The plant communities of Western Queensland and their relationships, with special reference to the grazing industry. *Proc.Roy.Soc.Q.*, 49, 156–204.

22. WOOD, J. G. (1939) Ecological concepts and nomenclature. *Trans.Roy.Soc.S.Aust.*, 63, 215–223.

23. WOOD, J. G. (1949) Vegetation of Australia, in *The Australian Environment*. (1 ed.), 77–96. C.S.I.R.O., Melbourne. 1950 (2 ed.), 77–96.

24. CROCKER, R. L. & WOOD, J. G. (1947) Some historical influences on the development of the South Australian vegetation communities and their bearing on concepts and classification in ecology. *Trans.Roy.Soc.S. Austr.*, *71*, 91–136.

25. BEADLE, N. C. W. & COSTIN, A. B. (1952) Ecological classification and nomenclature. *Proc.Linn.Soc.N.S.W.*, *77*, 61–82.

26. CHRISTIAN, C. S. & PERRY, R. A. (1953) The systematic description of plant communities by the use of symbols. *Journ.Ecol.*, *41*, 100–105.

27. WILLIAMS, R. J. (1955) Vegetation regions (map and notes) in *Atlas of Australian Resources*. Dept. of National Development, Canberra.

28. CHRISTIAN, C. S. (1959) The ecocomplex in its importance for agricultural assessment, in KEAST, A. *et al.* (eds.). *Biogeography and ecology in Australia*, 587–604. Den Haag, Junk.

29. WEBB, L. J. (1958) Cyclones as an ecological factor in tropical lowland rainforest, North Queensland. *Aust.J.Bot.*, *6*, 220-228.

30. WEBB, L. J. (1959) A physiognomic classification of Australian rain forests. *J.Ecol.*, *47*, 551–570.

31. WOOD, J. G. & WILLIAMS, R. J. (1960) Vegetation of Australia, in *The Australian Environment*, (3 ed.) 67–84. C.S.I.R.O., Melbourne.

32. SCHWEINFURTH, ULRICH (1962) Studien zur Pflanzengeographic von Tasmanien. *Bonner Geographische Abhandlungen*, Heft *31*, 1–61.

33. COCHRANE, G. ROSS (1963a) A physiognomic vegetation map of Australia. *Journ. Ecol.*, *51*, 639–655.

34. BRAUN-BLANQUET, J. (1932) *Plant Sociology: the study of plant communities*. McGraw-Hill, New York.

35. GOODALL, D. W. (1953a) Objective methods for the classification of vegetation. I. The use of positive interspecific correlation. *Austr.J.Bot.*, *1*, 39–63.

36. GOODALL, D. W. (1953b) Objective methods for the classification of vegetation. II. Fidelity and indicator value. *Austr.J.Bot.*, *1*, 434-456.

37. GOODALL, D. W. (1965) Plot-less tests of interspecific association. *Journ.Ecol.*, *53*, 197–210.

38. GREIG-SMITH, P., KERSHAW, A. W. & ANDERSON, D. J. (1963) The analysis of pattern in vegetation: a comment on a paper by Goodall, D. W. *Journ.Ecol.*, *51*, 223–229.

39. DANSEREAU, P. (1957) *Biogeography*. Ronald, New York.

40. SCHIMPER, A. F. W. (1903) *Plant Geography upon a physiological basis*. Transl. by Fisher, W. R., ed. by Groom, P., and Balfour, I. B. Oxford.

41. COCHRANE, G. ROSS (1963c) Vegetation studies in forest-fire areas of the Mount Lofty Ranges of South Australia. *Ecology*, *44*, 41–52.

42. RICHARDS, P. W. (1952) *The Tropical Rainforest: An Ecological Study*. Camb. Univ. Press.

43. GRUBB, P. J., LLOYD, J. R., PENNINGTON, T. D. & WHITMORE, T. C. (1963) A comparison of montane and lowland rain forest in Ecuador. *Journ.Ecol.*, *51*, 567–601.

44. BOYKO, HUGO (1947) On the role of plants as quantitative climate indicators and the geoecological law of distribution. *Journ. Ecol.*, *35*, 138–157.

45. THORNTHWAITE, C. W. & BLUMENSTOCK (1941) Climatic classification. in *Climate and Man*. U.S.Dept.Agric.Year Books, 195.

46. SPECHT, R. L. (1951) A reconnaissance survey of the soils and vegetation of the Hundreds of Tatiara, Wirrega and Stirling, *Trans.Roy.Soc.S.Austr.*, *74*, 79–107.

47. SPECHT, R. L. (1957) Dark Island Heath (Ninety Mile Plain, South Australia). V. The water relationships in Heath vegetation and Pastures on the Makin Sand. *Austr.J.Bot.*, *5*, 151–172.

48. SPECHT, R. L. (1958) The climate, geology, soils and plant ecology of the northern portion of Arnhem Land. *Records of the American-Australian Scientific Expeditions to Arnhem Land*. Vol. *3*, 333–414.

49. DAUBENMIRE, R. (1959) (2 ed.) *Plants and environment: a textbook of plant autecology*. Wiley, New York.

50. KLAGES, K. H. W. (1942) *Ecological Plant Geography*. Macmillan, New York.

51. HUNTINGTON, ELLSWORTH (1940) *Principles of Economic Geography*. Wiley, New York.

52. CANDOLLE, ALPHONSE DE (1875) Les groupes physiologiques dans le regne vegetal. *Rev.Scientifique*. Ser. 2, *16*, 364–372.

53. TRUMBLE, H. C. (1939) Climatic factors in relation to the agricultural regions of South Australia. *Trans.Roy.Soc.S.Austr.*, *70*, 313–347.

54. PRESCOTT, J. A. & THOMAS, J. A. (1949) The length of the growing season in Australia as determined by the effectiveness of the rainfall. A revision. *Proc.Roy.Geog.Soc. Austr.*, (S.Austr.Br.), *50*, 42–46.

55. LEEPER, G. W. (1960) Climates of Australia, in *The Australian Environment* (3 ed.), 19–28. C.S.I.R.O., Melbourne.

56. SLATYER, R. O. & MCILROY, I. C. (1961) *Practical Microclimatology*. U.N.E.S.C.O., Paris.

57. CARR, STELLA G. M. & TURNER, J. S. (1959) The ecology of the Bogong High Plains I and II. *Austr.J.Bot.*, *7*, 12–63.

58. RAUNKIAER, C. (1934) *The Life Forms of Plants and Statistical Plant Geography.* Clarendon Press, Oxford.

59. CAIN, S. A. (1950) Life-forms and phytoclimate. *Botanical Review*, *16*, 1–32.

60. ALLAN, H. H. (1937) A consideration of the 'biological spectra' of New Zealand. *Journ. Ecol.*, *25*, 116–152.

61. COCHRANE, G. ROSS (1966) Bushfires and vegetation regeneration. *Victorian Naturalist*, *83*, 4–10.

62. SPECHT, R. L. & PERRY, R. A. (1948) The Plant Ecology of part of the Mount Lofty Ranges (1). *Trans.Roy.Soc.S.Austr.*, *72*, 91–132.

63. PATTON, R. T. (1936) Ecological studies in Victoria; Part IV—Basalt Plains Association. *Proc.Roy.Soc.Vict.*, *48*, 172–190.

64. OLLIER, C. D. & JOYCE, E. B. (1964) Volcanic physiography of the Western Plains of Victoria. *Proc.Roy.Soc.Vict.*, *77*, 357–376.

65. WILLIS, J. H. (1964) Vegetation of the basalt plains in Western Victoria. *Proc.Roy. Soc.Vict.*, *77*, 397–405.

66. ZIMMER, W. J. (1946) The Flora of the Far North-West of Victoria. *Forests Commission of Victoria Bull.*, *2*.

67. RAYSON, PATRICIA (1957) Dark Island Heath (Ninety Mile Plain, South Australia). II. The effects of microtopography on climate, soils and vegetation. *Austr.J.Bot.*, *5*, 86–102.

68. ROWAN, J. N. & DOWNES, R. G. (1963) *Study of the land in north-western Victoria.* Soil Cons. Authority of Victoria, Melbourne.

69. C.S.I.R.O. (1953) *et seq. Land Research Series Surveys.*

70. DOWNES, R. G., GIBBONS, F. R., ROWAN, J. M. & SIBLEY, G. T. (1957) Principles and methods of ecological surveys for land use purposes. *Second Austr. Conf. in Soil Science, Melbourne, 1957.*

71. GIBBONS, F. R. & GILL, E. D. (1964) Terrains and soils of the Basaltic Plains of Far Western Victoria. *Proc.Roy.Soc.Vict.*, *77 (2)*, 387–396.

72. BEADLE, N. C. W., WHALLEY, R. D. B. & GIBSON, J. B. (1957) Studies in halophytes. II. Analytical data on the mineral constituents of three species of Atriplex and their accompanying soils in Australia. *Ecology*, *38*, 340–344.

73. LYON, A. V. (1932) The irrigation of horticulture community settlements. *C.S.I.R.O. Pamphlet*, *26*.

74. SPURLING, M. B. (1951) Irrigation efficiency in horticulture. *Dept.Agric.S.Austr.Bull.*, *420*.

75. SPURLING, M. B. (1952) Citrus irrigation part II: Sprinkler irrigation. *Dept.Agric.S. Austr.Bull.*, *423*.

76. TILL, M. R. (1960) Irrigation needs of fruit trees, vines and vegetables. *J.Agric.S.Austr.*, *64*, 89–92.

77. TAYLOR, J. K. & ENGLAND, H. N. (1928) A soil survey of Block E (Renmark) and Ral Ral (Chaffey) Irrigation areas. *C.S.I.R.O. Bull.*, *42*.

78. MARSHALL, T. J. & HOOPER, P. D. (1932) A soil survey of Blocks A, B, C, D and F, Renmark Irrigation District of South Australia. *C.S.I.R.O.Bull.*, *56*.

79. MARSHALL, T. J. & HOOPER, P. D. (1935) A soil survey of the Berri, Cobdogla, Kingston and Moorook Irrigation Areas and the Lyrup Village District, South Australia. *C.S.I.R.O.Bull.*, *86*.

80. HUBBLE, G. D. & CROCKER, R. L. (1941) A soil survey of the Red Cliffs Irrigation District, Victoria. *C.S.I.R.O.Austr.Bull.*, *137*.

81. SKENE, J. K. M. (1951) Soil Survey of the Robinvale Irrigation Area. *Dept.Agric.Vict. Technical Bulletin*, *10*.

82. COCHRANE, G. ROSS (1960a) Intensive land use in South Australia's Upper Murray. *Austr.Geogr.*, *8*, 25–41.

83. COCHRANE, G. ROSS (1960b) The Renmark fruit growing district. *Proc.Roy.Geog.Soc. Australasia,S.Austr.*, *61*, 21–36.

84. COCHRANE, G. ROSS & PRYOR, ROBIN J. (1964) Land use in the Silvan-Monbulk Region, Dandenong Range, Victoria. *Proc. Roy.Soc.Vict.*, *77 (2)*, 239–264.

85. TAYLOR, J. K. (1960) Soils of Australia, in *The Australian Environment* (3 ed.), 29–44. C.S.I.R.O., Melbourne.

86. CLARKE, G. R. (1957) (4 ed.) *The study of the soil in the field.* Clarendon Press, Oxford.

87. BRADE-BIRKE, S. G. (1944) *Good Soil.* Hodder & Stoughton, London.

88. LEEPER, G. W. (1948) *Introduction to Soil Science.* M.U.P., Melbourne.

89. JENNY, HANS (1941) *Factors of Soil Formation—A System of Quantitative Pedology.* McGraw-Hill, New York and London.

90. ROBINSON, G. W. (1932) *Soils, their origin, constitution and classification.* London.

91. HALLSWORTH, E. G. & COSTIN, A. B. (1950) Soil classification. *J.Aust.Inst.Agric.Sci.*, 16 (3), 84.

92. PRESCOTT, J. A. (1952) (2 ed.) The soils of Australia in relation to vegetation and climate. *C.S.I.R.O.Aust.Bull.*, 52.

93. CROCKER, R. L. (1946a) An introduction to the soils and vegetation of Eyre Peninsula, South Australia. *Trans.Roy.Soc.S.Austr.*, 70, 83–107.

94. DOWNES, R. G. (1954) Cyclic salt as a dominant factor in the genesis of soils in S.E. Australia. *Austr.J.Agric.Res.*, 5, 448–464.

95. STEPHENS, C. G. (1950) Comparative morphology and genetic relationships of Australian, North American and European soils. *J.Soil Sci.*, 1, 123–149.

96. STEPHENS, C. G. (1956) (2 ed.) *A manual of Australian soils.* C.S.I.R.O., Melbourne.

97. STEWART, G. A. (1954) The soils of monsoonal Australia. *Trans.V.Int.Cong.Soil Sci. Leopoldville*, 4, 101–8.

98. STEWART, G. A. (1959) Some aspects of soil ecology, in KEAST, A. *et al.* (eds.) *Biogeography and Ecology in Australia.* Den Haag, Junk, 303–314.

99. C.S.I.R.O. (1960) (3 ed.) *The Australian Environment.* C.S.I.R.O., Melbourne.

100. JOFFE, J. S. (1936) *Pedology.* Rutgers Univ. Press, New Brunswick, N.J.

101. NORTHCOTE, K. H. (1956) The solonised brown (Mallee) soil group of south-eastern Australia. *Sixième Congress de la Science du Sol, Paris, 1956*, 2, 9–19.

102. LITCHFIELD, W. H. (1956) Species distribution over part of the Coonalpyn Downs, South Australia. *Austr.J.Bot.*, 4, 68–115.

103. SPECHT, R. L. & RAYSON, PATRICIA (1957) Dark Island Heath (Ninety Mile Plain, South Australia). I. Definition of the ecosystem. *Austr.J.Bot.*, 5, 52–85.

104. SPECHT, R. L. (1963) Dark Island Heath (Ninety Mile Plain, South Australia). VII. The effect of fertilizers on composition and growth, 1950–1960. *Austr.J.Bot.*, 11, 67–94.

105. VICTORIAN DEPT. AGRIC. *Mallee Horticultural Digest & Victorian Horticultural Digest.*

106. CLEMENTS, F. E. & SHELFORD, V. E. (1939) *Bio-ecology.* Wiley and Sons, New York.

107. RATCLIFFE, F. N. (1936) Soil Drift in the Arid Pastoral Areas of S.A. *Coun.Sci.Ind. Res.Austr.Pamphlet*, 64.

108. RATCLIFFE, F. N. (1937) Further observations on soil erosion and sand drift with special reference to S.W. Queensland. *C.S.I.R.O.Austr.Pamphlet*, 70.

109. WOOD, J. G. (1936) Regeneration of the vegetation on the Koonamore Vegetation Reserve, 1926–1936. *Trans.Roy.Soc.S. Austr.*, 60, 96–111.

110. HEFFORD, R. K. (1961) An investigation into the need for, and use of, rural credit in selected areas in South Australia. Unpublished M.Ec. Thesis, University of Adelaide.

111. WILLIAMS, MICHAEL (1964) The historical geography of an artificial drainage system: the lower South East of South Australia. *Austr.Geog.Studies*, 2, 87–102.

112. DAVID, T. W. E. (1950) *The Geology of the Commonwealth of Australia.* Vol. 1. (Edited and much supplemented by Browne, W. R.). Arnold, London.

113. CROCKER, R. L. (1946b) Post-Miocene climatic and geologic history and its significance in the genesis of the major soil types of South Australia. *Austr.C.S.I.R.O. Bull.*, 193.

114. CROCKER, R. L. (1959) Past climatic fluctuations and their influence upon Australian vegetation, in KEAST, A. *et al.* (eds.) *Biogeography and ecology in Australia.* Junk, Den Haag. (Monographiae Biologicae, Vol. 8), 283–289.

115. WOOD, J. G. (1959) The phytogeography of Australia, in KEAST, A. *et al.* (eds.) *Biogeography and ecology in Australia.* Junk, Den Haag, 291–302.

116. JESSUP, R. W. (1948) A vegetation and pasture survey of Counties Eyre, Burra, and Kimberley, South Australia. *Trans.Roy. Soc.S.Austr.*, 72, 33–68.

117. BURBIDGE, N. T. (1960) The phytogeography of the Australian Region. *Austr.J. Bot.*, 8, 75–211.

118. CROCKER, R. L. (1944) Soil and vegetation relationships in the lower south east of South Australia. *Trans.Roy.Soc.S.Austr.*, 68, 144–172.

119. WOOD, J. G. & BROWNELL, P. F. (1957) Sodium as an essential micronutrient element for *Atriplex vesicaria* Hew. *Nature, 179*, 635–636.

120. MARTIN, HELENE A. & SPECHT, R. L. (1962) Are mesic communities less drought resistant? *Austr.J.Bot., 10*, 106–118.

121. CLEMENTS, F. E. (1916) Plant Succession. *Carnegie Inst.Wash., Publ. 242.*

122. CLEMENTS, F. E. (1928) *Plant succession and indicators.* Wilson, New York.

123. TANSLEY, A. G. (1948) The peculiarities of South Australian vegetation. *Journ.Ecol., 36*, 181–183.

124. WHITTAKER, R. H. (1951) A criticism of the plant association and climatic climax concepts. *Northwest Sci., 25*, 17–31.

125. WHITTAKER, R. H. (1953) A consideration of the climax theory: the climax as a population and pattern. *Ecol.Monogr., 23*, 41–78.

126. CURTIS, J. T. (1955) A prairie continuum in Wisconsin. *Ecology, 36*, 558–566.

127. ROBINSON, G. & COCHRANE, G. ROSS (1965) Water management and conservation in Hattah Lakes, National Park. Paper read at Conservation Symposium, Hobart, A.N.Z.A.A.S., Aug. 1965.

128. BEADLE, N. C. W. (1948) *The vegetation and pastures of New South Wales.* Sydney.

129. BEADLE, N. C. W. (1959) Some aspects of ecological research in semi-arid Australia, in KEAST, A. *et al.* (eds.) *Biogeography and Ecology in Australia.* Junk, Den Haag, 452–460.

130. DOWNES, R. G. (1959) The ecology and prevention of soil erosion, in KEAST, A. *et al.* (eds.) *Biogeography and Ecology in Australia.* Junk, Den Haag, 472–486.

131. STEWART, D. W. R. (1936) Notes on marsupial damage in pine plantations. *Austr. For., 1 (2)*, 41.

132. REID, P. A. (1953) Some economic results of myxomatosis. *Quart.Rev.Agric.Econ., 6*, 93–94.

133. MOORE, R. M. (1959) Ecological observations on plant communities grazed by sheep in Australia, in KEAST, A. *et al.* (eds.). *Biogeography and Ecology in Australia.* Junk, Den Haag, 500–513.

134. RATCLIFFE, F. N. (1959) The rabbit in Australia, in KEAST, A. *et al.* (eds.). *Biogeography and Ecology in Australia.* Junk, Den Haag, 545–564.

135. COCHRANE, G. ROSS (1964) European influence on the vegetation of Great Barrier Island. *Austr.Geogr.Studies, 2*, 103–109.

136. CUNNINGHAM, T. M. (1960) The natural regeneration of *Eucalyptus regnans, University of Melbourne School of Forestry Bull., 1.*

137. ASHTON, D. H. (1955) Some problems concerning the regeneration of mountain ash in Victoria. Paper presented to Section K, A.N.Z.A.A.S., Melbourne, 1955.

138. COCHRANE, G. ROSS (1963b) Commercial viticulture in South Australia. *N.Z.Geog., 19*, 60–82.

139. ALLEN, RUTH F. (1930) A cytological study of heterothallism in *Puccinia graminis. J. Agric.Research, 40*, 585–614.

140. DODD, ALLAN P. (1959) The biological control of prickly pear in Australia. in KEAST, A. *et al.* (eds.). *Biogeography and Ecology in Australia.* Junk, Den Haag, 565–577.

141. MCNALLY, J. (1957a) A field survey of a Koala population. *Proc.Roy.Zool.Soc. N.S.W.* May 8, 1957.

142. MCNALLY, J. (1957b) Koala management in Victoria. *Wild Life Circular, 4.* Fisheries and Game Department, Victoria.

143. MCNALLY, J. (1955) Damage to Victorian exotic pine plantations by native animals. *Austr.For., 19 (2)*, 87.

144. GOODING, C. D. & HARRISON, L. A. (1953) The wallaby menace in the Kimberleys. *J. Agric.W.Austr., 2* (3rd Series), 333.

145. GOODING, C. D. & HARRISON, L. A. (1955) Trapping yards for kangaroos. *J.Agric.W. Austr., 4* (3rd Series) (6), 3.

146. TOMLINSON, A. R., GOODING, C. D. & HARRISON, L. A. (1954) The wallaby menace. *J.Agric.W.Austr., 3* (3rd Series) (5), 609.

147. PRICE, A. GRENFELL (1963) *The Western Invasions of the Pacific and its continents, a study of moving frontiers and changing landscapes.* Oxford Univ. Press, Oxford.

148. TAYLOR, G. (1959) Human ecology in Australia, in KEAST, A. *et al.* (eds.) *Biogeography and Ecology in Australia.* Junk, Den Haag, 52–68.

149. KEAST, A., CROCKER, R. L. & CHRISTIAN, C. S. (1959) *Biogeography and Ecology in Australia.* Junk, Den Haag (Monographiae Biologicae, Vol. 8).

150. JONES, C. F. & DARKENWALD, G. G. (1950) *Economic Geography.* Macmillan, New York.

151. THOMSON, DONALD F. (1962) The Bindibu expedition: exploration among the desert aborigines of Western Australia: I. *Geogr. J., 128*, 1–14; II. 143–157; III. 262–278.

152. BIRDSELL, J. B. (1953) Some environmental and cultural factors influencing the structuring of Australian aboriginal populations. *American Naturalist, 87,* 171–207.

153. KELLY, J. H. (1952) *Report on the beef cattle industry in Northern Australia.* B.A.E., Canberra.

154. KELLY, J. H. & WILLIAMS, D. B. (1954) *The beef industry in Northern Australia.* B.A.E., Melbourne.

155. BOEREE, R. M. (1957) De extensieve Runderteelt in Noord-Australie. *K.N.A.G., 74,* 533–552.

156. BOEREE, R. M. (1959) Past and Present of rural Eyre Peninsula. *Proc.Roy.Geogr.Soc. Austr.(S.A.), 60,* 71–86.

157. BAUER, F. H. (1959) Sheep in Northern Australia. *Austr.Geogr., 8 (1).*

158. BAUER, F. H. (1963) Significant factors in the white settlement of Northern Australia. *Austr.Geogr.Studies, 1,* 39–48.

159. KING, H. W. H. (1959) Transhumant grazing in the snow belt of N.S.W. *Austr. Geogr., 8 (4),* 129–140.

160. KERR, A. (1962) *Northwestern Australia.* Govt. Printer, Perth.

161. STEPHENS, C. G. (1961) Soil landscapes of Australia. *C.S.I.R.O.Soil Publ., 18.*

162. RUTHERFORD, J. (1963) Group irrigation schemes and integrated uses of land in the southern Murray-Darling Basin. *Austr. Geogr.Studies, 1,* 65–83.

163. RYAN, JULIA M. (1963) Changes in intensity in land utilisation in the Otway Ranges. Unpubl. M.A. Thesis, Univ. of Melbourne.

164. COCHRANE, G. ROSS & MCDONALD, N. H. E. (1966) Regeneration in the Victorian Mallee. *Victorian Naturalist, 83,* 220–226.

165. WADHAM, S., WILSON, R. K. & WOOD, JOYCE (1957) (3 ed.) *Land Utilization in Australia.* Melbourne.

166. GENTILLI, J. (1958) Is the Western Australian wheatbelt a natural region? *W.A. Natur., 6,* 157–162.

167. GENTILLI, J. (1961) The survival of natural environment in W.A. *W.A.Natur., 7,* 179–190.

168. MEINIG, D. W. (1959) Colonization of the wheat lands. *Austr.Geogr., 8.*

169. THOMSON, K. W. (1959) Urban settlement and the wheat frontier in the Flinders Ranges, S.A. *Proc.Roy.Geogr.Soc.Austr. (S.A.), 60,* 25–37.

170. SCOTT, P. (1959a) Changes in Tasmanian Agriculture 1948-58. *N.Z.Geogr., 15,* 192–195.

171. PERRY, T. M. (1963) *Australia's first frontier; the spread of settlement in New South Wales, 1788–1829.* M.U.P., Melbourne.

172. THOMSON, K. W. (1957) The settlement pattern of the Barossa Valley, S.A. *Austr. Geogr., 7,* 51–58.

173. DAVIS, CHARLES M. (1959) Fire as a land use tool in north-eastern Australia. *Geogr. Rev., 49,* 552–560.

174. MEINIG, D. W. (1963) *On the margins of the good earth; the South Australian wheat frontier, 1869–1884.* Murray, London.

175. BIRD, E. C. F. (1961) Reedgrowth in the Gippsland Lakes. *Vict.Nat., 77,* 262–268.

176. POLUNIN, NICHOLAS (1960) *Introduction to plant geography and some related sciences.* Longmans, London.

177. HOWARD, R. A. & POWELL, DULCIE, A. (1963) The introduction of rubber producing species in the West Indies. *Econ.Bot., 17,* 337–349.

178. CHRISTIAN, C. S. (1957) Developments in Northern Australian Agriculture. *Proc.Roy. Geogr.Soc.Austr.(S.A.), 58,* 37–42.

179. WILLIAMS, M. (1965) South-east of South Australia. *Longman's Australian Geographies, 22.*

180. SMITH, R. H. T. (1964) The development and function of transport routes in southern N.S.W., 1860–1930. *Austr.Geogr.Studies, 2,* 47–65.

181. VICTORIAN SOIL CONSERVATION AUTHORITY. *Annual Reports.*

182. HEATHCOTE, R. L. (1964) Conservation or opportune use: the pastoralist's problem in semi-arid Australia. *Advancement of Science, 21 (89),* 47–60.

183. DEVERY, P. J. (1956) A geographical description of the flood problem in N.S.W. *Inst.Agric.Sci.J., 22.*

184. COCHRANE, G. ROSS, BURNARD, SALLY M. & PHILPOTT, JENNIFER M. (1962) Land use and forest fires in the Mount Lofty Ranges, South Australia. *Austr.Geogr., 8,* 143–160.

185. SAUER, C. O. (1950) Grassland, climax, fire and man. *J.Range Mgt., 3,* 16–21.

186. BEADLE, N. C. W. (1940) Soil temperatures during forest fires and their effect upon the survival of vegetation. *Journ.Ecol., 28,* 180–192.

187. BIRD, E. F. C. (1962) Water Supply and Waste Disposal. *Geography, 47,* 190–2.

188. WILSON, M. G. A. (1959) The coal fields of the Lower Hunter Valley. *N.Z.Geogr., 15,* 18–41.

189. WILSON, M. G. A. (1963) The changing La Trobe Valley. *Austr.Geogr.Studies, 1,* 31–38.

190. WILLINGTON, C. M. (1961) The mineral industry contribution to the development of S.A. *Proc.Roy.Geogr.Soc.Austr.(S.A.), 62,* 47–56.

191. DUNCAN, C. (1961) The aluminium industry in Australia. *Geogr.Rev., 51,* 21–46.

192. SOLOMON, R. J. (1959) Broken Hill: the growth of settlement, 1883–1958. *Austr. Geogr., 7,* 181–192.

193. THOMSON, K. W. (1955b) The changes in function of former mining settlements: the Wallaroo copper belt. *Proc.Roy.Geogr.Soc. Austr.(S.A.), 56,* 47–58.

194. DALE, M. B. (1959) The location of oil refineries in Australia. *N.Z.Geogr., 15,* 160–172.

195. BRITTON, J. N. H. (1961) The development of Port Kembla. *Geography, 46,* 247–250.

196. THOMSON, K. W. (1955a) Das Industriedreieck des Spencer-Golfs. *Die Erde, 55,* Heft 3–4, 286–300.

197. COGGINS, R. S. (1959) The Snowy Mountain Scheme. *Longman's Austr.Geographies.*

198. COCHRANE, G. ROSS (1960c) Water Storage plan for South Australia. *N.Z.Geogr., 16,* 217–219.

199. SUNDBORG, A. (1951) Climatological studies in Uppsala. *Geographica, 22.*

200. LANDSBERG, H. E. (1956) The climate of towns, in THOMAS, W. L. (ed.) *Man's role in changing the face of the Earth,* 584–606.

201. GEIGER, R. (1965) *The climate near the ground.* Harvard Univ. Press, Cambridge, Mass.

202. WESTERMAN, H. L. (1959) The future growth and expansion of the Metropolitan area of Adelaide. *Proc.Roy.Geogr.Soc. Austr.(S.A.), 60,* 59–70.

203. SCOTT, P. (1959b) The Australian C.B.D. *Econ.Geogr., 35,* 290–314.

204. DICK, R. S. (1960) *Five towns of the brigalow country of south-eastern Queensland.* Univ. of Queensland Press, Brisbane.

205. LINGE, G. J. R. (1961) Canberra after fifty years. *Geogr.Rev., 51,* 467–486.

206. ROBINSON, K. W. *et al.* (1963) *Readings in urban growth.* Univ. of Sydney and N.S.W. *Geogr.Soc.Res.Paps.,* 3–7.

207. MARSHALL, ANN (1958) Observations of indoor discomfort under conditions of dry heat. *Proc.Roy.Geogr.Soc.Austr.(S.A.), 59,* 23–34.

208. MARSHALL, ANN (1963) The prediction of indoor heat discomfort. *Austr.Geogr. Studies, 1,* 115–123.

209. HUMBOLDT, A. VON (1807) *Ideen zu einer Geographie der Pflanzen nebst einem Naturgemälde der Tropenländer.* Türbingen.

Two Studies in the Historical Geography of South Australia

MICHAEL WILLIAMS

THE GEOGRAPHY OF SOUTH AUSTRALIA: 1840

I can scarcely imagine a more interesting scene than to observe a country in the course of being rescued from a state of nature.—J. F. BENNETT, *South Australia* (1843), p. 74

Perhaps the most crucial geographical choice that faced the creators of South Australia was that of a site for the capital. The natural advantages of the area in which the first landing would be made, particularly in respect to water and soil, were of paramount importance, as had been demonstrated by early struggles at Sydney in New South Wales and at Swan River in Western Australia. Colonel Light, the Surveyor-General, who was sent to South Australia, considered various sites but rejected them on one ground or other. Kangaroo Island he thought a vast flat desert of sand and scrub, separated moreover from the mainland whence would come trade (Fig. 1). The Port Lincoln district was handicapped by unproductive hinterland and lack of water. The Murray mouth, long held to be the ideal location for the first settlement by reason of the trade flow expected on the river, was impractical on account of lack of a deep passage into Lake Alexandrina. The Encounter Bay district was rejected because of its exposure to south-westerly winds. These disadvantages were real. By contrast, positive advantages characterized the eastern shores of Gulf St. Vincent, where Light found wide, flat to gently sloping plains and an obviously fertile soil which supported long grass and savannah woodland, watered by many stream courses which, flowing off high, forested ranges, ensured a fairly constant supply of water. The one disadvantage seemed the lack of a harbour; but the subsequent discovery of the long, south-trending inlet of the

Port Adelaide River buttressed Light's original good opinion.

The Port River at first seemed the obvious site for the new town, but Light found it lacking in fresh water and in firm building ground; accordingly, he chose high ground alongside the Torrens River, some six miles southwest of the Port and in the centre of the plains, where there was ample fresh water. In eight brief weeks he laid out the town on a generous scale, with its twin foci in North Adelaide and the City, and with surrounding parklands.

Survey and apportionment of agricultural land was the next important step. Inefficiency, personal differences, and lack of resources acted however to delay the country surveys. Very little progress was made in rural settling through 1837 and 1838—a disastrous event for establishment of a colony dependent upon rapid agriculture for its prosperity.

During these two years, about 5000 of the 6000 inhabitants of South Australia were concentrated in Adelaide. Unable to get on the land, they were camped in the City, exerting themselves in building a town far larger than was needed at the time, and indulging in land speculation which quickly used up the limited capital of many.

Two of the reasons for the delay in survey and apportionment of rural land arose from the need to make certain specific provisions. Firstly, the preliminary purchasers who had paid money in Britain for South Australian land as yet unsurveyed could demand survey, regardless of distance from the original landing. This meant enlargement of the area first required by about two-thirds. Secondly, any settler who paid £4000 in advance could select at will an area of 15,000 acres, and when this had been marked into eighty acre sections, could select any 4000 acres in a compact block; the remainder became available to other settlers. Altogether, 450,000 acres had to be surveyed on this account in 30 Special Survey areas, only a small portion being taken up immediately. The preliminary purchasers and the Special Surveys alike put an intolerable strain on the survey teams.

The general framework for settlement appears in Fig. 2, which shows districts A to F surveyed for the Government and the areas covered by the thirty-three Special Surveys. The distribution of Government land, in which sections could be selected, shows a preference for the high-rainfall zone along the coast from Adelaide to Cape Jervis. The Special Surveys were located either in areas of assured rainfall, e.g. in the Mt. Barker District; or along water frontages, as with the five surveys along the Murray and those on either side of the Wakefield, Light and Gawler rivers. This framework of survey guided settlement for many years.

The Rural Scene: 1840

About half a million acres had been surveyed and subdivided into sections by 1840 of which about 160,000 acres had been selected and sold. The distribution of most of the sold land is shown in Fig. 3 [1].

The three environmental factors of slope, vegetation and water are reflected in the settlers' first choice of land. Preference for land with little slope was related to ease of cultivation. The Adelaide plain and the Willunga and Noarlunga Basins formed important zones of early settlement, whereas the steep slopes and broken relief of the western edge of the Mount Lofty Ranges and the Willunga scarp were avoided. The separate settlement at Mount Barker and near Strathalbyn, while high above the sea, occupied flat valleys and areas of locally subdued relief.

Preference for level land was perhaps secondary to assessment of agricultural and pastoral capabilities, as these were indicated by vege-

tation (Fig. 3, inset). The coastal plain and eastern margins of the upland block of the Mount Lofty Ranges, with less than 25 inches of rain a year, coincided with the red-brown loamy earths of moderate fertility and with open savannah woodland. On the coastal plains, *Eucalyptus odorata* (peppermint gum) predominated, to the east of the uplands lay a broad zone of *Eucalyptus leucoxylon* (blue gum). Beneath and around the trees occurred a largely herbaceous growth of kangaroo and wallaby grass *(Themeda triandra, Danthonia penicillata)* which Backhouse described in 1837 as 'growing up to our elbows and resembl[ing] two years' seed meadows, in England, in thickness'. The savannah woodland was easily accessible to the first settlers because the perennial grass provided feed for sheep without the expense and effort of clearing. If cultivation were however to be attempted, clearing was a simple matter. In contrast, the podzolized soils and the dense vegetation of the dry sclerophyll or stringy-bark high forests of the Mount Lofty Ranges, where rainfall exceeded thirty inches, were unattractive. Closer trees and dense and profuse undergrowth made these forests impenetrable, difficult to clear and highly combustible [2]. Indeed, the rugged and forested valleys and spurs of the ranges (or 'Tiers' as they were then known) formed a refuge for escaped convicts and other evaders of the law [3]. Another negative area for settlement was the scrubby, heath-like country on the deep podzolized sands of the southern Mount Lofty Ranges and Fleurieu Peninsula which carried a E. baxteri-E. cosmophylla association. In the plains about ten miles north of Adelaide, and away from the foothills of the ranges, diminished rainfall caused savannah woodland to give way to mallee.

Within the zones of fairly level land and open forest, final location was influenced by the availability of water. Nearly one half of the farms in 1840 obtained their water supply from rivers—particularly the Torrens, Sturt Creek, or the five small creeks that flowed off the Mount Lofty Ranges and across the Adelaide Plain. The Onkaparinga and Angas rivers were also drawn upon (Fig. 3). About one-tenth of the farms relied upon surface water, lagoons, swamps, or ponds, and three-tenths on wells. The character of water supply on the remainder

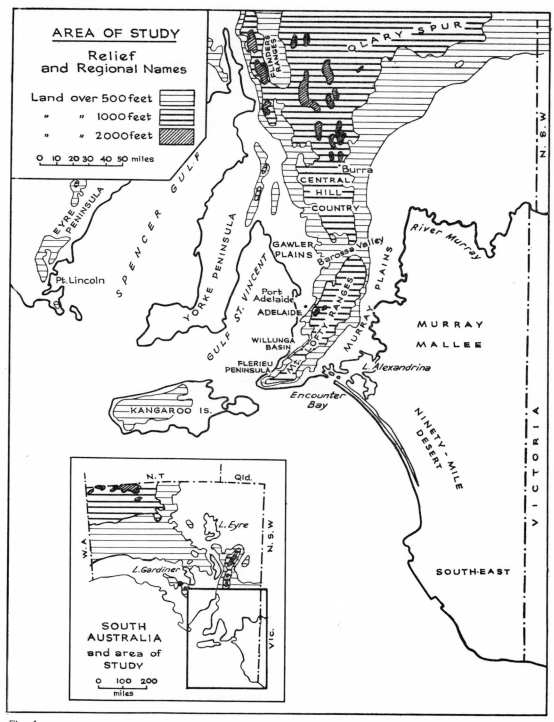

AREA OF STUDY
Relief
and Regional Names

Land over 500 feet
„   „   1000 feet
„   „   2000 feet

0 10 20 30 40 50 miles

Fig. 1

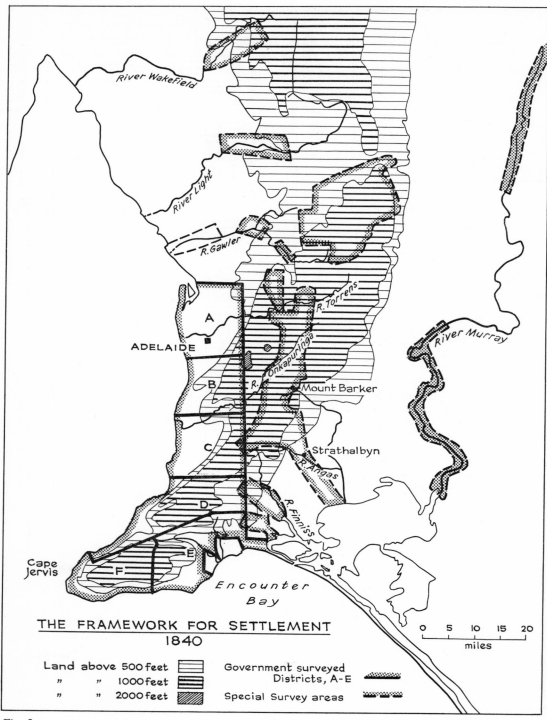

THE FRAMEWORK FOR SETTLEMENT
1840

Land above 500 feet   Government surveyed
  "   "   1000 feet   Districts, A-E
  "   "   2000 feet   Special Survey areas

Fig. 2

is not known. Wells were more numerous on the coastal plain (six out of every ten farms) than in the hill areas (only two out of every ten). The thick, porous sedimentary rock of the plains probably contained much more water than did the thin soils of the hills, where surface supplies were relied upon more heavily. Wells had to be sunk to 122 feet in the eastern portion of the plains near Tusmore, but most were but ten to forty feet deep.

Of the land that was sold, 15,706 acres were enclosed. 73 per cent were fenced by wooden post and rail fences, the remainder by stone walls, banks, ditches and iron bars, or by temporary fences made of piled-up scrub and branches. Enclosure was needed to stop stock from straying, to prevent damage by invading stock, and—on the Adelaide Plains—to exclude herds of feral pigs. Closely related to the amount of land in cultivation, the concentration of enclosed land was greatest in District A in the Adelaide Plains (9441 acres), District B (2832 acres), and the Mount Barker District (2036 acres).

In 1840 'cultivation of the soil commenced in earnest' [4]. The stagnation of the first four years was over. It was said that 'farming establishments are in active preparation on every side, and it is a matter not merely of hope but of sober expectation, that our magnificent agricultural valleys will soon be filled with produce sufficient for home consumption' [5].

The extent of cultivation is shown in Fig. 3. Local concentrations include the Reed Beds at the mouth of the River Torrens, where fertile alluvial land was subject to periodical flooding; the area immediately east of the parklands; the Tusmore areas three miles east of the City; the banks of the Torrens, particularly at Klemzig; and the Mount Barker district at Hahndorf. Both at Klemzig and at Hahndorf, German migrants had set up small farming communities and with great industry had already got into cultivation 156 acres at the one place and 201 acres at the other.

A Mediterranean type of climate had been inferred for this part of South Australia from the early explorations, but the summer season still came as a shock to migrants from well-watered and humid countries. 'I recollect', said John Morphet, 'the disconcerted and dismal look with which most of the party regarded from the deck of the ship, the dried and scorched appearance of the plains which to their English ideas betokened little short of barrenness' [6]. It took many years of experiment for the cultivators to fit their traditional agricultural practices to the new regime of seasons. Despite many widely-publicized reports on the farming calendar, the process of acquiring local knowledge was still in its early beginnings in 1840.

A great mass of detail about cropping techniques and times of sowing appeared in the 1840 survey of farms, but the correct time for sowing cereals was still not known—crops were being put in the ground from January to October, despite the hot winds and scorching sun which in the previous October had resulted in the loss of half of the late-sown seed. Crops sown too early or too late suffered badly from blight and smut [7]. Extreme timing was however exceptional; most crops were planted in the wet months between April and July, April and May seeming to give the most promising results. Barley was successful when sown a little later, even as late as June, while maize flourished after being planted in August and September. All of this is consistent with modern agricultural knowledge and practice. But the earliest cultivators had also to learn that delimitation of the extreme is not all; the rain needed to germinate seed can vary capriciously in South Australia. The skilful farmer had to adapt his seeding operation to current seasonal conditions, however unexpected.

Yields were as varied as were times of planting. Wheat yields in the Mount Barker district varied from fifteen or twenty bushels per acre for July planting, to forty bushels per acre for April planting. Five to twenty-seven bushels of wheat per acre were harvested near Gawler, and from six to twenty-seven bushels for wheat and up to forty bushels for barley along the banks of the Torrens, where, however, late-planted barley fell as low as sixteen bushels. Similar yields were recorded for Districts B and C.

Farmers were already learning much from experiments with types of seed—Tasmanian, South Australian Talavara, and South American rust-resisting wheat and Cape and English Barley. Seed pickled in lime or brine proved far superior to that untreated [8].

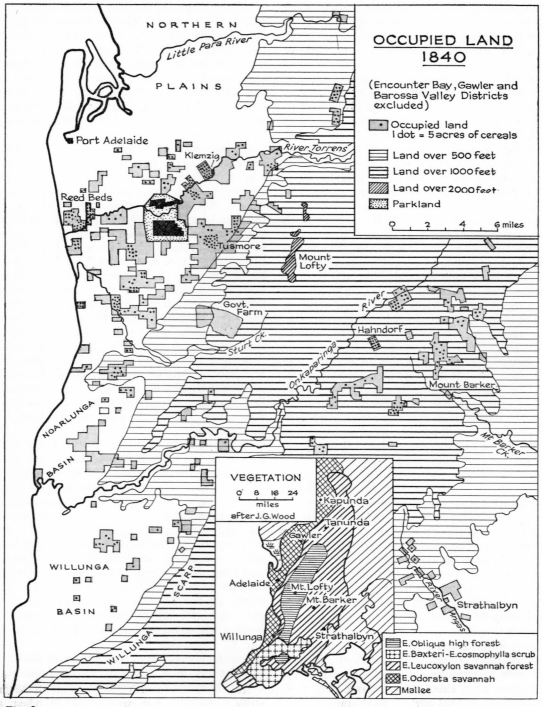

OCCUPIED LAND 1840

(Encounter Bay, Gawler and Barossa Valley Districts excluded)

- Occupied land 1 dot = 5 acres of cereals
- Land over 500 feet
- Land over 1000 feet
- Land over 2000 feet
- Parkland

0   2   4   6 miles

VEGETATION

0   8   16   24
miles

after J. G. Wood

- E. Obliqua high forest
- E. Baxteri–E. cosmophylla scrub
- E. Leucoxylon savannah forest
- E. Odorata savannah
- Mallee

Fig. 3

Of other crops, potatoes were perhaps the most common. Yields of two to two and a half tons per acre were usual, except when crops were attacked by grubs, and four tons per acre were produced in the high-rainfall zone of the hills near Kersbrook. While potatoes failed near Gawler, those planted at every six weeks throughout the year in the humid southern portion of the ranges, at Encounter Bay, were successful. Turnips, rape, vetches, and melons appeared amid the vegetables and fruit of small garden plots, while the 700 vines and 400 fruit trees at Mount Barker foreshadowed the later commercial production of grapes, olives, and citrus.

The survey of 1840 tells little of numbers and distribution of stock in the newly-settled areas of South Australia, but totals of sheep and cattle are known to have increased rapidly, particularly after overlanders brought stock to Adelaide in 1838 (Table 1).

Table 1 *Numbers of Stock in South Australia, 1838 to 1841*

	Sheep	Cattle	Horses
1838	28,000	2,500	480
1839	108,000	7,600	800
1840	166,770	13,957	659
1841	250,500	16,696	1,252

Sources: *South Australian Almanac, 1840,* for 1840.
South Australian Almanac, 1842, for 1838, 1839, 1842.

Stock totals by individual landowners, published in the *South Australia Almanac* for 1840, cannot be related to particular localities, other than in the broadest way. In Fig. 4, totals are shown for each of the eleven regions, with the distribution of known stockyards and pens—such as occurred in nearly three out of every four properties in the settled areas—and of dairies, all of which indicate animal husbandry.

The Adelaide District had the most stock—51,819 sheep, and 5876 cattle which the large number of dairies would suggest were for milk. The Northern District had 2210 cattle and 53,100 sheep, the flocks belonging to squatters who were rapidly taking up land in the high-rainfall area of the central uplands. Information on the early expansion of the squatter occupation is tantalizingly slight (see below), but the probable location of some outstations can be identified (Fig. 4). There is reason to suppose that squatters were already moving north to the head of Spencer Gulf, Horrocks being said to have reached Wilmington in 1840. The very few stockyards recorded in the Para district suggest that many of the 16,311 sheep and 2727 cattle there belonged to squatters, as did the 3000 sheep and 2200 cattle in the Port Lincoln District.

The remaining regional figures, more or less proportional to amount of settlement, are shown in descending order in Table 2.

Table 2 *Distribution of Stock in the Settled Areas of South Australia, 1840*

	Sheep	Cattle	Horses
Mount Barker	15,900	2,727	126
Strathalbyn	8,800	1,045	65
Onkaparinga	8,710	260	16
Hurtle Vale	3,530	522	32
Morphet Vale	3,850	194	21
Willunga	1,500	128	4
Encounter Bay	250	307	9

Source: *South Australian Almanac, 1840.*

In each case, however, the total number of stock is larger than might have been expected from the amount of land taken up and enclosed or from the number of stockyards; here again, the circumstance can only be explained by squatter occupancy.

The population of South Australia had risen by the end of 1840 to 14,610, of whom 6557 were in the City of Adelaide, 1932 in the municipal villages surrounding the City, 707 in Port Adelaide and Albert Town, and 5414 in the rural areas. The early massive concentration of population in the City was now past, even though some 44 per cent of the total population still lived there. People moved out to the country areas at a rate of between 160 and 210 a month. Wheeler, manager of the South Australian Company, stated in the following years that they were 'now going into the interior in shoals, cultivating and sheep farming in every possible direction' [9]. In 1840, District A contained 3152 country settlers, B had 839 and C had 259. In the upland areas, Mt. Barker had 819, the Northern District had 660, and Encounter Bay 106. There were in addition 186 at Port Lincoln and 90 on Kangaroo Island.

Only 97 of the 338 holdings marked in Fig. 3 carried no permanent dwellings; of these 97, 25 had houses under construction or had temporary dwellings, usually tents. Clearing, fencing and land preparation took precedence over house-building.

The rural living unit was variable, but such entries as these for Plympton, five miles southeast of Adelaide were typical of many others: 'There are on this farm two large and commodious dwelling houses, with a cottage for labourers; stable, cart shed, stock yard, etc.' or 'one very good dwelling house on the section with a cottage for labourers and a stockyard.' A few sections had more elaborate and specialized outbuildings—barns, dairies, fowl-houses or pigsties; some had two stockyards, and nearly all had a garden ranging from half to two acres. The best and most substantial houses were made of stone or brick, except that some near Willunga in the southern coastal plains were made of local slate. But stone and slab had to be quarried, and bricks to be made so most settlers, lacking for time, turned to the two easily-won natural materials of wood and mud. Many houses were made of reeds, stringy-bark, wood, log, lath and plaster, cob, or pisé. There were also some Manning's houses, pre-fabricated structures shipped out from Britain and erected in South Australia [10].

Despite the many temporary structures, the recorded impression is that of an ordered and substantial landscape, chequered into 80-acre sections and studded with substantial farmhouses, cottages and outbuildings. The temporary structures, increasingly numerous with distance from Adelaide, were later demolished or abandoned when settlers had time to build in the stone which they most preferred. In this way the South Australian landscape gained one of its most distinctive visual features, which contrasts it with other parts of rural Australia—an overwhelming preponderance of masonry farmhouses [11].

The Urban Scene: 1840

The overwhelming dominance of Adelaide in the urban scene of South Australia has led geographers and historians alike to regard secondary settlements as of little significance. Yet the embryo villages and towns of this early phase were in time to become service centres for the rural areas and to create an important aspect of the new landscape.

Town creation was left to private enterprise. Speculation over sites was rife. The Secondary Towns Association, formed in 1838 by capitalists in Britain, directed its agent in South Australia to select two Special Surveys in which two secondary towns would be laid out, one near the coast and one inland [12]. After an extensive search, the agent replied that 'There are too many devoted to that object already. The formation of Townships and Villages has been a favourite scheme of the speculative for some time past, although many of them will never have an existence but in name'. Along the banks of the Murray and on the shores of Lake Alexandrina, six townships were intended to be laid out 'of which I am doubtful if more than two will ever rise to importance'. With such a large area in which to choose town sites and with so many people already attempting to create towns, it was little wonder that the agent wrote 'I am quite at a loss to know where to direct my steps in search of a promising locality'.

Bennett, two years later, observed that it was a favourite scheme to lay out a section of land as a township and to sell small portions:

In this manner almost every district boasts its township, although in many cases the site is only discernible by the board containing its name, or the name of some of the streets, with the pegs which mark the boundaries of the lots [13].

Despite the superabundance of potential towns, some of the subdivisions succeeded in becoming actual towns, whether by virtue of site on a line of communication, by securing priority in a newly colonized area, or as a result of local initiative: this last factor, however, is difficult, if not impossible, to measure.

Naturally enough, the greatest speculative activity occurred in the zone of densest agricultural settlement. Within a radius of three miles of Adelaide, thirty villages were started (Fig. 5). Of these, only a few could hope to be economically viable. Hindmarsh (pop. 601), Bowden (pop. 393), and Prospect (pop. 109), assisted by traffic between Adelaide and the Port, were inhabited mainly by carriers, brickmakers and labourers [14] 'who have houses

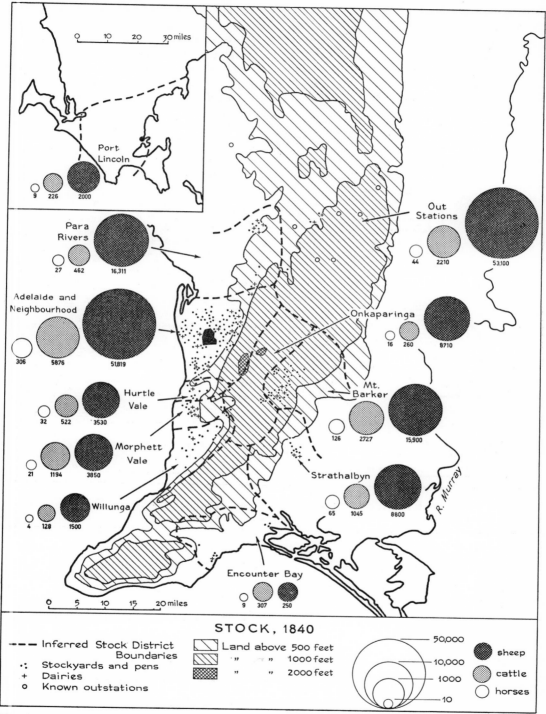

Fig. 4

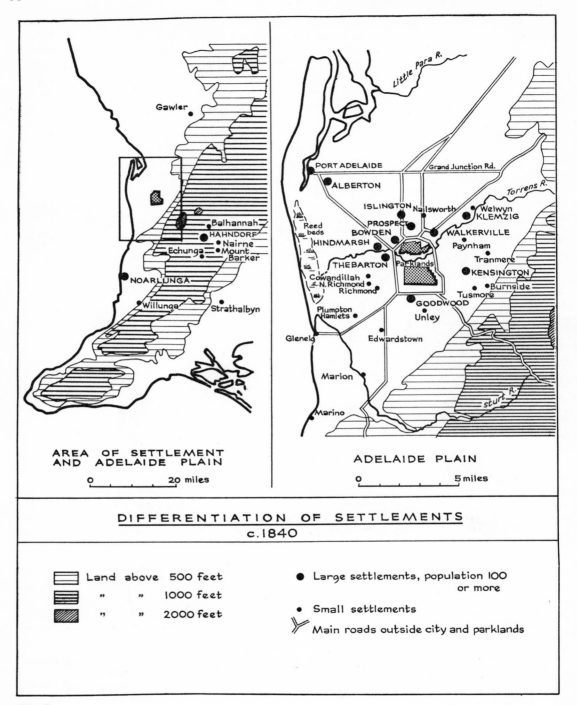

AREA OF SETTLEMENT
AND ADELAIDE PLAIN

0 ——————— 20 miles

ADELAIDE PLAIN

0 ——————— 5 miles

DIFFERENTIATION OF SETTLEMENTS
c.1840

▭	Land above 500 feet	● Large settlements, population 100 or more
▤	,, ,, 1000 feet	• Small settlements
▨	,, ,, 2000 feet	Y Main roads outside city and parklands

Fig. 5

of their own, cultivate small gardens [and] rear a few pigs and poultry' [15]. Thebarton (pop. 501) was an industrial settlement with tanneries, numerous brickworks and small workshops, inhabited mainly by labourers and mechanics who were attracted to cheap freehold blocks near the City. The process of residential differentiation was already at work. Kensington and Walkerville (pop. 202) were regarded as superior areas for business men and merchants having 'many genteel residences and beautiful gardens and altogether decidedly more aristocratic and English'. Walkerville was already destined to become a high-class residential suburb, with its acre blocks selling for as much as £120 while the highest figure in Hindmarsh was £80. Walkerville's 'smug-looking cottages' and substantial brick houses which seemed as though they had been 'built for future generations' [16] gave an air of comfort and prosperity. Islington (pop. 77), profiting from a site on the main road to Gawler and the Barossa Valley, had two inns. It was mainly occupied, however, by small-scale dairymen and agriculturists who were creating a belt of agricultural land around the settlement. Although small and founded fairly late, Islington progressed so markedly that it seemed to bid fair to pass most of its rivals in the race of improvement. Klemzig (pop. 209) was a village of German migrants, its orderly arrangement of houses, roads and gardens bespeaking a cooperative and communal settlement. There was, said one observer 'nothing English here—even from the picturesque kirk down to the pony cart, all is different' [17]. Much labour and capital had been applied; the settlement already possessed 230 acres of cultivated land and 190 horses and cattle. Finally, to the south of Adelaide lay another small settlement—Goodwood, with a population of about 100.

More important than any of these settlements was Port Adelaide. The site, proving difficult, had affected initial growth of the settlement. It was separated from the firm land of the plains by two miles of swamp which demanded expensive road work. The depth of water at the anchorage was insufficient, and dredging had to be started in 1839. Fresh water had at first to be carted from Adelaide so that not until a successful well was sunk on the north side of the creek, opposite the town, could extensive settlement occur.

As these difficulties were slowly overcome, the settlement grew. It had 472 inhabitants by 1840, when it was said to be increasing rapidly. The marine character of the town was reflected in the occupations of its inhabitants, who consisted of 'ships' carpenters, fishermen, boatmen, and ships' chandlers, three or four publicans, several shipping agents, the men employed in the harbour and custom's department, a couple of butchers, a sailmaker, a blacksmith, etc.' [18]. Albert Town (now Alberton) (pop. 235) was situated on the firm ground on the Adelaide side of the swamp, functioning basically as a residential suburb of the Port.

In addition to these villages, most of which could be regarded almost as suburbs of Adelaide, many other newly-emergent settlements dotted the plains. Most of these contained 'at least a few houses, the residences probably of a carpenter, a blacksmith or shoe-maker' [20], the indispensable hotel, and — later — the general store. Edward's Town, for instance, was divided into acre allotments on which lived eight families; Cowandilla had eight or nine pisé houses and a brickworks; New Richmond had three dwellings and two or three more in course of construction. Tusmore to the east of Adelaide had '3 cottages for workmen, a smith's shop, and a public house', while Plympton Hamlets had 'a considerable number of persons'. Payneham had eighteen cottages, one dwelling house and a public house. Welwyn was 'divided into small allotments for a township' on which there was already a public house and five cottages, and Unley (pop. 92), had twenty-two houses, all of which had been built during the preceding six months.

In districts B and C, the density of incipient towns was less (Fig. 5). Creighton had an hotel and the post office for the southern coastal plains. Marino was already 'a fashionable bathing establishment with an hotel and an inn', Marion was just taking a recognizable shape with two dwelling houses and two more in the course of construction, but already offered the services of a carpenter, a smith, and a wheelwright. Farther south lay Noarlunga, with a new bridge across the Onkaparinga River—a thriving settlement with an inn, an hotel, a general store and extensive stockyard, where it was 'proposed to hold periodic Markets for the sale of every description of stock'. In the southern extremity of the plains, beneath the Willunga scarp, lay the town of Willunga with a police station, 'a handsome and commodious inn and hotel', and eight dwelling houses in which lived the workmen of the nearby slate quarries.

In terms of distance from Adelaide, Gawler was the northern counterpart of Willunga, but was larger and more varied and it could boast 'a very good inn, one public house, police barracks, two smiths' shops, six dwelling houses, and thirty-four inhabitants'. Gawler stood at the junction of the main north road from Adelaide with the road to the River Murray.

Away from the plains and in the hills was another group of settlements. The German settlement of Hahndorf (pop. 300) was, like Klemzig, different from other villages not only in continental European architectural styles, but also in its orderliness. It was said of Hahndorf that 'all is foreign as well as pleasing' [22]. Echunga had three houses, and blacksmith's and wheelwright's shops; Balhannah contained an inn, an hotel and four dwelling houses; Nairne was recognizably larger with at least two houses, an inn, and smith's and carpenter's establishments. Strathalbyn and Mount Barker were barely beginning, one with a house and store, the other with an inn and a few houses.

The only other settlements of significance in the State were Port Lincoln on the southern tip of Eyre Peninsula, with a population of 195 and some forty houses, and the two creations of the Secondary Towns Association: Victoria and Wellington. Information is very scanty on both of these. Victoria remained unsettled, but

Wellington, in a strategic position at the lowest crossing of the Murray, had a few houses and an inn.

Town creation seems often to have preceded occupation of rural land. Further research might well reveal that the town was sometimes the incentive to the taking-up of land in a new area, as was the case with Kooringa and Kapunda in later years. The craftsmen and tradesmen quickly grouped together in communities to provide services for, and perhaps to stimulate the settlement of, the surrounding countryside. Only 56 per cent of all the male immigrants to South Australia up to 1840 could be classed as agricultural workers [21]— a low proportion for an infant colony that had to feed itself and pay its way. 20 per cent were building tradesmen, 12 per cent were tradesmen and artisans, and 6 per cent were mechanics—in other words, 38 per cent of the male population had followed some trade or craft prior to immigration. It was not surprising that some set up independent workshops and stores in the country, proving just as much pioneers as were the farmers.

The result of only four years of colonizing activity was observed by Bennett, who had watched the settlers move into the virgin land before 1838 and saw the same areas again in 1843:

I have seen the plains and forests around Adelaide changed from their original desolation into a continual mass of farms—some thousands of acres bearing their crops of wheat, maize and barley—while in the more distant parts in which no track or trace of human being could be found when I first rode through them, I ultimately saw spotted with sheep and cattle stations, with an occasional field of corn [22].

THE GEOGRAPHY OF SOUTH AUSTRALIA: c. 1855

In the fifteen years after 1840, South Australia underwent many changes: its geography became increasingly complex, the amount of land under cultivation increased slowly but substantially, pastoral activity spread in a rapid and spectacular manner, and minerals were discovered and exploited both in South Australia and in the adjacent colony of Victoria.

The rapid expansion of settlement in country areas in 1840 brought the colony near to bankruptcy in the following year, but primary production enabled the colony to overcome this financial crisis. By the end of 1842 the harvest was so abundant that the population of 16,000 was producing enough food for twice that number and had a surplus for export. From 1842

Table 3 *Details of the Extent of Cultivation and Per Cent Composition of Total Exports, South Australia 1840 to 1856*

Year	No. of Cultivators	Total Acres Cultivated	Value of Exports (£A)	Value Wool Exports as % of Tot. Exports	Value Wheat and Bread-Stuffs Exports as % of Tot. Exports	Value of All other Exports (Mostly Copper) as % of Tot. Exports
1840		2,687	15,650	55.8	4.7	39.5
1841		6,722	40,561	87.5	—	12.5
1842		18,940	29,070	75.8	—	24.2
1843		28,690	66,160	68.9	3.5	27.6
1844		26,906	82,268	52.0	14.0	34.0
1845	1,269	26,218	131,800	54.8	10.3	34.9
1846	1,714	33,292	287,659	37.0	4.2	58.8
1847	1,837	36,440	275,115	20.4	9.4	70.2
1848	1,846	48,912	465,878	21.1	4.3	74.6
1849		44,973	373,842	29.0	4.0	67.0
1850		64,728	545,040	24.1	10.9	65.0
1851	2,821	80,971	540,962	27.3	14.7	58.0
1852		97,214	736,899	15.7	31.0	53.3
1853		113,457	731,595	32.3	39.0	28.7
1854		129,699	694,422	26.3	49.0	24.7
1855	5,321	203,423 (est.)	686,959	41.3	35.0	23.7
1856		203,423	1,398,867	29.7	42.0	28.3

Source: S.A. Statistical Register, 1927-28

onwards the difficulty was to find markets for grain. Shipments went with little success to the Cape of Good Hope, New Zealand, Singapore, and to the other Australian colonies. The British market was virtually closed by the Corn Laws, but, with the repeal of the Navigation Acts in 1849, the competitive price of wheat fell. South Australian wheat exports increased four-fold, from £14,996 in 1849, to £59,769 in 1850 (Table 3).

Expansion of cultivation and scarcity of labour fostered the invention of agricultural machinery. In 1844, John Bull, a farmer from near Mount Barker, invented a harvesting machine or stripper which Thomas Ridley, a Hindmarsh miller, perfected and marketed. Although small, this device was well adapted to flat ground and to ripe dry grain, proving peculiarly suited to the climate and terrain of the Adelaide plains. Conflicting reports make the machine's effect on production difficult to assess. Undoubtedly it sold widely; machines were said in 1851 to be at work in almost every field of the Willunga Basin [23], but the cost of £50 each probably kept them out of reach of small farmers. Whatever its application and effects, however, the harvester serves at least to indicate the growing interest in cultivation as opposed to pasturing. The Wakefieldian

heritage was fostering a class of small, independent cultivators, who, although men of small means and limited power, were growing in numbers. These contrasted with the few but wealthy and influential pastoralists. South Australian agriculture thus came to differ strongly from that of other States. No better indication can be given of the growing importance of wheat, as opposed to wool, than the percentage which each contributed to the total exports of South Australia (Table 3).

Expansion of the pastoral industry was promoted by natural increase of flocks, and by the limited extent of the native grasses in the savannah woodland on either side of the Mount Lofty Ranges. Pastoralists pushed farther afield, away from the high-rainfall areas of the central uplands. Explorers and pastoralists alike quickly destroyed the prevalent idea that all valuable districts of South Australia were fully occupied. Burr discovered the fertile land north of Clare in 1842, Darke found grassy country as he penetrated inland from Port Lincoln, and squatters from the Western District of Victoria moved quickly into the fertile land of the ranges and flats of the South-East.

Disease in flocks, and transport of wool, alike set problems. Scab, scouring three-quarters of the flocks in 1843, was eventually cured with simple palliatives of corrosive sub-limate, tobacco, tar and turpentine. Transport of the wool clip was assisted by the development of Port Wakefield and Port Augusta as mineral exporters, and by the many bullock teams which the mines had called into existence. Moreover, since copper ore provided an excellent ballast cargo for wool, the cost of shipping wool came down. The problem of obtaining secure tenure of runs (see below) was less easily surmounted.

Development of mining ran through the events in South Australia between 1840 and 1855. Although it did not enable the province to recover from periodic financial crisis, mining did help to diversify the economy and to produce some unexpected prosperity. In addition, the discovery of copper at Kapunda in 1843 and at the Burra (Kooringa) in 1844 encouraged the spread of intensive settlement towards, and eventually in, these northern parts of the State. These rich discoveries came after more modest finds in the settled areas—silver-lead at Glen Osmond in 1841 and at Mont-acute in 1842, and copper at Kanmantoo, east of Mount Barker, in 1846.

Kapunda and Burra were the most important discoveries. A ready market was found for copper in Swansea; but the cost of ore was great, and local smelting obviously an economic proposition. Smelters were established in a short-lived venture at Yatala near Port Adelaide, and at Kooringa (Burra) and Apoinga south of Burra, the copper from these two works going by cart to Port Wakefield and then by barge to Port Adelaide for oversea shipment.

Table 3 lists the value of all exports other than wheat and wool; these were overwhelmingly of copper. By 1846 their value exceeded that of wheat and wool combined, a position held until 1852.

The discovery of gold in Victoria in 1851 had a profound effect on South Australia, when the population underwent a net outmovement, probably involving 10,000 people in the ensuing six years. This migration depressed the South Australian economy, particularly in the retail trade but farming was less affected, many of the farmers planting their crop before leaving and returning in time to harvest it. Yet South Australian citizens were not unresource-ful in countering the effects of the Gold Rush. They diverted the outflow of gold to Adelaide by offering a higher price than did Melbourne. They also attempted to open the navigation of the Murray in order to divert the trade and produce of the Murray Valley towards South Australia, and increased agricultural output to feed the thousands of migrants in Victoria. With a good harvest in 1851, rising prices, and a falling local market, South Australian growers and millers took good advantage of the new Victorian market.

Agricultural Occupation

The agricultural returns for 1855-6 show 203,423 acres under cultivation, of which 172,717 acres (about 85 per cent) were in cereal crops, nearly all wheat. The remaining acreage of cropland was under hay (11.5 per cent), potatoes (1 per cent), and vineyards, orchards, gardens and miscellaneous crops [24].

Cereal crops (Fig. 6) were concentrated on the drier, flatter and more easily cleared coastal plains and the eastern slopes of the central uplands. In the coastal plain south of Adelaide, all the land was well enclosed with post and rail fences, though near Willunga there was fencing of 'a slighter kind which marked the recent advance of many new comers' as they moved southwards [25]. In the foothills of the Southern Mount Lofty Ranges, extensive sheep and cattle runs were being rapidly enclosed for cultivation. The scattered scrub in the Willunga Basin was being cleared; such was the activity in this area, that nowhere in the colony did agricultural operations seem more vigorously pursued. Yields of between twenty and thirty bushels per acre were common; the threshing machine was used widely to cope with the abundant harvest [26]. Port Willunga was being developed at this time for the export of wheat directly overseas and to Port Adelaide. Some 10,500 acres of land were under wheat in this region, making it one of the core areas of South Australian agriculture. Here too, occurred the greatest density of well-developed towns, reflecting the agricultural productivity.

Northwards from Adelaide stretched the wide plains flanking Gulf St. Vincent. These had long been neglected, mainly on account of their low rainfall, scarcity of water, and

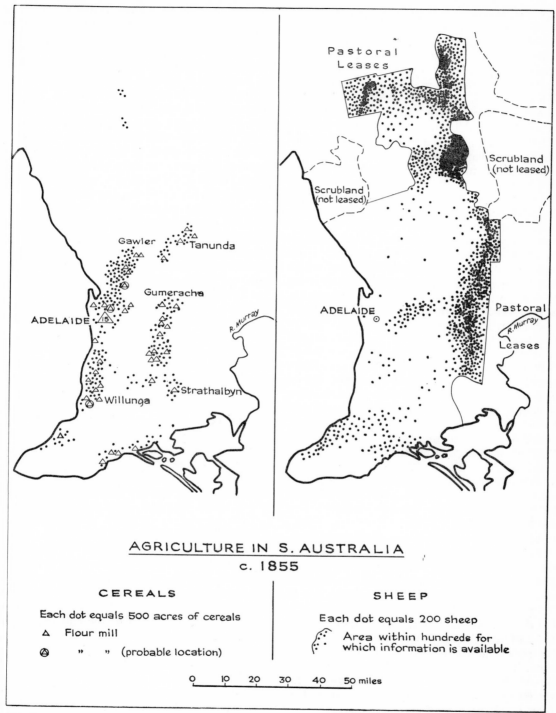

AGRICULTURE IN S. AUSTRALIA
c. 1855

CEREALS

Each dot equals 500 acres of cereals

△ Flour mill

⊕ " " (probable location)

SHEEP

Each dot equals 200 sheep

Area within hundreds for which information is available

0   10   20   30   40   50 miles

Fig. 6

exposure to the scorching summer northerlies. Their neglect was surprising, however, when the obvious fertility of the soil was taken into consideration, and the reporter of the *South Australian Register* who witnessed a ploughing match near Salisbury in 1851, where 'the fine rich mellow soil' was revealed for the first time, could only wonder why 'the greater portion of these plains had been passed over by settlers choosing land' [27]. But settlement was already edging northwards, particularly along the flank of the high ground, the plains were coming into cultivation in patches, and by 1856 there were some 15,000 cultivated acres between Grand Junction Road and Gawler. Plans were afoot to make a causeway through the mangrove swamps at Port Gawler, so that wheat could be sent by barge to Port Adelaide. The progress of the settlement of Salisbury which had 'sprung up like a mushroom' in the space of a few years and contained 200 inhabitants, 'several butchers, two bakers, two blacksmiths, as many wheel-wrights and carpenters, a tailor [and] one doctor' [28], was a good indicator of advance.

Cultivation in the Barossa Valley was firmly entrenched. Local concentrations of tillage were to be seen near Lyndoch with their 'succession of cornfields with farm houses and barns', and in the area bounded by the three German settlements of Langmeil, Tanunda and Bethanien. Groups of settlers penetrated eastward to Light's Pass, where Truro was said to be a rising town [29]. Beyond Truro, the land sloped away from the central uplands and before the settlers lay the panoramic view of the Murray Plains with their covering of mallee scrub which was long to bar settlement.

On the eastern side of the hill country in the broad valleys of the upper Onkaparinga and Torrens, and in the vicinity of the settlements of Gumeracha, Lobethal, Mount Torrens, Woodside and Birdwood (Blumberg), lay the newest and perhaps most rapidly-rising area of settlement, where wheat was grown 'to an extent hardly credible without inspection'. This 'eminently agricultural district' had nearly 15,000 acres under the plough, and 'probably more wheat has been grown here within a given limit, than in almost any other portion of the province'. The concentration of mills in this district would seem to justify its

claim to agricultural importance. Second-rate eighty acre sections were said to be selling for £200; labour was scarce, and Ridley's harvesting machine could not be bought here [30]. A secondary concentration of cultivation marked the edges of the hills near Strathalbyn, which sent wheat to Port Elliot.

Elsewhere in the settled areas, wheat was cultivated in small amounts for local domestic needs only. None was grown in the South-East which was regarded as being an exclusively pastoral district. Nor were there crop returns for the Port Lincoln district where the windmill had been 'in a state of unfinished ruin for five years' [31]. High rainfall in the central and southern ranges was unfavourable to wheat, although crops of potatoes were grown in the Inman and Hindmarsh valleys in the Fleurieu Peninsula. The Clare district towards the north had only 4000 acres under cereals because it was thought to be best suited to potatoes. But its future seemed promising, for its land had been 'exciting notice and competition' from settlers, who were willing to pay as much as £3 for an acre in this well-watered locality [32]. Vine culture, so highly characteristic of the Clare district today, was almost absent then, taking no more than eight acres, but was fairly common and widespread in the two other major areas of present production, the Barossa Valley and MacLaren Vale.

Hay, usually cereal hay (green-cut grain crops), was grown in every district but 36 per cent of all hay was grown within a six mile radius of Adelaide, presumably to feed the horses and working stock of the urban area.

Pastoral Occupation

Pastoralists with their sheep flocks moved beyond the confines of surveyed land and squatted on runs that were created in the virgin landscape. The pastoral occupation was technically illegal, and contrary to the stated principles of the foundation of the Colony, nevertheless, the rapid increase of flocks and the sale of the vastly increased wool clip meant an increase of wealth for the colony from which everyone benefited, and the illegality was tolerated. In any case the situation was reversible. Despite the squatter's occupance of the land, the title was still vested in the Crown. Cadastral units called Hundreds, in which land

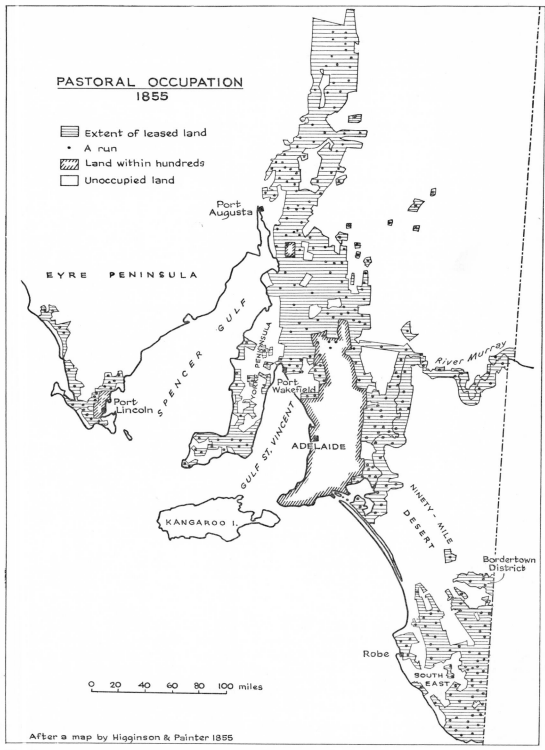

PASTORAL OCCUPATION
1855

Extent of leased land
A run
Land within hundreds
Unoccupied land

Port
Augusta

EYRE PENINSULA

SPENCER GULF

YORKE PENINSULA

Port Lincoln

Port
Wakefield

River Murray

GULF ST. VINCENT

ADELAIDE

NINETY - MILE DESERT

KANGAROO I.

Bordertown
District

Robe

SOUTH
EAST

0 20 40 60 80 100 miles

After a map by Higginson & Painter 1855

Fig. 7

was surveyed and could be bought, might be proclaimed and land resumed for agricultural purposes, at six months' notice. This insecurity of tenure was resented by the squatters, but caused real anxiety only to licensees close to settled areas. And because of the insecurity, squatters were not regarded so hostilely in South Australia as in the eastern States.

No record was kept of pastoral expansion until 1842, when it became necessary for a squatter to obtain an Occupation Licence for the nominal sum of £5. Lists of licensees were published in the *Government Gazette* of 22 December 1842 and for the subsequent three-year period, but give no locational details. Such details were added to the lists published from 25 July 1844 to 10 February 1848, but are too vague to form the basis of a distribution map. In addition to the licence fee, pastoralists were charged according to their own annual returns of stock, at rates of six-pence per head on large cattle and one penny per sheep; but much evasion and confusion accompanied the returns, making them at best unreliable, and at worst useless in reconstructing past geography.

Occupation Licences were exchanged in 1851 for leases. Pastoralists had to lodge plans of the runs with the Surveyor-General, and pay rental charged at ten shillings, fifteen shillings, or twenty shillings per square mile. The plans make it possible for the first time to plot the extent of pastoral occupation. The situation for 1855 is shown in Fig. 7. The outer edge of land reserved for permanent settlement (the Hundreds) is shown, although as some Hundreds had only then been proclaimed recently and the land not yet surveyed and sold, runs

within their boundaries were still in existence. The outer edge of the runs and a dot indicating the centre of each run give a generalized impression of pastoral occupation [33].

This map indicates a great expansion within twenty years of the initial landing. All the high-rainfall areas had been taken up, except for Kangaroo Island which carried but some 10,000 sheep. In Eyre Peninsula, the humid western coast attracted more settlement than the eastern coast, although the latter was the nearer to Adelaide. Pastoralists in the South-East quickly occupied the best lands along the Victorian border, and the Bordertown and Keith districts in addition. They were moving also northwards into lower-rainfall areas. The generally NW-SE trend of the run boundaries reflects the topographical extent of range and swamp flat that cover most of the area, the almost permanently water-covered flats near the coast and in the centre not being taken up at all.

The greatest continuous area of runs lay on the eastern side of Gulf St. Vincent and Spencer Gulf, extending nearly 350 miles north of Adelaide beyond Wilpena Pound. This vast pastoral domain was confined exclusively to the high-rainfall zone of the central uplands and the Flinders Ranges. A few runs were also being created to the northeastward, in the direction of what is now Broken Hill, along the high ground of the Olary Spur. Runs ranged less from east to west (from Spencer Gulf to the Murray River), the only areas not occupied were those of dense mallee scrub in Yorke Peninsula, the Gawler Plains, and the plains west of the Murray. The plains within the great loop of the Murray, and the forbidding Ninety-Mile Desert, were devoid of settle-

Table 4 *Number of Stock, Runs, Shepherds and Stockmen in Regions of South Australia in 1856*

	Dist. Councils	N. of Adelaide	South-east	Eyre Peninsula	Murray Mallee	Yorke Peninsula	Kangaroo Island	Total
Sheep	368,605	747,727	537,553	132,370	83,348	82,000	10,857	1,962,460
Cattle	100,084	66,557	80,185	4,640	20,368	920	None	272,746
No. of Runs	None	126	80	21	51	23	None	301
No. Shepherds	119	413	224	81	8	170		1,015
No. Stockmen	78	55	36	3	15	16		203

Sources: Sheep and Cattle—Return of Inspector of Stock, *South Australian Government Gazette*, 31-12-1856
Number of Runs—Based on map of pastoral occupation by Higginson and Painter, (1855) *S. Australian Archives*, C. 355.
Number of Shepherds and Stockmen—Census Return, (March 1855) *South Australian Parliamentary Paper*, No. 19 of 1855-56.

ment, as was the interior of Eyre Peninsula. These parts were remote and lacking in water.

The distribution of stock throughout South Australia in 1855 remains unknown. The only general indication comes from the returns of the Inspector of Sheep, supplemented by details of the number of runs, shepherds and stockmen (Table 4). The main pastoral area was the hill country north of Adelaide, but the flocks in the lower South-East (c. 537,000) were increasing faster than those elsewhere.

In contrast, detailed returns of 1855 for flocks in the Adelaide district can be mapped with fair accuracy (Fig. 6). Density is low in the well-settled areas and high in those unsettled. This pattern, recurring in later years, suggests a dramatic change in land use with the spread of settlement and wheat cultivation: wheat was grown principally on open ground that required little clearing—the same ground that, with natural pastures, had at first attracted sheepowners. For this land there was competition.

The contribution of the squatters to the geography of South Australia cannot be measured in terms of the value of the wool clip alone, for they must be regarded as the experimenters of the environment. Their testing of the capability and quality of the land, as indicated by rainfall and vegetation, provided invaluable information for later farmers. The squatters did much to determine the outer limits of settlement. The distribution of pastoral occupation in 1855 broadly resembles the distribution of proclaimed hundreds and agricultural settlement in 1880, but even in its most optimistic period between 1875 and 1880, agricultural settlement never got so far north in the Flinders Ranges as did pasturing.

Towns and People

The process of town creation was still in 1855 a speculative venture, speculation in land and in towns being surpassed only by speculation in minerals [34]. The Government neither curbed nor controlled the creation of towns. Too often, the stranger looking for a town was in the state of that traveller who, attempting to find New Glenelg, 'could not find its exact location unassisted', and when he did arrive found not one building erected. Empty blocks and derelict street signs signalized the failure of many

a scheme. It became evident that to subdivide a section and to call it a town was not enough. Investment in essential services then became a way of attracting buyers and settlers. The advice to 'put up a public house and a blacksmith's shop and village will soon follow' was adopted in some new subdivisions, among them Normanville, Auburn, Watervale, and Naracoorte [35].

The often very close spacing of these early private towns engendered competition for trade. The acquisition of a mill was eagerly sought after. The small scale of most mills at the time made the acquisition well within the range of an aspiring township, although, strangely enough, the large growing rural centre of Clare failed in this respect. A public house, places of worship, and later on a school and an Institute provided additional services, which helped to generate and attract trade from the surrounding rural areas. If at least some of these essentials could be obtained, supplemented by the usual array of tradesmen and storekeepers, then a town had a chance of growing to about 100 to 200 persons, and of achieving some degree of permanence as a nodal centre.

There was of course a limit, although it is difficult to set, to the number of towns and the complexity of services that any rural area could support. The question is especially difficult to discuss in the context of urban situations of a century ago, particularly as accurate census figures for most of the urban areas were not collected until 1871. Nor is there a consistent and comprehensive means of assessing the services offered. Yet it would be wrong not to examine what evidence there is of differentiation already effected by 1855.

Population, houses, and selected characteristics of towns are listed in Table 5, which ranks towns in order of population, where statistics permit. Although the table is compiled from a variety of sources and may be open to amendment in detail, the relative position of the towns within classes is probably correct. The information contained in the table for the central hill district is mapped in Fig. 8.

Adelaide and its suburbs, particularly Kensington, Norwood, Thebarton, Hindmarsh and Bowden, dominated the urban scene, both in size and in complexity. The total population of

D

Table 5 *Towns and Selected Features, c.1855*

Town	Population	No. of Houses	Post Offices	Flour Mills	Schools	Churches	Public Houses	Courts	Date Establishment of Institute
Adelaide & Environs	28,119	5,476	13	14	59	48	183	1	1853
Burra	c.4,300	c.850	1		4	4	8	1	1857
Pt. Adelaide & Alberton	3,507	733	2	1	8	4	18	1	1859
Kapunda	2,000	350	1		2	4	5	1	1858
Gawler	1,000	220	1	2	3	7	8		1857
Brighton	600	160	1	1	1	3	5		
Mt. Barker	c.400	80	1	2	3	5	5	1	1856
Willunga	—	—	1	2	2	4	2	1	1854
Angaston	c.250	—	1	1	1	2	3	1	1856
Port Elliot	—	—	1	1	1	1	2	1	1855
Morphett Vale	—	—	1	2	4	4	3	1	
Salisbury	220+	60+	1	2	1	1	9		1858
Nairne	—	—	1	1	2	2	3		1859
Macclesfield	—	—	1	1	1	1	2		1859
Aldinga	—	—	1	1		2	2	1	1860
Hahndorf	c.250	c.50	1	2	1	1	2		1859
Strathalbyn	—	—	1	1		2	3	1	1858
Penola	—	—	1		1	1	1	1	1860
Sturt	—	—	1	1	1	1	3		1853
Noarlunga	150	40	1	1	1	2	2		1859
Clare	—	—	1		1	2	4	1	
Maclaran Vale	—	—	1	2	3	1	5		
Tanunda	140	40	1	1	1	3	4		
Gumeracha	—	—	1	1	2	1	2		
Lyndoch	—	—	1	1	1	1	3		
Goolwa	—	—	1	1	1		1	1	
Glenelg	200	60	1		1		4		1859
Clarendon	—	—	1		1	1	1		1853
Port Lincoln	—	—	1			1	2	1	
Woodside	—	—		1		2	1		1859
Chain of Ponds	—	—	1		1	1	1		
Mt. Torrens	—	c.60	1	1	1		1		
Echunga	—	—	1		1	1	2		
Auburn	—	—	1		1		2		1859
Yankalilla	—	—	1	1	1		1		
Encounter Bay	—	—	1	2		1	1		
Lobethal	—	—	1	2		1	1		

Sources: Population and Houses: Census Return, (March 1855) *South Australian Parliamentary Paper*, No. 19 of 1855-56 and files of the *South Australian Register*.

Flour Mills, Public Houses and Institutes: *South Australian Archives*, A/495,B7; 1195,53D; and A/1094,C1 respectively.

Schools: *South Australian Government Gazette*, 1856, p. 20.

Post Offices, Courts and Churches: A. Garran, (1855) *South Australian Almanac*.

Note: Branches of Banks were not established in country towns until the later years of the decade.

28,119 (out of a State total of 85,189) contrasted with the population of the next largest town—Burra, with about 4300. The functional complexity and the service provision of Adelaide can be gauged from its share of various occupations, as recorded in the Census Abstract of 1855 [36]. Adelaide had then, as it has now, an overwhelming proportion of the political, economic, and social activity of the State. Its degree of concentration was, and is, barely surpassed by any other capital city of Australia, a characteristic then and now reflected in the paucity and poverty of substantial secondary settlements.

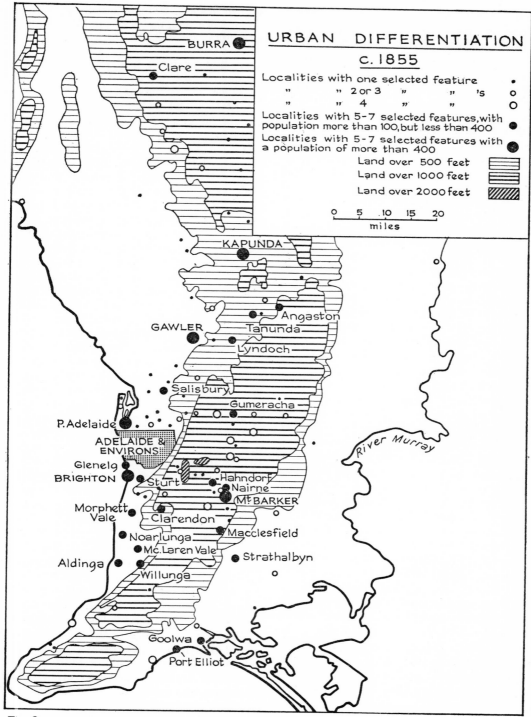

URBAN DIFFERENTIATION
c. 1855

Localities with one selected feature •
      "   " 2 or 3 " " 's ○
      "   " 4 " " ◉
Localities with 5-7 selected features, with
population more than 100, but less than 400 ●
Localities with 5-7 selected features with
a population of more than 400 ⬤

Land over 500 feet
Land over 1000 feet
Land over 2000 feet

0   5   10   15   20
        miles

BURRA
Clare
KAPUNDA
Angaston
GAWLER
Tanunda
Lyndoch
Salisbury
Gumeracha
P. Adelaide
ADELAIDE &
ENVIRONS
Glenelg
BRIGHTON
Sturt
Hahndorf
Nairne
Mt BARKER
Morphett
Vale
Clarendon
Macclesfield
Noarlunga
Mc. Laren Vale
Strathalbyn
Aldinga
Willunga
Goolwa
Port Elliot
River Murray

Fig. 8

Burra, Kapunda, Port Adelaide, Gawler, Brighton and Mt. Barker stood apart from the rest of these. Four of them were not part of the agricultural landscape. Port Adelaide was the main port of the whole province. Brighton constituted a seaside suburb, holiday, and health resort for Adelaide [37], and performed service functions for the wheatlands in the southern Adelaide plains. Burra and Kapunda, entirely dependent on mining and smelting copper, were true boom towns, with hastily-built temporary structures. Burra had grown from nothing to 4300 in four years. Somewhat under half of the population lived in small row houses in Kooringa itself, and in the small ill-formed surrounding villages 'or at least collections of dwellings', as one observer described them, of Redruth and Aberdeen. About 2600 people lived in dwellings hollowed in the soft earth at the sides of Burra Creek. Womenfolk on either side of the saffron-coloured stream from the mine could be observed 'washing and hanging out clothes, scouring pots, and [engaged in] other domestic occupations at every frontage'. For all the impermanency of their dwellings, the miners in the early fifties were among the best-paid labourers in the province; their prosperity was reflected in the good shops and stores of the main street. In addition, the settlement could boast eight inns, four churches and schools, six doctors, and two solicitors [38].

Kapunda, with a population of 2000, was an older, though much smaller, mining centre. Its high ratio of population to houses (1:5.7) can be explained by the very large number of tents, probably over one hundred, which surrounded the settlement and accommodated the temporary miners [39].

Gawler and Mt. Barker were the only two of this group of larger towns to be true service centres. Gawler had profited greatly from the transport of ore from Burra and Kapunda, the bullock wagons stopping there at about a day's journey from Adelaide and the Port. The transfer of the Burra copper trade to Port Wakefield and thence by the barge route to Port Adelaide had caused decline, and Gawler was said to be going back a little. Yet its future was assured, as:

the key to the north which can only be reached from Adelaide over the level country by passing through it, and it must inevitably concentrate the produce and the traffic of the surrounding agricultural and mineral districts [40].

A position on the very edge of the vast wheat-growing region that was to be developed to the north during the next fifteen years was to bring Gawler further prosperity, mainly in the role of manufacturer of agricultural implements [41].

A second level of development is suggested by the data for Port Elliot, Strathalbyn, Gumeracha, Willunga, Tanunda, and similar towns. These moderate-sized centres numbered about a score. Their size and degree of relative complexity reflected the agricultural productivity and length of occupance of their surroundings. The well-settled and well-developed wheatlands of the Willunga and Noarlunga Basins, and to a lesser extent the Barossa Valley from Lyndoch to Angaston and the eastern side of the central hills from Hahndorf to Strathalbyn, had concentrations of large settlements. The newly-rising wheat area to the east and south-east of Gumeracha had not yet progressed enough to produce and support well developed centres, but it nevertheless had the largest concentration of settlements in the next rank of the hierarchy, suggesting assurance of future growth. Some ten communities, resembling those near Gumeracha, had facilities which indicated a potential yet untested. Below these came nearly a hundred settlements, little more than crossroads communities. The majority of these offered the services of a public house, a post office, or both, and at the most, of a church or school.

Time would affect both the importance and the size of many of the towns, as new patterns of communication, particularly railway communication, emerged, as new areas were settled and colonized, and as geographical and social values changed. Yet it is remarkable how the process of town differentiation had already, by 1855, gone far enough to set the gross pattern of relative importance of the towns in the central and southern hill country of South Australia. Another foundation of the present landscape, the urban foundation, had by the middle of last century been laid.

German settlers had by 1855 made distinctive contributions to the landscape. Their con-

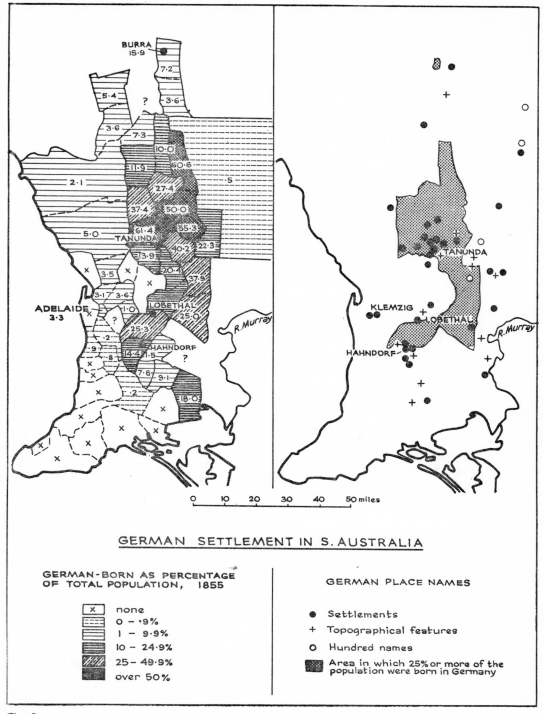

GERMAN SETTLEMENT IN S. AUSTRALIA

GERMAN-BORN AS PERCENTAGE
OF TOTAL POPULATION, 1855

☒	none
☰	0 − ·9%
☰	1 − 9·9%
▤	10 − 24·9%
▨	25 − 49·9%
■	over 50%

GERMAN PLACE NAMES

● Settlements
+ Topographical features
○ Hundred names
▨ Area in which 25% or more of the population were born in Germany

Fig. 9

cern to group together to preserve their language, religion, and customs led to the creation of compact nucleated settlements, Hahndorf and Klemzig, already noted above, and Lobethal, Grunthal (Ambleside), Blumberg (Birdwood), Friedrichswalde (Tarma) and Bethanien (Bethany). Germans became the dominant element in Tanunda and Nuriootpa, the two largest towns in the Barossa Valley, and in Stockwell and Eudunda farther north. The early Lutheran churches with their delicate eastern European spires, and Gothic script carvings, stained glass windows, and their headstones in the graveyards, all tell of a distinctive past. The settlers brought with them a tradition of intensive cultivation, adopting the vine culture so admirably suited to their new environment. In so doing, they created one of the most distinctive agricultural regions in South Australia, the Barossa Valley. The tradition of spade cultivation, and the practice of gavelkind, combined to produce the minute plots which are more fitted to the landscape of nineteenth-century Europe than to twentieth-century Australia [42].

The other German contribution to the geography of South Australia consists in non-British place-names, most of which came into existence during the early years. Their distribution (Fig. 9) corresponds well to the distribution of German-born in the total population of 1855. Many of these names were changed to more prosaic English names, and some others to aboriginal names in 1916, so that only Hahndorf, Klemzig, Lobethal and Langmeil are really known today [43].

Patterns of Communication

As the wheat farmers ploughed up more land, as the pastoralist moved away from the settled areas, and as the production of the mines increased, so the demand for more efficient means of transport and better communications grew. Particularly was this so, as nearly the whole of production was destined for oversea markets. Any reduction in transport costs enhanced the competitive strength of the products in the world market, and increased profit to producers. The 1850s brought in experimentation and introduced competition among road, tramway, railway, and navigation.

The road system was the first created and Fig. 10 shows the pattern of major highways of 1855. The principal all-weather roads were controlled and maintained by the Central Board of Main Roads, the district feeder roads were the responsibility of the District Councils and local authorities, and undefined tracks led beyond the settled areas into pastoral country. The radiation of roads from Adelaide reflects the location of the first place of settlement, and the subsequent dominance of the capital. Few cross-country roads did not lead to Adelaide. The only one of such importance was the Burra-Port Wakefield road, declared a Main Road in 1856 to ensure the repair of damage by the bullock teams which carted ore to Port Wakefield, and coal back to Burra [44].

New farming communities in the hill country to the northeast and east of Adelaide petitioned during the early fifties for the opening up of new roads down the steep face of the Adelaide scarp and for the improvement of existing roads, with a view to improving access to the City and the Port [45]. Similar demands for improvements and bridges came from Myponga in the south and from Port Gawler in the north [46].

The north-south elongation of the settled country roughly parallel to the coast, and the location of the major grain-producing areas on the coast, were responsible for the rapid development of many minor ports and the growth of coastwise shipping focussed on Port Adelaide. Jetties and loading facilities were in existence by 1856 at Port Willunga, Onkaparinga (Port Noarlunga), Yankalilla, Rapid Bay, Rosetta Head (Port Victor), Goolwa, Milang, and Robe. Others were being constructed at Glenelg and Myponga [47]. In addition, a causeway across the mangrove swamps at the mouth of the Gawler River gave a shallow anchorage at Port Gawler. At Port Wakefield, light barges could alone get near the very shallow estuary of the Wakefield River, and ships anchored eight or nine miles out at sea. The desire of wheat growers to obtain a local jetty is clearly shown by a petition presented by the residents of the Willunga Basin asking for the completion of their jetty at Port Willunga, which would cut down the costs and delays in the export of wheat and of the output of the four local slate quarries. A

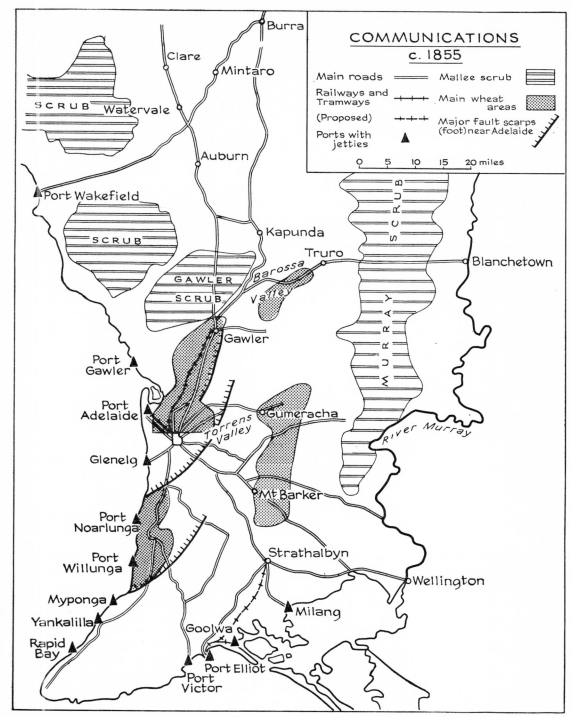

Fig. 10

similar request by the farmers in the eastern side of the hills near Callington for the jetty at Milang made the point that, although the district had a sufficient number of horses and bullocks for working the fields, they 'would be totally inadequate to transport its produce by land to Adelaide during the short period that intervenes between the harvest and seed-time,' to say nothing of 'the wear and tear of the roads' [48].

The ports situated along the south coast of the Fleurieu Peninsula and extending towards the Murray mouth were constructed to provide local export facilities, but were enlarged to cope with the trade anticipated when the River Murray was made navigable. The exploration voyages up-river, promoted by grain farmers at Gumeracha who wanted to send wheat up-river to the goldfields, suggested that inland navigation could succeed [49]. As the lakes at the Murray mouth were not open to ocean-going vessels, goods from the river boats were unloaded at Goolwa and transported by a tramway—constructed in 1854—to the ocean port of Port Elliot. None of the ports on the south coast had good natural harbours: all were exposed to the prevailing and often strong south-westerly winds, and expensive break-waters had to be constructed. Two thousand pounds were spent at Port Elliot on a sea wall, which however caused silting around the jetty and produced no marked improvement in the safety of the harbour. Consequently, Port Victor, seven miles distant, had to be developed after about 1862 [50].

The amount of trade through these ports is difficult to ascertain. The shipping returns for 1856 (Table 6) probably referred to overseas trade only, omitting the coastwise traffic which, for Port Noarlunga alone, was said to amount to 7000 tons of wheat and flour in that year.

Table 6 *Number and Tonnage of Ships in South Australian Ports, 1856*

Port	No. of Ships	Tonnage
Port Adelaide	397	166,741
Port Wakefield	17	4,388
Port Willunga	10	1,207
Port Elliot	15	127
Robe	5	1,200

Source: South Australian Blue Books, 1856, p. 351.

The respective merits of roads and of horse-drawn tramways and railways were considerably discussed in the mid-fifties. A government enquiry in 1856 fully endorsed the agitation for better transport, stating that, to develop the various resources of a country, the surest and best means were undoubtedly the improvement of the internal communications, and concluding that horse-drawn tramways at a cost of £2696 per mile held little advantage over well-surfaced roads at a cost of about £1800 or £2000 per mile. Tramways could carry only limited loads and set restrictions on traffic, while capital cost of rolling stock and stations was high. But if tramways were so constructed as to be eventually convertible to steam railways, which cost up to £4533 per mile, they were worth building [51]. But a proposal to extend the Port Elliot-Goolwa tramway thirteen miles northeastwards to the wheat growing areas around Strathalbyn, by which means it was hoped to reduce the cost of carting wheat from Strathalbyn to Adelaide from two shillings and sixpence per bushel to about sixpence, came to nothing and instead, the road was improved [52].

The first steam-locomotive railway in South Australia was laid from Adelaide to Port Adelaide in 1856. In the following year a new line was constructed through the wheat lands of the northern coastal plains, terminating at Gawler where some copper ore traffic was gathered. While these routes seemed logical and were constructed with little dispute, the next stage of construction was less obvious. Its objectives were to tap the Kapunda and Burra ore carriage and the Murray River traffic. Four routes were surveyed from Kapunda to Burra, and five through the Barossa and Torrens valleys to the Murray [53]. So bitter was controversy, and so uncertain were the advantages, that the Kapunda line was not completed until 1860, that to Burra not until 1870, and the first Murray link at Morgan not until 1878. The railway to Morgan immediately diverted the River Murray traffic to Port Adelaide. From this centralization of the railway system on the capital and its port, the small outports along the southern coast, Port Victor, Port Elliot and Goolwa, never recovered.

The Government from the start took a firm hand in the construction of railways, thereby coming to direct the pace and course of colonization. Whereas in well-settled countries such as Britain the railway was merely the last step in social progress, accommodating itself necessarily to centres of traffic and to existing masses of population, the Government in South Australia could, by means of the railway, determine the position of stations and consequently of future towns and villages.

The total net of communications was neither very complex nor very extensive. Yet, despite its meagre development, it represented the solution of certain problems and the pursuit of policies. Experience gained in the early years was to be drawn on for many subsequent decades in South Australia. Wheatfields close to the sea, and a multiplicity of small outports, foreshadowed the pattern of the great expansion into northern areas in 1869 to 1880, at which time the controversy about railways as opposed to tramways, the competition for and government control of railways, and the overriding desire of primary producers to lower transport costs, were all repeated. If there is one period which can be singled out as containing basic geographical patterns, and as sounding the beginning of many geographical themes which can be recognized throughout the history and geography of South Australia, that period is the mid-fifties of last century.

REFERENCES

1. This, and most of the information which follows on the geography of South Australia in 1840, is unless otherwise acknowledged, based upon the 1840 Survey of rural property in Papers Relative to South Australia *Brit. Parl. Paper, 505* (1843), 70–101.
2. For the original vegetation of the Adelaide area, see WOOD, J. G. (1937) *The Vegetation of South Australia*. Adelaide; and CLELAND, J. B. (1928) The Original Flora of the Adelaide Plains, *South Aust. Naturalist, 10*, 1–6, which is largely based on contemporary descriptions by BACKHOUSE, J. (1884) *A Narrative of a Visit to the Australian Colonies*, and BULL, J. W. (1884) *Early Experiences of Colonial Life in South Australia*.
3. PIKE, D. H. (1957) *Paradise of Dissent: South Australia 1829–1857*. Longmans, Melbourne, 286.
4. *South Australian Almanac, 1842*, 130.
5. Copies of any correspondence in the Colonial Department Relative to the Establishment of the Settlement of South Australia. *Brit. Parl. Paper, 129* (1841), 145.
6. Quoted in HODDER, E. *History of South Australia*. Sampson Low, Marston and Co., London, *1*, 91.
7. STEVENSON, G. (1840) Three lectures on agriculture and gardening in South Australia delivered to the Adelaide Mechanics' Institute during late 1839. Printed in *South Australian Almanac, 1840*, 21–56.
8. Based on PRICE, A. G. (1924) *Foundation and Settlement of South Australia, 1829–1845*. Preece, Adelaide, 161.
9. Second report of Select Committee on South Australia. *Brit. Parl. Papers, 394* (1841), 82.
10. CLELAND, J. B. (1955) Section Built Manning Cottages. *Proc.Roy.Geog.Soc.,S.A. Branch, 57*, 51–52.
11. ROSE, A. J. Some Boundary and Building Materials in South-eastern Australia, in Murray MacCaskill (ed.) (1962) *Land and Livelihood: Geographical Essays in Honour of George Jobberns*, Christchurch. 255–276.
12. The following account is based on the Statement of the Proceedings of the Directors of the *Secondary Towns Association formed for the Purchasing of one or more special survey or surveys of land in South Australia for sites for secondary towns, 1843*. Smith, Elder and Co., London.
13. BENNETT, J. F. (1843) *An Historical and Descriptive account of South Australia Founded on the Experience of Three Years' Residence in that Colony*. Smith, Elder and Co., London, 132.
14. Villages around Adelaide. *South Australian Magazine, 1*, (1841). 187.
15. BENNETT, [*13*], 132.
16. A Ride Through South Australia. *South Australian Magazine, 1*, (1842).
17. *Ibid.*, 344.
18. BENNETT, [*13*], 134.
19. *Ibid.*, 135.
20. The Germans at Hahnsdorf. *South Australian Magazine, 1* (1842), 255.
21. PIKE, [*3*], 181.
22. BENNETT, [*13*], 74.
23. *South Australian Register*, May 8, 1951.

24. Agricultural Statistics of South Australia. *Government Gazette*, Mar. 19, 1857 (stock) and May 28, 1857 (crops), supplemented by details from the Blue Books (holograph statistics compiled before Statistical Register) for 1855 and 1857. Deposited in Offices of Commonwealth Bureau of Census and Statistics, Adel.

25. *South Australian Register*, Mar. 14, 1851.

26. *Ibid.*, Mar. 26, 1851.

27. *Ibid.*, Sept. 13, 1851.

28. *Ibid.*, May 22, 1851.

29. *Ibid.*, June 21, 1851 & June 26, 1851.

30. *Ibid.*, July 21, 1851.

31. Flour Mills. Return of all erected and in the course of erection in South Australia, on May 30, 1854. *South Australian Archives*, A/495/B7.

32. *South Australian Register*, July 15, 1851.

33. The progress of pastoral occupation is based on Higgin's and Painter's map of South Australia in 1855, *South Australian Archives*, C. 355; and information supplied by Mr. W. R. Marchant of the Pastoral Division, Lands Department, Adelaide.

34. PIKE, [*3*], 351.

35. *South Australian Register*, Feb. 27, 1851; April 16, 1851; & July 15, 1851.

36. CENSUS (March 1855). *South Austr. Parl. Paper*, *19*, of 1856–56.

37. *South Australian Register*, Mar. 3, 1851.

38. *South Australian Register*, July 8, 1851.

39. BETTISON, I. J. *Kapunda: a study of the establishment of a community in rural South Australia*. Unpublished B.A. Dissertation, Dept. of History, University of Adelaide.

40. *South Australian Register*, June 3, 1851.

41. WILLIAMS, M. (1964) Gawler: The Changing Geography of a South Australian Country Town. *Aust.Geog.*, *9*, 195–206.

42. GILDING, G. F. (1961) *The German Settlement of Hahndorf*. Unpublished B.A. Dissertation, Dept. of Geography, University of Adelaide.

43. Nomenclature Committee's Report on Enemy Place-Names. *South Austr. Parl. Paper*, *66*, of 1916.

44. *South Austr. Parl. Papers*, *170*, 1856–57; and *93*, 1857.

45. *South Austr. Parl. Papers*, *23*, 1856; and *53, 106, 107, 112, 163* of 1856–57.

46. *South Austr. Parl. Papers*, *23*, 1856; and *174* of 1855–56.

47. *South Austr. Parl. Papers*, *154*, 1855–56.

48. *South Australian Archives*, A (1854), 3028, for Willunga. A (1855), 2800, for Callington.

49. *South Australian Register*, Feb. 22, 1853.

50. HODDER, [*6*], Vol. *1*, 277.

51. *South Austr. Parl. Papers*, *4*, 1856.

52. *South Austr. Parl. Papers*, *205*, 1855–56 & *20*, 1857–58. The tramway was finally built in 1868, after prolonged wrangling by Port Elliot and Goolwa as to which port would be the terminus of the new line. Eventually, as a compromise, it was joined to the existing Port Elliot–Goolwa tramway, at Middleton, thus not satisfying completely either of the rivals. For these later developments see HODGE, C. R. (c 1932) *Encounter Bay*. The Advertiser, Adelaide.

53. For the extension of the railway to Gawler, see *South Austr. Parl. Papers*, *87*, and *97*, 1857; and for the extension north of Gawler and to the Murray see *2*, 1856 and, *22*, 1857–58.

Murrumbidgee Land Settlement
1817 to 1912

TREVOR LANGFORD-SMITH

PART I: EXPLORATION 1817 TO 1830

Discovery of the rich pasture lands of the Murrumbidgee initiated the greatest wave of land settlement in Australian history. Murrumbidgee exploration and development was not, however, an isolated event. It was one of a series of outward movements, starting in earnest with the crossing of the Blue Mountains in 1813, and reaching its peak during the twenties and thirties. The origins of this general burst of activity have not been clearly understood. Perry [1, 2] has shown the fallacies in the traditional concept of the Sydney lowland as a natural prison, walled in by mountains and dense bush (Fig. 1). These natural barriers seemed important when curiosity was the only incentive to overcome them, but as soon as economic pressure began to make itself felt, settlement expanded in all directions with comparative ease and astonishing rapidity.

With some exceptions, it would appear that there was no general need for new land until about 1819, by which time a combination of adverse circumstances had brought serious hardship to many Sydney pastoralists. Severe and persistent drought, overstocking, and plagues of 'caterpillars' had wrought such havoc on the coastal grasslands that the original pastures known as oatgrass had been virtually replaced by hard, stringy varieties of little value for fodder. From this time on, there was constant and increasing pressure on the government to permit grazing outside the Cumberland Plain. Governor Macquarie wished to confine settlement to as small an area as possible for ease of administration, but agreed in 1820 to grazing outside the County as a tem-porary measure. This was the thin end of the wedge. Once under way, expansion gathered momentum, developing eventually into the uncontrollable invasion of the squatters.

Perhaps the first significant move towards the Murrumbidgee was by Charles Throsby, who in 1817 pushed through the bush of the southern tableland to Moss Vale and Sutton Forest. The following year Throsby and James Meehan (the Deputy Surveyor-General) attempted to find an overland route to Jervis Bay on the south coast [3]. In the Marulan area the party divided. Throsby proceeded to Jervis Bay by way of the Kangaroo River, while Meehan continued south along the tableland to reach Lake Bathurst and the Goulburn Plains (Fig. 2). In 1819, Governor Macquarie granted Throsby some land in the Moss Vale area. Throsby started a stock station there, and so appears to have been the first pastoralist to establish himself in the southern districts.

In a letter to Macquarie [September 4, 1820] Throsby mentioned that aborigines had reported the existence of a 'considerable river of salt water (except at very wet seasons) called by the natives Mur; rum; bid; gie' [4]. In 1821 Throsby set out in search of this stream. He crossed the Limestone (Canberra) Plains, and proceeding south came upon the Murrumbidgee in the Tharwa area. On his return, Throsby remarked:

the (stream) described by the natives to be salt . . . I found to be a broad but shallow river, and very rapid, issuing from extremely high mountains to the South-east [5].

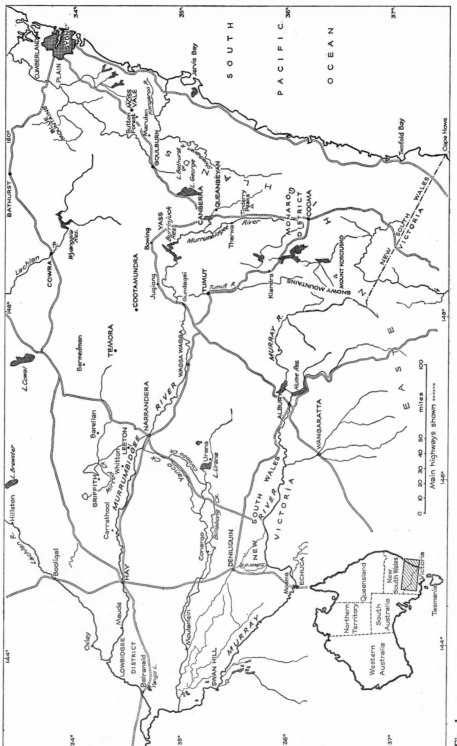

Fig. 1

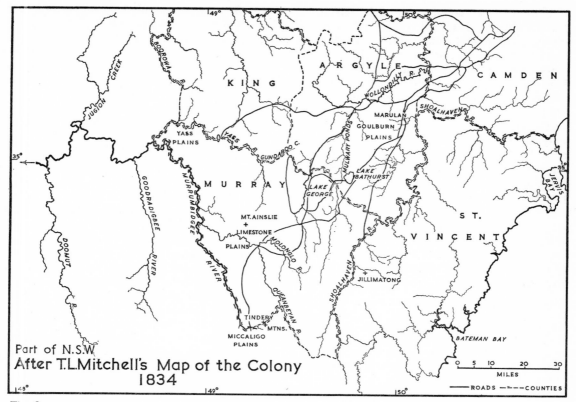

Fig. 2

It is understandable that further exploration, and initial settlement, followed this southern route of Throsby's through Canberra and thus into the upper Murrumbidgee. Had Throsby gone west rather than south he would have struck the Murrumbidgee near Yass Plains, and the rich pastoral country there would have attracted settlement downstream towards Gundagai and Wagga rather than upstream into the relatively second-class Monaro country. In 1823 Currie and Ovens extended Throsby's investigations by following the Murrumbidgee up to within a few miles of Cooma, and returned with glowing accounts of what they called the Brisbane Downs. This journey virtually concluded the era of exploration in the upper Murrumbidgee.

Settlement downstream was slower. The Yass Plains were first seen—or at least first reported—by Hume and Hovell during their journey in 1824 towards Port Phillip. They were described by Hovell [6] as consisting '. . . for the most part, of clear land generally level. The soil dry and good'. There were no more organized expeditions until 1829, when Sturt followed the Murrumbidgee to its junction with the Murray, and continued right down to the Murray mouth. Following Hovell's explorations, however, several enterprising pastoralists had pushed into new areas. On his journey [7a], Sturt called at stations owned by O'Brien at Yass Plains; Barber beyond the Yass River; Harris at Underaliga, some twenty miles north of the Murrumbidgee; and, continuing west, struck the Murrumbidgee at Tuggiong (Jugiong), where O'Brien had an outstation. Following downstream, he passed Whaby's station opposite the Dumot (Tumut) junction, and reached the extremity of settlement near Gundagai, where Stuckey and Roberts had just established themselves.

Sturt's periodic observations on the potentialities of the country through which he travelled reveal his inadequate understanding of an environment completely different from the European scene. In common with so many early colonists he thought in terms of *intensive* land use rather than the *extensive* grazing which was to prove so profitable in this new land. He considered the country between Yass and Underaliga to be very poor, and had eyes only for the alluvial soil of the valleys in the area from Underaliga to the Murrumbidgee. At Jugiong he remarked especially on the rich alluvial flats, and was most impressed by the Pondebadgery (Wantabadgery) plains, also alluvial [7b]. His reactions on reaching the great riverine plains just past the present site of Narrandera provide further evidence of his imperfect appreciation of the physical environment. He called this region Hamiltons Plains, and of it he remarked:

I think it very probable, that those lands which lie hardening and bare in a state of nature, would produce abundantly if broken up by the plough [7c].

Certainly, wheat has been grown successfully here for short periods in the past, but the climate is such that the area is essentially marginal, and unsafe for continued cultivation. On the other hand it is highly profitable pasture country. The great width of the Yanco Creek channel evidently puzzled Sturt considerably. He wrote:

Such a fact would argue that heavy rains fall in this part of the interior, to cut out such a watercourse [7c].

As it happens, the rainfall here is only sixteen inches. Yanco Creek channel is in fact overfit. It is a geological relic, and in former times carried the principal stream of this part of the Riverina [8].

Proceeding west, Sturt was disappointed at the country away from the river, and talked of:

. . . several plains, the soil of which was either a red sandy loam, bare of vegetation, or a rotten and blistered earth [7d].

The land 'bare of vegetation' to which he referred can only be what is known now as *scalded* country [9]. Sturt's observation there-fore refutes the commonly held supposition that this wind-eroded land type has resulted solely from erosion subsequent to white settlement. The 'rotten and blistered earth' is obviously the type now called *gilgai* or *crab-hole* country. The extensive salt-bush plains towards the Carrathool-Hay region had an extremely depressing effect on Sturt. He talked repeatedly of the inhospitable nature of the land, and said

It is impossible for me to describe . . . the dreari-ness of the view it presented [7e].

The vast area of flooded soils of the Low-bidgee, between Maude and Balranald, gave Sturt a lot of trouble, for his animals and the wheels of his drays sank repeatedly in the mud. The demoralizing psychological effect of this may have had some bearing on the fact that he made no reference to the potentialities of the soils, although in terms of fertility many of them are equal to the much praised narrow alluvial flats farther up the river. Just upstream from the Lachlan-Murrumbidgee junction, Sturt assembled a whale boat he had carried all this distance on the drays, and also fashioned a small skiff from some of the local timber. Proceeding by boat on 14 January 1830, he entered the Murray River—seven weeks and five days after leaving Yass Plains.

Because he was inexperienced in assessing agricultural and pastoral potentialities, Sturt was unduly pessimistic concerning the econo-mic wealth of the middle and lower Murrum-bidgee. Towards the end of his dairy [7f] he wrote:

Whilst the expedition was toiling down the rivers, no rich country opened upon the view to reward or to cheer . . .

and again:

The expedition returned to Sydney, without any splendid discovery to gild its proceedings . . .

He summed up his impressions in the words:

If I myself had entertained hopes that my researches would have benefited the colony, I was wholly disappointed. There is a barren tract of country lying to the westward of the Blue Mountains that will ever divide the eastern coast from the more central parts of Australia, as completely as if seas actually rolled between them.

In contrast to Sturt's deficiencies at land evaluation, he was exceptionally skilful at navigation and sound in his deductive reasoning concerning the other factors of the physical landscape. With scant evidence at his disposal, his theories concerning the course and ultimate fate of the Murrumbidgee, and especially those dealing with the relations of the Lachlan and the Murrumbidgee, were remarkably sound, and his charts and journal must have greatly assisted the squatters who followed him.

Following the work of Throsby, Currie and Ovens, Sturt's journey completed the exploration of the Murrumbidgee and opened the way for the settler along the whole course of the river.

PART II: EARLY SETTLEMENT AND THE SQUATTING MOVEMENT 1823 TO 1851

Land laws in New South Wales until 1847 reflected the confused thinking and continually changing administrative policy of that period, a condition often aggravated by lack of understanding on the part of the British Government. After 1847, matters improved somewhat, as the Regulations of that year for the first time attempted to deal with the squatting problem in a realistic manner.

A great pastoral expansion began in the twenties, due to the extraordinary success of Australian wool on world markets. The Sydney lowlands were too poor in quality to cope with the demands of new settlers, and by 1821 it was apparent that the limits of settlement, previously defined by the borders of the County of Cumberland, would need extending. Expansion to the south was at first somewhat tentative, and limited to pastoralists such as Throsby who were given special land grants and *tickets of occupation* to graze stock outside the County. Bigge's report of 1823 [*11*] dealt most favourably with the prospects of the New South Wales pastoral industry, and was instrumental in attracting English capital. Expansion was also encouraged by the favourable accounts of the explorers. As land grants or tickets of occupation were often difficult to come by, unauthorized settlement became rife, especially in the neighbourhood of licensed landholders. The Administration showed concern about the possible effects of unrestrained dispersion of settlement beyond the County of Cumberland, and in 1826 fixed the *limits of location* beyond which no land was to be sold or let [*12a*]. These limits were more precisely marked out in 1829 by a survey of the Nineteen Counties [*12b*], the extremity of settlement to the south being fixed by the borders of County Murray, i.e. a line from the Tindery peaks north of Cooma to the Shoalhaven River (Figs. 1 and 3).

By this time, however, unauthorized settlement was beginning to get out of hand, and was spreading up the Murrumbidgee towards the Cooma area, and downstream to beyond the Tumut junction. By 1830, the great expansion which was later to become known as the squatting movement was under way, and pastoralists were pushing out from the Sydney lowlands in all directions. By far the strongest movement was to the Murrumbidgee, where squatters raced madly to seize the rich, well watered pastures. In fact, the history of squatting in southern New South Wales is, to a very large degree, the history of Murrumbidgee settlement.

From 1830, progress downstream on the Murrumbidgee gained momentum, and soon outstripped that on the Monaro. As early as 1832 Tompson took up Oura station near Wagga [*13a*], and was closely followed by three other pastoralists. The rapidity of this movement led Governor Bourke [*14*] to note:

I would observe that it is not beyond the Southern boundary alone that Flocks and Herds of the Colonists have wandered for suitable pastures. They are numerous to the South West along the Bank of the Murrumbidgee . . . In every direction, the desire of procuring good pastures for Sheep has led the Colonists far beyond the limits of location. These unauthorised occupations must not, however, be permitted to continue so long as to create any title to the Land in the occupier. Under the Provisions of an Act of Council [15] passed last year [1833] . . . measures may be taken to prevent such a fraud on the Crown.

The colonists concerned, fully occupied by their scramble for new land, had little time to worry about titles, and the Act of 1833 had no effect on the spread of settlement. As early as 1835 Bourke was beginning to think realistically about the problem, for he said:

. . . I cannot avoid perceiving the peculiarities, which in this Colony, render it impolitic and even impossible to restrain dispersion within limits that would be expedient elsewhere [16].

On reaching Wagga the movement paused for a time [17a]. This is not surprising in view of the unfavourable change in physical environment a few miles downstream from there. The higher hills and ridges disappear, and, owing to a sharp drop in rainfall, the country tends to lose its green, well watered appearance. During this pause settlers filled up most of the open spaces to the east and south. By 1833 all the river frontages between Gundagai and Wagga were claimed by squatters, who also pressed up the Tumut River and intensified settlement on the Monaro.

In 1838 Mitchell journeyed south from the Murrumbidgee into Victoria and the rich pastures of *Australia Felix*, and his report [18] that: '. . . a land more favourable for colonization could not be found', attracted a wave of settlers who otherwise might have pushed down the Murrumbidgee into the drier land west of Wagga. A great overlanding movement began from Sydney, pressing down the Murrumbidgee through Yass and Gundagai, then across the river and south towards Port Phillip. A punt owned by Brodribb, a squatter on the Gundagai flats, was constantly in demand by stockmen wishing to cross the Murrumbidgee. During a period of three months in 1836 Brodribb claimed that 100,000 sheep crossed the river to be driven south [19]. Soon Gundagai was the accepted crossing place for all south-bound traffic. It was proclaimed a town in 1838, and with the establishment of an inn and store in 1839 its growth as an urban centre was firmly established. Sections of the town were subdivided into allotments in 1840, and

were auctioned the following year. The inconsistencies of administration at this time are exemplified by the fact that in 1840 permission to proclaim the town of Bowning, near Yass, was refused, the grounds being that it was outside the limits of location. It seems to have escaped notice that Gundagai, much farther west, had been proclaimed two years earlier in 1838.

By 1836 the Administration had decided that since nothing could be done to prevent squatting, all that remained was to accept it as an accomplished fact and bring it within the law. The Legislative Council accordingly passed the first Act [20] to legalize and regulate squatting. The country beyond the Nineteen Counties was to be divided into Districts, each under the control of a Commissioner for Crown Lands, and every squatter was to be compelled to pay a licence fee of £10 a year. All the Act really accomplished was to make it legal for squatters to occupy land. There was no restriction on area, and one licence entitled a man to occupation of as much land as he could manage to obtain. The Commissioners were merely figureheads, as there was no law to administer beyond the collection of licence fees.

During the late thirties, considerable friction developed between the squatters and the natives, and in 1839 an Act [21] was passed to provide a police force, the 'Border Police', for the Grazing Districts, and at the same time extend administrative control over the squatters. The Commissioners were given further powers, and were authorized to collect tax on stock carried—one penny for sheep, threepence for horned cattle, and sixpence for horses. Shortly after the passing of the Act, a Proclamation [22] delineated the boundaries of eight Grazing Districts, and named the Commissioners appointed to each (Fig. 3). Under the new regulations, then, a squatter had to pay both a fixed licence fee, and a tax on stock proportionate to the number carried. In return, he could claim police protection against assaults from aborigines or other white settlers, and, in the case of dispute over land holdings, had the right of appeal to the Commissioner.

The occupation rights of licensed squatters still savoured strongly of jungle laws, and the Commissioners had perforce to resort to des-

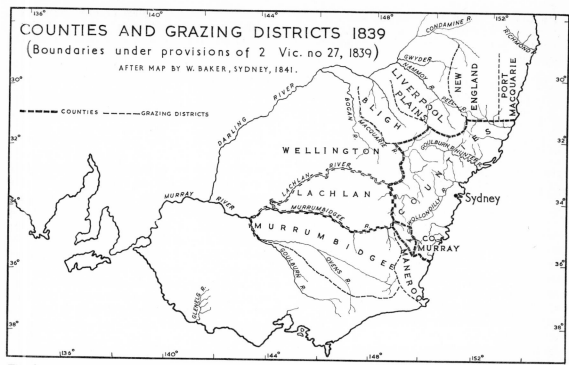

COUNTIES AND GRAZING DISTRICTS 1839
(Boundaries under provisions of 2 Vic. no 27, 1839)
AFTER MAP BY W. BAKER, SYDNEY, 1841.

Fig. 3

potic methods to achieve any measure of control. The case of John Spencer [23] near Gundagai was probably typical of this period. In 1841 he arrived with a few cows and horses, and established himself on land which had been claimed by Peter Stuckey since 1829. At first he was unmolested, but when he began to build up his stock, Stuckey objected. The issue was taken before the Commissioner at Yass in 1844, and it was decreed that Spencer could remain only on condition that his total stock did not exceed a dozen cows, a team of bullocks and three horses. The despondent Spencer was recorded as saying that his only chance of forming a station would be to move 300 miles down the river. Such was the fate of the squatter who arrived too late.

Once the better areas of the Murrumbidgee as far as Wagga had been appropriated, and the first mad rush into Victoria had slackened, squatters began to look to the drier lands of the Riverina. Details of expansion at this time are scarce, but records show that Uardry station near Hay was established by Edward Ray and Henry Angel [13b] in 1840, and that in 1845 Hobler [24] settled at Paika, just below the Murrumbidgee-Lachlan junction. Jervis [25a] notes that in 1842, Morris, Gwynne, and Walker explored the distributaries south of the Murrumbidgee main stream. They went from Brookong to Urana, and followed Billabong Creek for some distance, finally discovering the Edward River and Yanga Lake. Within a few years all the best land along these waterways had been settled. By 1848, almost all the land with water frontages on the Murrumbidgee inland plains had been taken up. Occupation of land away from the rivers came later. In 1847 Stewart, James and Gardiner [26a] explored the dry areas between the Lachlan and the Murrumbidgee in search of new pastures. Near Mirrool Creek, Stewart died of thirst, and the other two barely escaped with their lives. As late as 1875 this land was still unoccupied. A news item [26b] of that year stated:

. . . there is a large vacant space between the Murrumbidgee and Lachlan. It may seem incredible, but that part is so unknown and unfenced, that sheep from various stations are now running with two years' fleece on . . . There are at this date . . . one million acres unoccupied within two degrees of latitude.

The mallee to the west, and the badly watered plains to the south of the Murrumbidgee were also neglected for some years after the country with river frontages had been developed.

Economic Conditions in the Thirties and Forties

The basis of Riverina settlement in the thirties was the prosperity of the wool industry. Australian wool exported to England increased from two million lb. in 1830 to ten million in 1839. English market prices were high during this period, the peak being in 1836 when sales averaged two shillings per lb. This in itself was enough to encourage increased production, but development was further stimulated by English capital which was poured into the Colony [27].

Although settlement continued to spread down the Murrumbidgee in the forties, progress, particularly in the early years of the decade, was very much slower than in the thirties. One reason for this was that much of the better land had already been taken up; another, that economic conditions deteriorated and became most unfavourable to the pastoral industry. By 1840, economic circumstances forced England to restrict her interests in many avenues of trade. She continued to accept increased quantities of Australian wool, but at much lower prices. The 1836 price of twenty-four pence fell in 1840 to sixteen pence; in 1841 to fifteen pence; and, in 1843, to an all-time low of thirteen pence. Times were bad for the squatter, with sheep selling at sixpence a head, and scores of stations abandoned or handed over to creditors who didn't know what to do with them. Governor Gipps described the state of the period with characteristic realism in one of his despatches [28]:

The principal features which distinguish the present state of New South Wales are: 1st, The extent to which Insolvency has occurred amongst all Classes of the Community, even among men who were a short time ago considered in wealthy circumstances; and 2ndly, The great fall which has taken place in the price of every article of Colonial produce, and even also of Articles imported into the Colony . . . wages are falling; and persons who have nothing but colonial property (Sheep, Cattle, Houses or Lands) where with to meet pecuniary engagements, are driven in crowds to the Insolvent Court. Real property is scarcely saleable at any price, whilst Chattel property, including Sheep and horned Cattle, may be generally said to have fallen to one half or even to one third of the price it bore in 1840.

A slight improvement followed Wentworth's *Lien on Wool* Bill [29] in 1843, through which advances could be made to a mortgagor, using next season's wool clip as security. Then came a new method of disposing of sheep—boiling them down for tallow. This process was popularized by Henry O'Brien of Yass, who began large-scale operations in June, 1844. Boiling down made it possible to obtain at least saleable prices for stock which otherwise would not have reached the market. Another aid to recovery was a newly developed process of salting beef for export, which had some effect on improving conditions, particularly on the upper Murrumbidgee. By late 1844 the world trade situation was easing, and 1845 saw a keener English demand for wool, with prices ranging from sixteen to twenty-one pence per lb.

On the Murrumbidgee the depression was, in some ways, a blessing in disguise. The prosperous thirties had encouraged a miscellaneous collection of squatters with one aim—the breeding of vast numbers of sheep, regardless of quality. By harsh elimination, only the more astute or affluent pastoralists survived the early forties, and these in turn had either allowed their poorer quality stocks to perish, or had sold them for tallow. In consequence, the remaining flocks, although reduced in numbers, were on the average much improved in quality. Better sheep meant a better class of wool, which brought about a higher average market price. It was this higher price which enabled the industry to withstand a severe drought in 1846 that otherwise would have proved disastrous.

The middle and late forties were periods of fluctuating fortunes, but the pastoralists were now beginning to adapt themselves to the climatic vagaries of their new environment, as well as the inevitable fluctuations in market prices. Murrumbidgee settlement was gradually emerging from its pioneer phase and was beginning to acquire a semblance of stability.

Land Laws of the Forties, and their Effect on Murrumbidgee Settlement

The phenomenal expansion of the thirties was responsible for the emergence of the squatting class as the most influential pressure group in the Colony. The regulations under the Acts of 1836 and 1839 gave the squatter some legal standing and a voice in the community, but did not go far enough to satisfy him. What he wanted was security of tenure, compensation for improvements, and pre-emptive rights. These three points were the main political issues of the forties, and the agitation surrounding them kept the New South Wales political scene in a state of turmoil. Governor Gipps was faced with the difficult problem of dealing with these demands of the squatters without acting to the prejudice of other settlers.

Under the 1839 regulations, only one grazing licence was needed to permit squatting in any Grazing District of the Colony. This invited abuse, and by the early forties it was apparent that land control by monopoly interests was rapidly becoming a social evil. For example, a notorious character of the day, Benjamin Boyd, owned fourteen stations in the Monaro district alone, estimated at 231,000 acres, paying only four licence fees [30]. His interests extended well outside Monaro: he is reported to have claimed nearly two million acres elsewhere, with 8400 cattle and 142,000 sheep [31].

Gipps felt it his duty to attack such monopolies, and with this end in view and the backing of the Legislative Council he issued the *Occupation Regulations* [32] on 2 April 1844. These stipulated that each licence issued in future was to have effect for only one run, and that no run was to exceed twenty square miles or carry more than 4000 sheep or 500 head of cattle, or a mixed herd proportionate to these numbers. The following day, 3 April, Gipps issued a supplement which became known as the *Purchase Regulations* [33]. Under these, the squatter could purchase part of his run. After five years' occupation he was permitted to buy 320 acres at not less than the

established minimum price of £1 an acre, improvements being allowed for. This first sale was to be for a *homestead* block, and once completed, the squatter could retain undisturbed possession of the remainder of his run for eight more years, on the expiry of which he could buy another 320 acres, and so on. If, however, the squatter did not take advantage of the opportunity to buy when he was entitled to, anyone else could do so. If the homestead block had not been secured, the whole of the run would then go to the purchaser of the area which included it, the previous occupant retaining only the value of his improvements.

These two sets of regulations aroused such bitter opposition among the squatting class that at one stage armed rebellion was feared [17b]. Benjamin Boyd was a ringleader of the squatters, and travelled to England to obtain influential support in his fight against Gipps, but Gipps refused to be intimidated, and his stand was supported by Stanley, the Secretary of State. However, undercurrents stirred up by the wealthy pastoralists had their effect in English political circles, and squatter agitation of one kind or another was largely responsible for the Imperial *Waste Lands Occupation Act* of 1846. This was an attempt to embody most of Gipps' concessions, but without the clauses by means of which Gipps had hoped to keep the squatters within reasonable limits.

The Act was implemented in New South Wales through the *Order-in-Council* of 9 March, 1847 [34]. The old *boundaries of location* were abolished, and replaced by a new threefold division of land, known as *Settled*, *Intermediate*, and *Unsettled*. Unsettled lands were those in which pastoral settlement was still extending. In them, leases could be granted up to fourteen years for pastoral purposes, and for agricultural purposes to supply homestead requirements only. During these fourteen years the lessee alone had the right of purchase. Rent was proportionate to the estimated stock carrying capacity, which was determined by two valuators—one nominated by the squatter, the other by the Commissioner of Crown Lands. The basis of charge was £10 for the first 4000 sheep or its equivalent in cattle [one beeve to equal eight sheep], and £2.10.0 for each additional 1000 sheep or cattle equivalent.

To prevent a repetition of the scramble for water frontages that characterized Murrumbidgee expansion in the thirties, a provision stipulated that no lot was to include more than 440 yards of water frontage for each 160 acres. Landholders were asked to prefer claims for leases in respect of land to which they considered themselves entitled, and an expiry date of 30 September 1848 was fixed for lodgment of claims. As might be expected, there was considerable confusion in regard to the validity of claims, and investigations kept the Commissioners of Crown Lands busy for many years. In fact, some claims were not determined until after the passing of the *Crown Lands Act* of 1884 [*35*], which provided for subdivision of runs.

As some measure of the spread of pastoral settlement on the Murrumbidgee, the writer attempted to compare the numbers of depasturing licences issued as a result of the 1836 regulations with those following the 1839 regulations and the claims for leases under the 1847 Order-in-Council. However, compilation of the first of these lists was abandoned because the locations given on many of the licences were indefinite, the Grazing Districts not having been then clearly defined; while some licences appeared not to have been filed [*36*]. However, lists of licences issued following the 1839 regulations, and claims lodged under the 1847 Order-in-Council, have been compiled from the Government Gazettes by Campbell [*10a* and *10b*] and extracts are given below. Although not a precise record of settlement, these lists are believed to be sufficiently accurate to provide a reasonable assessment of settlement trends.

Grazing District	Licences issued 1840	Lease claims preferred 1848-9
Murrumbidgee	145	237
Lachlan	104	215
Monaro	150	172
	399	624

The lists reflect well the slowing down of settlement on the upper Murrumbidgee [Monaro] and the rush to secure land downstream on the Riverine Plains. Overall, development during the short eight or nine year period was more than 50 per cent—an extremely rapid increase. Since the purpose of the Order-in-Council was to assist orderly expansion in the newer districts, it certainly succeeded on the Murrumbidgee. But it went further than this, for it gave security of tenure to the powerful financial interests which had suffered a set-back by the *Purchase and Occupation* regulations of 1844. The prohibitive price of land which, under the 1844 Regulations, the large landowner had seen as a threat to his interests, now became his safeguard, for he could occupy leasehold land with little risk of losing it later. In effect, leasehold became almost as secure as land held on fee simple. Again to all intents and purposes the land was reserved for pasture; agriculture was virtually banned.

The security of the squatter's tenure under the Order-in-Council was the cause of considerable unrest between the poorer classes and the landed interests. It also proved a source of embarrassment to the Administration, which was anxious to encourage closer settlement and general rural development. By and large, however, the squatters enjoyed freedom from Government interference until the coming of free selection in 1861.

Maps and Surveys in the Forties

Prior to the 1847 Regulations, definition of property boundaries over the whole of the Murrumbidgee had been extremely vague, giving rise to constant disputes amongst rival landholders. Matters were not helped by the almost universal lack of fences, and with the rapid growth of settlement from the middle thirties onwards, sheep and cattle from neighbouring runs were in continual state of confusion.

Following the regulations and the gazetting of the lease claims, the Government initiated a series of surveys of the Grazing Districts, and gradually station boundaries were defined. Under the instructions of the Surveyor-General [Mitchell], Townsend began a survey of the Murrumbidgee Grazing District in 1848, and two years later completed a map of the district showing physical features and property boundaries. This was the first serious attempt to

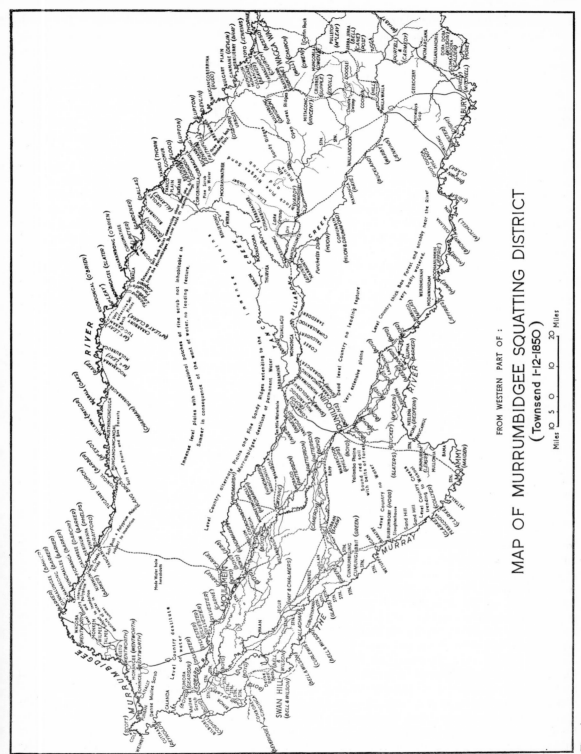

FROM WESTERN PART OF :

MAP OF MURRUMBIDGEE SQUATTING DISTRICT
(Townsend 1·12·1850)

Fig. 4

define pastoral holdings anywhere on the Murrumbidgee. The survey (Fig. 4) is a model of painstaking effort carried out under conditions which must at times have savoured of the hardships of Sturt and the early explorers: even sandhills and other minor features are delineated with remarkable accuracy. Pastoral holdings are denoted on the map either by the owner's name or by the name given to the station itself, sometimes by both. It is interesting to find the large numbers of pastoral holdings held by the same person or by families—an indication of the land monopolies of this period. Although property boundaries have changed over the years, many of the present-day stations bear the names shown by Townsend.

In a report issued early in his survey, Townsend stated emphatically that the plains of the lower Murrumbidgee, although rich in soil, were quite unsuited for cultivation on account of the severity of the climate [25a]. Subsequent attempts to establish wheat in these areas failed repeatedly, and Townsend's evaluation has proved substantially correct.

Townsend despatched his completed map to Mitchell in December 1850. A few days later, Mitchell instructed him to carry out a similar survey of the Monaro district. This second survey, finished in 1853, completed the delineation of pastoral holdings over the whole of the Murrumbidgee areas, and opened the way to a new and more quantitative approach to the assessment of land tenure.

Land Use and Station Management to 1851

Sheep and cattle were invariably run together on the early Murrumbidgee stations, but except in the Monaro District the economy was based substantially on sheep. Reasons for this are easy to find. In the first place, the great wool boom of the thirties encouraged the squatter to invest all his available capital on more and yet more sheep. Secondly, wool was much easier to dispose of than beef. It could be baled and loaded on the bullock wagons for despatch to Sydney with at least a reasonable chance of arriving safely at its destination. By contrast, cattle had to be driven great distances on the hoof, and without well established stock routes this at best was a hazardous undertaking. Then

again, there was an overseas market for wool which was seemingly inexhaustible. Beef on the other hand had only one market, Sydney, and a very limited one at that.

The exception was the Monaro District, where, in the early forties, sheep outnumbered cattle by only two and a half to one. Since it was customary to regard one beeve as equivalent to eight sheep (the ratio adopted in the 1847 regulations) the emphasis on cattle was well marked in Monaro. There would appear to be several reasons for this. In the first place, the lack of fences favoured the running of cattle in the type of country peculiar to this district. Sheep were difficult to round up in the mountain pastures, and more than the usual number of shepherds was needed to bring them back to the yards each night. Cattle, which could be left much longer without close supervision, were therefore cheaper to run. Then again, a type of catarrh, to which sheep seemed particularly subject at this stage, was worse in the upper Murrumbidgee than on the plains of the Riverina. Transport was another important factor. Although roads in all the Grazing Districts were bad at the time, in the Monaro they were quite abominable, and bullock teams were constantly getting bogged in the many creek crossings between Queanbeyan and Cooma. Transport costs in consequence were extremely high: one quote in the thirties was twenty-five shillings a hundredweight from Monaro to Sydney. Cartage of wool under such conditions was well nigh prohibitive, and it was often necessary to walk stock to market for sale as meat.

In the early forties, Benjamin Boyd established port facilities and a boiling-down works at Twofold Bay, and a trade movement developed down the mountain passes between the Monaro plateau and the coast. Sheep, as well as cattle, were marketed by this route. With the Twofold Bay outlet, and generally improving transport conditions on the Monaro, cattle were giving way to sheep by the late forties, and by 1850 the wool trade dominated the commerce of the whole Murrumbidgee.

Prior to 1851 there was very little cultivation in any of the Murrumbidgee districts. Small acreages of wheat were cultivated in County Murray and the Monaro District, while even smaller acreages of hay and a few potatoes were grown in Monaro. Elsewhere cultivation was negligible.

Station management during these early years of Murrumbidgee settlement was primitive to the extreme. There were no fences, sheep being tended constantly by shepherds, who, in the thirties, were mostly convicts under bond. Each shepherd looked after a flock which might vary from 400 to 1500 according to the nature of the country [17c]. Normally the sheep were taken to the grazing areas each day, being driven back at night to crudely constructed yards. The shepherds lived in huts nearby, and were responsible for the protection of their sheep from prowlers—animal or human. Cattle were allowed to run wild, and usually there was no attempt to muster them. The practice of a *general* muster began in the late forties and the fifties, when stockmen for many miles around met by arrangement, and did their best to draft out stock belonging to the various landholders. This somewhat chaotic state of affairs was typical of nearly all Murrumbidgee station management until the fifties, when numbers of runs were fenced.

ADDENDUM TO PART II: STATISTICAL SUMMARY TO 1851[1]

Stock

County Murray

Sheep. Pastoral stations had been established in County Murray for many years prior to 1843, the year of first recorded statistics. Sheep in 1843 numbered 184,000 and this figure rose to 267,000 in 1851.

Cattle. In 1843 cattle numbered 22,000, and showed very little increase during the period.

Monaro District

Sheep. Although the number of sheep in the Monaro District in 1843 (196,000) was much the same as in County Murray, increase for the Monaro was greater, the number rising to 369,000 in 1851.

Cattle. In 1843 cattle numbered 75,000, rose to a peak of 135,000 in 1846, then gradually fell away to only 69,000 in 1851.

Murrumbidgee District

Sheep. The increase in sheep during the period 1843 to 1851 was very much greater for the Murrumbidgee District than for any other division. In 1843 there were 227,000 sheep and, in 1851, 756,000.

Cattle. There was only a small increase from 93,000 to 114,000.

Lachlan District

Sheep. From 1843 to 1851, sheep numbers doubled, rising from 146,000 to 287,000.

Cattle. Numbers doubled rising from 54,000 to 104,000. The Lachlan District was the only division in which cattle showed a significant increase.

Cultivated Crops

County Murray

Wheat. The first returns for County Murray were for 1832, when 350 acres of wheat were grown for a yield of 6000 bushels of grain. During the ensuing years wheat acreages gradually increased to 2500 in 1842, and then fluctuated over the remainder of the period.

Other Crops. The only other significant crop was hay, the area of which increased from 1320 acres in 1845 to 1850 acres in 1849, falling back to 1500 in 1851.

Monaro District

Wheat. In 1843, the year of first returns, 1800 acres of wheat were grown for a production of 21,000 bushels. Acreages steadily declined to 1000 in 1851.

Other Crops. Hay was not important here as in County Murray, potatoes being the only other crop worth noting. There were 300 acres of potatoes in 1843, yielding 750 tons, and 380 acres in 1851 with 1000 tons.

---

[1]Based on figures extracted from New South Wales Returns, MS. (Mitchell Library) and Statistical Registers.

Murrumbidgee District

Prior to 1851, agriculture was of very minor importance in the Murrumbidgee Grazing District. There was a decline in wheat acreage from 2100 in 1843 to 1500 in 1851. Other crops were negligible.

Lachlan District

As in the Murrumbidgee District, there was very little cultivation in the Lachlan. The wheat acreage of 1500 in 1843 fell to 400 in 1851.

Population

County Murray

The first available population figures for the Murrumbidgee divisions are from the 1833 census, for County Murray. At this time the County had a total of 510 persons, of which 193 were under bond and 317 free. By 1836 the total had risen to 1728, 965 bond and 863 free. Thereafter the population rose steadily to 3886 in 1851, with only 43 under bond.

Monaro District

The earliest Monaro figures are for 1841, when of a total of 1883 persons, 502 were under bond and 1381 free. After a few years of slow increase, there was a rapid rise to 3689 in 1851 with only 48 under bond.

Murrumbidgee District

The population of the Murrumbidgee District increased from 1539 in 1841 to 2592 in 1846 and 4671 in 1851, a three times increase in ten years, which was at a faster rate than any of the other divisions. 485 of the population in 1841 were under bond, and as with Monaro and County Murray, this number fell very sharply to 65 in 1851.

Lachlan District

In 1841 the population of the Lachlan District at 1245 was lower than for any of the other Murrumbidgee divisions. The 1851 figure of 2892, however, shows an increase of nearly two and a half times. The ratio of bonded to free persons follows the trend of the other divisions.

Housing

The most significant feature of the housing statistics is the trend in materials used for the various divisions.

In 1841, County Murray, which was the first division settled, had 18 per cent of its houses built of stone or brick, and the balance of wood. The houses in the other three divisions were virtually all of wood. The position remained much the same over the period to 1846.

Over the next five years to 1851, the stone and brick houses increased to 21 per cent in County Murray. In the other three divisions, stone or brick houses rose from a negligible percentage in each case to 6 per cent in Monaro, 10 per cent in Murrumbidgee, 8 per cent in Lachlan. This trend towards more substantial dwellings in the pastoral districts is a reflection of the growing stability of the squatter in his new environment.

PART III: THE GOLD RUSH PERIOD 1851 TO 1861

Gold rushes in New South Wales were on a much smaller scale than in Victoria, a fact that is shown strikingly by a comparison of population trends in the two colonies. Population in New South Wales nearly doubled between 1851 and 1861, rising from 187,000 to 358,000. Although this is appreciable, it is after all what might be expected from natural growth in a young colony. Apart from the sensational but short lived boom at Kiandra in 1859 to 1860, New South Wales gold discoveries had little effect on Murrumbidgee land settlement. By contrast, due mainly to the discovery of gold, Victoria's population in 1861 was seven times that in 1851, increasing during this period from 77,000 to 540,000. By 1861, then, Victoria had a very much larger population than New South Wales. The rate of growth, however, had been far too rapid for such an insecure economic foundation to support it adequately, and thousands of new arrivals about this time began to look elsewhere for opportunities. From 1860, Victoria's population began to decline, while that in New South Wales continued to show a steady increase.

The Victorian boom of the fifties, and the ensuing decline in the sixties, each had profound effects on Murrumbidgee development. In the late forties, prior to the gold discoveries, small numbers of stock had been overlanded from the north through the Riverina and into Victoria. Following the 1851 boom in Victoria, pastoralists in Queensland and New South Wales discovered a lucrative market in Melbourne and the new Victorian settlements, and vast numbers of sheep and cattle were driven south by way of the central and western Riverina. Figures for the early years are not easy to obtain. It has been estimated, however, that 200,000 sheep crossed the Murrumbidgee in 1856, heading for Victoria. During a single fortnight in 1857, 42,000 sheep crossed the river, and it was considered that more than 300,000 would move south through the western Riverina during the season, quite apart from numerous flocks which were continually travelling via Wagga and points east [26c]. A single flock of sheep on the stock routes at this time usually numbered some 12,000 to 15,000, which were split into smaller units of about 2000, each under the control of a shepherd. The flock as a whole was under the supervision of an overseer, and a dray with its driver and a cook accompanied the party. Droving became an important avenue of employment for casual labour, which was drawn frequently from ex-sailors or disillusioned miners of many nationalities. Unskilled men of this type received about thirty-five shillings a week and experienced shepherds were given an extra five shillings.

New settlements sprang up at important points on Riverina stock routes, particularly at stream crossings, and settlements previously established on the routes grew into new importance. Near the present town of Hay on the Murrumbidgee there was a ford passable at low river, known as Lang's crossing, where stock coming from Queensland and northern New South Wales converged. A popular route was to proceed down the Lachlan as far as Booligal, cross, and then continue south to

Lang's crossing on the Murrumbidgee. In 1856 [26d] an enterprising settler established a punt at Police Point, near Lang's crossing, capable of carrying a dray and four bullocks, or alternatively 200 sheep. The popularity of the punt, at the time the only one below Wagga, is evidenced by the fact that during a six-week period in its first year of operation it carried a total of 150,000 sheep and 7000 cattle. Adjacent to the crossing a small settlement sprang up, and in 1858 a survey was carried out for a new town to be called Hay. Booligal, on the Lachlan, became firmly established as a staging post and river crossing on the southward route to Hay, and a punt was installed early in 1860. Later the same year a site for a village near the punt was gazetted [37a]. Once across the Murrumbidgee at Hay stock were driven due south to Deniliquin, which developed rapidly in the middle and late fifties as a stock selling centre.

During the late forties and early fifties, stock were usually driven to the outskirts of Melbourne itself. Then, as trade became brisk on the goldfields, dealers moved a short distance north to meet the incoming stock on the road. By the mid-fifties they had moved north again, and were buying at Moama on the Murray. Finally, by 1856, competition amongst the dealers had so intensified that they were establishing themselves at Deniliquin. As an index of business at this period, Jervis [25a] records the following stock sold at Deniliquin during the month of August 1856:

18,000	sheep	at	13/6
8,000	,,	,,	9/-
8,000	,,	,,	13/6
12,000	,,	,,	11/-
5,500	ewes	at	12/-
1,046	bullocks	at	£4

During a single month in the following year, stock valued at £100,000 were sold. Sales at Deniliquin continued very actively through 1858, and stock continued to stream southwards. During 1859, 439,185 sheep, 128,851 cattle and 5953 horses passed from New South Wales down into Victoria. By this time, however, the Victorian gold rush had passed its peak, and although the demand for stock persisted, the fantastic prices of the previous few years were sinking to a more moderate level.

Labour and Fences

As soon as news of the gold findings reached Murrumbidgee stations, stockmen and farm hands everywhere deserted their employers and joined in the rush. Flocks were left to look after themselves, and for a time chaos reigned. Squatters feared they would lose their investments, and complained bitterly, referring to the gold rush as a national calamity [26e]. As it happened, conditions did not deteriorate to the extent expected. The previously tended flocks were little the worse for the loss of their shepherds [27] and the squatters, mollified by the soaring prices for stock that accompanied the gold rush, began to talk hopefully of the future.

It seems to have taken several years to convince squatters generally that their loss of labour was other than a temporary inconvenience. However, with a big new demand for land closely following the high stock prices, eventually it became apparent to all that a substitute must be found for the shepherd system if heavy losses of sheep and cattle were to be avoided. And so at last fences began to appear.

One of the earliest records of fencing on the Murrumbidgee is from an advertisement of 1857, in which W. J. M. Stuckey calls for labour to erect wooden-rail fences on his Riverina property [38a]. Soon squatters everywhere were busily engaged in fencing, and recruiting labour of any kind available for this purpose. An article appearing in the *Sydney Morning Herald* in 1858 [26f] deals with the Murrumbidgee fencing problem in some detail. Its author draws attention to the enormous lengths of fencing which needed to be built. Then, fearing that this phraseology might fall on unaccustomed ears, he goes to some length to explain that 'fencing answers the purpose of the English hedge, or fence, in order to preserve the cattle in their proper boundary'. He describes the Riverina fence as a structure of two or three horizontal rails, with vertical posts, and notes that it costs him £60 to £100 a mile to erect. Two good workmen could complete a mile in six to seven weeks. Of considerable interest is this correspondent's note to the effect that Captain Francis Cadell, the river steamboat pioneer, was to undertake large

contracts for fencing under steam power. Steam was to saw the rails and the posts, and then dig the post-holes. By this time, Cadell had already established a steam-operated sawmill at Deniliquin, and fencing activities throughout the Riverina were gathering momentum.

Station Life and Management

Prior to 1851, many squatters lived away from their properties, and employed managers to look after their interests. This system worked fairly well when labour was plentiful, and management largely a matter of routine. After the gold discoveries things were very different, with many of the station hands away trying to make their fortunes and stock wandering about at will. The urgent need to fence, with labour at a premium, could only be dealt with satisfactorily by astute personal organization. Likewise, with soaring markets for stock, important snap decisions on sales were necessary to obtain the greatest possible profits. Owners found they could not afford to be absent.

Then again, the coming of the river steamers changed the whole complexion of station life. Goods could be transported from the coast at a reasonable price and with a minimum of damage. By 1858, station homesteads and outstation huts were assuming a new degree of comfort, and 'glass windows, wooden floors, lined walls, and many necessary comforts' [26g] were ushering in a new era of civilized living. Kitchen gardens appeared, and homegrown vegetables added variety to the once monotonous diet. The scarcity of labour added considerably to the workman's wages in the forties and fifties. Stockmen in the late fifties were receiving £60 to £80 a year; shepherds £40 to £45; a man and wife assisting on a station, £75 to £85, and casual labourers were paid from fifteen shillings to twenty shillings a week.

Although station life improved in the fifties, conditions were still extremely primitive in the Riverina at large. A report of 1857 [38b] notes that between the Murray and the Lachlan there were no churches, schools, police or postmen for hundreds of miles. The law was left to look after itself, and 'thousands of stockmen, shepherds, hut keepers, and bullock drivers who are quite nomadic' roamed the countryside, forming relationships with black women, and 'duffing' stock with the greatest of ease.

River Transport

The first steamboat to operate on the Murray River was William Randell's *Mary Ann* in 1852, closely followed by Francis Cadell's larger and more elaborate *Lady Augusta* in 1853. By the middle fifties, steamer transport on the Murray was well established, and had been responsible for reducing the price of goods delivered to river towns in New South Wales and Victoria by as much as 30 per cent [25a]. Boats from South Australia plied up the river as far as Albury. Soon steamer operators turned their attention to the tributary streams. Of these, the Murrumbidgee offered unusually good trade opportunities, but was badly cluttered up with snags. Early in 1856, work began on clearing the river for navigation from Wagga to the Murray Junction [38c]. In 1858, Cadell ascended the Murrumbidgee as far as Gundagai in his steamboat *Albury*, and started a transport service with small steamers between Gundagai and Adelaide, operating when the river was high.

By this time five steamboats were engaged in the river trade, and were bringing about notable changes in the transport and communication facilities of the Riverina and northern Victoria. Large numbers of stock were still crossing the Murray and proceeding on foot to Victorian markets, but squatters were finding it cheaper to send their wool by steamer to Adelaide than by bullock waggon to Sydney or Melbourne. On their return trips up the rivers the steamers brought stores and goods of all descriptions. By 1860, Wagga and Hay had developed into major ports for the despatch of wool produced on northern Riverina stations.

For all intents and purposes, Wagga became the head of navigation on the Murrumbidgee, as the voyage to Gundagai was found to be hazardous even at high river.

Early Water Conservation

Although Murrumbidgee water conservation has been generally regarded as a relatively recent innovation, one project of some importance was initiated as early as the 1850s.

As already noted, in former geological time Yanco Creek and its branch, Billabong Creek, were major Murrumbidgee distributaries. Subsequently, however, a mass of sediments blocked up the Yanco entrance channel, so that at the time of first settlement Murrumbidgee water was cut off except during unusually high floods. Jervis [25a] notes that during the early fifties squatters on the upper parts of Billabong Creek built dams across it, much to the annoyance of those downstream who were thereby largely deprived of the all too infrequent flow. Feeling on the matter reached such a pitch that raiding parties were frequently organized to destroy the dams, resulting on occasion in physical violence. 'Dam cutting' was still a popular pastime in 1866.

Faced with a serious water problem, squatters in the Yanco and Colombo Creeks area in 1855 conceived the idea of cutting a canal from the Murrumbidgee to Yanco Creek, thus supplying the smaller stream system with permanent water. This first attempt cost upwards of £8000. Another attempt in 1864 cost a further £5000. By 1867, a total of some £20,000 had been spent, and still an effective flow could not be obtained, although the water supply was much improved. At last, in 1879, a deep canal connecting the two streams was finished, and was filled with flowing water to a depth of six feet. This not only supplied Yanco and Colombo creeks, but augmented the flow of Billabong Creek and the Edward River.

Growth of Lower Murrumbidgee Towns and Villages

Deniliquin, Hay, Moulamein and Wagga were the principal urban centres for the Riverina during the fifties. Deniliquin originated from a small cluster of buildings in the late forties, and was proclaimed a town in 1850 [37b]. Population growth during the decade was slow, but as the stock traffic through to Victoria developed, the town became an important staging post and market centre. By the sixties Deniliquin was recognized as the principal centre for the western Riverina.

Jervis [25b, c, d, e] in an account of the growth of Riverina towns, describes how Hay grew first around a ford, and later around a punt used by stock on the route to Deniliquin. The town of Hay was surveyed in 1858, and proclaimed in 1859. Although important as a crossing and staging post at first, and in the late fifties as a river port, it did not really develop into a sizeable town until the sixties. Moulamein developed early as a junction between the traffic proceeding down the Edward River from Balranald, and that coming south from Hay en route to Deniliquin. In 1848 it had a lock-up and court house, and in 1851 was gazetted as a town. Wagga in 1849 consisted of a public house, a store and a blacksmith's shop [13b]. In 1852, the year of a great flood in which the town of Gundagai was inundated, Wagga had a population of about 50 [39]. Like Hay in the west, Wagga became an important crossing place for southward-bound stock in the eastern Riverina. It developed steadily during the fifties, and in 1858 a successful newspaper, the *Wagga Wagga Express*, was started there.

Several minor settlements became established in the fifties [25c]. Balranald was gazetted in 1851, and a mail service from Wagga was instituted in 1852. The settlement became a recognized crossing place on the river, and in 1859 a punt was installed. Oxley was gazetted in 1851, and Booligal in 1860; Conargo was laid out as a township in 1860.

Victorian Influence on Riverina Development

A dispute concerning the boundary between New South Wales and Victoria began in 1851, and proved a bone of contention for many years. An Imperial Act of 1850 [40] defined the boundary as '. . . a straight line drawn from Cape Howe to the nearest source of the River Murray, and thence by the course of that river to the eastern boundary of the Colony of South Australia'. The confusion arose from the phrase 'the nearest source of the River Murray', for the Victorians maintained that this referred to the upper Murrumbidgee which is nearer to Cape Howe than the upper Murray. In support of this interpretation, they quoted a letter dated 3 January 1851 from Mitchell, the New South Wales Surveyor-General, in which he states categorically that the upper Murrumbidgee was the river referred to in the Act. The official New South Wales view was to the effect that

the Murray had become well known long before Mitchell wrote his letter, and had been called by that name far above the junction with the Murrumbidgee. This being so, they maintained that the nearest source of the 'River Murray' could not be the upper Murrumbidgee.

As early as 1856, the residents of the southern Riverina were agitating for the separation of the region to Victoria. It was claimed that New South Wales had done nothing to develop the country, '. . . scarcely a single mile of road having been made or bridge built over any of the creeks and rivers' [38d]. Attention was also drawn to the fact that the Riverina was being settled rapidly from the Victorian side of the Murray, and that trade links were with Melbourne and Adelaide rather than Sydney. Added to this, it was felt locally that Sydney people had no idea of the increasing importance of the area. A particularly sore point with the majority of Riverina residents was the location of the place of nomination for the Murrumbidgee electorate at Tumut, well to the east of the geographical centre of the electorate. Communications at this time were so bad that it was often impossible for residents of Murray towns to reach Tumut in time to record their nominations. Dislike of the New South Wales administration, however, was not prompted by love for that in Victoria, as instanced by the observation: '. . . the residents in the northern part of Victoria are not one whit more contented than the people of this (N.S.W.) side of the Murray' [38e]. In fact, the *Ovens and Murray Advertiser* was quoted as saying that the river country should go to South Australia, as there was no gold duty there.

The close affinity between the Riverina and Victoria in the years immediately succeeding the gold rush cannot be questioned. To all intents and purposes Sydney was forgotten by settlers west of Wagga. Virtually all trade was with Victoria, and lines of communication ran south rather than east. Then again, from the middle fifties on, Victorians seeking land poured northward into the Riverina, strengthening by direct human relationship the contacts already established by commerce. In all but administration, Sydney's ties with the Riverina were broken. They have never been fully regained.

Monaro Settlement in the Fifties

Developments in the Riverina during the fifties tend to overshadow those in the upper parts of the Murrumbidgee Valley, which by comparison were slow and unspectacular. The one great event of the period was the discovery of gold at Kiandra in 1859 by the brothers James and David Pollock [41]. It is of interest to note that the Pollocks brought sheep every summer from the Murray to graze on upper Murrumbidgee pastures. In December 1859 and January 1860 the big Kiandra gold rush was under way. By February some 15,000 miners had established themselves in the Kiandra area, and fantastic finds were being made. One report [41] claims that 500 ounces of gold were being won daily. Winter snows drove away the majority of the miners, and by August only 4000 were still braving the elements. Before the winter was out many of them had died from exposure. With the melting of the snows in the spring many of the original miners returned. By this time, much of the readily accessible gold had vanished, and practically the whole population left the district for good before the winter of 1861.

The gold rush had the effect of accelerating the growth of Cooma, which, although surveyed as a village in 1849, had grown very slowly. Adaminaby owed its existence to Kiandra gold, and grew rapidly as a staging post on the road from Cooma to Kiandra.

ADDENDUM TO PART III: STATISTICAL SUMMARY 1851 TO 1861[2]

Stock

County Murray

Sheep. After the slow increase prior to 1851, numbers showed a slight downward trend during the period, from 267,000 in 1851 to 199,000 in 1861, with some fluctuation in the intervening years.

Cattle. After remaining more or less static in the previous period, numbers increased slightly from 22,000 to 56,000—a peak which was not reached again for another 13 years.

Monaro District

Sheep. Numbers continued to increase during the period from 369,000 in 1851 to 450,000 in 1855, then fell away again to 325,000 in 1861.

Cattle. Numbers had been decreasing for some years previously and reached a record low of 67,000 in 1852, then rose again gradually to 145,000 in 1861.

Murrumbidgee District

Sheep. The remarkable increase in sheep numbers during the forties continued in the early fifties. In 1851 there were 756,000; in 1854, 922,000. Then, with the stock movement into Victoria gathering momentum, numbers fell to nearly half in 1855, before beginning to rise again, reaching 708,000 in 1861.

Cattle. Numbers rose more rapidly than in the preceding period, increasing from 114,000 in 1851 to 323,000 in 1860—a peak which was not exceeded for many years thereafter.

Lachlan District

Sheep. During the period numbers which had previously been increasing rapidly, rose erratically from 287,000 in 1851 to 720,000 in 1860, but fell to 488,000 in 1861.

Cattle. Numbers also continued to rise, with ups and downs, from 104,000 in 1851 to a peak of 249,000 in 1860. The numbers continued to fall thereafter for many years.

Cultivated Crops
County Murray

Wheat. Acreages, which had been fairly static for some years prior to 1851, doubled during the period, rising from 2182 in 1851 to 4920 in 1861.

---

[2]Based on figures extracted from New South Wales Statistical Registers.

Other Crops. Hay, the only other significant crop, fluctuated but showed no marked trend. Acreages, mainly of oats, were 1500 in 1851 and 1200 in 1861.

Monaro District

Wheat. Acreages continued to decline during the early fifties, then rose again. There were 1000 acres in 1851; 700 in 1855; and 3100 in 1861. Apart from minor fluctuations, the latter figure remained much the same for a number of years thereafter.

Potatoes. Acreage, which had previously been fairly stationary, rose during the period. The 400 acres of 1851 rose to 800 in 1861, yielding 2900 tons.

Other Crops. These were relatively unimportant.

Murrumbidgee District

Wheat. Of very little significance prior to 1851, wheat showed considerable development during the period. The 1500 acres of 1851 increased, with fluctuations, to 9000 in 1861.

Other Grain Crops. In particular maize, barley and oats increased but by 1861 were still relatively unimportant.

Hay. The increase was from a mere 500 acres in 1851 to 2500 in 1861. Almost the entire hay crop was oats.

Lachlan District

Wheat. As with the Murrumbidgee District, wheat in the Lachlan District, which had been insignificant with only 400 acres in 1851, showed a marked development to 2200 acres in 1861.

Hay. There was an increase from 100 acres in 1851 to 600 acres in 1861. Only half of this was oats.

Other Crops. No other crops were significant.

Population

The persons under bond, who had formed a significant proportion of the population in all divisions during the thirties and forties, had decreased to an insignificant number by 1851, and subsequently were not recorded.

County Murray

Of the 3900 persons in 1851, females comprised nearly half. Numbers increased steadily to 6100 in 1861, the proportion of females remaining fairly constant.

Monaro District

The population in 1851 was 3700, of which between one third and one half were females. There was an increase to 9200 in 1861, the female component remaining the same.

Murrumbidgee District

Of the total of 4700 in 1851, only 1600 were females. The population increased to 6300 in 1856 and 12,900 in 1861, females remaining at one third of the total.

Lachlan District

The population in 1851 was 2900, a little over one third being females. There was a slow increase to 3100 in 1856, then a very rapid rise to 14,800 in 1861. Only one quarter of the latter were females.

Housing

The proportion of brick and stone houses in County Murray continued to increase during the early fifties, from 21 per cent in 1851 to 27 per cent in 1856. There was then a fall to 19 per cent in 1861.

In the case of the Monaro District, the proportion fell very slightly from 6 per cent in 1851 to 5½ per cent in both 1856 and 1861.

In the Murrumbidgee District, the percentage fell from 10 per cent in 1851 to 7 per cent in 1856, and then rose again to 11 per cent in 1861.

There was a decrease in brick and stone houses in the Lachlan District from 8 per cent in 1851 to 6 per cent in 1856 and 4 per cent in 1861.

These housing trends have some correlation with the social and economic reactions of the period. County Murray being one of the Nineteen Counties, and therefore an old established area, showed a tendency to follow the Sydney pattern where the well-to-do had a marked preference for brick or stone. Then, with great new developments elsewhere, new settlers with the means to build substantial homes tended to by-pass this 'in-between' area. For a region far removed from civilization, the proportion of brick and stone houses in the Murrumbidgee District was high. This seems to reflect the highly profitable activities of the large squatters there. The falling off in this type of house in the Lachlan District is indicative of the period of stabilization in this not-so-rich region following over-development in the thirties and forties. The relatively low but nevertheless stable position of brick and stone on the Monaro is symbolic of a region that was relatively second-class in soil and pasture, but safe climatically, and not subject to sudden booms and depressions.

PART IV: PERIOD OF LAND LAW REFORM 1861 TO 1884

The Background to Land Law Reform in New South Wales

Phenomenal agricultural development on the Murrumbidgee followed the land legislation of 1861, and some understanding of the principles of this legislation is essential to appreciate the trends of the period.

The land monopoly of the squatter, strengthened by the Order-in-Council, did not go unchallenged for long. For a time the gold discoveries provided a diversionary interest, but by the mid-fifties disappointed miners in rapidly growing numbers were seeking new sources of livelihood, and turning to the land as the obvious choice. Finding themselves frustrated, not by insufficient land, but by regulations weighted to the advantage of one privileged class, they expressed their disapproval with a directness and vigour that startled the Administration. Their case was strengthened by the support of certain influential members of the Council with marked democratic leanings, and even by isolated individuals amongst the squatters themselves. A 'Land League of New South Wales' was formed as a militant body pressing for land law reform, and this contributed notably to the pressure for a new land policy [42]. An extract from a League Manifesto reads:

. . . a great change is certainly wanted. Flocks and herds there are, indeed, to be seen here and there, but in miserable disproportion to the enormous extent of the public domain which is held by their owners, and held, too, at a rent or assessment to the Crown of the most trifling amount. Traces of agriculture there are, indeed, to be seen here and there, but in patches so few and far between that the great bulk of the people are still everywhere fed with imported bread-stuffs. And yet, monstrous and marvellous as it may appear, if the *bona fide* cultivator attempts to get a piece of land of his own, to produce his own loaf, he is at once met with difficulties which are all but insuperable.

Agitators for land law reform were well aware that the squatters' leases were for a fixed period of fourteen years, and that the first of them, issued in 1848, were due to expire in 1862. Substitute legislation of one kind or another would be necessary, and the reformers were determined that this would be on a more equitable basis than hitherto. Sir John Robertson, Secretary for Crown Lands and an ardent land reformer drafted the new Bills, and the Enactments which followed are now commonly known as the 'Robertson Land Acts of 1861'. There were two Acts, the *Alienation Act* [43] and the *Occupation Act* [44], the aims of which were, broadly to facilitate the settlement of an agricultural community alongside the established pastoralists.

The basic principle of the *Alienation Act* was free selection before survey. Selectors were entitled to apply for the conditional purchase of any Crown Land within the limits of 40 to 320 acres, provided the land was not under lease taken out prior to 1858, or reserved for some specific purpose such as town sites or water supply. Land was valued at £1 an acre, but the purchaser was required to pay a deposit of only five shillings an acre, with three years to make good the balance. If he wished, however, he could defer settlement for an indefinite period by paying five per cent interest on the sum outstanding. The purchaser had the additional privilege of grazing rights over three times the area of his purchase, provided this was not claimed by another selector. Certain improvement and residence conditions were specified, but these 'came to be honoured in the breach rather than the observance' [45]. The Act was subsequently amended twice, but the only significant alterations were the extension, in 1875, of the maximum area to 640 acres, and the fixing of an age limit of sixteen for persons qualified to select. The *Occupation Act* abolished the occupation provisions of the Order-in-Council, and limited the tenure of squatters' leases to five years—thus hastening the expiry date of recently issued leases. The only effective privilege awarded the pastoralist was under the Regulations of the *Alienation Act*, which gave a lessee pre-emptive right to purchase part of his holding which he had improved. He was permitted to purchase a maximum of one twenty-fifth of his run at a price not less than £1 an acre.

In spite of these new methods for land acquisition the old method of unconditional sale and sale by auction was allowed to remain, and in fact accounted for nearly 40 per cent of all New South Wales land sold while the Robertson Acts remained in operation [46a]. To safeguard their interests against the inroads of the free selector, squatters frequently took advantage of the auction clauses of the Act to have large sectors of their leasehold put up for auction, subsequently bidding for the land and purchasing it themselves, often at the upset price.

Much has been said, but little real research done on the operation and effects of the Robertson Acts. Roberts [17d] has stated bluntly that the acts backfired to the extent that they meant prosperity to the larger squatter, and that 'settlement under them was largely a fiction'. On the other hand, Clark [47a] has hinted that the squatters may to some extent have jeopardized their financial independence in their fight against infiltration by the selectors. Roberts and Clark agree, however, that the

Acts failed as a means of putting men on the land—an assumption that is queried by Burton [48] and others.

In assessing the results of the legislation it seems important to go beyond its immediate reactions, although Burton has suggested that even these were by no means unsuccessful. It is certainly clear that the benefits gained were not directly in line with those envisaged by Robertson and his reformers, for the majority of free selectors did not remain on their holdings, and the holdings themselves in the long term increased considerably from their intended size. However, statistics show a very marked increase in the total area under crop for the years following 1861, and there appear to be some grounds for questioning Clark's assertion that these increases do not indicate the success of the Acts. Clark [47b] argues that the financial difficulties of so many of the selectors would have precluded them as a class from contributing substantially to the increases, and suggests that significant additions would have come from farmers who purchased their land at auction, or from the squatters themselves. Although figures are not available to indicate the numbers of farmers who used the auction system to purchase land, it is difficult to imagine that many would have been willing to expend the considerable capital required for this form of alienation when the conditional purchase system was available, and offered such favourable terms.

Again, it would appear that in this early period of agricultural development small farmers in general were notoriously lacking in capital reserves, and thus would have been incapable of finding ready cash for purchase, even had they so desired. The supposition that squatters may have grown substantial quantities of wheat on their holdings is also difficult to countenance except in the case of some relatively small runs. Wheat was not an easy crop to grow as it required special supervision, and was difficult to market at a reasonable profit because of inadequate transport facilities. By comparison, wool raising was easy money. Added to this was a strong social rift between farmer and grazier which must have discouraged any serious attempt by the squatter to grow wheat. Right down to the present day, the Australian squatter has cherished the notion that cereal growing for cash sale is the role of the 'cocky' farmer, and that to lift hand to plough is to lose caste. Again, Clark's premise, that a low income and standard of living is inconsistent with overall development, cannot be applied universally. In fact, there are conspicuous exceptions in the growth of the New South Wales and Western Australian dairy industries, and the development of horticulture in the Murrumbidgee Irrigation Areas.

Quite apart from cultivation, the Acts were indirectly responsible for the closer settlement of *pastoralists* in some areas—a fact that seems to have escaped notice in the publicity given to alienation of huge holdings in the far west. The Acts were also responsible for pastoralists alienating vast areas of leasehold, with diverse side-effects such as the influx of a new pastoralist community into the pioneer 'squattocracy'. The Murrumbidgee provides many interesting examples of these varied reactions.

Free Selection and Conditional Purchase on the Murrumbidgee

The effects of free selection were very different in the various sectors of the Murrumbidgee. Reasonably good results appear to have been achieved in the upper reaches of the river, particularly the Monaro. Even the anti-selectionists Morris and Ranken [49] have conceded that '. . . upon the whole, Monaro exhibits substantial results from the Act of 1861'. These critics are quick to point out, however, that the selections of 640 acres or less which the Act proposed had, by 1883, grown to '. . . 1000 to 3000 and upwards', and that many of these blocks were owned by persons with primarily pastoralist backgrounds.

On the Monaro, there was bitter rivalry between selector and squatter right from the start. The selector took up either the maximum of 320 [later 640] acres, or as much of it as he could afford, and leaned heavily on his right to graze on three times the area so purchased. The squatter for his part did everything in his power to protect his own interests. Frequently his first reaction was to purchase the area adjoining a selector's land, thus taking away the selector's grazing rights and, on occasion, cutting him off

from access to roads, watering points, and other strategic areas. He did this by exercising his pre-emptive right to purchase part of his run (his pre-lease); by making his own conditional purchase; or by arranging to have the land concerned put up for auction and bidding for it himself. Both selectors and lessees frequently employed dummies to select for them, and until 1875 when the Act was amended [50], took out selections in the name of each member of their families, regardless of age. Unless a selector could build his block into at least 1000 acres he rarely survived, for the Monaro was not primarily agricultural land, and grazing required much more than even the increased area of 640 acres permitted.

McFarland [51a] likens this battle between squatter and selector to a game of chess; the selector would take up part of a squatter's run, and the squatter would retaliate by taking away the selector's grazing rights, whereupon the selector would sell out to the squatter and start again, perhaps on an adjoining run. Morris and Ranken have gone so far as to admit that this competition, while frequently proving severe on the individual, was very beneficial to the Monaro as a whole. By 1883 almost all the better Monaro land suitable either for agriculture or grazing had been alienated, and nearly all of the original runs had been fenced, improved, and at least partly subdivided. The new order did not, however, bring about an intensification of cultivation on the Monaro. It was *grazing*, and particularly sheepraising, that developed.

Farther down the Murrumbidgee, in the sector from Gundagai through Wagga to Narrandera, free selection by 1883 also resulted in the alienation of most of the land, and subdivisions of the order of 2000 to 3000 acres [49]. However, although many of these properties were acquired in the first place by conditional purchase, an appreciable number, unlike the Monaro, were bought at auction. Another marked difference between the central Murrumbidgee and the Monaro was the land use of the new holdings. Many holdings in the Gundagai area combined agriculture and grazing, while farther down towards Wagga and Narrandera there was a marked tendency to concentrate on agriculture alone.

E

Traditionally accepted authorities on the Land Acts, such as Roberts and Coghlan, have been prone to make generalized assumptions on the basis of New South Wales statistics *as a whole*. Certainly, it would appear that, during the time the Acts were in force, cultivated land in the Colony little more than doubled in area [52]. This result, however, can only be seen in perspective if returns are examined on a regional basis. New South Wales includes a relatively small area suitable for successful wheatgrowing, and it happens that the most important sector of this lies within the better-rainfall lands of the Riverina, particularly those lands associated with the Murrumbidgee and the Lachlan. Statistics for the Murrumbidgee Pastoral District over the period 1861 to 1874 show an increase in wheat acreages from 9000 to 28,000, and for the Lachlan District from 2200 to 12,000 over the same period. Regional statistics are not available thereafter for six years, but over a mere four years from 1880 to the close of the period in 1884, wheat in the relatively small Murrumbidgee Electoral District increased from 6400 to 11,800 acres (see Addendum to Part IV). It would seem, then, that in the area best suited to its cultivation, wheat acreages increased several times at least during the period concerned, which was no mean result from a crop with relatively unremunerative returns. The inference is that the Robertson Land Acts, with all their deficiencies, were primarily responsible for the early development of the Murrumbidgee wheat belt.

Farther downstream, on the great plains of the lower Murrumbidgee, the effects of the enactments were different again. Even the better-rainfall areas here were marginal for wheatgrowing, and almost all the selectors who depended on agriculture were unsuccessful. In fact, the only selectors who remained were those who managed to build up holdings for themselves greatly in excess of the conditional purchase block, and who relied mainly on sheep.

Prior to 1875, when every member of a family was entitled to select, family groups could, by using their additional grazing rights, amass appreciable areas of land. However, if the grazing lands were lost, even large families found that their purchase aggregations were insufficient for maintaining reasonable living standards, and there was a strong inducement to sell out to the original lessee, particularly if the offer was attractive. Morris and Ranken claim that of 1426 selectors who applied for land in the Counties of Wakool, Townsend, and Cadell (the south-western Murrumbidgee plain), only 244 were still in occupation by 1883, most of them living poorly.

In the drier country of the far north-western Riverina, i.e. the land in the triangle formed by the meeting of the Lachlan and the Murrumbidgee, the selector was particularly unsuccessful. This was a region of few leaseholders, a 'large vacant space' [26h]. Numbers of selectors were attracted there, however, by favourable seasons in the seventies, throwing the lessees into a panic. Some of these selectors succumbed to attractive offers to sell, and the ones who remained fell prey to a succession of bad years. This was no country for wheat; and grazing at the rate of one sheep to three or four acres required larger areas than the selector could hope to acquire. Today, large uninviting areas near Hay and farther north, almost denuded of topsoil, are a monument to the wheat farmer of the eighties.

A relatively small area meriting special note is the 'Yanco Reserve'. Efforts to provide a water supply in the Yanco-Colombo Creek areas have already been noted (Part III). Most of these areas were held under lease until 1865, when the leases expired. Because of the lessees' considerable capital investment in water schemes, the Government agreed to reserve from free selection narrow strips of land along the watercourses, amounting in all to some 120,000 acres. Adjoining lessees were given exclusive use of these areas. Because of public pressure, however, the Reserve was revoked in 1876, and made available for selection. It was quickly alienated. Works to improve the water supply continued, and by 1880 a steady flow of water along the creek was being maintained.

An outstanding feature of this period was the movement of Victorians northwards into the Riverina. Some of them came as free selectors with little experience or capital to back them; others were farmers and graziers with adequate means who were anxious and able to purchase large properties. As one report [26i] puts it, '...Riverina was receiving the very marrow of Victorian refugee leaseholders, draining the Colony of its best men. Many of the settlers had sold their lands and were taking up country in Riverina'. This migration from Victoria was but a new phase of the movement that followed the 'gold period'. It added further to the already strong Victorian character of the Riverina, a character that is evident from incidental mannerisms and cultural traits even at the present day.

The problem of station ownership during this period has received very little attention. Jervis [25a] refers to a report that between 1862 and 1872 almost all sheep stations in the western Riverina changed hands, only six of the original occupiers remaining, and this is supported by scrutiny of land maps of the Riverina which show many changes in the registered ownership of properties after 1850. Again, an 1881 report stated that '...more land was sold in the Murrumbidgee district in one year by public auction than in any other ten districts of New South Wales' [53]. Undoubtedly some of this land was bought by leaseholders in order to secure their holdings, but in view of the movement into the Riverina by persons other than impecunious free selectors, particularly the Victorians, it is apparent that much land must have changed hands. This may reflect, in part, the weakened financial reserves of the squatters.

Economic Development

The period 1861 to 1884 was essentially one of transition from the great expansion, crude living, and easy money of the fifties to a new era of land alienation, station improvement, and a more stable and civilized way of life. With the fantastic markets of the gold rush period a thing of the past, energies were channelled into raising the quality of stock, increasing carrying capacity, improving transport facilities, and developing properties and homesteads generally to a standard commensurate with the status of the owners as a newly evolved landed aristocracy. Fencing, especially following alienation, was the most important form of station improvement. Although there are records of wire fences elsewhere in New South Wales from as early as 1855 [54], the general style of fencing on the Murrumbidgee

until about 1870 comprised split rails set in posts. Often the fence was crudely built of logs. From 1870, the use of wire rapidly gained in popularity, and the saving in labour by this method was a strong inducement to complete the enclosure of runs.

Official records make only three references to station improvements prior to 1883 [55, 56, 57], and these give but an indication of trends for the Murrumbidgee regions. It is apparent, however, that from 1871 expenditure on fencing right down the river from Cooma to Balranald was second only to that on buildings. 'Water conservation' came next, followed by 'ring-barking' and 'grass seed sowing'. Pasture improvement in Australia is commonly regarded as a fairly recent practice associated with the broadcasting of superphosphate, and it is therefore interesting to note that as early as 1871 small but by no means negligible sums were being expended for this purpose. In the Cooma region the figure for seed sowing was £1,168, as opposed to only £187 for ring-barking, and McFarland [51a] notes at least some attempt to introduce new grasses into the Monaro at this time, and stresses the need for introduction of English species. As might be expected, expenditure on pasture improvement decreased downstream with the falling off in rainfall—£455 in the Gundagai region, £220 at Wagga, and nothing at all at Hay and Balranald.

Apart from the Yanco Creek project, already noted, water conservation was restricted mainly to well-sinking. By this time, periodic droughts had instilled into Murrumbidgee settlers the supreme importance of permanent water. In fact, McFarland [51b] notes that even on the Monaro, the best watered sector of the Murrumbidgee, everything had to take second place to water supply. He says:

There are . . . very few residences in Monaro in which much regard has been shown to the selection of 'sites', from which the beautiful scenery of the district . . . can be seen . . . Everything has been sacrificed to the securing of Water.

On the Riverina plains, where conditions were much drier, pastoralists paid increasing attention to the construction of dams and wells. They found they could strike water almost anywhere if prepared to go deep enough; 80 to 150 feet was usual. Wells of this depth, however, were expensive, and by 1870 bores were beginning to take their place.

This period marked a revolutionary change in methods of transport, for on the main lines of communication railways began to displace both bullock wagon and river steamer. Victoria was first to tap the Riverina by rail. In 1864 a line was built north to Echuca on the Murray. Echuca developed rapidly as a river port, and captured traffic from the Murrumbidgee and upper Murray which had been proceeding downstream to South Australia. With an eye to attracting the whole of western Riverina trade, Victorian interests completed an extension of this line to Deniliquin in 1876. Although the New South Wales Government had approved the Deniliquin-Echuca railway, the success of the venture caused some alarm, and hastened the extension of railways from Sydney. A line was completed to Wagga in 1879, marking the end of that town as a river port. Extensions from Wagga reached Narrandera in 1881, and Hay in 1882, and cheap freight rates were introduced to popularize the new service.

Murrumbidgee towns reflected the changing economic conditions of the period. Wagga, as the centre of a steadily developing mixed farming and grazing region, suffered little from ces-sation of the great stocking movements. From the eighties, it achieved added significance with its rail connections. Narrandera grew slowly but steadily as a railway town and minor regional centre. Hay developed as a prosperous river port in the sixties, but with the falling away in stock traffic in the seventies it lost some of its former significance. The railway in 1882 compensated in part at least for the loss of river traffic, and the town achieved stability as a centre serving the 'back block' areas, especially those to the northwest. Deniliquin and Moulamein were saved from probable decline by the railway connections with Victoria, and, like Hay, became effective regional centres.

A number of the other Riverina settlements such as Balranald, Oxley, Booligal, and Conargo failed, for a time at least, to fulfil earlier promises of development. Balranald subsequently received a new lease of life with a rail extension from Deniliquin in the 1920s.

Farther upstream, the towns of Gundagai, Queanbeyan, and Cooma experienced a slow, if unspectacular growth. Cooma suffered a minor set-back with the failure of Kiandra gold, but soon recovered and progressed steadily with the development of sheep-grazing on the Monaro. Adaminaby, badly hit by the Kiandra crash, reverted to a minor role as a sub-regional centre.

ADDENDUM TO PART IV: STATISTICAL SUMMARY 1861 TO 1874 WITH COMMENTS FOR 1880 TO 1884[3]

Note: Statistics for the Pastoral Districts are not available after 1874, and there follows a six year gap during which returns were collected in unsuitable units. From 1880, published figures are available for Electoral Districts, and where possible these have been extrapolated to give very approximate trends for the Pastoral Districts for the period 1880 to 1884.

Stock

County Murray

Sheep. There were fluctuations in numbers during the period 1861 to 1874, but there was a very slight overall increase from 199,000 to 251,000. The latter figure is still less than that for 1851 (267,000).

Cattle. The number of cattle dropped from 56,000 in 1861 to 23,000 in 1868 and then increased to 63,000 in 1874.

Monaro District

Sheep. There was a rapid and steady increase in sheep from 325,000 in 1861 to 1,038,000 in

---

[3]Based on figures extracted from New South Wales Statistical Registers.

1872, with a fall to 737,000 in 1874. Between 1880 and 1884 there was also a slight fall.

Cattle. Numbers fell from 145,000 in 1861 to 76,000 in 1868, building up again to 160,000 in 1874. Numbers fell rapidly between 1880 and 1884.

Murrumbidgee District

Sheep. The rapid increase in sheep evident before 1861 continued. Numbers rose from 708,000 in 1861 to 5,069,000 in 1874. Sheep numbers decreased between 1880 and 1884, but picked up again rapidly thereafter.

Cattle. Numbers decreased from 291,000 in 1861 to 191,000 in 1874. Numbers also fell between 1880 and 1884.

Lachlan District

Sheep. Following the same trend as in the Murrumbidgee District, numbers rose rapidly from 488,000 in 1861 to 4,291,000 in 1874. There was a fall between 1880 and 1884.

Cattle. After a sudden drop from 198,000 in 1861 to 75,000 in 1863, numbers rose again fairly steadily to 229,000 in 1874. As in the case of sheep, there was a fall between 1880 and 1884.

Cultivated Crops
County Murray

Wheat. Acreages rose steadily from 4900 in 1861 to 7500 in 1874; there was, however, only a slight increase in total yields.

Other Crops. As in the preceding period, the only other crop of any significance was hay, which showed no marked increase or decrease.

Monaro District

Wheat. Acreages and yields fluctuated slightly, but showed no marked trend either way. Acreage was 3100 in 1861 and 2700 in 1874. Between 1880 and 1884 there was a steady fall in both acreages and yields.

Maize. Although relatively unimportant in the fifties, there was a rise in acreage from 500 in 1861 to 4200 in 1874, with correspondingly increased yields. However, it would appear that most of this increase must have been on the coast, for the acreage in the Electoral District during 1880 to 1884 was small.

Murrumbidgee District

Wheat. Development was fairly rapid from 9000 acres in 1861 to 28,000 in 1874, with correspondingly increased yields. Both acreages and yields continued to rise rapidly between 1880 and 1884.

Other Grain Crops. Maize, barley and oats continued to increase between 1861 and 1874, but were very minor crops. They showed no significant trends between 1880 and 1884, and were still minor crops.

Hay. Mainly oats was grown for hay and areas increased from 2500 acres to 5800 acres between 1861 and 1874, and continued to increase between 1880 and 1884.

Lachlan District

Wheat. Acreages increased even more rapidly than in the Murrumbidgee District, rising from 2200 in 1861 to 12,000 in 1874. The rapid increase continued between 1880 and 1884.

Maize. There was an increase from an insignificant 170 acres in 1861 to 2600 acres in 1874. It was not important between 1880 and 1884.

Population

Population was not recorded in Pastoral Districts after the 1871 census. Comparative figures for the period are therefore restricted to the two censuses of 1861 and 1871.

County Murray

In 1861, the population was 6100 of which females comprised nearly half. The total rose to 7400 in 1871, sex ratios remaining fairly constant.

Monaro District

Of 9200 persons in 1861, between half and one third were females. There was a significant increase to 14,000 in 1871, the proportion of females remaining the same.

Murrumbidgee District

The population in 1861 was 12,900, one third being females. The number rose extremely rapidly to 25,000 in 1871, the female component rising slightly.

Lachlan District

The total in 1861 was 14,800, females comprising only one quarter. Of the 18,700 in 1871, more than one third were females.

Housing

Comparative figures are not available.

PART V: CONSOLIDATION OF SETTLEMENT 1884 TO 1912

By 1884, much of the present pattern of Murrumbidgee development, apart from irrigation, had been delineated. Stock routes, roads, railways, and towns in the eighties had functional relationships very similar to those of today. Such changes as have occurred since then have been concerned principally with intensification of development within the established framework, and in particular with closer settlement of the larger holdings.

The Crown Lands Acts of 1884 and 1889

The most significant developments may be traced, either directly or indirectly, to the Lands Act of 1884 [35], sometimes known as the *Division of Runs Act*. This is of particular interest because, in spite of violent opposition from vested interests, it reaffirmed the Government's confidence in the principle of closer settlement by small farmers at the expense of the large landholder. At the same time it side-stepped some of the more objectionable measures of the Robertson Acts, and experimented with new forms of legislation. The purpose of the Act was fourfold: to put a stop to wholesale alienation of land; to acquire large areas of land which could be made available for conditional purchase and settlement by small, resident landowners; to raise again the maximum area of conditional purchase blocks, already increased once by the Act of 1875; and to encourage settlement in the far-west by the establishment of an entirely new class, the small grazier.

Under the Act, the State was divided into three Divisions: Eastern, Central, and Western. The Eastern Division included the upper Murrumbidgee, the Central the western slopes and most of the Riverina, while the Western extended over far-western New South Wales, incorporating only a small part of the lower Murrumbidgee plains. The Act 'invited' lessees to divide their runs into two equal parts, and to surrender one of them to the Crown. In return, the lessee could apply for a new pastoral lease to cover the remaining part, with tenure fixed at five years for the Eastern Division, ten for the Central, and fifteen for the Western. Each case was to be considered on its merits. Should the Government decide that division was inexpedient, the part surrendered could be returned to the leaseholder, who would then enjoy the privilege of a new lease over the whole of his run. Technically the Act did not compel lessees to subdivide, but it was made clear that failure to do so would automatically disqualify them from further tenure on expiry of their current leases. In effect, then, the measure amounted to resumption of half all leasehold land, some of it, however, being returned to original run holders at Government option.

In the Eastern and Central Divisions, land acquired by the Crown was thrown open to Conditional Purchase at £1 an acre, payable by instalment. Eastern Division blocks remained within the range of 40 to 640 acres as determined by the 1875 Act [50], while in the Central Division the maximum was raised to 2560. In addition, in both Divisions, conditional leaseholds up to three times the purchase area could be applied for. Conditions of sale in these two Divisions included residence for at least five years, during the first two of which the whole block was to be fenced.

Land acquired in the Western Division was

not released for purchase, but made available under *Homestead Lease*. Areas here ranged between 5760 and 10,240 acres, tenure being fifteen years with the possibility of extension to twenty. Conditions included fencing within the first two years, and residence for at least six months in twelve during each of the first five years. This section of the Act was significant in that it was the first official acknowledgment that land in the far west was essentially grazing land, and quite unsuited in the long term to wheat growing. It opened the way to settlement by relatively small, resident pastoralists at the expense of the squatter, who often did not live continuously on his holding.

A number of minor amendments to this 1884 legislation were incorporated in the Act of 1889 [58], the most important being extension of leases in the Western Division from fifteen to twenty-one years. This was to encourage new pastoral development, for settlers were showing reluctance to establish under a system of short tenure.

Murrumbidgee Settlement Following the 1884 and 1889 Acts

These new enactments, while escaping the violent condemnation of the Free Selection Acts, were nevertheless much criticized. The general feeling of the times was summed up by Coghlan [46d], who remarked that the 1861 Acts 'conspicuously failed to encourage *bona fide* settlement; nor can it be said that the legislation of 1884 and 1889 succeeded'.

On closer examination, one senses the tendency, as with the 1861 Acts, to assess the results of the legislation by its deficiencies rather than its achievements. This, after all, must have been a natural reaction, for the defects were so very obvious, and were pounced upon only too readily by squatting interests whose land monopolies had suffered from the enactments. Critics have also been inclined to overlook the fact that the huge areas alienated prior to 1884, and therefore exempt from the provisions of the Acts, must have included a large proportion of the first class land originally available. It could hardly be expected that average returns from the newly acquired land would be as high as from the previously developed areas. Again, many of the blocks

thrown open to purchase were not applied for, and, being left unattended, rapidly deteriorated. A worse advertisement for the legislation could hardly be imagined than unkempt, idle blocks of land dotted here and there over the countryside. The conditions of the times were by no means propitious for new settlement, and aggravated these defects. Droughts during the eighties were the worst for many years. Rabbits for the first time assumed plague proportions, wreaking havoc in both cropland and pasture. And then, to add to all this, came the great economic depression of 1893.

All the worst features of this period were displayed in the Riverina, and particularly in the timbered areas north of the Murrumbidgee River. Numerous pockets of forest provided effective protection for rabbit burrows, and rabbits bred in thousands. Typical of the times were the experiences of the Barellan-Barmedman region [59] which up till then had proved most attractive to both pastoralists and free selectors. Rabbits appeared here first in 1885. Settlers were slow to react, and netting was not completed on most holdings until 1890, when it was already too late for preventive measures to be effective. Wheat farms were riddled with burrows, and pastures so depleted that stock had to be sent regularly to the neighbouring hills on agistment. Unclaimed conditional purchase blocks rapidly developed dense masses of scrub from secondary growth, and became ideal breeding grounds for rabbits which then spread into adjoining holdings. In this part of the Riverina, it was not until about 1910 that the pest was brought under some measure of control. South of the Murrumbidgee River, where there was less timber, rabbits were not so troublesome.

In view of these varied adverse circumstances, it is of great significance that of all the statistical areas in the State, the Murrumbidgee Electorate showed by far the greatest degree of development in the years following 1884 (see Fig. 5 and Addendum to Part V). The Electorate comprised most of the western slopes and both the eastern and central Riverina, including the Barellan-Barmedman region. Wheat acreages here increased no less than six times between 1884 and 1891, as compared with a mere 29 per cent increase for the State as a whole. After 1891, changed statistical

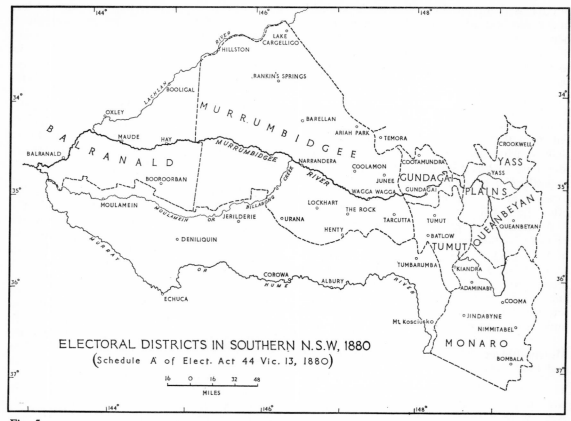

ELECTORAL DISTRICTS IN SOUTHERN N.S.W, 1880
(Schedule A of Elect. Act 44 Vic. 13, 1880)

Fig. 5

boundaries make the sequence difficult to follow, but one of the new Divisions that is at least partially comparable, the South-Western Slopes, showed a further threefold increase in acreage in the short period 1892 to 1895, stressing the phenomenal growth in farming settlement in the period 1884 to 1895. There were modest increases in wheat farming in a few neighbouring Divisions, but in most other parts of the State development during this period was either stagnant or negative. In fact, the upper Murrumbidgee was one region showing a decline.

It is obvious that any positive results achieved through the 1884 and 1889 enactments would have been most apparent in the case of subdivision of large holdings, particularly if these holdings included good farming land. Such holdings were outstanding in the Riverina, which was the home of the land monopolist. The fact, then, that the Riverina showed such rapid development of wheat farming settlement is in itself indicative of the success of the Acts in bringing about closer settlement. Except for the Western Division, the legislation was aimed primarily at stimulating *farming* activities, and therefore it is hardly surprising that stock development was not comparable with wheat. Nevertheless, over the period 1884 to 1891, both sheep and cattle increased steadily throughout the Murrumbidgee areas. After 1891 there was little development for some years, due in part to unfavourable markets.

It was essentially *wheatfarming* that dominated development trends in the central Murrumbidgee and eastern Riverina during the latter years of the century, and during this period the Murrumbidgee became established as one of the leading wheat-producing regions of Australia. Although the effects of the Free Selection Acts back in the sixties were considerable, it was the 1884 and 1889 Acts which were mainly responsible for bringing this about, for they resulted in the gradual ejection of the squatter from the areas physically suitable for wheatgrowing. From the nineties, pastoral monopolies were largely restricted to the areas in the Riverina receiving less than sixteen inches of rainfall. In view of Coghlan's reservations concerning the effectiveness of the 1884 and 1889 Acts, it is interesting to find his admission that:

. . . it is in the valleys of the Murray and Murrumbidgee that the struggle between selector and squatter has been fiercest, and where the most remarkable increase of agricultural settlement is now established [46b].

And again:

. . . we must look forward to that part of the country (the Riverina) as the future granary of New South Wales [46c].

Since most new settlement at this time was through Conditional Purchase, it would appear that, in spite of its faults, the 1884 and 1889 legislation proved remarkably effective in making development possible in the Murrumbidgee wheat farming areas.

A minor feature of the 1889 Act which was of some significance to the upper Murrumbidgee was the introduction of Snow Leases. For many years, settlers on the Monaro had been taking stock to the high mountain areas after the thaw in early summer, grazing them on the rich alpine pastures, and then removing them at the first sign of snow the following autumn. When the rabbit plague was at its worst in the Riverina, sheep from as far west as Barellan were sent to graze on the summer pastures of Tumut, Kiandra, and Kosciusko [59]. In order to place this activity under some form of control, Snow Leases were issued. For a nominal fee, pastoralists were authorized to graze stock on specified areas for a period of seven years, at the expiry of which another seven year tenure might be granted. Snow Lease grazing over the years has been responsible for burning out vast areas of alpine woodland, and for initiating soil erosion in the vital catchment

areas of the Murray and Murrumbidgee rivers. It was not until 1958 that complete restriction was imposed on snow grazing in areas more than 4500 feet above sea level.

Legislation and Murrumbidgee Settlement 1894 to 1912

The principal weakness of the 1884 and 1889 Acts arose from the fact that virtually all lessees were required to forfeit half their leasehold area to the Crown, and that embarrassingly large areas of this land remained unclaimed after being made available for conditional purchase. This idle land was of no use either to the former lessees or to the Crown, and became a serious liability. The lessee had his normal productive capacity reduced unnecessarily, and in some cases suffered hardship in consequence.

Under the Crown Lands Act of 1895 [60], this deficiency was rectified. The Crown still reserved the right to resume up to half the area of any leasehold in the Eastern and Central Divisions, but exercised this power only if land in a particular area was required for some specific settlement plan. The lessee affected could claim as his property any improvements on land taken over in this way, and in addition was compensated by an extension of the lease on the remainder of his holding proportionate to the area resumed. To avoid the possibility of land remaining idle even for a short period, the resumed land could be retained by the leaseholder under Occupation Licence until such time as it was actually taken over by a new settler.

It appears that the Acts of 1884 and 1889 were not sufficiently water-tight to prevent accumulation of enormous estates by a few entrepreneurs, backed by powerful financial institutions [46e]. In an effort to reduce this kind of speculation to a minimum, the 1895 Act introduced a radical change in the residence conditions. For original conditional purchases, the new Act required ten years residence, with a further term of five years for any additional purchases that might be made. These provisions had the effect of considerably reducing the transfer of conditional purchases—the factor most responsible for aggregation of holdings. In the Western Division, the

1895 Act provided for an absolute extension of seven years to leases, raising the total tenure to a maximum of twenty-eight years. A provision of the Act that had an immediate response concerned the lands already resumed but still unclaimed. These were once again thrown open to pastoral lease, and therefore came into production after years of idleness. Renewed control of these areas also helped to reduce the breeding of rabbits.

Wheatfarming in the Central Murrumbidgee and Riverina continued to expand very rapidly during the nineties. Between 1894 and 1900, the two statistical divisions of South-Western Slopes and Riverina accounted for approximately half the total increases of wheat acreages in New South Wales. Districts which showed very marked developments were those north and northwest of Wagga around Narrandera and Whitton, and south of the Murrumbidgee through Narrandera and Urana towards the Murray. There was also a concentration of settlement on the Lachlan between Hillston and Booligal, but much of this region proved marginal and suffered severely in the great drought of 1901. Between 1900 and 1912 the same general trends in wheat expansion continued, although at a somewhat reduced tempo in the areas west of the sixteen inch isohyet.

One of the most interesting features of the period was the remarkable increase in wheat yields in the Murrumbidgee wheat belt between 1898 and 1903. There was an understandable decline due to the 1901 drought, but apart from this yields rose steadily, increasing nearly three times in the South-Western Slopes Division, and seven times in the Riverina. Increase in the total area sown to wheat could have had very little bearing on this trend, for although wheat acreages continued to rise up to 1900, they fell rapidly for two or three years thereafter, the areas sown in 1903 being approximately equal to those in 1898. The first of the new Farrer wheats (Federation) was not released until 1901, and could have had no appreciable effect. Likewise, it was not until well after 1900 that superphosphate was used to any extent in New South Wales. In any case, if factors such as these were significant, their effects would not have been restricted to the Murrumbidgee. The explanation may be concerned with more efficient methods of farming. Prior to

1898 areas sown to wheat in this region had been expanding at an extremely rapid rate. For efficient production, new farms would have required clearing, erection of rabbit proof fences, and the installation of farm machinery —all of them time-consuming operations. Mechanized farming, pioneered in South Australia, was rapidly gaining ground in New South Wales in the nineties, and probably had a more immediate effect on production in the new farming areas than in other parts of the State where old fashioned methods had become established routine.

As in the eighties, wheatgrowing in the upper Murrumbidgee showed very little if any overall increase between 1880 and 1912. There was little inducement to cultivate in the cold and relatively wet lands of the Monaro, when conditions of climate and soils were so much more favourable down the river.

During this great development of the Murrumbidgee wheat belt, it is significant that pastoral development, as reflected by stock carried, remained relatively static in all Murrumbidgee regions from the Monaro to the Riverina. Lack of expansion should not, however, be interpreted as evidence of relatively low economic return. The fact is that development of both sheep and cattle had reached a very high order prior to the eighties, when wheatfarming for the first time really gathered momentum. Apart from a few Homestead Leases in the Western Division, closer settlement played a very small part in pastoral development. The explanation is simple. Taken as a whole, prior to 1884 the upper Murrumbidgee was already divided into runs that could give but little overall return from subdivision, and the few larger runs that survived were largely freehold. Down the river in the better areas of the Riverina, a large number of affluent pastoralists had alienated their holdings prior to 1884, in order to keep the free selector at bay. There was further aggregation into freehold during the eighties and early nineties on the part of vested interests, and after 1894 large holdings of good land suitable for closer pastoral settlement were largely unavailable without resorting to resumption.

Even to the present day the Riverina remains the home of the land monopolist. In excellent grazing country, with a rainfall from 13 to 17 inches, and with abundant sub-surface water, a property of 10,000 acres is regarded as small.

Economic Conditions and Pastoral Ownership

It has already been hinted that the struggle with the free selector had a serious crippling effect on the financial reserves of many individual pastoralists, and it has been inferred that in consequence many pastoral properties may have changed hands during the seventies and eighties. Whatever the vicissitudes of individual pastoralists, until 1884 at least there is no doubt whatever of the general prosperity of the wool industry. Production was good, prices were high, and there seemed no limit to opportunities for further development. There was, however, a most important change in pastoral economy between 1865 and 1900. Before free selection, comparatively little capital was required to operate even the largest of the Riverina stations. The need to alienate, following the 1861 Act, brought with it an immediate demand for capital, and in many cases pastoralists were compelled to seek this from external sources. The United Kingdom was only too ready to invest in New South Wales at this time, and between 1874 and 1890 provided £44 million of private capital [61], a large part of which went to the pastoral industry.

Fitzpatrick [62, 63] expresses the commonly held view when he relates this inflow of capital to a gradual change to bank ownership of pastoral properties. Butlin [64] disputes this, however, and claims that so-called 'company ownership' was in most cases merely the possession of property as collateral security held under mortgage. Whatever the true position, it is startling to note from Butlin's figures that land registered as company holdings in 1890 comprised 40 per cent of all holdings in the Central Division, and 50 per cent in the Western.

An outstanding case of complete company ownership was that of Yanga Station, near Balranald in the western Riverina [65]. In 1897, the English Scottish and Australian Bank sought and gained approval for the exchange of 36,000 acres of freehold in the New England region for the same area of Riverina Crown Land on Yanga Station. The reason given by the Bank for wishing to alienate the Yanga land was that it already owned property adjoining the Yanga blocks. In other words, the Bank wished to agglomerate vast areas of land into one Riverina freehold station, which, incidentally, included much of the fine 'flooded' country of the Lowbidgee. This proposition was finalized in spite of considerable opposition, both within the House and also in the Balranald area itself. A typical reaction was that of John Hudson [65]:

It would be a national sin and loss to futurity to barter land in this manner . . . it would be . . . playing into the hands of speculators . . . The fact is well known that no shareholders in the 'E.S. and A' Bank reside in this part of the globe.

Whether as owner or mortgagee, company investment in the Riverina did much to expand wool production there, and for a time returns to all concerned were generous. Prices rose steadily from 1868 to a peak in 1875, when wool fetched sixteen and one half pence per lb. in London. Then came the recessions which history has now shown to be typical of the Australian land industries. Prices fell; droughts, especially those of 1877, 1884 and 1892, caused hardship, rabbits accounting for a good deal of the pastures still remaining; the *Division of Runs Act* considerably curtailed workable assets; and, finally, the depression of 1893 added its burden to an economy already almost at breaking point. The eighties and nineties saw many foreclosures or surrenders of mortgaged Riverina stations, and the ruination of pastoralists who had over-extended their credit.

With the turn of the century emerged a new, much more balanced approach to station enterprise. The pastoral industry was learning the hard way; and the lesson it learnt was that in Australia, the land of extremes, both investment and returns must be averaged over many years if long term stability is to be achieved. In many ways this period of stabilization, interrupted by an unusually severe drought in 1901, was analogous to the years following the reckless Riverina expansion of the 1830s. The difference lay mainly in economic status. The earlier squatter was essentially an individualist, a capitalist dependent on his own resources. The pastoralist of 1912, although still of a

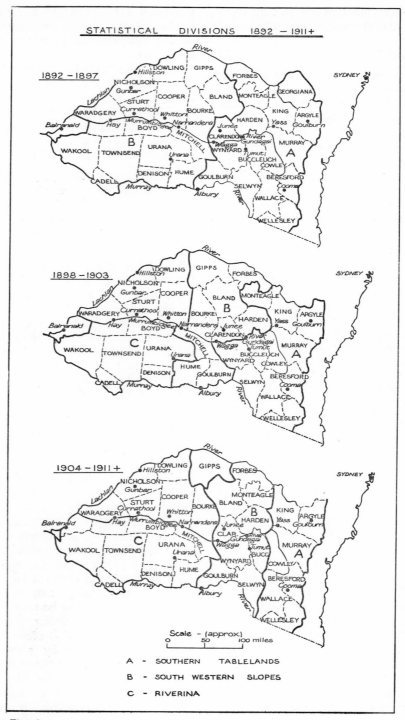

Fig. 6

markedly individual character, was more or less (according to the point of view) a servant of his creditors. Fitzpatrick [63] has said '. . . it was the pastoralist who did the work, the financier who got the money'. But the financier got by no means all the money. By 1912, the Murrumbidgee grazier, in common with many large scale graziers from other Australian regions, had established a pattern of life perhaps unique to newly developed countries. This involved a curious combination of hard and often disagreeable physical work with a form of gracious and sometimes luxury living that still savoured of the English landed aristocracy. On many large holdings, whether company owned or not, this pattern survives today.

ADDENDUM TO PART V: STATISTICAL SUMMARY 1884 TO 1912[4]

There were four changes in statistical areas during the period (Fig. 6) and an analysis of trends on a regional basis is therefore extremely complicated. All that is possible is a generalized commentary.

It should be noted that the official designations for Statistical Divisions during the period 1892 to 1897 are misleading. The so-called 'Southern Tableland' includes much of the western slopes of the ranges, and the 'South-Western Slope' is in reality nearly all *flat* country, being in effect the region traditionally known as Riverina, and including the Murrumbidgee inland plains.

In the following discussion, the regions used for locational purposes are by intent somewhat vague. They have been referred to as 'Upper and Central Murrumbidgee', and 'Western Slopes', and 'Riverina'. It can be assumed, however, that they approximate to the Statistical Divisions of 1904 to 1911, viz. 'Southern Tableland', 'South-Western Slopes' and 'Riverina' respectively.

Stock

Upper and Central Murrumbidgee

Sheep. During the period, sheep numbers varied somewhat from season to season, but overall the position was static. The decline already evident in 1884 continued until about 1886; from then numbers increased steadily to 1891. There was then a further decline, which continued, with fluctuation, to 1903. Very slight increases followed to 1911.

Cattle. As with sheep, cattle generally were static during the period. The decline evident in 1884 continued to 1886. Recovery, however, was rapid, with some notable increases to 1891. From then, numbers fluctuated to 1911, with a very slight decline.

Western Slopes

(From 1884 to 1897 trends are incorporated with the Riverina Region.)

Sheep. From 1898 to 1911 numbers fluctuated, with no very marked trend one way or the other.

Cattle. As with sheep, cattle numbers fluctuated from 1898 to 1911 without any marked trend.

Riverina

(From 1884 to 1897 trends include the Western Slopes.)

Sheep. From 1884 to 1891 the joint regions showed an approximate 60 per cent increase, which was followed by a decline to 1897.

This decline continued in the Riverina until 1899. In 1900 and 1901 numbers were higher, but there was a 50 per cent fall in 1902. This was followed by a rapid recovery, then a slow but fairly consistent increase to 1911.

Cattle. From 1884 to 1891 the trend for cattle in the joint regions closely followed that for sheep, numbers during the period being doubled. This was followed by fairly static conditions to 1897. The Riverina remained comparatively static from 1898 to 1902, in

---

'Based on figures extracted from New South Wales Statistical Registers.

which year numbers fell (as with sheep) by about 50 per cent. There was steady recovery to 1906; from then numbers fluctuated to 1911, without any obvious trend.

Cultivated Crops

Upper and Central Murrumbidgee

Wheat. The decline evident in 1884 continued, with seasonal fluctuations, to about 1891, the acreage in 1891 being about half that in 1884. There were marked seasonal fluctuations from then until 1911 without any definite trend either way.

Oats. The acreage of oats, which was recorded as negligible in 1884, remained fairly static from then until 1911. Oats attracted attention from about 1891 only because of the comparatively low acreages of other crops.

Hay. As with oats, hay attracts attention towards the turn of the century only because of low acreages of other crops. From about 1900, however, hay increased rapidly, and in 1911 the area sown was three times that of wheat for grain.

Western Slopes

(From 1884 to 1897 trends are incorporated with the Riverina.)

Wheat. From 1898 to 1903 acreages remained much the same, *but yields were trebled.* From 1904 to 1911 acreages fluctuated, but showed an overall increase of 70 per cent, while during the same period yields were doubled.

Oats. Acreages were very small compared with wheat acreages, but showed a steady increase from 1898 to 1911.

Hay. From 1898 to 1911, the acreages of hay remained at about 20 per cent to 25 per cent that of wheat for grain.

Riverina

(From 1884 to 1897 trends include the Western Slopes.)

Wheat. Wheat acreages in the composite region increased six times from 1884 to 1891, and more than three times from 1892 to 1897. From 1898 to 1903 Riverina acreages remained static overall *but production rose seven times.* Between 1904 and 1911 both acreage and production rose by 30 per cent.

Other Crops. Except for hay, other crops were relatively unimportant. Hay showed steady, if unspectacular increases, and by 1911 the area sown was about 20 per cent of that sown to wheat for grain.

Population

In the censuses of 1881 and 1891 population is recorded in Electoral Districts. In 1901 a start was made to record in Statistical Divisions, but this was discontinued. Analysis of general trends during the period is therefore of doubtful value. An interesting individual feature is the increase in the proportion of females in the Murrumbidgee District between 1881 and 1892; during this period the percentage rose from 37 to 41.

REFERENCES

1. PERRY, T. M. (1955) The Spread of Rural Settlement in New South Wales, 1788–1826. *Hist.Stud.Austr.and N.Z.*, 6, 377–395.
2. PERRY, T. M. (1957) Climate, Caterpillars, and Terrain. *Austr.Geog.*, 7, 3–14.
3. MEEHAN, J. *Memorandum . . . Made on a Tour . . . 3rd March to 14th April, 1818.* M.S. (Mitchell Library).
4. THROSBY, C. (1820) Letter to Governor Macquarie, Sept. 4, 1820, M.S. (Mitchell Library).
5. THROSBY, C. (1820) Letter in *Australian Magazine*, Vol. *1*, 60.
6. BLAND, W. (ed.) (1831) *Journey of Discovery to Port Phillip, New South Wales, by Messrs. W. H. Hovell and Hamilton Hume in 1824 and 1825.* A. Hill, Sydney, 6.
7a. STURT, C. (1833) *Two Expeditions into the Interior of Southern Australia*, Vol 2. Smith, Elder and Co., London, 13–29.
7b. *Ibid.* 35.
7c. *Ibid.* 48.

7d. *Ibid*. 49.

7e. *Ibid*. 59.

7f. *Ibid*. 223–4.

8. LANGFORD-SMITH, T. (1960) The Dead River Systems of the Murrumbidgee. *Geogr.Rev.*, *50*, 368–389.

9. BEADLE, N. C. W. (1948) *The Vegetation and Pastures of Western N.S.W.* Govt. Print, Sydney, 55–63.

10a. CAMPBELL, J. F. (1929) Squatting on Crown Lands in New South Wales. *Journ.and Proc. Roy.Austr.Hist.Soc.*, *15*, 93–120.

10b. CAMPBELL, J. F. (1931) Squatting on Crown Lands in N.S.W., Supplementary Paper, *Journ. and Proc.Roy.Austr.Hist.Soc.*, *17*, 43–86.

11. *Report of the Commissioner of Enquiry on the State of Agriculture and Trade in the Colony of New South Wales*. (J. T. Bigge), 1823, London.

12a. *Sydney Gazette and New South Wales Advertiser*, Sept. 6, 1826.

12b. *Ibid*., October 17, 1829.

13a. BAYLIS, J. J. (1927) The Murrumbidgee and Wagga Wagga. *Journ.and Proc.Roy. Austr.Hist.Soc.*, *13*, Part 1, 253–256.

13b. *Ibid*., Part 2, 294–304.

14. Bourke to Stanley, July 4, 1834. *Hist.Rec. Austr.*, Ser. *1*, *17*, 470.

15. An Act for Protecting the Crown Lands of this Colony from Encroachment, Intrusion, and Trespass, 1833. 4 Willm. 4.

16. Bourke to Glenelg, October 10, 1835. *Hist. Rec.Austr.*, Ser. *1*, *18*, 156.

17a. ROBERTS, S. H. (1924) *History of Australian Land Settlement*. Macmillan & Co., Melbourne, 57.

17b. *Ibid*. 182.

17c. *Ibid*. 169.

17d. *Ibid*. 230.

18. MITCHELL, T. L. (1839) *Three Expeditions into the Interior of Eastern Australia*, Vol. 2. T. & W. Boone, London, 271.

19. BRODRIBB, W. A. (1883) *Recollections of an Australian Squatter: Leaves from my Journal since 1835*. John Woods, Sydney, 17.

20. An Act to Restrain the Unauthorized Occupation of Crown Lands, 1836, 7 Willm. 4.

21. An Act further to restrain the unauthorized occupation of Crown Lands, and to provide the means of defraying the expense of a Border Police, 1839, 2 Vic. 27.

22. Proclamation of May 21, 1839. *N.S.W. Govt. Gazette, 418*, May 22, 1839.

23. KENNEDY, R. T. (1947) The Earliest Gundagai Medical Practitioners. *Journ.and Proc. Roy.Aust.Histr.Soc.*, *33*, 117–147.

24. HOBLER, G. Journal, M.S. (Mitchell Library).

25a. JERVIS, J. (1952) The Western Riverina: A History of its Development. *Journ.and Proc. Roy.Austr.Hist.Soc.*, *38*, Part 1, 1–30.

25b. *Ibid*. Part 2, 78–103.

25c. *Ibid*. Part 3, 127–150.

25d. *Ibid*. Part 4, 181–193.

25e. *Ibid*. Part 5, 235–244.

26a. *Sydney Morning Herald*. Feb. 22, 1847.

26b. *Ibid*. Dec. 9, 1875.

26c. *Ibid*. July 18, 1857.

26d. *Ibid*. July 30, 1856.

26e. *Ibid*. Sept. 13, 1851.

26f. *Ibid*. July 2, 1858.

26g. *Ibid*. Nov. 30, 1858.

26h. *Ibid*. Dec. 9, 1875.

26i. *Ibid*. July 14, 1875.

27. ROBERTS, S. H. (1931) The Australian Wool Trade in the Forties. *Journ.and Proc.Roy. Austr.Hist.Soc.*, *17*, 337–368.

28. Gipps to Stanley, Aug. 19, 1843. *Hist.Rec. Austr.*, Ser. *1*, *23*, 84.

29. An Act to give a preferential Lien on Wool, from season to season, and to make mortgages of Sheep, Cattle, and Horses valid, without delivery to the Mortgagee, 1843, 7 Vic. 3.

30. Gipps to Stanley, May 17, 1844. *Hist.Rec. Austr.*, Ser. *1*, *23*, 603.

31. WELLINGS, H. P. (1934) Benjamin Boyd in Riverina. *Journ.and Proc.Roy.Austr.Hist. Soc.*, *20*, 114–121.

32. Regulations of April 2, 1844. (Occupation Regulations). *Votes and Proc.Leg.Coun. N.S.W.*, 1844, Vol. 2, 4.

33. Regulations of April 3, 1844. (Purchase Regulations). *Votes and Proc.Leg.Coun. N.S.W.*, 1844, Vol. 2, 25.

34. Order-in-Council of Mar. 9, 1847. *Votes and Proc.Leg.Coun.N.S.W.*, 1847, Vol. *1*, 285.

35. Crown Lands Act, 1884. 48 Vic. 18.

36. New South Wales Archives (Mitchell Library).

37a. *New South Wales Government Gazette*, July 18, 1860.

37b. *Ibid*. Mar. 11, 1850.

38a. *Border Post*, Albury, April 4, 1857.

38b. *Ibid*. Mar. 21, 1857.

38c. *Ibid*. Jan. 3, 1854.

38d. *Ibid*. Oct. 11, 1856.

38e. *Ibid*. Jan. 3, 1857.

39. GORMLY, J. (1906) Exploration and Settlement on the Murray and Murrumbidgee. *Journ.and Proc.Roy.Austr.Hist.Soc.*, *2*, 34–43.

40. An Act for the better government of Her Majesty's Australian Colonies. Aug. 5, 1850.

41. *Back to Cooma*. Back to Cooma Executive Committee, 1926.

42. *Manifesto of the Land League of New South Wales*, April 26, 1859. F. Cunninghame, Sydney.

43. An Act for Regulating the Alienation of Crown Lands, 1861. 25 Vic. 1.

44. An Act for Regulating the Occupation of Crown Lands, 1861. 25 Vic. 2.

45. COGHLAN, T. A. & EWING, T. T. (1903) *Progress of Australasia in the 19th Century*. W. R. Chambers, London, 375.

46a. COGHLAN, T. A. (1892) *Wealth and Progress of New South Wales*. Govt. Print, Sydney, 238.

46b. *Ibid.* 299.

46c. *Ibid.* 290.

46d. COGHLAN, T. A. (1900-01) *Wealth and progress of New South Wales*. Govt. Printer, Sydney, 436.

46e. *Ibid.* 455.

47a. CLARK, C. M. H. (1955) *Select Documents in Australian History 1851–1900*. Angus and Robertson, Sydney, 95, 96.

47b. *Ibid.* 154.

48. BURTON, H. (1938) The Development of Australian Industry, in *Australian Economic Policies*. Australian Supplementary Papers, Series B, Aust.Inst.Internat.Affairs, Sydney, 1–17.

49. Report of Inquiry into the State of the Public Lands and the Operation of the Land Laws. (A. Morris and G. Ranken) May 2, 1883, Vol. *2*, 71.

50. An Act to Declare and Amend the Laws Relating to Crown Lands, 1875. 39 Vic. 13.

51a. MCFARLAND, A. (1872) *Illawarra and Monaro: Districts of New South Wales*. W. Maddock, Sydney, 124.

51b. *Ibid.* 102.

52. COGHLAN, T. A. (1918) *Labour and Industry in Australia*. Oxford University Press, Oxford, 1362.

53. Parliamentary Debates, New South Wales, 1881, Vol. *1*, 1303.

54. WRIGHT, P. P. Papers, M.S. (Mitchell Library).

55. Report of Chief Inspector of Stock. *Votes and Proc.Leg.Coun.N.S.W.*, 1870/71, Vol. *3*, 941.

56. *Ibid.* 1871/72, Vol. *2*, 53.

57. *Ibid.* 1882, Vol. *2*, 1386.

58. Crown Lands Act, 1889, 53 Vic. 21.

59. Gow and Gow's Quarterly Gazette, Barellan, Jan. 1924.

60. Crown Lands Act, 1895, 50 Vic. 18. See also Synopsis of Crown Lands Bill, 1894, *Votes and Proc.Leg.Coun.N.S.W.*, 1894/95, Vol. *3*, 1361.

61. HARRIS, H. L. (1927) The Financial Crisis of 1893 in New South Wales. *Journ.and Proc.Roy.Austr.Hist.Soc.*, *13*, 305–343.

62. FITZPATRICK, B. (1941) *The British Empire in Australia: An Economic History*. Melbourne University Press, Melbourne, 384–388.

63. FITZPATRICK, B. (1950) Note on 'Company Ownership' of N.S.W. Pastoral Stations, 1865–1900. *Hist.Stud.Austr.and N.Z.*, *4*, 111.

64. BUTLIN, N. G. (1950) Company Ownership in New South Wales Pastoral Stations, 1865–1900. *Hist.Stud.Austr.and N.Z.*, *4*, 89–111.

65. Exchange of Land on Yanga Station near Balranald, Oct. 7, 1897. *Votes and Proc. Leg.Coun.N.S.W.*, 1897, Vol. *3*, 607.

Government Irrigation and its Physical Environment

JOHN RUTHERFORD

Water is a key resource in economic development, especially when it is scarce relative to other inputs. The conservation of water, and its use for irrigation, domestic and stock needs have long been considered vital problems in Australia where a dearth of water hinders economic activity over vast areas, and where the variability of rainfall, even in humid zones, frequently causes serious setbacks to primary industries and urban development. With such a paucity of water supplies there is little hope that irrigated farming will occupy a large portion of the continent or contribute a major share of its gross national product. However, because of its labour-intensive character and high yields per acre irrigation has already played an important part in closer settlement, especially by encouraging relatively decentralized growth. This is especially true of the Southern Murray-Darling Basin which contains about eighty per cent of the nation's irrigated land; a region where irrigation farms are found mostly in group settlements embracing numerous farmers and set up with considerable assistance from State Governments. The present essay is concerned solely with these settlements and the water conservation projects that serve them; it seeks to outline their salient structural and locational features and so pinpoint the major ways in which their geography reflects regional differences in the impact of the physical environment on land settlement policies pursued by government.

By their aggregate size and volume of output the group irrigation schemes of the Southern Murray-Darling Basin (Fig. 1) overshadow all other water projects in Australia; yet, it is erroneous to identify the nation's irrigation solely with these largest schemes. Aside from a number of other group schemes on rivers outside the region under review, of growing importance in humid and drier parts of the continent are unit-farm projects developed by 'private diverters' with access to streams, or by farmers using other small water resources such as farm dams and bores. In many instances these single-farm projects are developed under licences or permits granted by the Crown and most of them have benefited from various types of government assistance, especially advice and financial aid [1]. Single-farm irrigation schemes are much more scattered than are the group projects discussed in this essay, mainly because they are locationally less-restricted by physical conditions, and because they depend on the initiative of individual farmers rather than on State action.

Group Irrigation and the Regional Structure of Economic Development in Australia

Rather than view them in isolation there is much to commend a study of the group irrigation schemes of the Southern Murray-Darling Basin as part of the regional structure of economic development in Australia. Of particular importance are the ways the structure has been moulded by policies implemented by State authorities—by 'State socialism' as it has been called [2]. The irrigation schemes of the Southern Murray-Darling Basin reflect a common feature of Western economic growth, i.e. the growing specialization of area [3], itself a manifestation of a highly-modified law of comparative advantage [4]. They take on a richer meaning when viewed as examples of the so-called structural and locational attributes of growth in technically advanced countries [5].

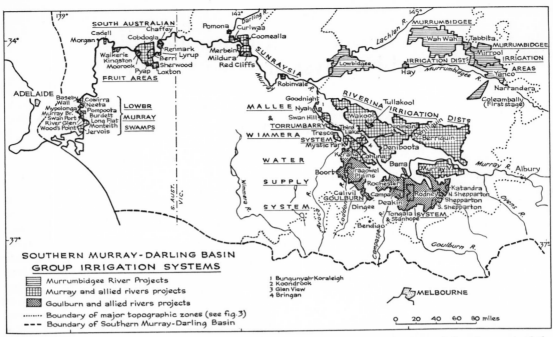

Fig. 1—(Adapted from the Department of National Development, *Resources and Development of the Murray Valley*, Vol. 2. D.N.D. Canberra)

Along with other farming regions of south-eastern Australia these group irrigation schemes have emerged as a result of important structural changes. In particular, the schemes are responses to the growing demand in Australia and abroad (especially in the United Kingdom) for foodstuffs such as milk and milk products, wool, sheepmeats and a wide range of fruits. In addition, Australian irrigation reflects profound changes in the character of agricultural supply as new forms of capital have been evolved and substituted for land and labour. The use of large quantities of conserved water for irrigation and the adoption of a complex range of improved systems of crop and animal husbandry are classic examples of the structural changes that typify Western societies.

As Philbrick [6] has stressed, it is important for the geographer to recognize complex functional regions, for example, the ways in which small, medium and large units of an economic system are connected to form a functional system. Economists proposing the so-called 'centre-periphery' thesis of growth [7] argue

that a useful approach to these functional regions recognizes salient locational attributes of change, i.e. rural development focussed on growing urban industrialized centres. In technically advanced societies each agricultural area becomes increasingly tied to core urban industrialized regions, both for the farming inputs (labour and capital) it needs and for the farm products it sells. In an open economy such as Australia it is usual for these ties to involve both overseas and domestic core regions. Most Australian farming areas are linked to common yet distant urban markets, notably those in the United Kingdom. Within Australia the same farming areas are linked to a number of widely-separated metropolitan regions which act as end and intermediate product markets for the farms.

The coastal metropolises of southeastern Australia, Sydney, Melbourne and Adelaide, are vital to the group irrigation schemes of the Southern Murray-Darling Basin because they act as important sources of ideas, money and goods moving onto irrigation farms and as major end-markets for things farmers sell [8].

These urban nodes are also the seats of State Government, and a striking feature of Australian agriculture is the extent to which farmers have long relied on State authorities to initiate and manage numerous forms of rural development, including the larger water projects. Close cooperation has existed between the Commonwealth and State Governments for the diversion of water from the Murray River under terms laid down in the River Murray Waters Agreement [9]. However, the decision how to use waters diverted from the Murray, the finest stream in southern Australia, or from rivers not subject to inter-State agreement has always been the prerogative of each State.

The socialistic character of larger water projects in southeastern Australia stems primarily from social pressures to underwrite closer settlements. The harsh physical conditions necessitated large-scale investment in water storage and reticulation as well as active centralized control over water use within projects. Competing users were then ensured of an adequate supply and equitable distribution of water. A high level of government participation in the water projects of the Southern Murray-Darling Basin has profoundly affected how they exhibit structural and locational attributes of Australian economic development. The following are some examples:

1. Much of the irrigation farming in the region has involved group or community schemes. Each scheme affects many farmers unless water supplies have made this difficult, as has been the case for streams of low and irregular flow or streams serving country of very uneven relief.

2. Whenever the occasion has permitted it group irrigation has been sponsored by the States with the expressed aim of underwriting closer settlement of the relatively dry arable farming regions of southeastern Australia. These settlements have aimed at maximizing opportunities for settlers with limited capital or previous farming experience (if any). Between 1910 and 1928 and for a time after 1945, large immigration and soldier-settlement programmes were associated with such projects.

3. State authorities centred in the three coastal metropolises of southeastern Australia have played major roles in shaping the location and social and economic structures of the various group irrigation projects. They have afforded much assistance to farmers especially through highly-centralized research and extension services, financial and other institutions. State and Commonwealth Governments have greatly influenced the availability of and farmers' participation in various markets at home and abroad, especially by promoting trade agreements and price-support schemes.

4. Through numerous economic, political and social ties, the major irrigation schemes of the Southern Murray-Darling Basin are grouped within three important regional structures ('matrices' of growth). Each structure is focussed chiefly on a single metropolis, though border zones are important where two or even three regional structures overlap. For example, irrigation communities in the Riverina of southern New South Wales are politically linked to Sydney yet owe much economic allegiance to Melbourne. Interstate competition is extremely keen in southern New South Wales, closer to Melbourne than to Sydney [10].

Irrigation and Zones of Production Uncertainty

A primary purpose of the group irrigation schemes of the Southern Murray-Darling Basin has been to achieve patterns of rural and urban development impossible without much more abundant and reliable water supplies than prevail under natural conditions. Initiated by forces centred in the three metropolitan centres, the water schemes of the Basin have emerged as a result of massive regional transfers of capital and human resources. The results have been striking examples of leap-frogging by land uses with pockets of intensive (irrigated) farming springing up in zones characterized by extensive, dryland farming. These pockets have developed well inland from the natural limits of comparable land uses closer to the seaboard. Leap-frogging of this type is a form of sequent occupance in which the frontier of each land-use system has not moved inland from coastal metropolises in a simple 'crest-of-the-wave' fashion. Marked discontinuities and multiple-nucleated patterns have occurred which are aberrations from simple normative models that arise especially because of the three-fold political division of the region and deliberate exploitation of only parts of lands naturally suited to irrigated farming.

The Southern Murray-Darling Basin occupies a strategic position since it embraces major parts of the hinterlands of the three port capitals of southeastern Australia. It also includes much interior country which has posed serious problems for land settlement as it has spread out from and has subsequently been linked to these port capitals. The main problems of the interior are, of course, climatic and production uncertainty. Although the hinterlands comprise uplands, peripheral slopes and better-watered plains that have proved to be relatively safe regions for the systems of land use established there, towards the north and northwest, the Southern Murray-Darling Basin includes much relatively dry country unsuited to closer settlement without irrigation. In the interior lowlands, a sub-humid to semi-arid climate is experienced by Riverine plain and Mallee areas, the scenes of numerous unsuccessful attempts to push unirrigated arable farming beyond the long-term no-rent margins. To the northwest, the plains include parts of the semi-arid country that skirts the Dead Heart of Australia; a belt whose outer boundary has fluctuated markedly over time with consequent hardship for rural settlers. Regional shifts of 'climatic years' have been documented for New South Wales [11], as have some of the problems of land settlement in the economically submarginal wheat regions greatly handicapped by these shifts [12].

Thus the Southern Murray-Darling Basin provides excellent examples of the climatic difficulties that have beset land settlement of the inland plains of southern Australia over the past 100 years. Much of these plains experience a variability of rainfall equal to or below the 'world standard value' for regions of comparable mean annual rainfalls [13]. Bearing in mind the kinds of farming made possible during years of average or above-average rainfalls, it is obvious that the Basin contains lowlands with a high degree of climatic uncertainty.

Except in restricted upland areas and other small regions, where low temperatures during winter are a handicap for some crops, rainfall is the most critical element of climate in the Southern Murray-Darling Basin, as it is for Australia at large [14]. In common with North American lands of similar economic development, if somewhat different terrain and climate, the Basin experiences climatic uncertainty that is the compounded result of three major components: a highly variable timing of rainfall, a highly uncertain geographic spread of rainfall, and the tendency for like seasons to bunch into sequences of very irregular length. These conditions of production uncertainty have produced in this Australian region problems of maladjusted land settlement very similar to those experienced in the western half of the U.S.A. [15].

A zone of particular climatic uncertainty flanks the present day interior (arid) margin of commercial wheatgrowing. It will be seen from Fig. 2 that the group irrigation schemes of the Southern Murray-Darling Basin occupy strategic positions in relation to marginal wheat regions, here distinguished by major statistical units. These uncertain regions (unstable for cereals such as wheat and for allied forms of land use such as meat production from sheep and cattle) include the western Riverina and lower Western Statistical Divisions of New South Wales, the northwestern parts of the Northern and Mallee Divisions of Victoria, and much of the Murray-Mallee of South Australia. Closer settlement for arable farming based on 640-acre or 320-acre properties has been tried and has failed beyond the present day inland wheat margin (compare Figs. 2 and 9). In addition, tremendous stock losses have been suffered by the more extensive system of Merino woolgrowing which occupies the region in the northwestern corner of the Southern Murray-Darling Basin.

Over the years, farmers have adjusted to production uncertainty in the interior lowlands of southeastern Australia, both by adapting to, and by modifying, their physical environment. Adjustments include, contractions of closer settlements from submarginal zones, increases to farm sizes (both within and beyond the limits of closer settlement), and changes in production techniques to make crops and livestock less vulnerable to climatic hazards. However, the effects of the drought of 1965 made it very evident that the region is still vulnerable. The general run of farmers have adopted a number

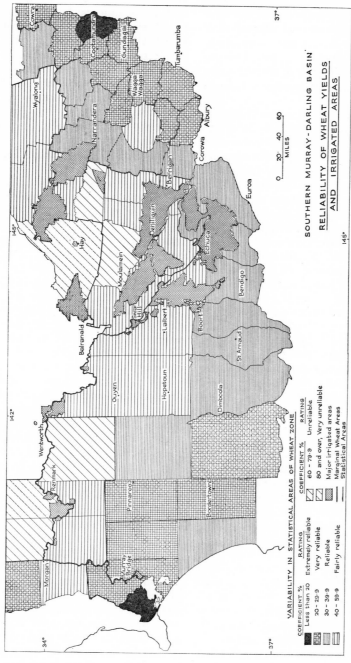

Fig. 2—(Data on wheat yields from the Bureau of Agricultural Economics, Canberra; and Dunsdorfs, E. (1950) *The Australian Wheat-Growing Industry 1788-1948.* Melbourne University Press, Melbourne

of carefully-developed adaptations to semi-arid regimes [16]. However, during a long run of good seasons, such as between 1946 and 1956, some farmers in the drier sections of the wheat belt adjusted the timing and character of their sheep enterprise to the earlier and more abundant growing seasons then prevalent. This increased their vulnerability when normal years of later and less-abundant growing seasons returned.

A key problem of production uncertainty in the interior lowlands of the Southern Murray-Darling Basin is the common incidence of a single growing season from April to November followed by a period of dormancy for plants during the hot months. This greatly restricts the range of production possibilities under rainfall and limits the scope for enterprise diversification. A key aim of irrigation has therefore been to enhance the normal autumn to spring production period, especially for sheepraising, or to permit production during the hotter months from spring to autumn, thus reversing the seasonal character of production in the region. The latter is very characteristic of fruit-growing and dairying.

Irrigation can be used to establish widely different types of farming. For instance a system of irrigation supplying enormous amounts of moisture could be employed to displace dryland systems of production entirely, or it could be used to aid rather than displace dryland techniques. It is, however, not fully recognized that a decision in favour of one pattern of investment poses important problems related to opportunity costs, i.e. the returns that could have been achieved by adopting the best of the available alternative lines of investment.

As in many parts of the world, group irrigation schemes in the Southern Murray-Darling Basin have often been used to promote resource development. Under political pressures for new farming opportunities, and influenced by value systems which place a high esteem on relatively small-scale farms, irrigation in the region has been employed in many instances to promote fruitgrowing, dairying, vegetable and rice production in closer settlements more or less divorced from, and with very different patterns of rural and urban development to, adjacent dryland economies. These closer settlements would be impossible

without irrigation sufficient to at least double or treble moisture supplies available from rainfalls in the average growing seasons. Frequent corollary developments have been politically-contrived systems of 'cheap' water supplies in which direct beneficiaries are charged rates barely sufficient to cover district running costs, and capital costs are a charge on the State. Most of these settlements have also depended on active government intervention to give irrigators accesses to markets for their factors of production and products that they would not otherwise enjoy.

Although their interest in, and political pressures for, irrigation facilities have varied with the seasons, farmers on broad acres have participated in systems of group irrigation. Especially is this true of wheatgrowers and pastoralists running sheep for wool and meat. Irrigation systems of the group type first evolved in northern Victoria with the establishment of ninety Irrigation and Water Supply Trusts between 1886 and 1905. These Trusts arose from a majority request of the dryland farmers concerned. They depended greatly on local farmer initiative and their operation was essentially under the control of the farmers affected, although the State supervised their development and provided the major enabling-works for water conservation and reticulation to districts. Most of these Trusts failed and were taken over by the State Rivers and Water Supply Commission in 1906. Similar systems of irrigation to aid dryland farming emerged in southern New South Wales between 1935 and 1955 by the development of Irrigation Districts such as Berriquin, Wakool, Denimein, Deniboota, Wah Wah, and Benerembah. Projects such as these have been much more affected by State controls than were the earlier Victorian Trusts. However, in both States, the essential aim was to promote *partial* irrigation of dryland properties to aid sheepraising or mixed cereal-growing and sheepraising, rather than to displace dryland systems of production with enterprises impossible under existing rainfall. Victorian authorities have not been very sympathetic to this form of development over the past sixty years and, in recent times, authorities in New South Wales have expressed their disapproval of the so-called 'District' mode of development [17].

Intensive and Extensive Irrigation Compared

Any discussion of the geography of irrigation in the Southern Murray-Darling Basin cannot overlook an important politically-contrived division of projects, especially important to regional patterns throughout the interior lowlands. Though they fall along a continuum, there tends to be a well-recognized distinction between *intensive* irrigation schemes on the one hand and *extensive (partial)* irrigation schemes on the other hand. In New South Wales, the distinction is emphasized in project names. All *intensive* irrigation tends to occur in 'Irrigation Areas'; whereas most *extensive* irrigation occurs in so-called 'Irrigation Districts'. The problem is confused however because, in Victoria all schemes are called 'Districts', and in South Australia all schemes are called 'Areas'.

Most *intensive* irrigation, both on the Riverine plain and in the Wimmera-Mallee zone, is to be found in projects developed by very active State socialism, including the resumption by the State of dryland farms and their subdivision into relatively small family farms geared to artificial water supplies well in excess of rainfall. The system is basic to most fruitgrowing and dairying on the lowlands, yet it is also of some importance for fat lambraising and ricegrowing in selected areas. In short, *intensive* irrigation is to be associated with massive State closer settlement schemes and the large water conservation and reticulation systems feeding them.

The bulk of the *extensive* irrigation on the plain occurs in projects that were not initially closely settled. On the whole, State enterprise has been limited to bringing water supplies to the boundaries of existing dryland properties and to supervising the continued supply of water and to promoting any land drainage schemes that have emerged. Though *extensive* irrigation schemes have relied on a great deal of State help in the matter of water supply, they have not been affected to any extent by State-promoted closer settlement. In fact, it was not the initial intention of authorities to supply water in order to alter patterns of dryland farming; on the contrary, early aims were to stabilize and enhance this farming. However, following the provision of limited facilities for irrigation, and a growing appreciation by farmers of the value of irrigation, general pressures to close-settle many of the old *extensive* irrigation schemes have occurred. Systems of *extensive* irrigation are found only on the Riverine plain, but they occur in both Victoria and New South Wales. In these States, programmes to intensify land uses in *extensive* irrigation areas have been associated with pressures for water supplies superior to those on which the schemes were first designed. In the long run this has given rise to serious problems of water supply and, in some instances, to problems of uncoordinated land drainage. Political reactions to these and other problems have recently led to a reversion to *intensive* irrigation methods in New South Wales [18].

THE GEOGRAPHIC PATTERN OF GROUP IRRIGATION AND ADJOINING FARMING

As stressed in Fig. 3, the landscapes of the Southern Murray-Darling Basin can be divided into three major zones: peripheral uplands, riverine plain, and Wimmera-Mallee lowlands. Each zone has a distinctive physical geography and mode of economic development. Briefly, it is evident that conditions of climate and terrain have not been conducive to group irrigation schemes in the peripheral uplands but these regions are the major source of water to serve the needs of the interior lowlands. The main

water conservation projects are located in the Eastern Highlands on the Murray, Murrumbidgee and Goulburn rivers. We have noted key problems of climatic uncertainty in the interior lowlands and the promotion of large group irrigation schemes here has been a main line of attack on these problems. Related systems of water supply for domestic and stock purposes have also been used. Not only have these works allowed land uses impossible without irrigation but, as typified by the Victorian

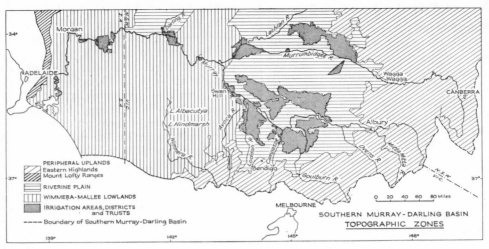

Fig. 3

Mallee, they have promoted intensities of dry-land settlement impossible under rainfall alone.

The combination on the riverine plain of specific conditions of relief, surface water supplies and soils has encouraged a pattern of water projects characterized by a widespread delivery of water by gravity in open earthen channels. Relatively cheap water supplies that have resulted from this permit a wide range of irrigated land uses in five riverine sub-sections of the plain. By contrast, physical conditions in the Wimmera-Mallee zone have meant that most group irrigation is concentrated along one stream, the Murray River, and it is confined to a relatively narrow range of products in small compact group irrigation schemes located close to the river. These Murray-Mallee schemes are mostly supplied by pumps. The contrasts between the riverine plain and Wimmera-Mallee zone form a major interest of this essay and are emphasized by a comparison of Figs. 1, 3, 8 and 9.

Peripheral Uplands

The Southern Murray-Darling Basin is flanked in the east, south and west by highlands. To the east and south, these peripheral uplands are the southern extremity of the Eastern Australian Highlands and, for the purposes of this discussion, are termed Eastern Highlands.

The Eastern Highlands have several key features for the present essay. Firstly, they are the main sources of water used in the water projects of the interior lowlands. Secondly, with the notable exception of limited alpine areas with low winter temperatures, the Eastern Highlands have climates conducive to year-round and reasonably safe rural production. Hence, there is relatively little need for large-scale irrigation or for developing a permanent link with other rural areas (as happens with some upland areas, such as those of the western U.S.A.). However, while climate poses less need for irrigation, and broken relief rules out large water supply schemes, many farmers in the peripheral uplands are finding value in unit-farm irrigation to supplement rainfall. Also, in some regions problems of great seasonal ranges of temperature impose systems of transhumant grazing [*19*]. Because of climatic uncertainty there are, on the whole, no serious maladjustments of land settlement, chiefly because the difference between short- and long-term climatic experiences is not great in the peripheral uplands.

The Eastern Highlands trend southward in New South Wales, and turn sharply at the southern border to trend westward across central Victoria, terminating in the Grampian Ranges. Astride of the border between the two States these highlands include the only truly alpine regions of the continent, forming a relatively small belt of high country generally 3000 to 6000 ft. above sea level and reaching the

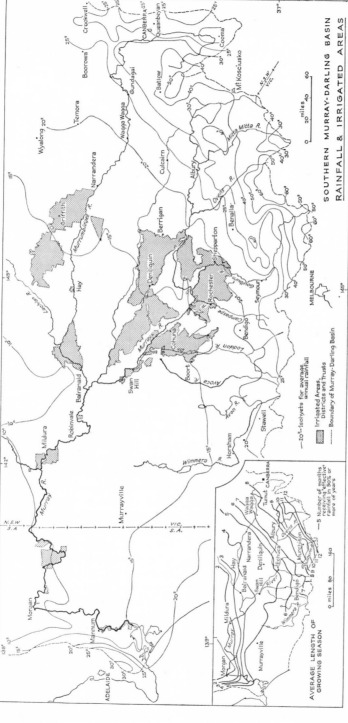

Fig. 4—(*Source*: Department of National Development (1947) *Resources and Development of the Murray Valley*, Vol. 2. D.N.D., Canberra)

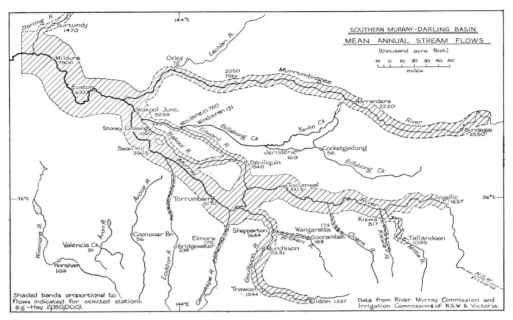

Fig. 5

maximum elevation of 7305 ft. at Mount Kosciusko. Much of the Eastern Highlands is dissected plateau little more than 2000 ft. a.s.l. A striking feature of the country is a 'gorge-and-basin' relief where river valleys often form a sequence of alternating gorges and basins. Later discussion stresses the hydrological significance of this. The junction between the Highlands and riverine plain occurs at about 500 ft. a.s.l. in New South Wales and 625 ft. a.s.l. in Victoria [20].

The Western Highlands are of little significance to the present discussion primarily because they do not form catchments for streams draining onto the interior lowlands.

As stressed by Fig. 4, the peripheral uplands are the wettest parts of the Southern Murray-Darling Basin, peak falls occurring in the alpine areas of the southeast where rains up to eighty inches per annum are recorded in the average year. Most of the uplands experience average rainfalls in excess of twenty-five inches and leaving aside problems of winter temperature stress, a growing season from autumn to spring and lasting more than nine months is commonplace. The bulk of the moisture supplies of the uplands are derived from the interaction of air-masses moving across southern Australia from

west to east. The interaction is accentuated by local orographic effects to produce relatively high falls on high windward-slopes and frequent 'rainshadow' areas in sheltered basins.

Two major characteristics of rainfalls on the Eastern Highlands have great hydrological significance for water schemes in the Southern Murray-Darling Basin. Firstly, there is a marked tendency towards a winter maxima. Snow cover and alpine bogs produce some delayed run-off but not sufficient to give the double-maxima river flows found in some highlands regions of the world. Secondly, the most elevated highlands astride of the border between New South Wales and Victoria tend to have the highest and most reliable rainfalls. Less elevated uplands, especially to the north and west of the alpine core region, experience lower and less reliable rainfalls.

All the streams of the Southern Murray-Darling Basin rise in the Eastern Highlands but although they travel long routes they are puny by world standards. All the streams can also be classified as perennial, yet they suffer from low run-off. The average annual run-off from the uplands of the entire Murray Basin (408,000 square miles and embracing much country to the north of the region under review) is only

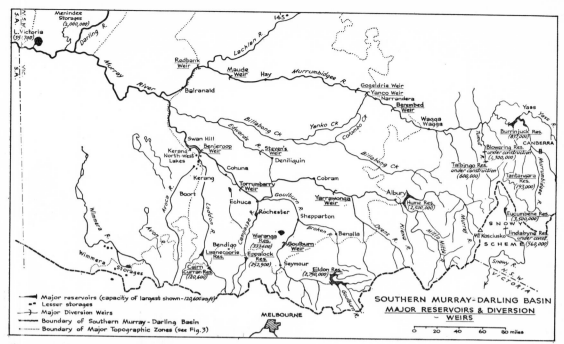

Fig. 6—(Adapted from Department of National Development, (1947) *Resources and Development of the Murray Valley*, Vol. 2. D.N.D., Canberra)

nineteen million acre feet. The alpine areas receiving an average of sixty inches or more of rain experience a mean annual run-off of about thirty inches. The balance of the uplands, with average annual rainfalls of more than twenty inches, experiences an average annual run-off of between two and ten inches per year [21].

Stream flows from the Eastern Highlands vary greatly from season to season and from year to year, due largely to the fact that the typical river basin comprises a relatively small upper catchment and a large lower region with little or no run-off [22]. Rivers rising in the alpine regions of 4500 or more ft. a.s.l. have the greatest and most reliable flows and this accounts for the dominance of the three streams of alpine yet relatively large catchments, i.e. the Murray, Murrumbidgee and Goulburn rivers (Fig. 5). Smaller streams of alpine origin, such as the Ovens and Mitta Mitta, are of much less significance primarily because of limited catchment areas. Other streams, such as the Lachlan in New South Wales and the Campaspe, Loddon, Avoca and Wimmera in Victoria, suffer from relatively low and variable flows mainly because limited upland catchments experience low and erratic rainfalls. Little wonder that the chief sites for the largest dams in southern Australia occur on the Murray, Murrumbidgee and Goulburn rivers (Fig. 6).

Peak 'natural' flows in all streams of the Southern Murray-Darling Basin occur during and immediately after the winter rainy season. However, the season of greatest water need, and therefore of greatest artificial diversion to meet this need, is the spring-autumn period. This strategic lack of coincidence between the season of stream flow and the season of maximum water reticulation to the interior lowlands is emphasized in Fig. 7. It is a key reason why relatively large headwater structures to store water from the winter until the following summer have been a minimum pre-requisite of large-scale irrigation of the interior lowlands. Even larger structures, storing water during floods for later use, have become necessary to bridge the years. Seasonal and yearly variations of stream flow are key reasons why water conservation has proved so costly in southern

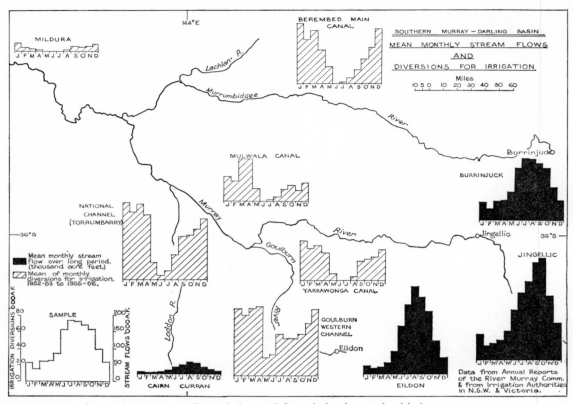

Fig. 7—(Data from River Murray Commission and State irrigation authorities)

Australia. Added to this is the need to divert water over long distances to serve the dry interior lowlands, and the necessity to maintain a relatively high ratio between headwater storage on the one hand and irrigation need on the other. Herein are important explanations for the degree of State socialism associated with major water projects in southern Australia [23].

The new Eildon Dam in Victoria [24] illustrates the type of carry-over headworks now developed on the three key streams of the Southern Murray-Darling Basin. This dam is comparable in many respects to the enlarged Hume and Burrinjuck dams (Fig. 6). An original dam at Eildon, storing some 306,000 acre feet, was built early this century to allow closer settlement schemes in the Goulburn Irrigation System after 1910. Rapid increases in farmers' demands for water (associated both with closer settlement and a growing awareness of the merits of irrigation) tended to accentuate problems of water shortage experienced during

the major droughts between 1938 and 1945. This influenced the Victorian Government's decision to erect a larger structure at Eildon.

The original Eildon Dam was first filled to capacity in 1927 and it had the modest aim of storing winter and spring flows for use throughout the Goulburn System during the subsequent dry summer and early autumn. The new Eildon Dam was completed in 1956 and has a maximum storage capacity of 2,750,000 acre feet. It is a large structure designed to achieve much more than an ironing out of the fluctuations of river flows in any year. A key aim is to store surplus waters in rainy years to meet needs during later dry years. Its erection meant a doubling of total storage capacities of all Victorian reservoirs and a doubling of the water available to the Goulburn Irrigation System. The highland catchment of the new Eildon Dam covers some 1500 square miles of country experiencing average annual rainfalls of between 30 inches (Eildon) and 80 inches

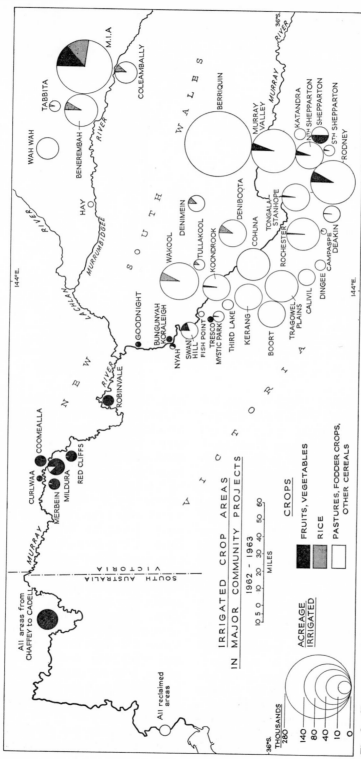

Fig. 8—(Pastures are here classed as crops)

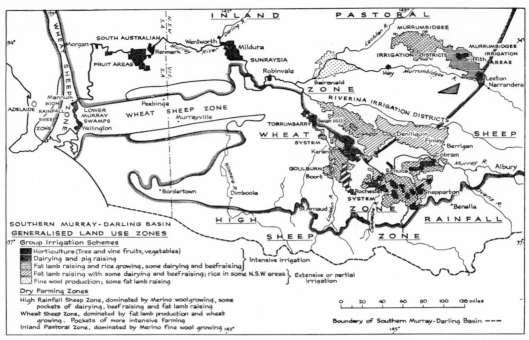

Fig. 9—(Adapted from fieldwork and Department of National Development, *Resources and Development of the Murray Valley*, Vol. *2*. D.N.D., Canberra)

(Mount Buller). Although Eildon Dam has gone a long way towards ensuring permanent supplies of water to the interior plain and Mallee served from the Goulburn River, there is still need for the greatest care in distribution and on-farm use of water, as was demonstrated during the drought of 1965. However, the new Eildon Dam serves to iron out much of the normal fluctuation of flow in the Goulburn River. The average flow at Eildon is about 1,425,000 acre feet, yet this previously varied from as high as 3,350,000 acre feet in 1917 to as low as 450,000 feet in 1938.

The siting of the large headworks of the Southern Murray-Darling Basin (Hume Dam on the Murray River, Eildon Dam on the Goulburn River and Burrinjuck Dam on the Murrumbidgee River) reflects a typical compromise between various physical and economic variables. Each dam exploits gorge-like terrain of the 'fall' zone between the Eastern Highlands and the riverine plain. Location of a dam in a natural gorge or narrow valley ensures maximum upstream storage for a given cost per cubic foot of storage wall. In each

case, a suitable site as close as possible to the irrigable lowlands has been chosen to minimize the distance between the site and points of major water diversion, and also to ensure maximum upstream catchment. Although hydrological conditions in southeastern Australia tend to make major water conservation an expensive task, calling for corporate action of a scale only to be tackled by government enterprise, the region is favoured by two factors. Firstly, the sudden change of gradients between peripheral upland and riverine plain. Secondly, the very rapid change from relatively well-watered uplands in the east and south to the much drier lowlands to the north and west. These conditions make for juxtaposition of water-surplus and water-deficit areas, though Victoria is much better-endowed in this respect than is southern New South Wales. In the latter region, it is necessary to take water relatively long distances from upland storages to points where it can be used most effectively on the riverine plain.

Whilst nature has provided relatively abundant surface water resources in the Eastern

Highlands of the Southern Murray-Darling Basin, a variety of political, social and economic factors has determined the timing and character of the use of these resources. Physical conditions pose the possibility of major dams on the three finest streams of southeastern Australia. These physical conditions alone don't explain why, nor all aspects of how, this development has taken place. In particular, they don't explain why Australians have actively developed these southern water supplies over the past century when more abundant resources in northern Australia have only just begun to be mapped and developed. Certainly, a key reason for water projects on the Murray, Murrumbidgee and Goulburn rivers is that they permit active closer settlement of important elements of the three leading regional structures of economic growth in Australia. As Tisdall [25] has stressed, there has been a natural tendency for State authorities in southeastern Australia to concentrate first on the easiest and most fruitful sites for headwater storages, then gradually to move into more difficult and less-abundant sites. More recent work on Eppalock Reservoir is an example of the latter.

Riverine Plain

As shown in Fig. 3, the riverine plain of southeastern Australia lies inside of the Eastern Highlands and to the east of the Wimmera-Mallee lowlands. With its upland flanks at between 500 and 650 ft. a.s.l. the plain slopes gently to the northwest to a mean elevation there of about 100 ft. a.s.l. The longitudinal gradients of the plain (Fig. 10) are generally from south to north over much of northern Victoria, but swing to an east-to-west direction in Victorian country flanking the Murray and in much of southern New South Wales. These gradients are very slight, ranging from about four feet to the mile near the Eastern Highlands to as little as one foot per mile in the extreme northwest. At Kerang in northern Victoria, the average northern gradient is about twenty feet in fourteen miles. Transverse gradients are also slight but diminish with increasing distance from the upland. At Kerang the transverse gradient from 'high' plain towards the shallow defiles of Calivil and Pyramid creeks is only six feet in sixteen miles [26].

As stressed by Fig. 4, the riverine plain receives moderate moisture supplies from rainfall. Average annual rainfall of about twenty to

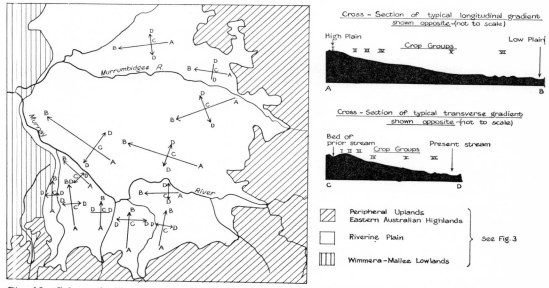

Fig. 10—Schematic illustration of longitudinal and transverse gradients of surface of riverine plain, and typical crop groups under sound irrigation. Crop groups are: I = Citrus; II = Peaches; III = Lucerne and Apricots; IV = Perennial Pastures, Pome Fruits, Vines and Vegetables; V = Annual Pastures, Fodder Crops and Paspalum; VI = Rice and other cereals

twenty-five inches on the upland flanks declines to about ten inches over much of the north-western corner. Isohyets tend to parallel the Eastern Highlands in New South Wales but this is less true of northern Victoria. Growing seasons on the upland flanks of the plain are between five and nine months, sufficient to support dryland closer settlement based on broad-acre cerealgrowing and associated sheepraising. However, semi-aridity enforces more-extensive farming for fine wools in the northwest. Reliability of rains tends to be closely correlated with total rains, and therefore diminishes towards the northwest, although as was stressed earlier, the economic and social repercussions of unreliability of rainfall tend to be felt most acutely along the arid margins of each land-use area. This is especially so between the wheat belt and the inner pastoral belt, because it is in such margins of transference that maladjusted forms of settlement are most likely to arise.

At first sight the riverine plain seems featureless except for occasional hills; yet, closer inspection reveals numerous forms of relief, many of which have had major effects on the layout and mode of development of water projects. For example, a number of macro-relief forms have greatly determined the economic locations and shapes of water supply channels and irrigation districts, as the following examples indicate:

1. In parts of the plain outcrops of bedrock occur as low hills; a good example is the Terricks Range, between the Loddon and Campaspe rivers in northern Victoria, which delimits the eastern edge of the Tragowel Plains Irrigation District making up sections of the Goulburn Irrigation System. Such outcrops cannot readily be commanded by the gravity systems typical of the plain.

2. Between Echuca and Deniliquin in southern New South Wales occurs the Cadell Tilt Block [27] producing steeper than usual gradients on the plain. Such gradients cause a break between the Berriquin and Deniboota irrigation districts, as well as a major diversion in the course of the Murray River in this region.

3. As streams flow out across the plain they tend to form braided channel patterns, the complexity of the drainage increasing with increasing distance from the highlands. Streams flow generally northwards in Victoria, but westwards along the Murray and in southern New South Wales. River frontage land (locally termed 'black' or 'lignum' country from its soils and vegetation) tends, therefore, to be relatively uneven and subject to flooding from streams, hence, it is difficult to irrigate. Where this river-frontage land is irrigated, holdings tend to be large and given over to *extensive* irrigation.

4. In northwestern Victoria, in a triangle between Kerang, Boort and Swan Hill, the country is broken by frequent lakes or salt pans and associated dunes (lunettes). The latter occur typically on the eastern edge of each depression [28]. Though some dunes have been developed for irrigation, on the whole much of this Northwest Lakes Region is difficult to command by relatively compact systems of gravity water supply and remains undeveloped except for dryland farming.

One vital topographic feature of the riverine plain is the asymmetrical pattern of streams, many of which act as sources of water or as outfalls for irrigation and other water projects. The regional pattern of streams has a strong influence on the pattern of water development, especially as it shows strong accordance with micro-relief (see below). There is a natural conformity between longitudinal gradients and directions of stream flow over the plain. As a result, the general direction of stream flow is from south to north in Victoria south of the Murray River, and from east to west along and north of the Murray River.

It has been stressed elsewhere [29] that there is an intimate association on the riverine plain between regional variations of soils, micro-relief, vegetation, and the suitability of land to various forms and intensities of irrigation. The present discussion seeks to clarify this relationship in a broader context than that of the earlier review. Much of the present day surface materials of the plain are derived from deposits laid down by prior streams. There has also been aeolian activity, both to resort alluvial deposits and to bring in materials ('parna') from the west. It is now recognized by Butler, Langford-Smith, and other workers [29] that the plain can be divided into 'high', 'intermediate' and 'low' elements according to small yet vital differences of elevation and associated natural features. The country flanking the Eastern Highlands (Fig. 10) is dominantly 'high' plain, consisting of coarse-textured and well-drained materials laid down by prior streams as they suddenly changed gradients on debouching from the uplands. This country is now dominated by the great soil group, red-brown earths. Further inland, between levee-like deposits of red-brown earths, and ultimately dominating the whole landscape, is 'low' plain formed originally as the floodplains of the prior streams but now composed of grey and brown relatively low-lying, heavy-textured soils. In the transitional country between these two great soil groups, i.e. regions between true 'high' plain and true 'low' plain, it is common to find interlacing strips of the two types of land. For example, in the country served by the western parts of the Goulburn Irrigation System in the southern parts of the Boort and Tragowel Plains irrigation districts and in the Calivil Irrigation District, long narrow strips of 'high' plain trend from south to north and are separated by strips of 'intermediate' and 'low' plains (Fig. 11).

The old beds of prior streams usually occur on 'high' plain and are nominated in soil surveyors' reports as 'high level depressions'. The occurrence on 'high' plain means that the old beds are usually in the interfluvial areas between present day streams, though this is not always the case. Fingering out across the plain as sinuous depressions, the elevated beds of the prior streams are flanked by relatively elevated and well-drained soils. Moving at right angles to the old stream beds, down towards present streams (down the transverse gradients shown in Fig. 10), one at first encounters 'intermediate' plain which is usually quite evenly graded and composed of soils of intermediate elevation and permeability. Close to present day streams the landscape is usually dominated by 'low' plain, composed of low-lying and relatively impermeable soils; much of this latter country is very uneven, mainly because of stream braiding (but also because of 'crabhole' formations), and it is subject to flooding from present day streams.

Regional changes in the suitability of the riverine plain to irrigation are governed by various physical and economic considerations; and it is clear that these bear a close relation to the aforementioned patterns of landforms and to prior and present day streams. Major controls of land-type suitability for irrigation include the following [30]:

1. The texture and structure of soils, notably:
(a) depth with free drainage.
(b) degree of aeration in the root zone.
(c) infiltration capacity.
(d) tilth and stability of the surface.

2. The nature of macro- and micro-relief, particularly as they affect slope and evenness of the land surface. These features influence problems of land grading, water reticulation and land drainage.

3. The degree of accumulation of toxic salts in the root zone of soils. Though this tends to be greatest in regions of the lowest elevation, this is by no means always the case, especially where 'perched' water tables occur.

4. Liability to inundation from streams and conditions of surface drainage.

5. Accessibility to water supplies, particularly as problems of distance and other factors affect the cost per acre foot of water delivered and the speed and timeliness of water deliveries. These conditions are by no means a function solely of channel distance between farm and major points of water diversion.

6. Subsoil drainage and deep drainage.

7. The effects of climatic and other agronomic conditions on the range of crops and systems of agriculture possible. Under this heading one would consider production functions (input-output relations) technically possible and economically desirable.

8. Social and economic conditions that govern the feasibility and desirability of developing lands in certain ways.

Having regard to the existing technical and economic conditions in Australia, modern research suggests that it is possible to take the abovementioned variables into account in a SCALE OF CROP EXCLUSION developed to assist the classification of lands in terms of suitability for different kinds of irrigation farming. In this scale, systems of irrigated farming are grouped as follows:

Group I—Citrus.

Group II—Peaches.

Group III—Lucerne and apricots.

Group IV—Perennial ('permanent') pastures, pome fruits, vines and vegetables.

Group V—Autumn and spring (so-called 'annual' or 'temporary') pastures; various fodder crops such as sorghum, and paspalum (a perennial pasture, but less-exacting than *Group IV*).

Group VI—Wheat, oats, and rice.

Country dominated by 'low' plain and relatively inferior physical conditions can often be used for Group VI, but much of it is not very suited to other Groups I to V; country that is somewhat better, and suited to Group V, is usually quite suited to Group VI but not suited to Groups I to IV; and so on up the scale. Country suited to Group I tends to have very superior physical conditions. If market conditions warrant it, this land has a comparative advantage for citrus but it is very suited to other crops, except rice which requires relatively impermeable soils to enable deep and prolonged inundation of the land.

On the riverine plain, land types tend to be arranged in an orderly fashion, with recurring combinations of 'high', 'intermediate' and 'low' plain. The patterns are to be observed along both the longitudinal and transverse gradients (Fig. 10). A corollary of this is an orderly arrangement of the suitability of the land to different irrigated crops or pastures. Much of the 'high' plain is very suited to citrus, especially if dunes occur; 'intermediate' plain is suited progressively down the slopes to Groups I, II III and IV; whilst 'low' plain, if suited to irrigation at all, is best developed for Groups V and VI

In terms of the above factors, therefore, it would tend to pay best to locate land uses of Groups I to IV (*intensive* irrigation for fruits, vegetables, or dairying) on 'high' plain closest to major water supply channels. It is fortunate that main channels tend, if often mainly for engineering reasons, to be located near the Eastern Highlands and along prior stream levees where they have the greatest command

over the riverine plain as this ensures major water supplies to land types agronomically best-suited to *intensive* irrigation. Although the early planners, working mainly between 1905 and 1928, made many mistakes in project location, there is little doubt that *intensive* irrigation and closer settlements, such as those of the Murrumbidgee Irrigation Areas in New South Wales and the Victorian schemes in the Murray Valley, Katandra, North Shepparton, Shepparton, Rodney, Tongala-Stanhope, Rochester, Dingee, Cohuna, Koondrook and Swan Hill irrigation districts, were designed to exploit 'high' plain with advantages of land type and proximity to major water points. This fact is revealed in numerous records, especially in early official plans which showed closer settlements on 'red loamy soils' near existing or proposed major channels. As stressed elsewhere [23], Elwood Mead, an early Commissioner of the Victorian State Rivers and Water Supply Commission, and planners concerned with the Murrumbidgee Irrigation Areas [31] used as precepts experience in the U.S.A. and other places (including embryonic irrigation schemes at Australian centres such as Mildura and the Goulburn Valley). They deliberately located *intensive* irrigation schemes and major water channels so as best to exploit 'high' plain which they believed lent itself to the kinds of closer settlements being developed. Obviously they were not aware of sophisticated appreciations of land types and problems of land drainage that arose in the wake of these first settlements, especially through the work of irrigation authorities and the Council for Scientific and Industrial Research (now the Commonwealth Scientific and Industrial Research Organization, C.S.I.R.O.). The writer agrees with his colleague, Langford-Smith [29a], that a much better appreciation of the complex problems of irrigation development could, and probably should have been developed prior to the implementation of the major *intensive* irrigation schemes promoted in Australia between 1910 and 1930. However, it would be wrong to imply that early planners gave little thought to physical and economic questions. Voluminous official reports, both at the time and after the event, clearly demonstrate that these issues were closely studied. Subsequent history proved that serious mistakes were made, both

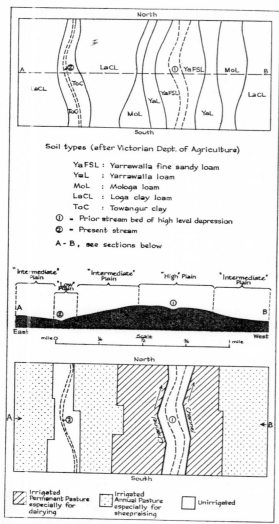

Soil types (after Victorian Dept. of Agriculture)

YaFSL : Yarrawalla fine sandy loam
YaL   : Yarrawalla loam
MoL   : Mologa loam
LaCL : Loga clay loam
ToC   : Towangur clay
① = Prior stream bed of high level depression
② = Present stream
A - B, see sections below

Fig. 11—A typical association of soils, landforms, and land-uses along transverse gradients (west-east section) of riverine plain between zone of red-brown earths and zone of grey and brown soils of heavy texture, Calivil Parish, Victoria

as to project location and the sizes of farms and systems of land uses encouraged on them. Whether early planners could reasonably have anticipated all of these problems is a moot point.

Towards the interior, lowlands become dominated by 'low' plain generally unsuited to crops and pastures in Groups I to IV. Given adequate water supplies these interior regions are best developed for Groups V and VI.

Hence, mixed fat lambraising, ricefarming, or fine woolgrowing (Merinos) tend to dominate in irrigation projects such as Benerembah, Wah Wah and Wakool in the Riverina of New South Wales, and in comparable schemes of the Goulburn System in Victoria, such as the Tragowel Plains and Boort irrigation districts, especially in parts of the schemes most remote from major diversion channels. The trend from relatively *intensive* irrigation on the upland flanks of the riverine plain to more *extensive* irrigation of interior plain stems from the fact that land and water supplies in the upland flanks are more suited to irrigation than they are in the interior plain, because of the physical factors already mentioned.

A major exception to the pattern outlined above is the Torrumbarry Irrigation System, flanking the Murray River between Echuca and Swan Hill (Fig. 1). In this System it has been possible to develop a number of closer settlements based on *intensive* irrigation (both fruitgrowing and dairying), despite the position of the area remote from the Eastern Highlands. The development arises partly because the area is located close to the Murray River, ensuring an abundant and regular water supply; and partly because the Torrumbarry System serves a tongue of 'high' plain, supposedly a legacy of an active prior Goulburn River [32]. This ensures superior land types for a wide range of irrigated land uses, in sharp contrast to adjacent 'low' plain served by irrigation in the northern Tragowel Plains Irrigation District.

The systematic arrangement of land types and irrigation suitability described above, is best seen on the riverine plain in a progression down the various longitudinal gradients (Fig. 10). Generally the progression from 'high' plain to 'low' plain is from south to north in the Goulburn System of Victoria (Fig. 1) and east to west in all other Murray and Murrumbidgee systems in Victoria and New South Wales. Slight modifications include the fact that the trend from 'high' plain to 'low' plain occurs from southeast to northwest in the extreme eastern elements of the Goulburn System (near and east of the Goulburn River), and from northeast to southwest in the Murrumbidgee Irrigation Areas and the new Coleambally Irrigation Area.

Movement down the transverse gradients of the plain produces a similar, and often much more abrupt, systematic change from 'high' to 'intermediate' to 'low' plain; with changes in land-use suitabilities from Group I to Group VI. Figure 11 illustrates one such transverse gradient, selected from the Calivil Irrigation District. As in other parts of Victoria, rice is not grown on 'low' plain here, this being purely a politically-contrived difference between Victoria and New South Wales. In such an area, the change from 'high' to 'low' plain is so rapid that it often occurs within the one farm. In this situation it is common to find that irrigation land, whatever its use, is concentrated on the more-easily watered parts of the 'high' and 'intermediate' plain (excluding prior stream beds that are difficult to drain), whereas unirrigated land occupies 'low' plain or prior stream beds. Within the irrigated sections of the farm, crops or pastures exerting the greatest demands on land and water supplies tend to occupy the highest plain which possesses superior conditions of land type and water supply. Less-exacting systems of irrigation occur on somewhat lower plain, more remote from major water channels.

The aforementioned discussion of land type and regional zonation of land uses has tended to overlook the exceptions to the rule. There are some areas where State authorities have established irrigation schemes in poor locations. For instance *intensive* schemes are found where *extensive* would have been more appropriate (witness fruitgrowing on the Swan Hill Flats at Speewa) and *extensive* schemes where no irrigation might have been appropriate. Much of the northern Tragowel Plains Irrigation District and parts of the Wakool Irrigation District come into the latter group. Likewise, the individual farmer has not always developed his land for the best uses, especially over the long-term. There has been a tendency for many of these maladjusted patterns of irrigation development to be corrected over time, at considerable cost to authorities and individuals. The high fixed social and economic costs embedded in irrigation schemes impose rigidities however, so poorly-sited land uses tend to persist, unless physical conditions (including induced ones) make this economically impossible.

Riverine Plain: Water Conservation and Irrigation

The major State-sponsored water conservation and irrigation projects of the riverine plain are shown on Fig. 1 (compare Fig. 3 for topographic divisions). With the exception of several modified natural basins, the so-called 'headworks' on the plain are not conservation sites, they are merely diversion weirs and ponds to facilitate the gravity supply of water from streams. It is both convenient and realistic to list the major irrigation works under three *systems*, distinguished according to the stream serving as the major source of water:

Murray Irrigation System

Projects here rely mainly on water conserved by Hume Reservoir; and they fall into two gravity systems:

1. *Yarrawonga*. The diversion of water at Yarrawonga Weir supplies schemes in two states:

(a) *New South Wales*. The Berriquin, Denimein, Deniboota, and Wakool irrigation districts, and the Tullakool Irrigation Area; all are in the southern Riverina. Some water is supplied via the Edwards River (Steven's Weir).

(b) *Victoria*. The Murray Valley Irrigation District.

2. *Torrumbarry*. Water diverted at Torrumbarry Weir serves the Cohuna, Koondrook, Kerang, Third Lake, Fish Point, Mystic Park, Nyah and Swan Hill irrigation districts; in-transit storage is supplied by Kow Swamp (a modified natural basin).

Murrumbidgee Irrigation System

Projects here rely on headwater storage at Burrinjuck Reservoir; but supplies are soon to be greatly augmented by the emergent Snowy Scheme, via the Tumut River (Blowering Dam being built). The system can be divided into schemes north and south of the river respectively.

Berembed (northern). Diversion from the Murrumbidgee River at Berembed Weir serves the Murrumbidgee Irrigation Areas (Yanco and Mirrool), and the Benerembah, Tabbita and Wah Wah irrigation districts.

Gogeldrie (southern). The new Gogeldrie Weir serves the emergent Coleambally Irrigation Area.

Completion of connections between the Murrumbidgee River and the Snowy Scheme will allow further development north, and especially south, of the river [17].

Less-important irrigation projects further down the Murrumbidgee include the Hay Irrigation Area, supplied by a local pump, and the Lowbidgee Irrigation and Flood Control District, supplied by diversions at Maude and Redbank weirs.

Goulburn Irrigation System

Projects in this massive system extend throughout large parts of the Goulburn, Campaspe and Loddon river valleys, and include the Katandra, North Shepparton, Shepparton, South Shepparton, Rodney, Tongala-Stanhope, Deakin, Rochester, Dingee, Calivil, Boort and Tragowel Plains irrigation districts. They rely mainly on the headworks at Eildon on the Goulburn but are supplemented by smaller headworks on the other streams mentioned. In-transit storage occurs at Waranga Reservoir, and diversion from the Goulburn River is achieved by Goulburn Weir. The old structure on the Loddon River has been superseded.

Most of the Goulburn System is supplied by the Waranga Western Main Channel which runs approximately due west from the Goulburn River, skirting the foothills of the Victorian uplands but with a slight fall northwards. Subsidiary channels feed north down the longitudinal gradients of the plain, often following prior stream levees to give them maximum command over 'high', 'intermediate' and 'low' plain. Minor channels follow both longitudinal and transverse gradients of the plain and, unlike major channels, they often adopt zig-zag courses to skirt the boundaries of the grid-like property subdivisions typical of the plain. Apart from the important feature of its main channel cutting across the longitudinal gradient of the plain, the general relationship of channel patterns to micro-relief is very similar in the Goulburn System to that developed in other projects, including the Murray Valley Irrigation District depicted in Fig. 12. In the latter, channels run along high plain from east to west.

A comparison of Figs. 1 and 3 emphasizes how the group irrigation schemes of the riverine plain are much larger and more scattered than those of the Wimmera-Mallee lowlands. This contrast is primarily due to differences of physical geography between the two regions. The shallow incision of streams and the generally even macro-relief throughout the riverine plain have greatly facilitated distribution of water by gravity systems. On the whole, this has been aided by the relatively impervious character of soils permitting the use of unlined earthen channels. Losses of water and damage to land through water percolation have sometimes occurred, especially where major channels occupy prior stream levees with very permeable soils. The fact that it has been possible to exploit water resources of five riverine situations—those of the Goulburn, Campaspe, Loddon, Murray, and Murrumbidgee rivers—also makes for a much more scattered pattern of irrigation on the plain than occurs in the Mallee. Later discussion stresses the more limiting physical possibilities of the latter region. Of course, it would be naive to attribute these differences in the patterns of irrigation projects between the riverine plain and the Wimmera-Mallee lowlands purely to physical factors. In both regions, the fact that water projects have been sponsored by several States (three for the Wimmera-Mallee lowlands) has been a prime reason why scattered physical resources have been exploited. For example, the concentration of much early Victorian effort on the Goulburn System, and most early effort in New South Wales on the Murrumbidgee System, led to widely-separated developments. This stemmed largely from active intervention by two sovereign States, each deliberately focussing its efforts on the best stream completely under its control. In fact, until the mid-1930s most irrigation effort in New South Wales was centred on the Murrumbidgee Irrigation Areas (M.I.A.) based on water resources often less-abundant than those of the Murray further south. However, this was a deliberate policy to give attention to regions not subject to problems of uncertainty of water supplies stemming from inter-State disagreement that plagued the development of the Murray for decades. For New South Wales, concentration on the Murrumbidgee had the

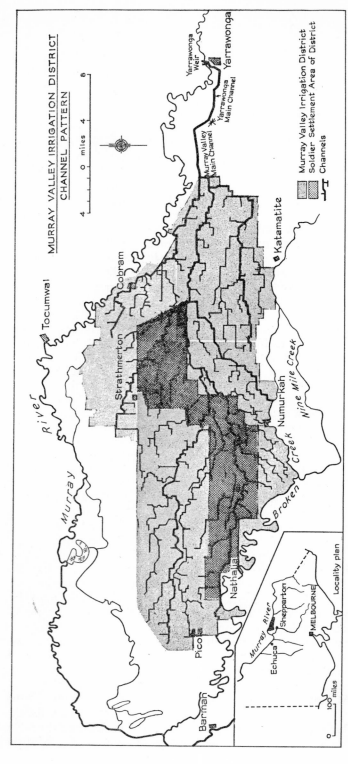

Fig. 12.—Water flow is from east to west down longitudinal gradient of plain. Central, levee-like formations of high plain are exploited for Soldier Settlement by *intensive* irrigation for fruits and dairy products. (*Source:* States Rivers and Water Supply Commission, Melbourne)

added advantage that the products of investment there were more likely to enhance regional development centred on Sydney than would have been the case if a similar investment had been made in the southern Riverina, which comes more under the influence of the rival entrepôt—Melbourne.

Intensive irrigation projects on the riverine plain rely on basic water allocations of about 1 acre per foot per annum; i.e. enough water to irrigate each acre, classified by the State authority as 'commanded and suited to irrigation', to a cumulative depth of 1 foot. Commonly, farmers receive as 'sales' much more than this basic allocation; this is especially true of ricegrowers who need up to 7 acre feet per year for every acre in rice. The major examples of *intensive* irrigation on the plain are:

1. *Murray System*—Murray Valley, Cohuna, Koondrook, Swan Hill and Nyah irrigation districts in Victoria, and the Tullakool Irrigation Area in New South Wales.

2. *Murrumbidgee System*—the Murrumbidgee, Coleambally and Hay irrigation areas.

3. *Goulburn System*—the Katandra, Shepparton, Rochester, Tongala-Stanhope, Dingee, and Calivil irrigation districts of Victoria.

In some cases true *intensive* irrigation occupies central, and *extensive* irrigation peripheral, pockets of these projects: the Murray Valley Irrigation District, west of Cobram in Victoria, is the best example of this. Note the centrally-located Soldier Settlement Area of *intensive* irrigation of 'high' plain flanked by *extensive* irrigation of 'low' plain (Fig. 12).

Extensive or *partial* irrigation is typical of all other projects on the riverine plain, but the reliance on irrigation as opposed to dryland farming varies considerably from project to project. For example, relatively *intensive* forms of irrigation (particularly for fat lambraising and dairying) are common in districts such as Berriquin and Calivil; by contrast, irrigation is fairly *extensive* (dominated by broadacre farming for lambs and Merino wool) in projects such as Tragowel Plains and Wakool. On the whole, schemes tend to be most *extensive* farthest from the Eastern Highlands, i.e. on the poorer land types with the least abundant and least reliable water supplies; they tend to be most *intensive* closest to the Eastern Highlands (or to the Murray River) where superior land types and water supplies can be enjoyed.

There have been important historical changes in the location of irrigation projects and the works that serve them. For example, most of the earliest schemes were developed by Trusts in northern Victoria, between 1886 and 1900 [23]. It was common for these Trusts to depend on relatively primitive works, such as small diversion weirs on modified natural streams used as water carriers. This meant a concentration of irrigation development on relatively 'low' plain, remote from the Eastern Highlands; early development in the northern parts of the Boort and Tragowel Plains irrigation districts in the Goulburn System, and in the Kerang Irrigation District in the Torrumbarry System are good examples. During this century, after the inception of the State Rivers and Water Supply Commission in Victoria and the Water Conservation and Irrigation Commission in New South Wales, irrigation came to depend on much more-active State socialism. In particular, this meant more profound government intervention to build larger diversion structures and major artificial channels, primarily to allow exploitation of 'high' plains better-suited to closer settlement for dairying, fruitgrowing and fat lambraising. A vital geographic effect of this was that irrigation schemes became increasingly focussed in regions closer to the Eastern Highlands and near large prior stream beds; the Murrumbidgee Irrigation Areas in New South Wales, and Victorian projects such as the Dingee, Calivil, Rochester, Tongala-Stanhope, Shepparton and Murray Valley irrigation districts are examples of this. The emergent Coleambally Irrigation Area in New South Wales is the latest stage of this trend for the focus of irrigation of the plain to shift closer to the Eastern Highlands: to move into regions better-suited, by land types and water supplies, to the widest range of irrigated land uses (Groups I-IV).

Though the large *extensive* irrigation projects ('Districts') of the Riverina of New South Wales have produced marked changes in the agricultural landscape along the Murray and Murrumbidgee rivers, it is clear that this mode of development has lost favour with officials [17,

18]. There is some doubt as to whether water conservation and agricultural authorities in New South Wales have ever been very enthusiastic about projects of this type, possibly with the notable exception of L. A. B. Wade; however, it is only fairly recently that they have publicly expressed their opposition to new 'Districts' and their preference for 'Areas', as embodied in the new Coleambally Irrigation Area being developed along the Murrumbidgee River. Objections to *partial* or *extensive* irrigation of the 'District' type are directed mainly at issues such as: the high capital costs of channels (much longer per acre irrigated in this system than in the 'Areas'); great wastage of water in-transit (by percolation and evaporation) through the excessively-long supply lines; a tendency for irrigators to make erratic use of water (so creating difficulties for the supplying authority) and to use water in a relatively indifferent fashion; and the fact that 'Districts' have not really produced a significantly improved range of production possibilities for farmers. In the latter context, authorities argue that, under *partial* or *extensive* irrigation of the type found in schemes such as Berriquin and Wakool, the farmer tends to be limited to fat lambraising in the autumn to spring period.

A further official objection to 'Districts' is that most of the schemes were first designed on the assumption of very limited dependence on artificial water supplies; in the main, *partial* irrigation was to be used for several waterings of land, mainly to boost the normal production season made possible by rainfall between autumn and spring. More stable production of wool, and to a lesser extent fat lambs, on 'annual' pastures was to be the key aim; an enhancement of land uses prevalent before irrigation. Small size of channels and lack of prior drainage facilities were keynotes of this unambitious form of *partial* irrigation. However, since the late 1930s, and especially since 1945, farmers throughout the riverine plain have become increasingly aware of the production benefits of irrigation and, as a result, there has been a rapid increase in the seasonal demands for water.

A corollary, but more significant trend is the gradual development of irrigated 'permanent' pasture, i.e. *intensive* irrigation, especially during the summer months. These trends have posed a number of serious problems for 'Districts'; initial channels have been unable to cope with heavier and seasonally more-concentrated demands for water. More intense irrigation has posed the need for land drainage but this has been difficult to implement in a coordinated fashion, because of the scattered pattern of irrigation adopted by 'District' methods. Irrigation authorities in New South Wales now argue that all these drawbacks of *extensive* irrigation can only be met by planning projects as 'Areas' (*intensive* irrigation) from the outset, by anticipating the long-term trend towards more intensive use of land and water, and by implementing, from the start, a system of channels and drains to cope with it. The new Coleambally Irrigation Area reflects this policy. It is argued elsewhere [*29a*] that, despite a number of commendable features, this new official preference for 'Areas' rather than 'Districts' seems to play down some of the merits of the latter, especially integration of irrigated and dryland farming.

Irrigation Farms on the Plain

Comparison of Figs. 1, 8 and 9 provides a summary of the dominant types of farming in the group irrigation schemes of the riverine plain. It will be seen that these projects have allowed a number of land uses to be extended well inland into regions where unirrigated farming is of a much more extensive character; witness intensive fruitgrowing and dairying on small farms (30 to 100 acres) in country where dryland wheatgrowing or woolgrowing occur on farms of many hundreds or thousands of acres. On the other hand, especially in the old wheat belt *partial* irrigation has tended merely to accentuate land-use trends already under way without irrigation. Hence, we may observe that new modes of occupance, including leap-frogging of land uses well beyond normal (unirrigated) limits, as well as new *types* or *phases* of occupance by consolidation behind old frontiers, are products of group irrigation on the riverine plain. In essence, irrigation here is a major example of technical change occurring in southeastern Australia since 1900, but more especially since 1930, i.e. the very active substitution of capital for land or, as one writer has termed it, the 'purposive change of the environment' [33]. Partly because such investment has occurred only in selected and widely-scattered localities, and particularly because it reflects the differential impact of State socialism, group irrigation schemes have proved a major agency distorting a more simple concentric zonation of land uses around the coastal metropolises of southern Australia.

Although some farms in the group irrigation schemes produce a wide variety of products, it is more common for farms to specialize in one product or a limited range of joint products. Since it is rational for planners to encourage a measure of economic homogeneity within projects or large sub-sections of them (if only to simplify problems of water control), the geographer can observe a marked tendency for specialization of area. It is more than a matter of taxonomic convenience therefore to discuss irrigation farms in terms of product groupings, since these best reflect formal and functional regions [34] occurring on the plain (and in the Mallee discussed later).

Fruit and Vegetable Areas

A comparison of Figs. 1, 3, 8 and 9 emphasizes that irrigation has produced important pockets of fruit-vegetable production on the riverine plain. The farms involved range between 30 and 200 acres for the most part, much smaller than the 650 to 1500 acre wheat farms common under nearby dryland conditions. The accepted 'living' or 'home maintenance' area for Soldier Settlement in a very modern scheme—the Murray Valley Irrigation District of Victoria (Fig. 12)—was 40 to 50 acres of irrigable country, depending on soil types.

Most of the *intensive* irrigation farms on the plain were set up between 1910 and 1925 by State closer settlement schemes. After 1918, and again after 1945 (the Murray Valley Irrigation District being the largest project in the latter period), such closer settlements were important ingredients of War Service Land Settlement Projects. At other times, they formed one aspect of a very general drive by governments to encourage local farmers and immigrants to settle on the land in southern Australia.

Group irrigation schemes emphasizing fruit-growing on the riverine plain rely on heavy application of artificial water supplies; average application is between two and three acre feet in addition to rainfall during the normal growing seasons (mainly between October and March inclusive). Most of the settlements depend on gravity irrigation throughout (from initial diversion on streams to single farm fields); however, it is often necessary and economic to use pumps to command some highly-prized country (such as dunes) to permit citrus growing.

The main horticultural settlements practising group irrigation on the plain are as follows:

Murrumbidgee Irrigation System. The closely-settled parts of the Murrumbidgee Irrigation Areas (Yanco and Mirrool) focussed on settlements such as Leeton and Griffith.

Murray Irrigation System. Pockets of closer settlement near Cobram (Murray Valley Irrigation District) and Koondrook (Koondrook Irrigation District) in Victoria; and the Barma, Bringan and Glenview irrigation trusts of New South Wales (these three exploit dune formations mentioned above).

Goulburn Irrigation System. All or part of the Shepparton, Rodney, Tongala-Stanhope and Rochester irrigation districts of Victoria. Fruit-growing tends to form scattered and declining pockets in the latter three projects, where sheepraising and dairying are in the ascendancy.

Tree fruits (pome, stone and citrus) and some vines (wine and table mainly) are the chief products of horticultural settlements under irrigation on the plain. Where soil types permit, it is common for farmers to achieve greater income stability by growing a wide range of fruits; many farmers, especially those of southern European extraction, also grow vegetables for canneries and large city markets. Climatic and pedological conditions on the plain do not favour dried vine fruits, though these were attempted on a major scale early in some projects, especially those of the M.I.A. The key drawbacks of the plain for dried fruits are heavy-textured soils (giving late seasons) and marginally-severe hazards of excessive

F

humidity and rainfall during spring and autumn. Relatively cheap water supplies possible on the plain allow a concentration on fruits for canning, two major focal points being the M.I.A. and the Goulburn 'Valley'. Local processing (weight-cost reduction) enables these products to command scattered markets throughout Australia and abroad (especially in the United Kingdom).

Micro-variations of land type greatly influence the detailed spatial arrangement of fruitgrowing within the one compact settlement; or, for that matter, within the one farm where it possesses a range of physical conditions. Surveys of these patterns are rare; however, some appreciation of them can be gained from the recommendations of extension services on the M.I.A. [35]. The detailed spatial variation of land-type suitability on the M.I.A. for fruitgrowing under *intensive* irrigation is largely a function of two variables: soil characteristics (especially soil permeability) and the slope of the land. Classification of soils recognizes permeabilities ranging from very high to very low; classification of slope recognizes lands that are steep (slope of more than 3 inches per chain), moderate (3 to 1½ inches per chain), and flat (less than 1½ inches per chain). Hollow lands are recognized as being drainable or undrainable. Within these ranges of conditions, horticultural land on the M.I.A. has been classified into five classes:

Class 1—Land suited to general horticulture, especially citrus: country with all the very permeable soil types (especially most sands) regardless of slope, except for hollows.

Class 2—Land suited to general horticulture but only fair for citrus—most of the fairly permeable soils of good slope.

Class 3—Land useful for non-citrus tree and vine crops—gentler slopes of the relatively permeable soils or the steeper slopes of relatively impermeable soils.

Class 4—Land not suited to citrus or stone fruits but adapted to vines and pome fruits—much of the impermeable soils of gentle slope or the very impermeable soils regardless of slope. If the grade is slack, prunes do best where soils are relatively impermeable. Table grapes and some of the more-exacting wine and spirit grapes do not tolerate very impermeable soils in this class.

Class 5—Poorly-drained land, especially undrainable hollows, are not rated as being suited to fruitgrowing. Much of this land, if it is used at all, is under vegetable growing.

An important feature of the economy of most of the horticultural settlements, both on the riverine plain and in the Mallee, is vegetable production. Irrigation and local climates aid year-round cropping, but especially production at times of short supplies from other producing areas that tend to compete for the main markets (notably the metropolises and large towns of southern Australia). The inland irrigation schemes possess the key advantage that their land is relatively cheap and is not subject to pressure from advancing urban uses; this gives the vegetable grower of inland areas a competitive edge over his counterpart in the rural-urban fringes of major cities. The growth of vegetable growing in the group irrigation schemes was stimulated by army contracts during the 1939 to 1945 War (especially with American troops in the Southwest Pacific area). Since the War, the industry has been encouraged by an influx of southern Europeans (particularly Italians) coming to Australian areas by a 'chain-migration' process [36].

Though a wide range of vegetables is grown in the inland irrigation districts, main crops are tomatoes (fresh, canned and processed for sauce and pulp), and root vegetables, i.e. crops that can stand long transport by train and truck to major cities as far afield as Brisbane. On the M.I.A., two systems of vegetable growing persist. Firstly, mixed fruitgrowing-vegetable growing on so-called Horticultural blocks in which all the crops tend to be produced by the one farmer (commonly a landowner of Italian extraction). Secondly, specialized vegetable growing, usually by recently-arrived Italian migrants on land leased from the owner of a Large Area block which is otherwise given over to rice and fat lambs. There is some evidence of an agricultural ladder in which farmers move upwards from specialist vegetable growing under lease on Large Area farms to their own mixed fruit and vegetable properties (Horticultural blocks). And in some cases the final rung is specialist Large Area farming [36a].

Dairying Areas

It will be seen from Figs. 1, 3 and 9 that the group irrigation schemes of the riverine plain support important pockets of dairying, especially in northern Victoria. Like fruit-vegetable production, most dairying depends on copious summer irrigations and a reversal of the annual production cycle; production between spring and autumn rather than between autumn and spring. As shown in Fig. 19 for the Tongala-Stanhope Irrigation District, most dairying was based initially on lucerne and fodder crops; since the late 1920s, these have gradually been replaced by 'permanent' (summer-growing) pastures, both introduced and volunteer (spreading through districts from farms where first sown). Such pastures provide grazing for the milking herd and a source of hay for winter feeding. Key plants in them are white clover (such as Irrigation White), ryegrass, cocksfoot, *Paspalum dilatatum*, *Phalaris tuberosa*, kikuyu, and rhodes grass [37]. Pastures have several advantages over lucerne, including greater longevity, more satisfactory grazing qualities, greater variety of fodder and palatability, and equal suitability as hay.

The main dairying areas rely nowadays on *intensive* irrigation schemes which permit pastures to be watered heavily between September and March (inclusive) with between two and three acre feet of water per annum and waterings of about three or four inches every ten to fourteen days in the hot months. In these schemes, dairy properties enjoy one of three systems of *water rights* [37, 38]:

1. For properties of 40 acres or smaller (now rare, but very common earlier this century) a basic water right of 1¾ acre feet for every acre assessed by irrigation authorities as 'commanded and suited to irrigation'.

2. Nowadays, properties specializing in dairying under *intensive* irrigation are between 40 and 100 acres in size and receive an average annual water right of 70 acre feet plus 1 acre foot for every 2 acres in excess of 40 that are rated as commanded and suited to irrigation.

3. Rare properties that are over 100 acres receive 100 acre feet plus 1 acre foot for every

3 acres in excess of the basic 100 rated as commanded and suited to irrigation.

Though some specialist dairying without irrigation has developed in better-watered upland regions of northeastern Victoria and the 'Hills District' of South Australia, all the major dairying areas on the riverine plain are akin to fruit-vegetable production in that they represent relatively intensive land uses in dry sub-humid to semi-arid regions (Fig. 4) impossible without massive irrigation schemes. The chief dairying settlements listed below have deliberately been sponsored to exploit 'high' plain or Recent alluvials (as at Swan Hill) suited initially to lucerne and later to improved 'permanent' pastures, both by the character of land types and by nearness to major sources of water. These settlements are:

Murray Irrigation System. Pockets in the Murray Valley, Cohuna, Koondrook and Swan Hill irrigation districts of Victoria supplied by gravity diversions from the Murray at Yarrawonga and Torrumbarry weirs.

Goulburn Irrigation System. Pockets in the Katandra, North Shepparton, Shepparton, South Shepparton, Rodney, Tongala-Stanhope, Rochester, Dingee and Calivil irrigation districts of Victoria, supplied by gravity diversion from the Goulburn at Goulburn Weir.

Murrumbidgee Irrigation System. A small scheme in the Hay Irrigation Area. It should be noted that dairying was once very active on the M.I.A. in country now developed for Large Area farming (rice/fat lambs); the industry declined there in the early 1920s, because land types proved unattractive to lucerne and economic conditions were adverse to dairying in poor locations; at that time 'permanent' pastures had not yet been evolved to replace lucerne on heavier-textured soils.

The development by *intensive* irrigation for fruit-vegetable production and dairying on the lowlands of the Southern Murray-Darling Basin (riverine plain, and Mallee discussed later) are classic examples of how regional transfers of capital and State developmental policies can produce major aberrations from simpler land-use patterns around key urban nodes. It was noted earlier that the concentration of most dairying and fruits for canning on the riverine plain reflects the fact that gravity water supplies in open earthen channels make for relatively 'cheap' water there. However, the very existence of large water projects to underwrite these industries, as well as the exploitation of five scattered riverine situations, ranging from the Murrumbidgee in the north, to Victorian areas along the Murray, Goulburn, Campaspe and Loddon rivers in the south, are to be explained by forces of State socialism that have encouraged Governments in the two States to push closer settlement, based on small-scale family farming, much farther inland than normal rainfalls will permit.

When most of the irrigated dairying was first established between 1910 and 1928, modal farms—then 'living' areas, now 'home maintenance' areas of closer settlements—were between 40 and 60 acres, depending on land types. Most of each farm was under lucerne. Especially with the gradual displacement of lucerne by 'permanent' pastures, but also with declining net returns per acre as production costs have risen, authorities have been forced to allow increases in farm sizes to the present-day averages of between 75 and 100 acres. These enlargements occurred as some farmers went out of business or sold out and their land was subdivided and added to adjacent blocks.

Dairying often forms a 'beginning' enterprise in new land settlements; this has been true of some irrigation projects now dominated by sheepraising and discussed below. Because it has been at a comparative disadvantage, dairying has tended to decline as a specialist or sideline activity under *extensive* irrigation in dominantly sheep-raising districts; however, where it does persist, as in some projects in northern Victoria, and southern New South Wales [39], it depends on the typical 'annual' pastures to be found there. Since these pastures have a low carrying capacity dairy farms geared to them are relatively large—generally between 100 and 300 acres.

It has been stressed elsewhere that the settlement of coastal dairying areas in New South Wales (to take one example) has been designed to allow each farm to exploit a combination of land types, where diversity of land occurs over short distances [40]. Such widely-varying yet contiguous types of land do not exist on the riverine plain; nevertheless, it is common for dairying under *intensive* irrigation to adapt detailed features of land use to micro-variations of land type. For example, farmers will commonly locate pastures with the most-exacting physical requirements on 'high' plain close to the major water channels normally found there; as a rule, this means that such pastures (or lucerne) are usually also close to the homestead and the farmer can give them the fairly constant attention they need during the main irrigation season. If a property also possesses 'low' plain, it is common for it to be used for 'annual' pastures or fodder crops, although, in Victoria, some 'low' plains possess soils that have superior self-mulching characteristics, making them more suited to 'permanent' pastures and lucerne than are most 'low' plains in southern New South Wales. Butler [41] suggests that this could perhaps be due to the presence of more *parna* in some of the soils of 'low' plains of northern Victoria.

Sheep and Cereal Areas

The largest and most-scattered irrigation schemes of the riverine plain are dominated by sheepraising, with or without other activities (such as ricegrowing in New South Wales). Most sheep-cereal production relies on *extensive* or *partial* irrigation and occurs in the 'Districts' of New South Wales or the projects of northern Victoria with poorer land and water supplies. In both States, where the one group irrigation scheme embraces a diversity of land uses, it is the rule for *intensive* irrigation for fruits, vegetables or dairy products to be located in central zones of 'high' plain enjoying abundant water supplies. Most sheepraising and ricegrowing are found on 'low' plain which is handicapped by greater distance from major water channels and greater difficulties of water supply. An example is the Murray Valley Irrigation District (Fig. 12).

In the sheep-cereal areas, group irrigation has had several major effects. Where pre-irrigation landuse was dominated by Merino woolgrowing or risky fat lamb production, *partial* irrigation has tended to aid a drift into more specialized fat lambraising. The trend has been most marked where land types and water supplies have made *partial* irrigation easiest;

least marked where land types (such as river-frontage land of broken micro-relief and heavy-textured soils) impose more reliance on a mixture of unirrigated and partially irrigated land. A classic example of this contrast can be observed in the Tragowel Plains Irrigation District. The drift into irrigated fat lambraising and closer settlement is most marked on the higher and more evenly-graded plain in the east; less marked for the 'lignum' or 'black' country nearer the Loddon River in the west.

Where pre-irrigation farming involved wheat-growing and fat lambraising (the typical *ley* agriculture of the better-watered plain), *partial* irrigation has assisted a drift into specialized fat lambraising, except where rice is now combined with sheep. Over the years, as in the wheat belt, rice/fat lamb farms have tended to adopt wider rotations to assist the build-up and maintenance of soil fertility.

Leaving aside special water supplies necessary for rice, most *partial* irrigation for sheep-cereal production involves much less water than is used for fruits, vegetables, and dairy products. Generally the aim has been to supply an average of about four waterings per year, so ensuring that rainfall plus irrigation totals about four inches per month in the March, April, September and October periods. This means that *partial* irrigation has allowed the establishment of high-quality 'annual' pastures (notably Subterranean clover and Wimmera ryegrass) conducive to the rapid and early production of high-quality lamb which enjoys an advantage over lamb from non-irrigated country in both domestic and overseas markets. The need to irrigate 'annual' pastures, and winter or summer fodder crops common on sheep farms, varies with the seasons, so that irrigation is much more supplementary in character than it is for the *intensive* irrigation projects dominated by dairying or fruitgrowing. In essence, *partial* irrigation has aimed to modify, not to drastically change, the autumn-winter-spring production period made possible by rainfall alone on the riverine plain. Such an aim is not very ambitious and explains why *partial* irrigation can be achieved over wide areas of relatively poor country.

Because of their size, location, and conditions of water supply, it is common for sheep farms under *partial* irrigation to display much

internal variation of land uses. Most graziers aim to grow some lucerne or 'permanent' pasture and these are best located on the highest plain that is commanded and suited to irrigation and is close to major water supplies. The dominant source of improved feed—'annual' pasture under irrigation—is usually located on the more even intermediate plain under average-to-favourable conditions of land type and water supply. Irrigated fodder crops and native pastures, and unirrigated country, occur on poorer 'low' plain subject to problems of poor water control, bad land drainage and inferior soils. Occasionally, that 'high' plain which is difficult to command and drain (such as high-level depressions or prior stream beds) is left unirrigated. The relative importance of these associations of land use and other conditions varies from farm to farm and from project to project.

Occasionally, sheepraising is practised under *intensive* irrigation, as in parts of the Rochester and Tongala-Stanhope irrigation districts. This usually happens where farms possess superior 'high' plain and abundant water supplies—legacies of earlier closer settlement for dairying. Better physical resources make for an emphasis on summer fattening based on 'permanent' pastures, though it is common for graziers to combine this with winter fattening on 'annual' pastures. Given larger areas, farms of this type indicate the great flexibility of land uses possible by the combination of 'high' plain and superior water supplies, and they point to the great possibilities posed by the new Coleambally Irrigation Area where authorities have deliberately sought flexibility. Here we observe a conscious effort to encourage sheepraising by *intensive* irrigation of the upland flanks of the riverine plain in order to sponsor farms with a far wider range of production possibilities than is normally available to their counterparts relying on *partial* irrigation of 'low' interior plain.

Irrigated sheep farms vary greatly in size, more or less in direct correlation with land types, water supplies and the relative emphasis on *intensive* as distinct from *extensive* irrigation. For example, in the Rochester and Tongala-Stanhope irrigation districts [29b] *intensive* irrigation of 'high' plain occurs on farms generally between 100 and 500 acres. On 'intermediate' plain where projects have fair water supplies (basic rights of between 1 in 2 and 1 in 5) sheep farms generally range between 250 and 900 acres. Where the poorest land types and water supplies combine sheep properties are much larger, usually between 900 and 2000 acres, though some are up to 10,000 acres and more as in Tragowel Plains. Moving between these three groups, in the same order, one also notes a declining emphasis on 'perennial' pastures as opposed to 'annual' pastures; irrigated land as opposed to unirrigated land, and crossbred sheep and beef for meat as opposed to Merino sheep for wools. The contrast is essentially one of varying levels and reliability of stock nutrition.

Geographic Patterns of Irrigation on the Plain

When the aforementioned features of land types, water supplies, and irrigation farms are borne in mind, it is clear that there is a far-from-haphazard pattern of farms in the group irrigation schemes of the riverine plain. Superior land types and water resources tend to encourage smaller farms, more populous settlements, and greater emphasis on *intensive* irrigation (fruit-vegetable production, dairying, and summer fattening of lamb and beef) on the 'high' plains, especially near the peripheral uplands but also in the favoured 'tongue' of country developed in the Torrumbarry Irrigation System along the Murray between Echuca and Swan Hill (Figs. 1 and 8). The interior plain is dominated by 'low' plain and relatively inferior water supplies, which encourage a greater emphasis on *partial* irrigation for lamb, rice and fine wool. Farms are also larger and regions less-densely populated. The contrast between 'high' and 'low' plain is most pronounced along the longitudinal gradients of the plain (Fig. 10). However, a similar contrast is to be observed along the transverse gradients, especially the further the section is from the peripheral uplands.

Though the aforementioned patterns reflect the strong influence of physical conditions, it would be naive to base a geographic appreciation too much on this side of the problem. Obviously, State authorities have long been aware of physical variations throughout the plain, and even without the modern appreciation of land types, they tended to seek out 'high' plain and good water supplies when pro-

moting closer settlement by *intensive* irrigation. However, by their timing of major schemes and the development of only parts of suitable land types, State authorities have greatly influenced the geography of irrigation of the plain. Several major effects of planning can be stressed at this juncture and some more detailed influences will be examined in the final section of this paper.

Irrigation tends to be more intensive in northern Victoria than in southern New South Wales. Not only are there more *intensive* irrigation schemes in northern Victoria but also the *partial* irrigation schemes in this area depend on higher water rights, more intensive land uses, and smaller farms, than do comparable schemes in New South Wales. Perhaps the most obvious explanation of this inter-State difference is that for Victoria, irrigable plain forms a much more important section of the State's land resources than it does for New South Wales. A further factor is that the riverine plain is much closer to Melbourne than it is to Sydney. When coupled with the longstanding disagreement over the use of the Murray River waters, this is a key explanation why Victoria has concentrated so much on the water of the Goulburn River and New South Wales on the waters of the Murrumbidgee River. In addition, proximity of the Riverina to Melbourne has tended to discourage investment there from Sydney. The fairly inexpensive 'District' mode of development has been preferred in the southern Riverina though it has some land types just as capable of supporting *intensive* irrigation as the adjacent Victorian regions watered by diversion from the Murray at Yarrawonga and Torrumbarry weirs.

Two further effects of broad political influences on irrigation warrant stress. Although Victorian authorities have long displayed a preference for *intensive* irrigation, they have elected to use new water resources available to the Goulburn System (by improved headworks on the three streams involved) to grant additional water rights to the *entire* System. This action means intensifying land uses rather than merely concentrating on 'high' plain better-suited to *intensive* irrigation, either by a modification of earlier irrigation or by completely new projects. In sharp contrast to this policy, authorities in New South Wales have elected to use new water resources (currently available in the Murrumbidgee River) not for new or old *partial* irrigation projects but for a new *intensive* irrigation scheme—the Coleambally Irrigation Area. In both States, modern policy reflects a preference for 'Area' or *intensive* irrigation methods, yet contrasts of policy affecting the allocation of new water resources is tending to produce differences in the geography of irrigated land uses in each State. In New South Wales, the current policy is tending to emphasize, even more strongly than in the past, the difference between and spatial separation of *intensive* and *extensive* irrigation schemes. In Victoria, current policy is tending to undermine longstanding differences between the two modes of development as reflected in long-established projects. Again, the contrast between the States would appear to stem from the fact that the demands of *partial* irrigation areas (existing or potential) are stronger in the State-wide scheme of things in Victoria than they are in New South Wales.

Wimmera-Mallee Lowlands

A comparison of Figs. 1, 3, 8 and 9 emphasizes that group irrigation schemes in the western lowlands (the Wimmera-Mallee region) contrast in many respects with those of the riverine plain. Though strongly influenced by political considerations, this contrast is very much a product of the different physical resource bases of the two areas.

Most of the Wimmera-Mallee lowlands once formed part of a Tertiary Murravian Gulf [20] which occupied this part of the continent. From late Pliocene times, as the peripheral uplands were being formed, the sea gradually retreated southwestwards from this gulf and materials once deposited on the sea-floor were affected by differential elevation and compaction and by faulting of bedrock. This resulted in a pronounced series of ridges and intervening troughs which trend generally from southeast to northwest over much of northwest Victoria and northeastern South Australia. Also, the entire area was gently uplifted. However, the Murray River was able to maintain a course to the retreating sea, though tortuously as it negotiated the northern extremities of the ridges and was turned sharply southwards at

Morgan in South Australia by the newly formed Western Uplands.

A number of detailed features of the Wimmera-Mallee country warrant emphasis. Aside from the ridges, of notable impact in the present context are the numerous west-east dunes of the northern Mallee close to the Murray. Both formations strongly influence the pattern of water supply channels which becomes increasingly more complex from the south (Wimmera) to the north (Murray-Mallee). Except for the Avoca (and then only in high flood) no tributaries reach the Murray from the south across the Wimmera-Mallee lowlands, all the small streams end in lakes or salt pans. In fact, except for the Murray country, the entire region is much more water-starved than is the riverine plain, particularly with increasing distance from the peripheral uplands, because the average annual rainfall declines, and the variability of rains increases, in this direction. The porous soils of the Mallee modify this factor. On the whole, the light-texture of solonized brown mallee soils tends to reduce the problem of aridity for dryland crops such as wheat but to increase it for irrigated crops.

We saw earlier that irrigation on the riverine plain is assisted by shallow incision of streams and relatively heavy-textured (fairly impervious) soils. The contrary condition applies to the Mallee. Downstream from Swan Hill, the Murray has been forced to become entrenched below the moderately-elevated surface, and the depth of entrenchment increases downstream. The river flows between a series of terraces separated from each other by sharp rises or bluffs until at Morgan it reaches a maximum depth of about 100 feet below the general land surface. Relatively expensive pumping has been necessary to command irrigable terrace land from the Murray except for limited gravity-diversion and siphon-drainage possible for the reclaimed swamps of the lower Murray.

The general pattern of rainfalls (Fig. 4) in the Wimmera-Mallee lowlands is somewhat similar to that of the riverine plain: high and more reliable falls close to the uplands; low and less reliable falls further from the uplands. However, this means that the chief irrigable country—the northwest near the Murray—is more water-starved than is much of the riverine plain. In addition, it has a much more pronounced seasonal pattern of rainfall (winter maxima) than has the plain, and this is of considerable relevance to the prevalence of dried fruitgrowing in the Murray-Mallee.

Important variations in the physical suitability of the land to irrigation occur throughout the Wimmera-Mallee zone. The combination of relatively low and erratic rainfalls and very porous soils makes the Mallee very hostile to closer settlement without artificial water supplies. As a result, a number of large domestic and stock water supply projects have been necessary to underpin closer settlement for cereal growing and/or fat lambraising. In both Victoria and South Australia, several such schemes rely on water pumped from the Murray River; however, by far the largest scheme is the Wimmera-Mallee Stock and Domestic Water Supply Scheme relying mainly on water diverted from the Eastern Highlands (Grampians) in western Victoria, but with augmenting supplies from the Goulburn Irrigation System after it has served the riverine plain. As mentioned later, only very limited irrigation can be allowed in these Domestic and Stock Water Supply schemes.

In sharp contrast to the plain, only one stream—the Murray River—provides an economic source of water for major group irrigation schemes in the Wimmera-Mallee lowlands. Hence, though such schemes are very scattered on the plain they occur in a shoe-string pattern along the Murray in the Mallee region (Fig. 1). Along the river frontages between Swan Hill and Mannum occur a series of small, compact and high-populated group irrigation schemes, dominated by fruit-vegetable production on elevated terrace soils commanded by pumps on the Murray. The expense of high or low-lift pumping make irrigation costly, as does the need to resort to concrete-lined channels to prevent excessive water percolation (with accompanying water losses and land deterioration) in the very porous solonized brown mallee soils of the region. These are key reasons for the small size, restricted location and intensive land uses of closer settlements along the Murray between Swan Hill and Mannum. The major exception in terms of water supply is the fruit area of the Swan Hill District (Woorinen) supplied by gravity in the large Torrumbarry

System. Compact settlements close to the river and devoted to tree and vine fruits (mainly for drying) and vegetables give the high net returns per acre foot and per acre irrigated necessary under the physically-exacting conditions of most of the Murray-Mallee country.

However, downstream from Mannum, South Australian authorities have been able to develop cheaper irrigation schemes by the reclamation of swamplands now served by flood-control levees, gravity water diversion and siphon-drainage of land. Though more expensive than comparable projects on the riverine plain, they permit dairying with lower incomes per acre foot or per acre than obtain for dried fruit production. However, it is milk-zone dairying and this gives relatively high gross incomes per acre.

In the irrigable Mallee country the spatial arrangement of land types and their suitability for irrigation is not very unlike that described earlier for the riverine plain, even if contrasts between 'high' and 'low' elements of the landscape are very much more pronounced in the Mallee and occur over shorter distances. Few, if any, areas commanded from the Murray below Swan Hill are naturally-suited to rice. However, the general absence of products in Groups V and VI (see pp. 154 to 155) here is primarily due to cost of water delivery rather than the character of land types encountered after water has been diverted from the river. Partly because of high costs imposed by primary pumping, and subsequent lifts in many cases, the most elevated of the commanded Mallee areas tend to be dominated by citrus. Not only does this crop give an adequate return for costly irrigation (costs being magnified by the common use of spray equipment) but it is very suited to the deep, well-drained soils characteristic of the 'high' Mallee slopes. Down the Mallee slopes, closer to the Murray, costs of water supply diminish, so does the natural suitability of land to the more-exacting crops. A movement down slope means a progressive change in the crops for which the country is naturally and economically best endowed: first to peaches, then to apricots, then to pome fruits and vines, and finally to vegetables. The only areas that lend themselves to extensive development for pastures are the reclaimed swamps below Wellington.

The aforementioned spatial arrangement of land uses by land types is obscured somewhat because of the smallness of farms and the economic incentive to diversify land uses wherever practicable. Hence, farmers often plant to vine fruits, country suited to tree fruits and vice versa. Nevertheless, the broad pattern still remains and has been documented in several land-use surveys [42].

Water Conservation and Irrigation in the Mallee

All of the group irrigation schemes along the Murray in the Mallee zone are devoted to *intensive* irrigation by State-sponsored closer settlement; they have strong affinities with the fruit-vegetable and dairying settlements of the riverine plain. In both regions, irrigation of this type emerges largely because of political forces; yet, the dominance of very *intensive* irrigation in the Mallee is also a reflection of the much more limited scope for irrigation there and the need to select land uses which will best justify the high costs of large water projects in this physically more hostile region. The overall pattern of group irrigation in the Murray-Mallee region is greatly affected by the three-fold political division of the region, one obvious effect of which is a scattered pattern, with *intensive* irrigation schemes in each of the States. A further, perhaps more subtle, effect is that investment for *intensive* irrigation of the Murray-Mallee lands has been much more active in Victoria and South Australia than it has in New South Wales. There seems no doubt that this contrast stems from the fact that the Mallee country is much closer to the State capitals, and is much more important in the total land resources, of the two southern States. On the whole, the Murray lands of far southwestern New South Wales are more peripheral in terms of the 'centre-periphery' thesis of economic growth [7]. To some extent, of course, farmers in far southwestern New South Wales tend to enjoy some of the facilities offered by the neighbouring State, such as rapid transport and large, centralized processing for dried fruit production and related urban facilities.

As mentioned earlier, the very extensive Domestic and Stock Water Supply schemes in the Wimmera-Mallee region are not designed to cater for irrigation, though limited and uncertain supplies for this purpose are sometimes made available along major channels such as the western extension of the Goulburn Irrigation System. The main reason for this is that it is uneconomic to supply water throughout the system during the hot months because evaporation and seepage losses then would be prohibitive. The problem is aggravated by the very tortuous nature of channels, especially in the northern Mallee, a direct reflection of the numerous ridges and west-east dunes. The porous character of most soils in the Mallee is an added difficulty.

Because of costs of basic works—initial pumps, concrete-lined channels and pumping costs—authorities have to charge high rates for water to farmers in the Murray-Mallee group irrigation schemes. Generally rates are two to three times those common for farmers on the riverine plain. This is a basic explanation for the dominance in the Murray-Mallee settlements of citrus, dried fruits and vegetables, giving the highest gross returns per acre foot and per acre irrigated of all irrigation activities in the Basin under review. An additional factor, of course, is that farmers in the Mallee use more water than do many farmers on the plain, partly because of their greater emphasis on summer irrigation and because of higher losses of water through percolation and evaporation. It is common for the Mallee fruitgrower to apply up to seven inches of water in the August-September period; eight inches in each of December and January; and a further eight inches in the March to April period. Part of the last-mentioned irrigation is for leguminous cover crops.

As stressed earlier, the main source of water for the Mallee settlements is the Murray River and its headwater control—Hume Dam. Local weirs and locks provide limited ponding but no real storage. Barrages at Murray Mouth serve, *inter alia*, to freshen the river for 50 miles upstream and facilitate irrigation on the reclaimed swamps. Under the River Murray Agreement, signed in 1914 by the three States concerned, N.S.W. and Victoria share the waters of the Murray less an amount sufficient to maintain specified winter and summer flows in the South Australian Murray. This is being supplemented by Chowilla Dam, under construction near the Victorian-South Australian border. Nowadays, a significant proportion of the Darling River waters stored in the Menindee Lakes Scheme is used to fulfil the obligations of New South Wales to South Australia, so releasing Murray waters further upstream for diversion into southern New South Wales.

Irrigation Farms in the Mallee

Except for their emphasis on tree and vine fruits especially suited to drying, the Murray-Mallee settlements are similar to those fruit projects encountered in the M.I.A. and the Goulburn Valley. However, because of the comparatively high net returns per acre achieved with dried fruits, irrigated farms in the Mallee are much smaller being about 20 to 40 acres as a rule (including some 18 to 25 acres under fruit).

The emphasis on dried fruits in the Mallee settlements is usually explained on climatic grounds. However, compared with leading world areas, such as Fresno, California, the best Mallee settlements ('Sunraysia' and those of South Australia farther down the Murray) are at the lowest end of the scale of suitability—measured mainly in terms of the amount of solar heat during the growing season. The Mid-Murray Dried Fruits Area near Swan Hill is sub-marginal by these standards, because of a 10 to 14 day delay in the season and greater incidence of damaging rains and humidity during the growing season [43]. On the whole, it is more reasonable to explain the Mallee dried fruits settlements in terms of State socialism and strong political pressures to create opportunities for small family farms. Dried fruits take advantage of local climate, such as it is, and they give a fair return over-and-above the high costs of water in the region. The persistence of the Mid-Murray Area, in spite of continued economic losses and a harsh environment, is a classic case of State intervention for the purpose of maintaining closer settlements developed fifty years ago, and of saving farmers from the great social and economic costs that large-scale farm abandonment would pose. It is clear that adjustments needed to produce farms which would be viable under present economic circumstances would necessitate a metamorphosis of the Area, since 20

acre blocks would have to be increased in size to 70 or 100 acres or more to permit a change at least to dairying.

A further factor that aided an initial emphasis on dried fruits in most of the Mallee settlements was their remoteness from major markets and lack of rapid transport. Dried fruits, with local weight-cost reduction, meant the production of a high-valued commodity that could withstand the long transport to overseas and major local markets.

One can discern three major groups of fruit-vegetable settlements in the Murray-Mallee:

1. The *Sunraysia* settlements of two States between Robinvale in the east and the junction of the Murray and Darling rivers; these include Mildura, Merbein, and Red Cliffs in Victoria, and Coomealla and Curlwaa in New South Wales. Pomona is a small settlement on the Lower Darling River.

2. The *South Australian Fruit Areas* which include Chaffey, Renmark, Lyrup, Berri, Cobdogla, Loxton, Sherwood, Media, Pyap, Moorook, Kingston, Waikerie, Cadell and Mypolonga. The last-named is remote from the rest and part of it forms the dairying regions of the Lower Murray Swamps.

3. The *Mid-Murray Fruit Areas* which embrace all or parts of the Tresco, Swan Hill and Nyah irrigation districts in Victoria; and several small Trusts at Goodnight, Koraleigh and Bungunyah, in New South Wales.

Though dried fruits are the key to the economies of these settlements, it should be noted that additional important sources of income are tree fruits, fresh grapes and vegetables. Part of the fresh fruit and fruit for wine comes from dried fruit crops that prove unsuited, physically or economically, for the dried fruits trade; part comes from plantings developed especially for the fresh fruit trade. The Mallee settlements are also able to command good city and other urban markets for vegetables in competition with centres closer to the markets. The main advantage in the Mallee is a long growing season, assisted by assured water supplies.

Aided by proximity to the Adelaide milk market, and by State closer settlement schemes, long narrow strips of swamplands on the Lower Murray have been reclaimed for dairying. The settlements occur downstream from Wellington, and include Cowirra, Baseby, Neeta, Wall, Pompoota, Mypolonga (part), Murray Bridge, Burdett, Long Flat, Swan Port, River Glen, Monteith, Wood's Point and Jervois. With their emphasis on 'permanent' pastures developed by *intensive* irrigation, dairy farms on the Lower Murray Swamps are akin to those mentioned earlier for the riverine plain. However, a key difference is that most farms possess additional Mallee country, usually not irrigated, and abutting the irrigated lowlands. These Mallee rises are used for 'dry' runs, flood relief, grazing for young stock and as a source of 'hard' (cereal) feed. Thus, they complement and supplement the irrigated lowlands; and this form of 'on-farm' *integration* has proved of considerable economic benefit [29c]. It has been stressed

elsewhere that integration of this type is to be regarded here as a fortuitous result of adjacent but contrasting land types and of an earlier land settlement policy by which authorities attempted to encourage mixed irrigated farming, i.e. dairying on the flats and fruitgrowing on the Mallee rises. Most farmers found this diversification uneconomic, mainly because of a clash of work loads, hence, they tended to concentrate on irrigated dairying and to use Mallee country as an additional land resource, both to add to irrigated lowlands and to relieve the latter, especially during floods and wet winters. It has been noted that many Victorian dairy farmers are now trying to acquire dryland to achieve similar benefits, yet, they are handicapped by the common lack of juxtaposition of suitable land types. This is a major developmental problem warranting more attention in any future scheme to sponsor dairying.

SELECTED IRRIGATION PROJECTS: EXAMPLES OF SEQUENT OCCUPANCE

Since the 1830s agriculture, in the broad sense, has been the dominant mode of occupance of the Southern Murray-Darling Basin. However, as stressed earlier in this paper, State intervention after 1886 to achieve group irrigation schemes has produced profound changes in the sequent occupance of the interior lowlands. Most *intensive* irrigation projects for fruitgrowing, dairying or intensive fat lambraising have meant completely new modes of occupance in areas previously settled for *extensive* pastoralism or for extensive pastoralism then cereal-fat lambraising on large farms. On the other hand, most *partial* or *extensive* irrigation has produced new *types* and *variants* in older classes of occupance [44]; on the whole, an intensification and increased stability of stockraising for meat and wool. However, *partial* irrigation has often resulted either in a complete drift out of cropping (i.e. wheat and oats) or a change from wheat-sheep farming into rice-sheep farming. Both types of development —new modes of occupance or new types and variants of an older occupance—form part of the 'agricultural revolution' in southern Australia, especially since about 1930, typified by relatively more emphasis on 'purposive change

of the environment' rather than 'adaptations' to it [33].

In this final section space will not permit a full-scale discussion of irrigation and sequent occupance, however, it is the intention briefly to stress several major impacts of irrigation on the landscapes of selected parts of the region under review. The first theme to be emphasized is that there has been a very longstanding interest in group irrigation in the region. On the whole, schemes that have emerged over the past five to six decades, or those that are now just unfolding, are essentially modifications of much earlier plans. The Areas and Districts of the Central Murrumbidgee Valley are classic examples of how changes of visible landscape features emerge from forces long latent to the area. In particular, major developments now under way south of the river—notably the Coleambally Irrigation Area—are not to be taken merely as products of the mid-twentieth century but are more correctly viewed as fulfilments of plans first extensively canvassed a half century and more ago, but adapted to modern conditions and policies. The second theme is that detailed features of the landscape produced by group irrigation schemes strongly reflect two practicalities of the local Australian scene. The fact that man's awareness of and reactions to his physical environment have changed radically, even in a few decades, and the fact that much of the intensified pattern of occupance induced by irrigation has involved rectangular subdivisions within pre-irrigation patterns of settlement. Contrasts of landscape among the contiguous Mildura, Merbein and Red Cliffs settlements in the Murray-Mallee of Victoria are cited as classic examples of the first trend. Landscape patterns in the Tongala-Stanhope Irrigation District of the riverine plain in Victoria are discussed as examples of the latter trend.

The Murrumbidgee Irrigation Areas

The period since 1906 has seen the emergence of most of the group irrigation schemes of New South Wales. The chief schemes are in the Central Murrumbidgee valley, particularly the Murrumbidgee Irrigation Areas (Yanco and Mirrool).

The increasing tempo of government interest in water development in Australia early this century formed part of a more general process of closer settlement promoted under various enactments. The droughts of the period 1897 to 1902 had a great impact on the Riverina, and the very active water projects by Trusts in Victoria after 1886 drew attention to the scope for State-assisted irrigation north of the Murray. However, when conditions became ripe for major State investment from Sydney, it was natural that efforts should at first be directed to the Murrumbidgee rather than to the Murray. As stressed earlier, the Murrumbidgee is one of the three finest streams in southern Australia, yet, unlike the Murray, it was not plagued with problems of inter-State disagreement about its use. Also, with direct rail connection it was significantly closer to Sydney (the M.I.A. region being about equidistant from Melbourne and Sydney) so that investment along the Murrumbidgee would not mean an outflow of benefits through the rival capital— Melbourne.

A variety of factors conditioned the detailed design of irrigation works along the Murrumbidgee. For a rounded picture it is necessary to look both at plans first laid in 1906, then at plans which emerged as farm settlement began after 1912, and finally to the shape of schemes now unfolding, especially in the Coleambally Irrigation Area (compare Figs. 14A and 14B, and note Fig. 13). Here we have splendid examples of the impact of physical factors discussed early in this paper; also, we can observe how early-laid plans have taken decades to reach fruition and have been modified by man's new awareness of his resource bases and the roles that group irrigation can fulfil in government-sponsored social and economic change.

Timing of Development

The group irrigation schemes of the Murrumbidgee Valley were first planned in some detail soon after 1900, i.e. at a time when Victorian irrigation policy was undergoing profound changes; notably a drastic increase in the degree of State intervention, with much wider acceptance of State-sponsored closer settlement [23]. Much of the new thinking of the day can be seen in the Minutes of Evidence of the 1906 Public Works Enquiry, set up to study plans for irrigation along the Murrumbidgee [31]. It is clear that there had been an important switch of official policy away from limited government intervention (mainly to construct works to supply water to schemes managed by Trusts of farmers) to much more sweeping State socialism for *intensive* irrigation. However, as first planned, the M.I.A. was based on a modification of the Victorian Trust system, in that both *intensive* and *extensive* irrigation were to be combined but with more active State promotion of closer settlement of the land.

State Developmental Policy

Though one has to search through many published and unpublished papers (some relating to completely different issues, such as new railways for the southern Riverina) it is clear that detailed planning for the Northern Murrumbidgee Irrigation Scheme (Fig. 14A) was influenced by a combination of physical and cultural factors by no means peculiar to the region but typical, in important respects, of conditions prevalent in the Southern Murray-Darling Basin as a whole.

Choice of dam site. After careful study over many years of the Eastern Highlands, and

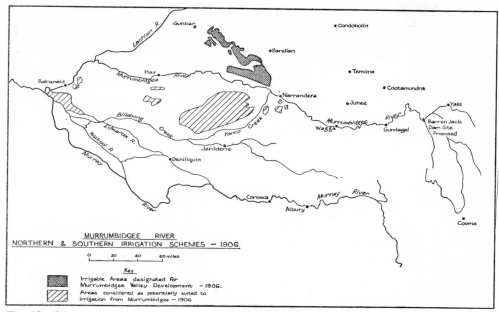

Fig. 13—(*Source:* New South Wales, Parliamentary Standing Committee on Public Works, Report ... Relating to the Proposed Barren Jack Storage Reservoir and Northern Murrumbidgee Irrigation Scheme, *Papers and Proceedings of the N.S.W. Legislative Assembly*, 1906)

much argument as to the geological suitability of the area, the decision was finally made to select Barren Jack (Fig. 13) as the site for the main headworks on the Murrumbidgee River between Barren Jack and Black Andrew mountains. This was a classic example of an efficient dam site: an expensive concrete structure was to be placed in a narrow and deep gorge, with a hard granite floor and walls giving firm foundations, as well as materials for dam construction and a high ratio of storage to cubic capacity (cost) of dam wall. The dam was suitably located fairly close to irrigable lowlands and well downstream to ensure maximum upstream storage, especially from the combined run-off of the Murrumbidgee, Goodradigbee and Yass rivers. Some concern was expressed in 1906 about possible water losses through fissures, faults and limestone materials, but it was generally agreed that Barren Jack was an ideal dam site, 'as if Nature had made it so' [31].

Choice of Site for Diversion Weir. Having regard to potential irrigable lands (discussed below), Berembed Weir was to be located at the head of Bundidgerry Creek with a number of factors in mind. As is frequently the case, final location was a compromise. The site formed the narrowest point of the valley between Wagga (lower slopes) and Narrandera ('high' plain). It was sufficiently downstream to reduce the risk of flood damage to the offtake canal and to ensure reasonable proximity to irrigable plain, thus lowering reticulation costs, and it was sufficiently upstream to give the greatest command over the widest area of potential irrigation land. Very significant in alluvial country, the site possessed a rocky outcrop close to the surface, ensuring firm foundations with minimum costs. In addition, it was possible to save on reticulation costs by using Bundidgerry Creek as a main channel almost as far as Narrandera.

Choice of Channel Route. To facilitate a start on irrigation north of the river—a key decision and discussed below—the main offtake channel (canal) was located around the foothills of the McPherson and Cocoparra ranges (spurs of the Eastern Highlands) ensuring easy gravitation from behind Berembed Weir via Bundidgerry Creek and maximum command over socalled 'first', 'second' and 'third' class irrigation

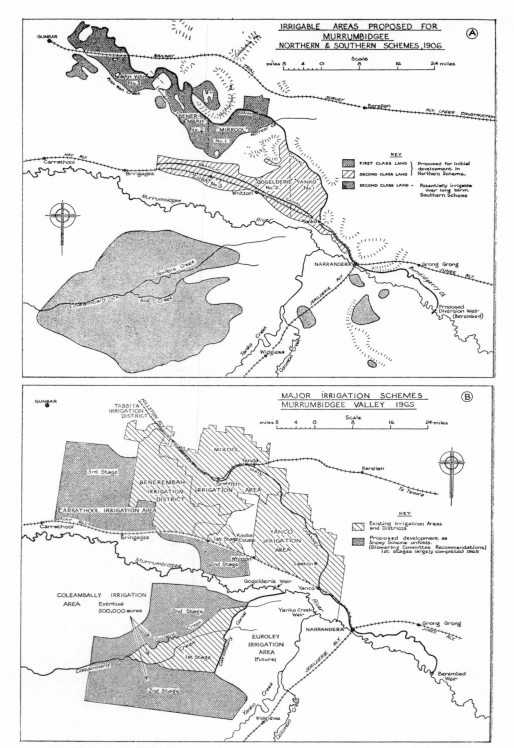

Fig. 14—Contrasts between old and modern irrigation projects, central Murrumbidgee Valley, N.S.W. (*Source:* (A) As for Fig. 13; (B) England, H. N. (1960). The Agricultural Use of the Snowy Waters: II—Irrigation Plans and Policy, *Austr. Journ. Agric. Econ.*, *4* p. 63

land between these uplands, the Murrumbidgee River, and Gunbar. The main channel was. to run about 132 miles from Berembed towards Gunbar. A subsidiary channel was planned to run parallel to the Murrumbidgee towards Hay, this being the only real concession authorities were prepared to make to strong claims made by the so-called Gibson group interested in *partial* irrigation to assist dryland farming (domestic, stock, and limited irrigation supplies) rather than closer settlement by *intensive* irrigation (to use the terms of this essay and not of Gibson and his advisers) [*31*].

Choice of Irrigable Land. Surveys carried out by the New South Wales Department of Public Works, aided by the New South Wales Department of Agriculture, were quoted in the 1906 Enquiry as indicating that there were about 356,870 acres of irrigable country on the riverine plain to be commanded by the planned canal west of Narrandera (Figs. 13 and 14). This land was divided into classes, and it was determined that about 196,000 acres were 'first-class' irrigable land, extending as a narrow, essentially continuous strip in the northwest. Closer to Narrandera, surveys indicated some 160,870 'second-class' land; in addition, a very large region of 'second-class' land was located to the south of the Murrumbidgee River, flanking Coleambally and Spillers creeks. It is evident that early estimates of these land types were governed largely by engineering considerations and that opinion was not unanimous as to the qualities of the various classified lands. The 1906 Committee, for example, reported to Parliament that there was not much difference between the two land classes [*31*]. It seems that irrigation engineers first selected the lands and agricultural authorities later confirmed their choice [*29*].

The original scheme pointed to the scope for diverting water from the Murrumbidgee to the irrigable lands north and south of the river, as part of the Northern and Southern schemes outlined in 1906. In view of the lack of experience with irrigation on this scale in New South Wales, it was decided to begin well to the north of the river on 'first-class' land. Should this prove successful, further development would spread to 'second-class' land to complete the Northern Scheme proposed in 1906, and,

perhaps later, to 'second-class' land to fulfil plans for the projected Southern Scheme not planned in any detail that year.

Irrigation north of the Murrumbidgee was to be tried in the two major zones shown in Fig. 14A. In the northernmost region, a start was planned for 'first-class' land on 'high' plain closest to the Eastern Highlands, i.e. in the so-called Mirrool District No. 1 which more or less conforms to central and eastern parts of the presentday Mirool Irrigation Area (Fig. 14B). Further expansion on less-elevated plain was to take up other 'first-class' land designed in 1906 as the so-called Benerembah District No. 2 and Wah Wah District No. 3, now projects of similar names (without numbers). The second major area of development was proposed for land south of Mirrool Creek, closer to Yanco and the Murrumbidgee River. This was to be on allegedly 'second-class' land in projects called Yanco District No. 1, Gogeldrie District No. 2 and Cuba District No. 3. It will be noted from Fig. 14 that these projects covered important elements of what are now the Yanco Irrigation Area (including the new Kooba Estate) and the Benerembah Irrigation District.

In 1906, the decision to start the Murrumbidgee Northern Scheme in the Mirrool District No. 1 was based on two factors. Firstly, it was believed that land here was naturally as well-suited to irrigation as any other in Australia. Secondly, that resumption of the northernmost land would be easier than resuming land south of Mirrool Creek because more of it was Crown Land and less was in private holdings. Authorities believed that landholders closer to Yanco would subdivide lands for irrigation, after the northern pilot scheme succeeded and the application of compulsory water rights stimulated interest in irrigation (as had happened in Victoria).

Planners concerned with the Murrumbidgee Irrigation Scheme proposed in 1906 seemed to follow a somewhat unbalanced approach typical of contemporary planning in Australia and abroad, and not greatly corrected until very recent times. A tendency to give disproportionate weight to engineering issues and too little weight to problems of crop and animal husbandry, soil science and economic prospects for irrigation [*29*]. However, it is obvious from the Minutes of Evidence of the 1906 Public

Works Enquiry that many people with expert and practical experience testified to the suitability of selected lands on the Murrumbidgee to irrigation of the type planned. Nor did many people raise doubts about the likely economic merits of the proposals. From hindsight, one can observe numerous defects in the initial planning. How much of these defects could have been foreseen by Australians, under the social and economic conditions of 1906, is a moot point. However, more recognition of variations of soil types and problems of drainage was quite possible, even in those days.

Officials concerned with irrigation planning in New South Wales early this century offered one reason for public investment between Yanco and Gunbar, namely that it would ensure financial salvaging of the Narrandera to Hay railway, then running at a loss. However, there is some doubt that this factor really played a part, compared with the desire of ruling politicians to retain power at the coming elections. For public investment of this type, it is very difficult to get at the real causes for decisions and to determine how important were factors mentioned by officials close to the projects.

Choice of Types of Farms. Experience in Victoria and western America, coupled with the then current programmes to aid closer settlement generally throughout the State, persuaded the New South Wales Department of Public Works to favour *intensive* irrigation as the basis of the Northern Murrumbidgee Scheme. Failure or serious difficulties of Irrigation Trusts in Victoria between 1886 and 1900 led to official opposition to much *extensive* irrigation to aid dryland farming as proposed by some of the witnesses to the 1906 Enquiry.

Early this century, the Government of New South Wales was engaged in broad programmes to sponsor closer settlement in humid and semi-arid areas, particularly by British immigrants; but it was at first hampered by a lack of suitable Crown Land in the better-watered parts of the State. Irrigation in the drier interior was welcomed as a means of providing more-abundant land resources for closer settlements. Authorities in New South Wales were convinced therefore that State-sponsored irrigation schemes would succeed only if based on the rapid purchase and closer settlement of country

by the State, after initial works had been implemented. The plans to begin on the Murrumbidgee largely with *intensive* irrigation for fruits and vegetables was also based on a strong local desire to make New South Wales independent of imports from other States. Mildura and Wyuna in Victoria and Salt Lake City in the U.S.A. were cited as examples of likely benefits in the Mirrool District No. 1.

However, the promotion of *intensive* irrigation of fruits was not the sole aim of the Murrumbidgee Northern Irrigation Scheme of 1906. Because of cheap water supplies, it was thought that dairying and fodder crop production (the latter for fattening stock and for sale to dryland farmers) would be major activities farther west on heavier soils of 'intermediate' and 'low' plain (as they are termed in this essay) and also as 'beginning' industries for some fruit-growers.

The scheme in 1906 was to develop several towns and outlying villages as compact nuclei. And around them, to set up concentric belts of farming: very small suburban 2-acre blocks for urban workers; small fruit-vegetable blocks of 5 to 20 acres abutting the towns on the better soils favoured by proximity to water supplies; and, in the outer ring, larger farms (20 to 100 acres) given over to dairying and fodder crop production using *partial* irrigation. Pre-irrigation farmers were to be offered 100 acres in the new venture.

Having regard to earlier discussion of land types on the riverine plain, it might seem that planners in 1906 were aware of detailed variations in the suitability of land for urban and rural settlement under irrigation. However, it is erroneous to read too much modern thinking into old schemes. The siting of the major channel on 'high' plain close to the peripheral uplands was an engineering decision designed to ensure that the gravity water supply system would serve the greatest area of 'fertile' land. Positioning of major towns near this channel ensured that the classic hubs or nodes of a closer settlement, as developed in Australia for nearly a century, would be closest to the major lines of water supply, on unirrigable land yet close to many irrigation farms. The concentration of farms on what is now seen as 'high' plain, with the widest range of physical suitability to most land uses, was mainly aimed in

1906 to ensure the easiest water supply to the largest number of farms; however, planners were also aware that this elevated plain was most suited to fruitgrowing. The 1906 proposal to promote larger farms with increasing distance from the major urban centres was based mainly on the need to compensate farmers for being farther from the major source of water and the towns. Evidence given by Wade [31] suggests that authorities regarded 'first-class' land as homogeneous, it might be false to conclude that planners were completely unaware that greater distance from the main nodes and channel also meant less-elevated country with a somewhat narrower range of production possibilities. Of course, in 1906, they were not aware that this 'low' plain would prove unsuited to *intensive* irrigation for lucerne, or that some soils (notably solonized brown Mallee soils) would be poor for fruits. Though it is difficult to understand fully the outlook of planning in 1906, it seems that concentric zonation of land uses for the Northern Murrumbidgee Irrigation Scheme mainly reflected an awareness by civil and hydrological engineers of the benefits of compact settlement and of the difficulty of effective water supply on the peripheries of a scheme. Micro-variations of land type seem to have been secondary considerations after engineers had selected country, though they were more obviously influential by the time the project got under way. Nevertheless, it would be erroneous to assert that the planners of 1906 knew nothing about differences of land type and their effects on the kinds of irrigation then proposed for the Murrumbidgee.

At least as it was planned in 1906, the Murrumbidgee settlement was influenced more by niceties of some aspects of engineering design and architectural layout than by attempts to take full advantage of detailed variations of land types. For example, as was the case at Mildura (discussed below), the plan for Griffith laid down by Walter Burley Griffin showed a system of radial and circumferential roads bisecting smaller blocks as the town centre (a circular town square) was approached. The pattern of subdivision of the rural area was then a logical extension of urban subdivision, based on a simple, if aesthetically pleasing design. The early planning also revealed a tendency to subdivide land on paper even before

channels had been surveyed, so imposing a far greater simplicity of layout than later conditions of channel design and efficient land and water use dictated. Griffith was to be sited on the foothills of the peripheral uplands on inexpensive land occupying a limited site of easily-drained land commanding breezes and views [45].

It is important to realize also that the Murrumbidgee Irrigation Areas were greatly affected by developments elsewhere, especially at Salt Lake City in the U.S.A. [31]. Local planners felt that the Murrumbidgee scheme would only prove a success if it were based on 'a close population and intense culture'. However, the aim was to achieve greater compactness than could be attained by a simple grid-like subdivision with uniform block sizes, irrespective of distance from urban nuclei and main channels (as happened at Mildura). L. A. B. Wade, the then Principal Engineer for Rivers, Water Supply and Drainage in N.S.W., referred to Smythe's *The Conquest of Arid America* [46]; Smythe is here speaking of Salt Lake City, which has become a model for similar settlements:

The city blocks consist of 10 acres, each divided into eight lots of 1¼ acres . . . There were two tiers of 10 acres and 20 acre lots. They went to farmers according to the size of their families [31].

Wade noted that, at Salt Lake City, the smaller the blocks the greater the settlers' neighbours; very small farms made it possible for farmers to live in the town. Thus each 4000 or 5000 acres will support 'a thrifty and beautiful hamlet'. It is clear from the 1906 Enquiry that experts wished to avoid, on the Murrumbidgee, a key source of difficulty which occurred in the early days of Mildura—over-ambitious extensions of subdivisions beyond the bounds of assured water supply. The new aim was gradually to expand on the edges of the nucleus of closer settlement, as water supplies to farm lands became more abundant. However, though Wade saw great economy of water distribution arising from compact settlement, he expressed the view that intensive land uses would 'not . . . be the best thing for the country' [31].

After the 1906 decision to go ahead with the Northern Murrumbidgee Irrigation Scheme, many years elapsed before headworks were built and farms settled. In the interim, important changes of policy occurred and, in part, these modifications reflected changing awareness of, and reactions to, physical conditions. Work on Burrinjuck Dam was started in 1907 to 1908 followed by work on Berembed Weir and the Main Canal. Water was first supplied to farms in 1913, when the Murrumbidgee Irrigation Scheme was opened. Prior to this, an Agricultural Experiment Farm was set up in 1908 at Yanco under the Department of Agriculture. It was located on land made available by McCaughey—a pioneer of irrigation on the Murrumbidgee—and its purpose was to explore agricultural problems of local irrigation development and to give advice to new settlers. At first, the Murrumbidgee scheme was administered by a Trust (as had been the case with earlier Victorian ventures). In 1913, the project came under the control of the Water Conservation and Irrigation Commission, with Wade as its sole member. After Wade's death the Commission was established with three members in 1914, along present lines.

Contrary to the 1906 plans, the Murrumbidgee closer settlement first began south of Mirrool Creek, i.e. on the land earlier classified as 'second-class', in country now included in the Yanco Irrigation Area but then termed Yanco District No. 1. It was not until the soldier settlement after 1918 that the so-called 'first-class' land north of Mirrool Creek was closer-settled to form the present day Mirrool Irrigation Area. This change of policy seems to have occurred for several reasons, though it must be admitted that these reasons have been inferred from public statements by officials close to the project; statements often made out of context. The true reasons for changes of government developmental policy are difficult to establish from the reports of commissions and bodies of enquiry or from newspaper articles, and other sources. However, plausible explanations for the major changes in the location and character of Murrumbidgee irrigation development are:

1. The fact that McCaughey readily agreed to let the State resume his land at North Yanco for the relatively low value of £3.10.0 per acre.

2. Rising costs of development between 1906 and 1912 which meant that it was more economic by the later year to develop as close as possible to the diversion weir.

3. The suitability of the soils near Yanco to *intensive* irrigation. It is clear that, for many years, the quality of soil closer to Yanco had been the subject of debate. For example, several witnesses at the 1906 Enquiry contended that all of the land shown as 'second-class' to the north of the Murrumbidgee River should have been rated as 'first-class'.

The report to Parliament of the 1906 Enquiry summed up by stressing that there seemed little difference between the two classes of land but that:

The Department [of agriculture] appear to have been guided in their classification by the question of subsoil, and the facility with which the land could be worked with the aid of water supplied for irrigation purposes [31].

It is clear from the Carmichael Commission's report of 1915 to 1916 that considerable variations of soil and land-use capabilities were then observed throughout country earlier classified as 'second-class', though there was much disagreement about the overall comparison between land in the Yanco and Mirrool areas [47].

In 1916, a Royal Commission enquiring into irrigation observed [48]:

Had it been feasible, before opening the settlement to selection, the proper course would have been to have made exhaustive soil-surveys of the whole Area; to have conducted practical tests of the various descriptions of soils; and then to have divided the land up into living areas suitable for the intensive farmer, the fruitgrower, dairyman, and stockraiser with holdings varying in size according to the quality of the soil and the requirements of those industries.

As this procedure would have necessitated prolonged delay, its adoption was impossible.

This frank admission by the Commission negates the judgment of later writers that variations of soils were not known to the irrigation authorities at the time of major closer settlement; however, it also suggests that such variations did not play a major role in shaping the location of embryonic development and the different land uses within it.

By the time the Murrumbidgee scheme got under way after 1913, Victorian policy towards irrigation development had changed radically under the influence of Elwood Mead [49]. This change greatly affected the decision of the New South Wales authorities to abandon their earlier intention of promoting *partial* irrigation on the peripheries of the Murrumbidgee settlements and to concentrate on *intensive* irrigation throughout. Also, the 1906 policy of ultimate development south of the Murrumbidgee, should the northern scheme prove successful, was changed to complete concentration on the north. The main canal, as originally designed, proved inadequate and was enlarged to cope especially with the new emphasis on *intensive* irrigation, and extensions of settlements into the Mirrool District [50]. By the time of farm settlement, the rigid equal block subdivision was also modified somewhat to take account of variations of land types [51]. Also, to minimize problems of transport, closer settlement tended to occur near railways, at some distance from the new urban centre, and move back towards it [36b].

During the 1920s and 1930s, physical and economic problems enforced many radical changes in the pattern of farming in the Murrumbidgee Irrigation Areas [51, 49]. Major difficulties were the economic problems of the depression years as well as waterlogging and damage to soils by salt accumulation. Although these problems were felt especially by the fruit industry, a drastic change occurred on the outer edges of the Murrumbidgee settlements, at first developed for dairying by *intensive* irrigation. A major factor was that heavier soils of 'intermediate' and 'low' plain (as they now appear) proved unsuited to lucerne, the key to the success of all irrigated dairying of southeastern Australia at the time. Lewis explains this for the M.I.A. in terms of soil impermeability, the flat terrain conducive to bad drainage, and the tendency for poor irrigation and water lying on the land to 'scald' lucerne crops [52]. Attempts to organize cooperative marketing of lucerne (an early aim of the project) had failed, but 'permanent' pastures, destined to become the mainstay of Australian dairying, had not then

been developed. As a result of these problems, and general economic difficulties, the dairying industry declined on the M.I.A. and was painfully replaced by a new industry, involving radical alterations to farm sizes and land uses. The general trend was towards improved pastures and sheep, then mixed rice-fat lamb-raising; and the trend meant increases in modal farm sizes on 'intermediate' and 'low' plain, from the initial 100 acres under dairying to 400 to 600 acres and more—the present day Large Area Blocks. Though still geared to *intensive* irrigation, these farms now concentrate on 'annual' pastures rotated with rice in a five to seven year rotation. However, 'permanent' pastures are becoming of increasing importance as a basis of a more flexible system of stock fattening, including the fattening of purchased store beef and sheep.

The Coleambally Irrigation Area shown in Fig. 14B is the largest scheme of its type ever attempted in Australia and is the first of a long-term series of projects in southern New South Wales to make fuller use of waters in the Murrumbidgee and Murray rivers, especially as the Snowy scheme unfolds. In general location, the scheme coincides with the Southern Murrumbidgee proposals sketched, but not planned, in 1906. However, in several ways, the Coleambally Area is a major departure from past practice in New South Wales. It reflects the aforementioned resurgence of interest in *intensive* irrigation and the economic need to concentrate on sheep, beef, and rice, products which have proved fairly successful in the past and which don't pose the same marketing difficulties that face fruits and dairy products [18]. The Coleambally Irrigation Area exploits 'high' plain close to the Eastern Highlands, favoured by land types with a wide range of production possibilities and close and abundant water supplies. Its site offers greater flexibility of land uses than land farther west, shown as potentially irrigable in 1906.

Contrasts of Landscape in the Mildura, Merbein and Red Cliffs Irrigation Districts, Victoria

Most obvious products of government planning are sharp boundaries to formal and functional regions. Striking examples of these occur along the Murray River, where Mallee country

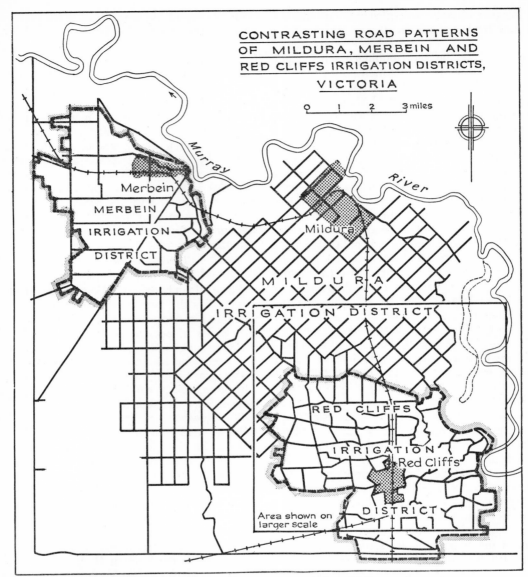

Fig. 15—(*Source*: State Rivers and Water Supply Commission, Melbourne)

has been developed for the *intensive* irrigation of small farms devoted to vine and tree fruits and associated vegetable production.

The Mildura, Merbein, and Red Cliffs irrigation districts of Victoria exhibit two very noticeable features. Firstly they stand out like oases of intense activity in an otherwise sparsely populated and relatively little developed region. Secondly the three settlements reflect important changes in man's apprecia-

tion of and reactions to his physical resource base. The projects arose in the last major phase of sequent occupance of southeastern Australia, as arable farming was displaced, or in their case as irrigation leapt well beyond the economic limits of an earlier type of occupance—broadacre farming for wheat and associated crops. Mildura was first designed in the late 1880s; Merbein (at first, White Cliffs) in 1907, but with post-1918 extensions; and Red

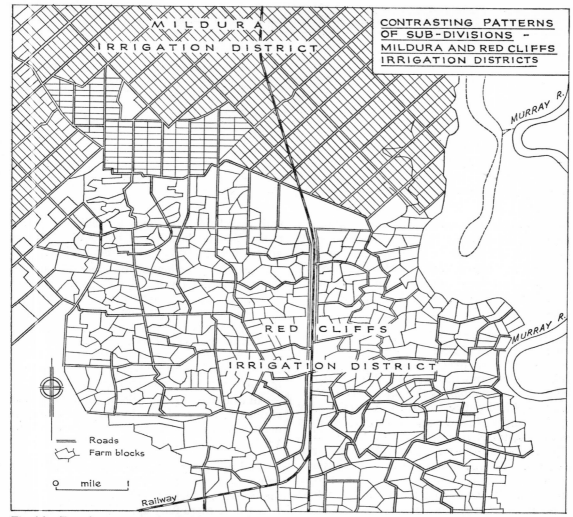

Fig. 16—(Based on a map supplied by State Rivers and Water Supply Commission, Melbourne)

Cliffs in 1920. Considerable changes occurred over this 35-year period, especially in man's awareness of micro-regional variations of soils, conditions of ground drainage and the economy of design of irrigation projects. These changes are still reflected in visible landscape forms of the three projects, some elements of which are emphasized by Figs. 15 and 16.

It is clear that the basic design of the Mildura District was made by the Chaffey Brothers, especially George Chaffey, under their agreement with the Victorian Government [53]. A very simple, gridlike subdivision was followed, the irrigated fruit blocks being a logical extension of

Mildura township (node of the settlement). In laying out the form of the project, the Chaffeys created a fruit settlement with various features:

1. Following the pattern they had adopted for the Ontario scheme, California, the Chaffeys aimed to create a settlement focussed on a main, straight-line road upon which a rectangular grid was superimposed [54]. It seems that this form was strongly influenced by the gridlike pattern common to much American settlement and to the wheat areas of Victoria of the day.

2. The settlement was to contain a modified concentric zonation of blocks, ranging from

Table 1 *Details of Lands Purchased and Subdivided by the State for Closer Settlement in the Irrigation Schemes of the Far North-West of Victoria, under the Closer Settlement Act, 1915. As at 1922.*

Closer Settlement Estates	Area of Land Purchased by the State in Acres	Properties Subdivided							
		Area in Acres	Number	Number of Families Thereon When Purchased	Subdivided Into		Number of Closer Settlement Blocks Now Occupied	Present Increase In Number of Families
					Number of Closer Settlement Blocks	Average Area In Acres		
Merbein	8,300	8,300	—	—	384	21	384	384
Red Cliffs	33,000	12,700	1	3	702	16	702	699

Source: Annual Report of the State Rivers and Water Supply Commission for 1921-22, Melbourne, 27-28.

'town' blocks of $\frac{1}{8}$ acre in the centre, through adjacent 'villa' lots of $2\frac{1}{2}$ acres, to 'agricultural' blocks of 10 acres; a pattern akin to that adopted at Ontario [55]. Blocks increased in size with increasing distance from the town, as happened later for the M.I.A. (see earlier discussion).

3. No attempt was made to adopt a relatively complex pattern of land subdivision, with farms orientated to an irregular pattern of channels following tortuous routes dictated by the west-east dune formations of the region. The settlement was laid out and allotted to farmers very rapidly and its broad forms were decided even before distributaries were surveyed [55, 56]. The channels were superimposed on the grid-like pattern of roads and property subdivisions, with some cutting many properties into two or more pieces and sometimes not reaching properties. In fact, there was a tendency to try to make channels follow fencelines rather than contours. The basic aim was to give each property a road frontage rather than a channel frontage.

The Merbein Irrigation District was first planned along very different lines to those finally adopted by farmers and persisting to the present day. Initially called White Cliffs, its farms were each to have 50 acres of irrigated land (mainly for fodder crops) and 640 acres of unirrigated Mallee country [57]. However, the project quickly switched to closer-settled fruit production along the lines adopted at Mildura. Yet, unlike the latter, Merbein grew slowly from an initial scheme close to the river,

with peripheral extensions as additional water reticulation made this possible. Red Cliffs has always been designed as a fruit project.

A careful examination of Figs. 15 and 16 shows that the layout of settlements became increasingly complex over time: a simple grid-like pattern at Mildura and the early (near-river) part of Merbein; a somewhat irregular pattern in the peripheral (later) parts of Merbein; and a very complex pattern at Red Cliffs. The contrast is most striking when viewed from the air or from aerial photographs.

An examination of official reports shows that various factors explain why the form of settlement became increasingly complex over the 1887 to 1920 period.

1. Perhaps the most important consideration was the question of producing a more efficient means of reticulating water to farms. Various issues were more fully appreciated and handled in later projects: by adopting a fairly complex pattern of distributaries in Red Cliffs, with each channel positioned to take advantage of micro-relief, and with properties subdivided to allow for this, it was possible to minimize channel lengths and so to reduce water losses and ground damage through evaporation and seepage. Later decision to line all channels with concrete was another way of overcoming the problem. However, gradually, authorities became aware of the need to lay out distributaries and main channels to ensure command of the greatest area per mile of channel and to minimize water losses, especially seepage losses in very sandy soils. By 1905 Victorian authorities accepted the principle of laying out

blocks so that at least one channel commanded a portion of every allotment, preferably by gravity supply, rather than have channels bisect some farms with distributaries along fences, as was done at Mildura. Before Merbein and Red Cliffs were finally developed, it was decided that each new property was to have a channel rather than a road frontage.

2. Mildura was criticized for being laid out on too ambitious a scale at the outset [56]. All settlements after it were developed by gradual extensions of channels and closer settlement, rather than by a blanket design of a large area.

3. In Victoria after 1905, all projects incorporated the concept of property subdivision after channel survey. In order to minimize the number and cost of road bridges over channels, and to ensure that properties had sufficient area and types of land to permit efficient farming, it was necessary to adopt a rather complex pattern of laying out roads and property subdivisions. The complexity reached a peak at Red Cliffs and is to be contrasted with the much simpler, yet less effective pattern of subdivision of the adjacent Mildura settlement.

4. After Mildura was first established, farmers and authorities became increasingly aware of the need to overcome growing problems of land drainage. The Red Cliffs settlement was the first Victorian scheme to begin with a planned drainage scheme; and the basic design of the settlement was largely influenced by the requirements of land drainage. For example, rather than adopt a simple channel pattern or simple layout of properties, it was necessary to adopt complex channel routes and to so locate property boundaries as to avoid unnecessary combination of elevated, permeable soils with lower-lying land subject to waterlogging from irrigated lands above it. Variations in property sizes throughout Red Cliffs reflect the varying quality of land. The fact that considerable differences in productive capacity could occur over short distances was not obvious to the architects of Mildura.

Landscape and Sequent Occupance in the Tongala-Stanhope Irrigation District, Victoria

The two case-study areas discussed above are splendid examples of how closer settlement

with irrigation has wrought such changes that the presentday landscape bears little signs of the earlier dryland occupance. A prime reason for this, of course, is that the change was from a very extensive system of dryland farming, with huge farms and a sparse-settled landscape, to a very intensive system of irrigated farming, with very small farms and the usual complex maze of structures associated with intense closer settlement. By contrast, the Tongala-Stanhope Irrigation District provides an excellent example of a region that was fairly closely settled for dryland farming before the advent of Government-sponsored irrigation. It is a region that initially had experienced two modes of dryland occupance; where irrigation then produced closer settlement, but the character of the final landscape was dictated by the three modes of occupance. The detailed formal and functional regions contained within the Tongala-Stanhope Irrigation District have been influenced greatly by man's adaptations to the physical environment for both dryland and irrigation farming; and the project provides numerous demonstrations of changes in this relationship over time with changing technology and new social and economic conditions.

Prior to the 1870s, the country now incorporated in the Tongala-Stanhope Irrigation District was first settled by 'squatters' pioneering the first mode of occupance: extensive pastoralism for Merino wool production. As in other parts of the riverine plain, initial settlement focussed on the river frontages which afforded superior water supplies and, in most seasons, the best feed conditions. However, even by the 1850s and 1860s, infilling of the 'back' or interfluvial country was well under way. It is difficult to obtain a precise account of the pattern of subdivisions and general land settlement promoted in this 'squatting era'; however, one account [58] shows that the extensive belt of country now covered by the Goulburn System, between the Goulburn and Campaspe rivers (Fig. 1), was held in only six pastoral runs. From east to west, *Ardpatrick, St Germains, Wyuna, Merrigum, Tongala,* and *Cornelia Creek.* The settlement pattern comprised very scattered farmsteads, widely-spaced roads (usually running as the crow flies, directly between important nodes), and infrequent property boundary lines.

Table 2 *Details of Lands Purchased and Subdivided by the State for Closer Settlement in the Irrigation Schemes near Tongala and Stanhope, Victoria, under the* Closer Settlement Act, 1915. *As at 1922.*

Closer Settlement Estates	Area of Land Purchased by the State in Acres	Properties Subdivided						
		Area in Acres	Number	Number of Families Thereon When Purchased	Subdivided Into		Number of Closer Settlement Blocks Now Occupied	Present Increase In Number of Families
					Number of Closer Settlement Blocks	Average Area In Acres		
Stanhope	20,900	20,900	6	12	309	62	302	297
Kyabram	3,000	3,000	7	10	56	53	56	46
Tongala	16,300	16,300	33	31	263	59	263	232
Koyuga	4,200	4,200	} Part 1	—	52	77	52	52
Cornelia Creek	2,500				14	176	13	14

Source: Annual Report of the State Rivers and Water Supply Commission for 1921-22, Melbourne, 27-28.

During the 1870s and 1880s, much of the region and huge parts of like riverine plain in northern Victoria were transformed by closer settlement for a radically new mode of occupance, that of wheat growing founded on farm units of 320 acres (best areas) or 640 acres (poorest areas). Modern cadastral maps bear witness to the imprint on the landscape of this mode of occupance; and the regular gridlike subdivisional patterns, arranged in a simple-to-survey north-south alignment, are strikingly borne out in present day road patterns, roads being built so that intersecting pairs contain about one square mile (2 'blocks' here). This dramatic feature of closer settlement for arable farming on riverine plain is clearly visible from the air or air photo maps and is summarized for Tongala-Stanhope in Fig. 17. Both Holt [59] and Meinig [60, 61] suggest that the 320 acre or 640 acre rectangular grid, used so much in the Australia wheat lands, was adopted with modifications from the U.S.A. 'grid-iron' system used for the Prairies.

It is not clear how much of the region was actually settled for wheatgrowing on 320-acre or 640-acre blocks, or how much of it was merely so surveyed in anticipation of a development which never ensued. Old and new cadastral maps do not decide the issue, since many maps reproduced years after the event perpetuate plans rather than achievements. However, that closer settlement for wheat, under

The Land Act, 1869 and subsequent legislation, did occur in and around the region now covered by the Tongala-Stanhope Irrigation District is borne out in several ways. For example, in 1880, the Victorian Parliament was presented with evidence [62] that the rate of selection of lands for wheat growing in the Echuca district had slackened because of adverse seasons. Similar reports were tabled for the same region in 1881, 1882, 1884, 1885 and 1886. The reports stressed problems of crop failures, farm abandonment and reversion to grazing, because of droughts. It is a well-documented fact that the impact of these droughts on closer-settled wheat farms of the northern plains of Victoria triggered off the first major plans to develop irrigation in northern Victoria [23].

Proposals in 1881 to bring State-sponsored water supplies to the northern plains of Victoria showed that most of the far northern plain between the Goulburn and Campaspe rivers was then subdivided according to the basic 320 acre or 640 acre grid pattern. In 1916, a Royal Commission attributed a failure of lucerne growing in the Rochester, Tongala, and Kyabram districts, 'not so much to the quality of the soil, but more to the utilization of old wheat paddocks' [63]. There seems little doubt, therefore, that the gridlike pattern of roads and basic property subdivisions in the modern Tongala-Stanhope Irrigation District is a legacy of an earlier wheat-growing era. Nor is there any doubt that, where possible, the pattern assumed a very regular form. The most obvious distortions to the simple north-south grid occur where a less-regular alignment of property boundaries was necessary to take advantage of river frontages or to adapt to infrequent hilly areas. Major roads, first surveyed in the squatting era, also break the regular pattern, as many run diagonally across the plains from southeast to northwest or from southwest to northeast. The most marked disturbance to the regular north-south alignment of wheat properties occurred where major roads ran close to rivers.

Between 1885 and 1905, mainly as a result of serious droughts, many wheat farms were abandoned and much property amalgamation took place, along with a fairly general reversion to pastoralism [62, 64]. However, these changes did not disturb the basic farm pattern; they merely altered the effective sizes of farms as economic units. (Of course, it should be stressed that even at the height of the early wheat era, single farms comprised a number of contiguous or scattered 320 acre or 640 acre lots.)

In the period of climatic adversity of the 1870s and 1880s, the United Echuca-Waranga Waterworks Trust emerged and some of the works laid down by this Trust were later incorporated, with modifications, in the Tongala-Stanhope Irrigation District. The aim of the Trust, as with many other similar ventures of the day in Victoria, was to provide domestic and stock water supplies and a basis for limited irrigation; mostly *extensive* or *partial* irrigation as it is now termed. In many respects such a project resembles the irrigation 'Districts' sponsored in southern New South Wales after 1935. In 1906, the State Rivers and Water Supply Commission, recently established to overcome problems that brought the downfall of most of the early Trusts [23], reported a moderate amount of irrigation in the Echuca and Waranga Trust. Though irrigation of scattered pockets of fruits and lucerne had developed, the most significant trend had been the irrigation of native pastures and fodder crops, as an adjunct to dryland farming (for sheep or for sheep and wheat). The total irrigated area was

only a small fraction of the territory covered by the scheme. On the whole, *extensive* irrigation of this kind produced little disturbance to the orderly gridlike pattern of land settlement and it merely produced a variant of the wheat-growing mode of land occupance.

Beginning in the first decade of this century in northern Victoria, and in the second decade in southwestern New South Wales, large areas of riverine plain experienced profound changes of land settlement induced by State-sponsored irrigation schemes, far more ambitious than those of the early Victorian Trusts. The displacement of broadacre pastoralism or more-closely settled wheatgrowing by a new mode of occupance—dairying or fruitgrowing on much smaller farms—was a common aim. The development of the Tongala-Stanhope Irrigation District was a Victorian counterpart (in some respects, a predecessor) of the Murrumbidgee Irrigation Areas outlined earlier. However, though few signs of pre-irrigation farming exist now on the M.I.A., the landscape of Tongala-Stanhope bears many legacies of the dryland farming era.

In many respects modern closer settlement for irrigation at Tongala and Stanhope has involved relatively simple rectangular subdivisions within the gridlike pattern first laid down for unirrigated wheatgrowing. A comparison of parts B and C of Fig. 17 bears witness to this. Nevertheless, the change to closer settlement based on *intensive* irrigation resulted in some drastic changes of the cultural landscape. One important development was that, instead of the new settlements being aligned in a relatively simple north-south fashion, it was necessary for irrigation engineers and irrigationists alike to pay close attention to a less-regular spatial arrangement of land types, particularly as it impinged on the economic layout of channels and the positioning of the new land uses to be sponsored by *intensive* irrigation. Tongala-Stanhope provides an interesting case of a compromise between investments made earlier for dryland farming and later investments for irrigated agriculture. In some respects, this compromise posed costs, the full import of which only became evident much later.

As an administrative unit, the Tongala-Stanhope Irrigation District came into being in

G

1939 to 1940; however, modern closer settlements there date back to the period 1909 to 1928, when State-sponsored irrigation schemes sprang up in numerous parts of northern Victoria, partly to replace older Trusts, but mainly to facilitate a general State-wide campaign to encourage the closer settlement of dryland and irrigated lands. As described in some detail elsewhere, these schemes involved numerous forms of State socialism, including large migration and soldier settlement programmes [23]. Active subdivision of lands for the modern type of *intensive* irrigation at Tongala-Stanhope began with the purchase and subdivision of lands of the Koyuga Estate in 1909. The Koyuga Irrigation District was formed in 1911-12; in 1912-13 it was amalgamated with the newly-formed Tongala District, both having being developed from an earlier Deakin Irrigation District (excised from the Echuca-Waranga Trust). The Stanhope Irrigation District emerged in 1918-19, primarily to cater for soldier settlement. As for the M.I.A. and Red Cliffs, and in contrast to Mildura, closer settlement by irrigation spread slowly out from Tongala and Stanhope, keeping pace with new water resources and the demand for land by settlers.

The Tongala-Stanhope Irrigation District forms a bi-nodal or disconnected pattern of closer settlement. Tongala is the centre of northern closer settlement, Stanhope of southern. Both closer settlements have affinities with those of the M.I.A., at Leeton and Griffith. Not only were all four settlements sponsored for similar reasons and based on the *intensive* irrigation of fruit and dairy farms, but all were designed in a modified concentric zonal pattern. At Tongala and Stanhope, the pattern is not truncated as it is at Leeton and Griffith, because land types change fairly uniformly in all directions from the urban nodes; hence, each town is surrounded by irrigated closer settlements. The concentric zones of land uses around Tongala and Stanhope were designed to surround each town with an innermost ring of workers' allotments and town allotments, averaging 3 acres; surrounding this was an intermediate ring of horticultural blocks averaging some 28 acres; and the outmost ring of closer settlement was of dairying or mixed farming blocks averaging about 68 acres. As

stressed earlier for the M.I.A., there seems little doubt that the design of these closer settlements was based largely on the engineering considerations of how best to reticulate water to the largest number of farms and how best to locate channels and farms so as to exploit land types most favourable to the then-accepted ideal forms of irrigated closer settlement of the riverine plain—intensive fruitgrowing or dairying.

Unlike the M.I.A. as planned in 1906, but identical to the M.I.A. as they were finally implemented (contemporaneously with the emergence of the Tongala-Stanhope Irrigation District), the success of closer settlement was thought to depend on farmers making a considerable and consistent use of irrigation water. Officials thought that farmers would be so dependent on irrigation that they would exert persistent and predictable demands for water (so facilitating delivery by State authorities), and that they would be happy to pay the compulsory charges for water. In other words, closer settlements of this type were designed to overcome several major problems that plagued the earlier Trusts [23].

That conditions of water supply and soils were important considerations affecting the design of the Tongala-Stanhope project is made clear by the following assertion by the State Rivers and Water Supply Commission [65] in 1912:

The conditions which govern the success in irrigation in this State are well established but are not everywhere understood. This warrants their restatement. In the selection of irrigable areas suitability of soil should be one of the prime considerations. Land suited to intense culture should, as far as practicable, be first supplied, and for such lands the water supply must be ample and reliable. For intense culture to be profitable holdings must be small. The success of irrigation is therefore closely associated with closer settlement. As to the success of irrigation there need be no misgiving if it is restricted to areas of good land, and settlers are given a proper water service.

In this part of the riverine plain of northern Victoria, the prior stream beds and associated levees recognized by modern surveys do not run from south to north, as they do farther west in the Goulburn Irrigation System. On the contrary, these relief forms, and the longitudinal gradients of the plain with which they are associated, run from southeast to northwest as long narrow tongues of 'high' plain interspersed by strips of 'intermediate' and 'low' plain. Referring to Fig. 18 as an example, it is clear that Tongala and Stanhope were each located on such a tongue of 'high' plain, as were major subsidiary water channels, feeding northwest from the Waranga Western Main Channel (Fig. 17A), located so as to give maximum command over the plain (note the similarity with the main channel of the M.I.A.). In the early part of this century, such 'high' plain was said to possess 'good red and sandy loam' or 'good red loam'. With such soils, and because of nearness to existing (Trust) or planned channels, the 'high' plain was considered ideal for fruit-growing and/or dairying. A node such as Tongala was located on the crest of a levee of 'high' plain to ensure a position central to the maximum number of farms arranged in a compact manner to exploit 'high' and 'intermediate' plains nearby. 'Low' plains were said to have 'stiff clayey loam' or were classed as 'swampy' and were considered to be generally unsuited to closer settlement. On the whole, the latter regions were to be served by only *extensive* or *partial* irrigation facilities and were not to be closer settled.

The ways in which closer settlement blocks formed rectangular subdivisions within earlier wheat blocks, and major irrigation channels cut diagonally across this gridlike farm subdivision, are stressed in Fig. 17C and Fig. 18. Minor channels and most roads followed a much more tortuous ('zig-zag') pattern, skirting rectangular blocks. For minor channels, such a pattern was adopted so as to minimize fragmentation of allotments. In the case of roads, the tortuous pattern reflected a new mode of occupance making use of existing social investments. However, reference was later made [59] to problems of transport posed by this road pattern in Victorian wheat areas.

The adoption of a modified concentric zonal pattern of settlement around Tongala and Stanhope was obviously an attempt to graft a new occupance onto an old one; to take advantage of existing roads, yet to develop farms of a size and with land uses best designed to serve the needs of *intensive* irrigation. As central places,

Tongala and Stanhope were positioned to best serve the two closer settlements. Though engineering problems of water supply figured prominently in the location and detailed design of the settlements, it would be foolish to assert that land types played no part in influencing the water engineer in his designs of channels, farms, land uses and town locations.

Conclusions

State governments in Australia have long played vital roles in the development of major water projects and farm settlements dependent on them. Active State socialism of this type stems in part from social pressures for enhanced opportunities for closer settlement based on family farms, longstanding models in Australian agriculture. Government intervention for water projects also results from the need to take corporate action to overcome the very considerable physical problems confronting any large water conservation and irrigation schemes in Australia.

Irrigation schemes have aroused great public debate in Australia; argument that has waxed and waned for more than eighty years. The mid-1960s have seen a major revival of the debate, partly because of diverse reactions to proposed schemes for northern Australia and partly because of recent serious droughts. Much of the argument about irrigation has concerned the wisdom of large public investment for water schemes. Some protagonists of irrigation tend, on occasions, to verge on hysteria when faced with objections to irrigation as one of the various alternative forms of public investment. Perhaps at another extreme, some of those who stress the economic drawbacks of irrigation, compared with non-irrigated types of development, tend to overstate their case that government intervention has been based on a myopic appreciation of the physical, social, and economic difficulties to be faced.

This paper has not entered the central arena of the general controversy on Australian irrigation. However, in stressing the obvious ways in which government water conservation and irrigation schemes have developed in response to salient factors of the physical environment, it has drawn attention to some features of Australia that are little publicized.

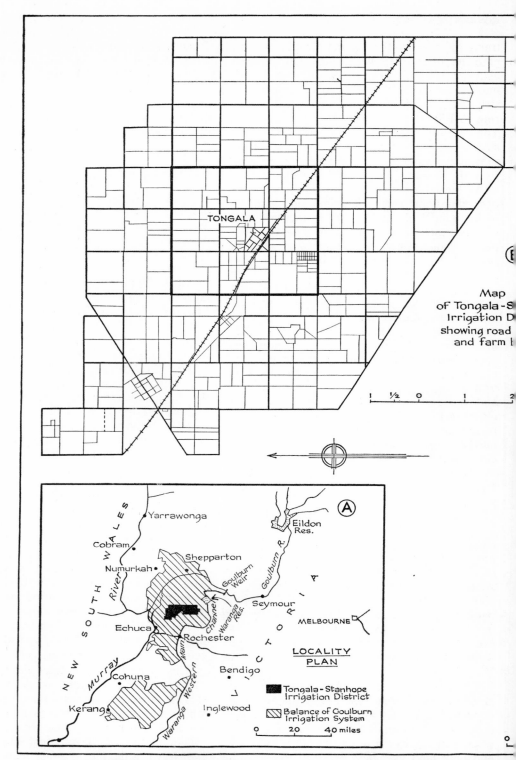

Map
of Tongala-S
Irrigation D
showing road
and farm

TONGALA

LOCALITY
PLAN

■ Tongala-Stanhope
   Irrigation District

▨ Balance of Goulburn
   Irrigation System

0   20   40 miles

Fig. 17—Three maps of the Tongala-Stanhope Irrigation District, Victoria: (A) positi
subdivisions; (C) a detailed example of roads, channels and property subdivisions res
Supply Commission, Melbourne)

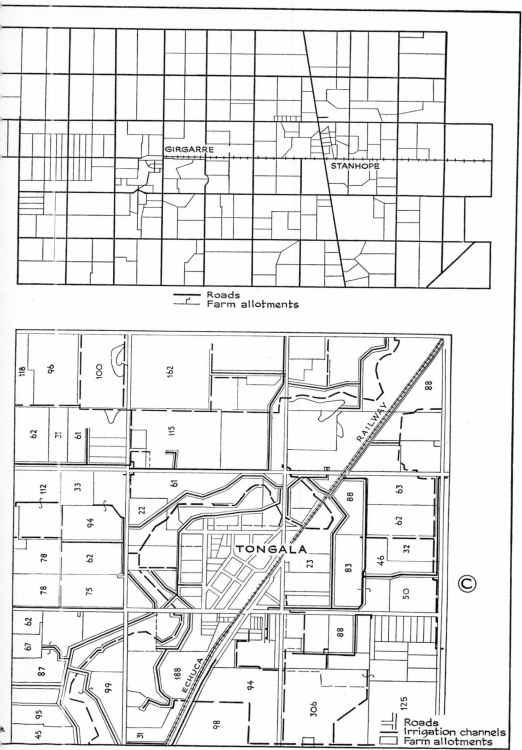

GIRGARRE

STANHOPE

Roads
Farm allotments

118 96 100 162

62 31 61 115

RAILWAY 88

112 33 61 88 63

22 94 88 62 32

78 62 TONGALA 23 83 46 50

78 75

62 88

67 188 ECHUCA

87 94 306 125

95 99 98 Roads
Irrigation channels
Farm allotments

45 31

ⓒ

heme in the Goulburn Irrigation System; (B) grid-like pattern of major roads and farm
om irrigated closer settlement. (Adapted from maps supplied by State Rivers and Water

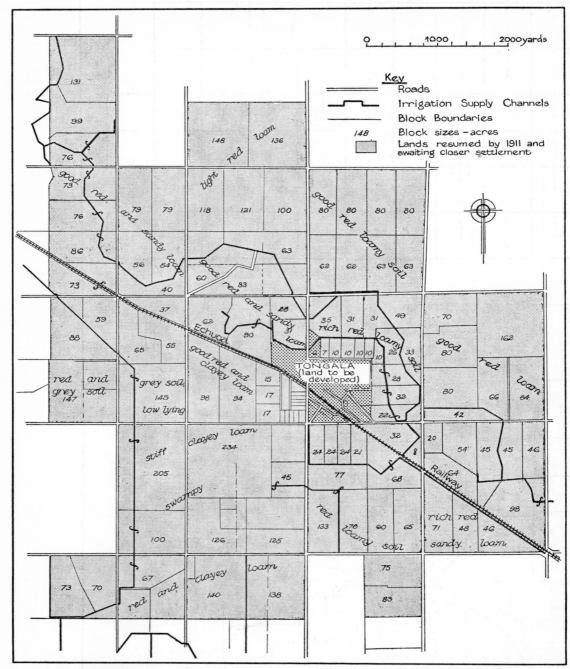

Fig. 18—Early plan of closer settlement to be centred on Tongala. (*Source: State Rivers and Water Supply Commission, Annual Report 1910-11.* Govt. Print., Melbourne)

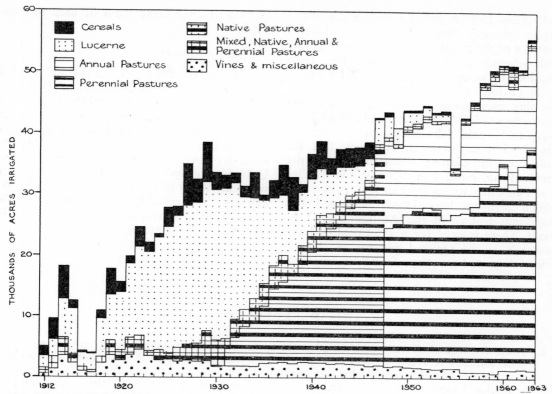

Fig. 19—Trends in areas irrigated, Tongala-Stanhope Irrigation District, Victoria, from the date of first State-sponsored closer settlement. Note how this scheme, always dominated by intensive grazing, has exhibited a dramatic replacement of lucerne by improved pastures (annual pastures for sheep and perennial pastures mainly for dairying.) (*Source:* State Rivers and Water Supply Commission, Melbourne)

The three-fold division of the Southern Murray-Darling Basin — peripheral upland, riverine plain, and Wimmera-Mallee lowland—has had profound effects on the pattern of water development in a region that presently contains some 80 per cent of the land regularly irrigated in the continent. Most of the economic development of southeastern Australia is focussed on the three port cities of Sydney, Melbourne and Adelaide. The Southern Murray-Darling Basin comprises large parts of the rural hinterlands of these ports and irrigation within the region has played important roles in the social and economic development of these hinterlands, especially by underwriting a degree of closer settlement and decentralization of settlement otherwise impossible. Even a cursory inspection of the basin-wide maps presented in this paper will confirm that the overall pattern of water conservation and irrigation schemes has been a rational response to major physical variations throughout the region.

A great deal of the intensive research work on soils and hydrology, and to a lesser extent on plant and animal husbandry, in Australia over the past five decades was triggered off by problems that arose in the wake of the first major State-sponsored irrigation schemes of the Southern Murray-Darling Basin. Though early architects of these schemes were obviously alive to some of the detailed variations of land types to be encountered on the riverine plain and Murray-Mallee lowlands, serious mistakes of land settlement stemmed from either a failure by planners and farmers to apprehend soil-plant-water relations vital to the success of irrigation schemes, or a tendency for the same people to be swayed largely by engineering considerations and an undue optimism about the future of irrigation. Nevertheless, detailed features of the location and land uses of irrigation schemes in the region have long been moulded by many subtle features of land type. It is obvious that physical factors are now exerting even more vital influences as man learns more of the economies and other advantages to be gained by intelligent responses to his physical environment. However, that the influences of climatic uncertainty have not received major stress in this paper is perhaps a sad commentary on the fact that, so far, irrigation planners have largely neglected this important feature of the Australian environment. There is need for a great deal of basic research on the regional patterns of climatic uncertainty and on ways in which irrigation

and land management might be used to combat it.

Acknowledgements

This paper is based largely on research carried out with the generous assistance of The Australian National University and the New South Wales Department of Agriculture, although the writer accepts full responsibility for the views expressed. The maps were drawn by Mr. A. Bartlett of the Department of Geography, The University of Sydney; and typing of the paper was carried out in this Department. Mr. B. W. Higman gave valuable research assistance in relation to the several case studies discussed in the last section of the paper. In this respect the author is indebted to the Research Grant of The University of Sydney.

REFERENCES

1. The most fruitful source of information on these schemes is *Water in Australia* which incorporates *The Australasian Irrigator*, and is published monthly in Melbourne.

2. EGGLESTON, F. W. (1932) *State Socialism in Victoria*. King and Sons, London.

3. BUCHANAN, R. O. (1959) Some Reflections on Agricultural Geography. *Geography, 44*, 1–13.

4. MIGHELL, R. L. & BLACK, J. D. (1951) *Interregional Competition In Agriculture . . . .* Harvard University Press, Cambridge, Mass., especially ch. 3 for a useful discussion of this law.

5. SCHULTZ, T. W. (1953) *The Economic Organization of Agriculture*. McGraw-Hill, New York, especially ch. 9.

6. PHILBRICK, A. K. (1963) *This Human World*. John Wiley, New York, especially chs. 1, 2, 11 and 20.

7. FRIEDMAN, J. (1963) Regional Economic Policy for Developing Areas. *Papers and Proceedings of Regional Science Association, 11*, 41–62 for a development of the concepts put forward by Schultz, op. cit.

8. RUTHERFORD, J. (1963) Metropolitan Sydney and Economic Growth in Western Communities, in *Readings on Urban Growth*. Research Papers 3 to 7, 38–69. Department of Geography, University of Sydney and The Geographical Society of New South Wales.

9. COMMONWEALTH BUREAU OF CENSUS AND STATISTICS. (1963) *Year Book of the Commonwealth of Australia, No. 50 for 1964*, 239–41. Government Printer, Canberra.

10. SMITH, R. H. T. (1962) *Commodity Movements in Southern New South Wales*. Australian National University, Canberra.

11. LAWRENCE, E. F. (1937) A Climatic Analysis of New South Wales, *Austr.Geog., 3*, No. 3, 3–24.

12. CALLAGHAN, A. R. & MILLINGTON, A. J. (1956) *The Wheat Industry in Australia*. Angus and Robertson, Sydney, especially ch. 9.

13. C.S.I.R.O. (1960) *The Australian Environment*, 23. C.S.I.R.O., Melbourne.

14. WADHAM, S. M., WILSON, R. K. & WOOD, J. (1964) *Land Utilization In Australia*, ch. 13. Melbourne University Press, Melbourne.

15. For examples see the following:
    GREAT PLAINS COMMITTEE (1936) *The Future of the Great Plains*. Government Printer, Washington.
    THORNTHWAITE, C. W. (1941) Climate and Settlement in the Great Plains. *U.S.D.A. Yearbook of Agriculture 1941*, 177–87. Government Printer, Washington.

16. ANON. (1955) *Final Report of the State Development Committee on the Development of Western and North-Victoria*, 15. Government Printer, Melbourne.

17. ENGLAND, H. N. (1960) Agricultural Use of the Snowy Waters: III–Irrigation Plans and Policy. *Austr.Journ.Agric.Econ.*, 4, 52–67.

18. NEW SOUTH WALES MINISTER FOR CONSERVATION (1956) *The First Report of Committee Appointed by the Minister for Conservation to Advise on the Use of Additional Water Available Within the Murrumbidgee Upon Completion of Blowering Dam.* Department of Conservation, Sydney.

19. KING, H. W. H. (1959) Transhumant Grazing in the Snow Belt of New South Wales, *Austr.Geog.*, 7, 129–40.

20. EDGEWORTH DAVID, T. W. (1950) *The Geology of the Commonwealth of Australia.* Vol. 2. Edward Arnold, London.

21. GREEN, K. D. (1954) Water Resources Investigations in Victoria: Availability of Hydrological Data. *Journ.Inst.Engineers (Aust.)*, 26, 1–10.

22. CRAFT, F. A. (1939) Elementary Hydrography of South-Eastern Australia. *Proc. Linn.Soc.N.S.W.*, 64, 498.

23. RUTHERFORD, J. (1964) Interplay of American and Australian Ideas for Development of Water Projects in Northern Victoria. *Annals Assn.Amer.Geog.*, 54, 88–106.

24. STATE RIVERS AND WATER SUPPLY COMMISSION (1956) *Eildon Dam.* S.R.W.S.C., Melbourne.

25. TISDALL, A. L. (1960) Water. *Austr.Irrigator*, 5, Pt. 10, 17–22.

26. GARLAND, K. R. (1953) Macorna Land-Use Survey. *Journ.Dept.Agric.Victoria*, January, 1953. See also first part in November, 1952.

27. HARRIS, W. J. (1938) The Physiography of the Echuca District. *Proc.Roy.Soc.Victoria*, 51, 45–60.

28. HILLS, E. S. (1940) The Lunette, A New Land Form of Aeolian Origin. *Austr.Geog.*, 3, 15–21.

29a. LANGFORD-SMITH, T. & RUTHERFORD, J. (1966) *Water and Land: Two Case Studies in Australian Irrigation*, chs. 2 and 7. A.N.U. Press, Canberra.

29b. *Ibid.* ch. 14.

29c. *Ibid.* ch. 15.

29d. *Ibid.* ch. 13.

30. BUTLER, B. E. (1950) Land Classification. *Technical Conference on Irrigation Held at Griffith . . . 1950*, 68–74. C.S.I.R.O., Melbourne.

31. N.S.W. PARLIAMENTARY STANDING COMMITTEE ON PUBLIC WORKS (1906) Report . . . Relating to the Proposed Barren Jack Storage Reservoir and Northern Murrumbidgee Irrigation Scheme, *N.S.W. Joint Parliamentary Papers*, 5, 531 et seq.

32. BUTLER, B. E. (1958) Depositional Systems of the Riverine Plain of South-Eastern Australia in Relation to Soils. *C.S.I.R.O. Soil Publication*, 10.

33. DONALD, C. M. (1965) The Progress of Australian Agriculture and the Role of Pastures in Environmental Change. *Austr.Journ.Sci.*, 27, 187–198.

34. HARTSHORNE, R. (1960) *Perspective on the Nature of Geography.* Rand McNally, Chicago, 131–45.

35. M.I.A. RESEARCH EXTENSION COMMITTEE, (undated). *Advice on Horticultural Land-Use in the Murrumbidgee Irrigation Areas.* Area Press, Griffith.

36a. RUTHERFORD, J. et al., (1955) Survey of Vegetable Growing on the Murrumbidgee Irrigation Areas. Unpublished report submitted to the Irrigation Research Extension Committee. Ref. [36a].

36b. BUTLER, M. (1965) An Historical Perspective on Murrumbidgee Settlement Patterns. Unpublished B.A. Honours thesis (Geography), University of Sydney, 103.

37. MORGAN, A. (1956) Victorian Irrigated Pastures and Fodder Crops. *Australasian Irrigator*, 1, No. 3, 7–12.

38. MCCOLL, J. C. (1963) Dairy farming with Less Water. *Ibid.*, 9, No. 1, 17–21.

39. RUTHERFORD, J. & DILLON, L. (1954) Dairy Farming in the Berriquin and Denimein Irrigation Districts. *Rev.Market.Agric.Econ.*, 22, 87–164.

40. RUTHERFORD, J. (1951) Some Aspects of Land Utilization on Dairy Farms on the Lower North Coast. *Ibid.*, 19, 179–247.

41. BUTLER, B. E. Private Communication. Canberra.

42. MACDONALD HOLMES, J. (1948) *The Murray Valley*, Figs., 26, 31 and 32. Angus and Robertson, Sydney.

43. BUREAU OF AGRICULTURAL ECONOMICS, (1951) *Australian Dried Vine Fruit Industry.* B.A.E., Canberra.
BUREAU OF AGRICULTURAL ECONOMICS, (1956) *Dried Vine Fruit Industry: Management Practices in Victoria and New South Wales 1956.* B.A.E., Canberra.
VICTORIAN PREMIER'S DEPARTMENT, (1955) *Report of an Interstate Committee of Enquiry–Mid-Murray Dried Fruits Area.* Premier's Department, Melbourne.

44. The concept of modes, types, and variants of occupance are discussed in literature such as: WHITTLESEY, D. (1929) Sequent

H

Occupance. *Annals.Assn.Amer.Geog.*, *19*, 162–5; DODGE, R. E. (1938) The Interpretation of Sequent Occupance. *Ibid.*, *28*, 233–37; and JEANS, D. N. (1966) Sequent Occupance in Geographical Study, in DURY, G. H. (ed.) *Aspects of the Content of Geography in Fifth and Sixth Forms*, 7. 10–7. 23. Dept.Geog.,Univ.Sydney and Geog.Soc. N.S.W. Sydney.

45. GRIFFIN, W. B. (1915) The Town Plan of Leeton. *Irrigation Record*, *3*, Nos. 4 and 5. Similar factors affected the planning for Griffith. See GRIFFIN, W. B. (1915), *ibid.*, *3*, No. 6.

46. SMYTHE, W. E. (1899) *The Conquest of Arid America*. Macmillan, New York.

47. NEW SOUTH WALES, (1916) Final Report of the Hon. A. C. Carmichael, M.L.A., as a Royal Commissioner Regarding the General Administration of the Water Conservation and Irrigation Commission. *N.S.W. Joint Parliamentary Papers*, 8, 140–765.

48. NEW SOUTH WALES, (1916) Report of the Royal Commission of Inquiry into the Claims Made By Certain Settlers on the Murrumbidgee Irrigation Area, With a View of Ascertaining Whether Such Settlers Could Prove That They Were Entitled to be Compensated by Reason of the Unsuitability of the Soil of Their Farms for the Growth of Lucerne. *N.S.W. Joint Parliamentary Papers*, 6, 136.

49. RUTHERFORD, J. (1960) Integration of Irrigation and Dryland Farming in the Southern Murray Basin. *Rev.Market.and Agric.Econ.*, *28*, 97–150.

50. NEW SOUTH WALES, (1915) Report Relating to the Proposed Enlarging of the Northern Canal, Murrumbidgee Irrigation Scheme. *N.S.W. Parliamentary Paper*. Evidence by H. H. Dare and L. A. B. Wade.

51. LANGFORD-SMITH, T. (1958) *Landforms, Land Settlement and Irrigation on the Murrumbidgee, New South Wales*, 142. Unpublished Ph.D. thesis submitted to the Australian National University.

52. LEWIS, A. D. (1935) *Irrigation in Australia*, 35. Interior Department, Pretoria.

53. VICTORIA (1886) Agreement Between the Government of the Colony of Victoria and George and William Benjamin Chaffey. *Victoria Votes and Proceedings, Legislative Assembly*, *1*, (1887) 971–85.

54. ALEXANDER, J. A. (1928) *The Life of George Chaffey*. Macmillan, Melbourne; VICTORIA (1889) Victorian Water Supply, Third Annual Report. *Victoria Votes and Proceedings, Legislative Assembly*, *4* (1889), 939.

55. VICTORIA, (1888) Mildura Irrigation Colony–Report by Chief Engineer of Water Supply. *Victoria Votes and Proceedings, Legislative Assembly*, *1*, (1888) 860.

56. VICTORIA, (1896) Mildura Settlement–Report of the Royal Commission. *Ibid.*, *3*, (1896) 33–440.

57. VICTORIA, (1907) State Rivers and Water Supply Commission Annual Report 1906–7. *Ibid.*, *2*, 140.

58. BOSSENCE, W. H. (1963) *Kyabram*, 18. Hawthorn Press, Melbourne.

59. HOLT, A. J. (1947) *Wheat Farms of Victoria–A Sociological Survey*, 23. University of Melbourne, Melbourne.

60. MEINIG, D. W. (1959) Colonization of Wheatland–Some Australian and American Comparisons. *Austr.Geog.*, *7*, 211.

61. MEINIG, D. W. (1963) *On the Margins of the Good Earth*, 26. John Murray, London.

62. VICTORIA, (1880) Report of Proceedings Taken Under the Provisions of the Land Act 1869, During the Year Ended 31st December 1879. *Victoria Votes and Proceedings, Legislative Assembly*, First Session, *1*, (1880) 450.

63. VICTORIA, (1916) Final Report From the Royal Commission on Closer Settlement as to the Workings of the Closer Settlement Acts in the Irrigable Districts. *Victoria Votes and Proceedings, Legislative Assembly*, *2*, 517.

64. See comparable reports to that quoted in [62] relating to later years.

65. VICTORIA, (1912) *State Rivers and Water Supply Commission Annual Report 1911–12*, 25. Government Printer, Melbourne.

Secondary Industry in Australia

G. J. R. LINGE[1]

This chapter is divided into six main parts. After a brief introduction which endeavours to indicate the position of secondary industry in the Australian economy, the development of manufacturing and the emerging pattern of location are traced from 1788 onwards. There follow two sections which give some account of the location of manufacturing and the influences that have brought this pattern into being, and this discussion is illustrated by an account of the locational decisions being made in the Australian aluminium industry. The final section takes up the question of decentralization—a topic of constant comment, much promise, but little achievement.

Introduction

Secondary industry includes all the activities involved in turning materials into more useful products for further processing or fabrication or for final consumption. There is often no sharp distinction between primary and secondary industry. In the case of minerals, for example, a fairly arbitrary line has to be drawn between initial stages, such as crushing and concentrating, which are usually included as part of mining, and subsequent stages which are included as part of manufacturing. It is also difficult to know whether to allocate some activities into the secondary or into the tertiary sectors. In Australia the repairing of motor vehicles, shoes, watches; laundering and dyeing; and tyre retreading (which together employ 7 per cent of the factory workforce and occupy 26 per cent of the factories) are included within secondary industry whereas in some other countries they are included in the tertiary sector. There are similar difficulties, too, about the classification of firms engaged in the production of heat, light, and power. Moreover, a company whose main interest is in manufacturing may integrate backwards (by owning farms or forests) or forwards (by owning wholesale or retail outlets), and be active in all three sectors.

Within the general classification of secondary industry a distinction is sometimes made between manufacturing and process industries. Manufacturing industries are those in which the materials used are not in themselves altered during the stages of production and examples are motor vehicle assembly, and the making of textiles and furniture. In contrast, the process industries physically or chemically convert the materials used into different substances such as occurs during the production of petroleum, paint, and fertilizers. The manufacturing industries tend to be more labour-intensive and to operate for perhaps a quarter of the total hours in a week, whereas the process industries tend to be capital-intensive and to operate more or less continuously. In practice the distinction is not always clear because some industries have both process and manufacturing stages. In this chapter the term manufacturing is not used in this special exclusive sense.

In Australia in 1965/66 there were 61,700 factories (establishments where at least four persons worked or where power was used), and 1,293,000 workers of whom a quarter were females. In *absolute* terms Australia has a lowly place among the world's industrial nations for although international comparisons are difficult it can be estimated that Australia probably employs only about one per cent of the world's factory workers. There are a few cities, such as Greater London (with an area of 720 square miles) or Tokyo Prefecture (525

[1]Some of the research for this chapter was carried out by Mrs R. Dowie, whose assistance is gratefully acknowledged.

square miles), which *each* have more factory workers than there are in the whole of the Commonwealth of Australia. However, in *relative* terms Australia is among the leading nations: for instance, the annual value of production [1] per worker (about $A4,100) is not far behind that of the United States and Canada, and is about four times the world average.

Manufacturing plays a significant and fairly constant role in the internal economy as Table 1 indicates. The proportion of the Australian workforce so engaged (27·5 per cent) is higher than in countries such as Japan (25·0 per cent), Canada (25·4 per cent), and France (26·4 per cent), but lower than in West Germany (36·2 per cent), United Kingdom (36·1 per cent), Sweden (34·2 per cent), Netherlands (29·9 per cent), and the United States (29·1 per cent). Between 1947 and 1961 the total labour force and the total factory labour force both grew at an average annual rate of 2 per cent, but the tertiary workforce increased more rapidly at 2·7 per cent per annum. Meanwhile the primary and mining workforces decreased by 0·5 per cent and 0·2 per cent per annum respectively.

One of the special characteristics of Australian factory industry is its economic isolation from the rest of the world—it does not form part of any regional economy. In contrast the secondary industry of Canada, for example, has to be viewed in the light of the role it plays in the North American economy, and Switzerland's manufacturing has to be seen as part of the West European economy. Moreover, unlike the United Kingdom and Japan, Australian manufacturing does not depend on overseas markets. Only 10·3 per cent ($A280,000,000) of the exports of the nation in 1963/64 consisted of manufactured goods (mainly metal products, implements and machinery, drugs, chemicals, and paper and stationery). In addition, of course, there were exports of processed primary products such as flour, sugar, canned fruit, scoured wool and tops, canned meats, lead, zinc, and copper which made up another 23·6 per cent of exports (or 25·0 per cent if refined petroleum products are also included). It tends to be overlooked that a considerable proportion of the primary produce processed in Australia is also consumed here: such is the case with about 65 per cent of the butter, 60 per cent of the cheese, 60 per cent of the flour, and 55 per cent of the preserved fruit. It is difficult to calculate precisely the proportion of the nation's factory workforce concerned with exports because some goods, such as canisters, cartons, and chemicals, find their way overseas incorporated in or associated with other products; a reasonable estimate is about 5 per cent.

The Development of Manufacturing and the Emerging Pattern of Location
(a) 1788 to 1900

The first settlers arrived in Sydney Cove on 26 January 1788 and before long several industrial undertakings were supplying the simple needs of an isolated, pioneering community [2]. The Government itself undertook brickmaking, flour milling, brewing, and the manufacture of

Table 1 *Gross National Product and Employment by Main Industry Groups per cent*

Industry	Gross National Product (a)		Employment (b)	
	1948-49	1961-62	1947	1961
Primary production	21.3	12.6	15.8	11.1
Mining and quarrying	2.5	1.6	1.8	1.3
Manufacturing	26.3	28.2	27.6	27.5
Electricity, gas, water	1.9	3.5	1.1 (c)	2.3
Building and construction	6.0	7.7	8.4 (c)	9.0
Other tertiary	38.0	42.0	45.3	48.8
Ownership of dwellings	4.0	4.4	—	—
Total	100.0	100.0	100.0	100.0

(a) At factor cost—derived from *Australian National Accounts 1948-49 and 1961-62*.
(b) Derived from censuses of population 1947 and 1961.
(c) Water supply, etc. included in building and construction.

woollen cloth, clothes, and boats. But the population grew very slowly and industrial opportunities were limited. Even by 1825, when Tasmania separated from New South Wales, the total population was only 50,000 persons of whom 14,000 were in the new island colony.

Industrial activity was at first largely confined to Sydney and the other settlements in the County of Cumberland which in 1836 contained 40,000 of the 77,000 people in New South Wales. During the 1830s and 1840s there was a 'pastoral exodus from the overgrown jail and the Nineteen Counties'. Between 1836 and 1851 the population of the County of Cumberland grew by 41,000 but in the rest of New South Wales it increased by 61,000. This growth and spread of population was accompanied by the development of manufacturing in the country areas both to serve the new markets and to make use of raw materials: between 1840 and 1850, for example, the number of breweries in New South Wales outside Sydney grew from three to sixteen and the number of flour mills from 68 to 130. Most country towns and many of the villages, particularly in New South Wales, Victoria, and South Australia, had small factories producing such goods as beer, flour, aerated waters, bread, leather, saddlery, wooden products, and sometimes even woollen cloth and simple agricultural implements.

The population of New South Wales reached 181,000 in 1851 but the population of Victoria, which had been settled for only fifteen years, had barely reached 77,000. Gold discoveries were announced in 1851 in both New South Wales and Victoria; not enough is yet known in detail about how the social and economic upheaval that followed these discoveries affected the development of manufacturing, but there were some obvious conse-

quences. The rush of able-bodied men to the diggings, the very rapid rise of wages and other costs, and the increase of imports slowed industrial progress in New South Wales, particularly in Sydney. Some industries virtually faded away; in 1852, 234,000 yards of cloth and tweeds were produced in New South Wales but by 1856 output had fallen to only 27,000 yards. In contrast, industries making metal goods were stimulated both by the demands of the miners and also by the demands of other manufacturers who were turning to mechanization as a way of overcoming both the shortage and the high cost of labour. Between 1851 and 1861 the population of Victoria increased sevenfold to 539,000 while the population of New South Wales increased by only one-third to 351,000. During this period seven times more gold was produced in Victoria than in New South Wales; while the Victorian fields were fairly close together and not far from Melbourne, those in New South Wales were separated from each other and from Sydney. In the light of these circumstances it is not surprising that 'the growth of population and wealth encouraged an expansion of commercial activity and the promotion of trading and financial enterprises which placed Melbourne in a position of financial leadership in the Australian colonies' [3]. The very rapid increase in Melbourne's population is shown by Table 2.

The passage of the *Australian Colonies Government Act* in 1850 and the subsequent separation from New South Wales of Victoria in 1851 and Queensland in 1859 paved the way for the introduction of protective tariffs. Their importance differed between the colonies. Victoria became ardently protective after 1871 (the tariff of 1867 was hardly protective), whereas New South Wales remained staunchly free trade until the 1890s. The other colonies

Table 2 *Population of Capital Cities, 1841 to 1891*

City	1841	1851	1871	1891
Sydney	29,973	53,924	137,776	383,283
Melbourne	4,479	23,143	206,780	490,896
Adelaide	8,480	14,577	42,744	153,896
Brisbane	500	2,543	15,029	93,657
Perth	not stated	not stated	5,244	8,447
Hobart	not stated	not stated	19,092	33,224

Source: Coghlan, T. A. and Ewing, T. T. (1903), *Progress of Australasia in the Century*. London, 446.

included some elements of protection in their schedules. It is difficult to know to what extent industrial development was affected by the Victorian policies as the structural and cyclical changes are hard to unscramble. Moreover, because the operation of tariffs in Victoria made the whole of Australia less attractive to British exporters the other colonies may in fact have had an indirect measure of protection. Although these reservations must be borne in mind, it has been argued that in the short run protection seems to have caused a more rapid development in Victoria than would have otherwise taken place, made for a higher level of factory employment, and brought about an earlier development of some kinds of manufacturing than took place in New South Wales [4].

Other influences were also at work. During the 1860s and 1870s the colonial governments offered various incentives to entrepreneurs. For example, Victoria, South Australia, Tasmania, and Queensland each offered a bounty of £1000 to the first mill to produce a stated quantity of cloth; the first such award was made to the Victorian Woollen Company of Geelong which commenced operations in 1868. Considerable promotional activity went on in country towns. In Victoria, in particular, local businessmen sponsored the development of manufacturing to maintain population and prosperity when they saw that the gold boom was coming to an end: Ballarat had a woollen mill by 1873, Geelong had four mills by 1874, and Castlemaine and Warrnambool each had a mill shortly afterwards.

Between 1861 and 1890 manufacturing was the fastest growing sector of the Australian economy (though, of course, during this period there were both years of recession and of more rapid expansion). Butlin has shown that manufacturing's share of the gross domestic product rose from 3.9 per cent in 1861 to about 8.0 per cent in 1870, to 9.8 per cent in 1880, and to 10.5 per cent in 1890 [5]. The definitions of manufacturing used in the colonies differed and were varied from time to time along with the methods of collection so that there is little point in trying to determine in detail which colony was industrially supreme. Suffice it to say that New South Wales and Victoria were fairly evenly matched industrially during the 1880s and 1890s [6]. In both colo-

nies metal working and engineering, building materials, clothing and textiles, and food and drink were the leading industries. However, in all categories, apart from clothing and textiles, and the production of light and heat, New South Wales had a greater value of plant and machinery per worker; probably this reflects the move towards mechanization that occurred in New South Wales factories during the gold rush period and also the shortage of capital and the greater availability of labour in Victoria when the gold fever had died down.

During the 1890s manufacturing made little progress. In Victoria manufacturing had been stimulated, particularly during the 1880s, by the demand stemming from the building of Melbourne. But whereas the population in the Greater Melbourne area (as defined by the colony's statistician) increased by 208,000 between the censuses of 1881 and 1891, it grew by only 5000 between 1891 and 1901. The slump caused employment in manufacturing in Victoria to fall from a peak of 57,400 in 1889 to a low point of 41,700 in 1893 and it was not until 1899 that the total of a decade earlier was again exceeded. Sinclair has suggested that Victoria's recovery from the slump was aided by the diversification of the economy which had come about as a result in part of industrial expansion, and also because some industries (such as the manufacture of woollen goods) recovered early and quickly expanded output [7]. In New South Wales the effect of the slump on factory employment was neither so marked nor so prolonged.

It has been indicated already that from about 1840 onwards there was a considerable growth of manufacturing activity in the country areas of New South Wales, Victoria, and South Australia. In 1880, for example, there were 137 flour mills in the country areas of New South Wales (compared with 13 in Sydney), 37 breweries (compared with 8), 74 sugar mills (compared with two refineries), and 117 aerated-water factories (compared with 26). But the average size of the country factories was much smaller than those in Sydney. The country breweries had an average of 7 workers as against 42 in those in Sydney, and the country flour mills had an average horsepower of 15.9 (compared with 36.7 in Sydney), an average of 2 stones operating (compared with

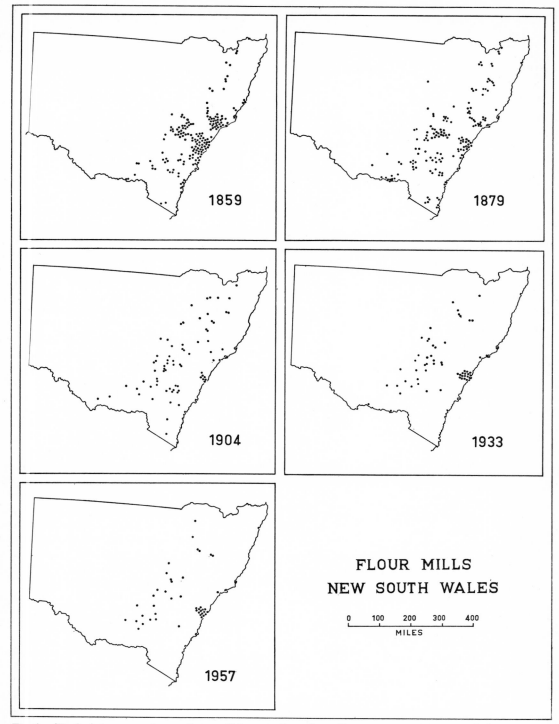

Fig. 1—(Each dot represents one flour mill irrespective of employment, output, or capacity)

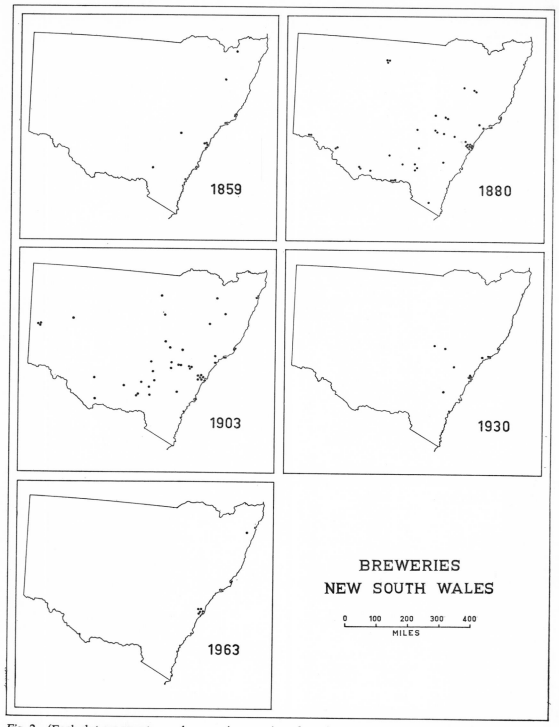

Fig. 2—(Each dot represents one brewery irrespective of employment, output, or capacity)

5), and an average of 3·2 workers (compared with 9·1). In only a few instances did the country workforce in an industry exceed that employed in Sydney. Overall 36 per cent of the factories and 58 per cent of the manufacturing workforce of New South Wales were in the capital city where there was also considerable additional employment in the form of out-workers.

During the last three decades of the nineteenth century several circumstances reinforced each other to deter the further development of manufacturing in country areas while at the same time encouraging it to grow more rapidly in the capital cities. Firstly, there was an increasing proportion of the population in the metropolitan areas: between 1871 and 1901 Sydney's share of its State's population increased from 26·7 to 35·6 per cent; Melbourne's from 28·9 to 41·5 per cent; and Adelaide's from 23·0 to 44·8 per cent. In the capital cities were the main markets, the main sources of labour and capital, and the greatest development of services such as gas, electricity, telephones, sewerage, and even hydraulic power. Secondly, a railway system was being built in each State that focussed on the capital city. In New South Wales railway route-mileage increased from 74 in 1861 to 996 in 1881, and to 2846 in 1901. In Victoria at these same dates the route-mileage was 114, 1247 and 3237. The effect of the railways was not so much to stimulate manufacturing directly, except in a few cases (barely 10 per cent of government demand for railway equipment was placed in the colonies [8]), but to reduce the protection of distance and cost which had allowed small country factories to compete with their larger metropolitan counterparts. Thirdly, technical and managerial developments affected industrial location. For instance, during the 1880s in the flour milling industry the replacement of grindstones by roller mills necessitated not only a greater outlay of capital, but also more space and more motive power. At the same time the wheat in some areas, such as the Hunter Valley and Illawarra districts, had been or was being affected by rust which forced farmers to turn to other crops or to livestock. Thus, a mill at Wollongong in 1882 was buying all its wheat from Sydney [9]. The small country mills, some of which were already in

difficulties due to changes in land use, were unable to compete with the large-scale mills, often electrically powered, erected in the capital cities, and over seventy ceased operations in New South Wales alone during the last two decades of the century. Generally technical innovation militated against small privately owned country works and encouraged concentration in fewer and larger units financed by city interests (see Figs. 1 and 2). Less commonly innovation worked in favour of country industry. One such example was the invention overseas in 1877 of the centrifugal cream separator; overnight butter-making was transformed from a cottage into a factory industry, and the advent of refrigerated ships soon afterwards made the market an international as well as a local one. In 1888 there were eight butter factories in New South Wales but twelve years later there were 168; ironically some of these were established in disused flour mills (Fig. 3).

The growth of the dairy, meat freezing, and other primary processing industries appears to have made little impact on the overall tendency for manufacturing to concentrate in the capital cities. Between 1877 and 1900 the factory workforce in Sydney grew by 24,000 (to 39,000) whereas in the remainder of the State it increased by only 11,000 (to 22,000) [10]. As Coghlan noted in the 1890s:

There has been some tendency for the number of hands employed in the metropolitan district to increase faster than those in the other portions of the Colony. The facilities for the establishment of large industries in and around Sydney are considerable—a commanding position as regards communication with the outside world, propinquity to the coalfields, easy communication with the chief seats of raw production in the Colony, density of the population, and abundant water supply—these have tended to centre in the metropolitan district all the chief industries. In the extra-metropolitan districts the principal works are saw-mills, smelting works, sugar-mills, and flour-mills, or industries of a domestic character intended to meet a day-to-day demand, or for the treatment of perishable goods [11].

By the end of the nineteenth century the broad locational pattern of Australian manufacturing had emerged. Much of the secondary industry was already concentrated at the capital cities. Sydney had about 63 per cent of the

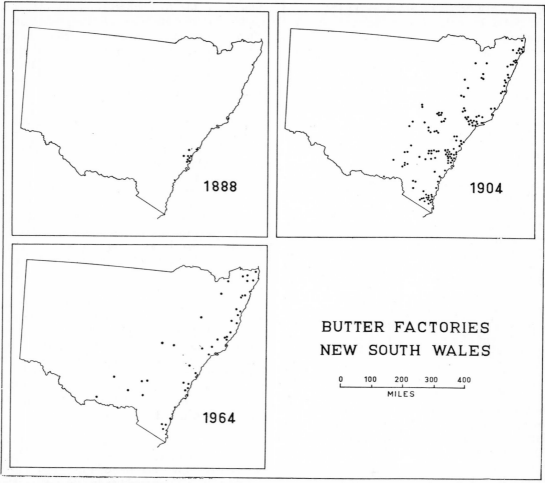

Fig. 3—(Each dot represents one butter factory irrespective of employment, output, or capacity. Cheese factories and creameries have been omitted)

New South Wales factory employees, and Melbourne an even greater share (about 76 per cent) of Victoria's. Newcastle (with shipbuilding, engineering works, and foundries), Geelong (with woollen mills, cement works, a paper mill, tanneries, and a salt works), and Port Pirie (with smelters and refineries) were established manufacturing cities. Whyalla was about to be developed as a shipping port for iron ore which at this time was used as a flux at the Port Pirie silver-lead smelters, and Port Kembla had been chosen as the site for an iron and steel works—a proposal, however, that was stillborn [12]. Many of the industrial concerns associated today with smaller towns were

already there in the nineteenth century such as Walkers Ltd., shipbuilders, at Maryborough (Queensland) in 1868; John Shearer & Sons, agricultural machinery, at Mannum (South Australia) in 1877; and E. Lucas & Co. Pty. Ltd., textiles, at Ballarat (Victoria) in 1878. Coghlan summarized the state of manufacturing in 1900:

The greater portion of the manufactories of Australasia may be classified as domestic industries—that is to say, industries naturally arising from the circumstances of the population, or connected with the treatment of perishable products; but there are nevertheless a fair number of industries of a more complex character which have been firmly established [13].

It was also a time of experimentation. The first zinc smelter in Australia began operations in 1897 at Cockle Creek (Newcastle) but it was not a commercial success and the company converted to lead smelting and refining. The first heat of open-hearth steel was made at Lithgow in 1900. And several locally designed and constructed cars (including one built by a Mr Holden at Geelong) had already made an appearance [14].

(b) 1900 to 1939

The economic crisis of the early 1890s showed that industrial expansion was being retarded by trade barriers between the colonies and competition from overseas exporters. Increasing unemployment in factories weakened opposition in New South Wales to protective tariffs and this in turn removed one of the obstacles to federation.

stimulus to manufacturing. Between 1904 (the first year for which satisfactory statistics become available) and 1913 employment in manufacturing grew at an average annual rate of 5·8 per cent compared with 2·3 per cent for population. This kind of differential in growth rates was true of all States (Table 3).

It is sometimes suggested that the expansion of secondary industry quickened as a result of the First World War. In fact, employment in manufacturing fell by 20,000 between 1913 and 1916 and the value of production remained at about the 1913 level until 1917. In the short run, therefore, industrial development was impeded—employment did not reach the 1913 level again until 1919. However, the war had two main long-term consequences [16]. Firstly, it accelerated the existing trend towards heavy industry. Thus, although the Newcastle iron and steel works was planned and partly

Table 3 *Factory Employment and Population 1904 to 1913*
(000's)

State	Factory Employment			Population		
	1904	1913	Average Annual Increase (%)	1904	1913	Average Annual Increase (%)
New South Wales	68	120	6.5	1457	1832	2.6
Victoria	76	119	5.0	1210	1412	1.7
Queensland	20	42	8.7	522	660	2.7
S. Australia	18	29	5.1	373	440	1.9
W. Australia	13	17	3.5	242	321	3.1
Tasmania	8	10	1.9	180	202	1.3
Six States	203	337	5.8	3984	4867	2.3

Source: Year Book of the Commonwealth of Australia.

The first Federal tariff, in 1902, was essentially for revenue purposes and 'its level of duties fell between those which Victoria, South Australia, and Queensland had charged and the small revenue duties which had been levied by New South Wales and Tasmania' [15]. The lowering of tariffs may have done Victorian manufacturers some harm (though the evidence is confused because 1902 was a drought year) but this was probably more than offset by the increased size of the market which allowed increased economies of scale and greater specialization. The tariff of 1908 gave further

constructed before the war, its output was expanded and its products diversified more quickly than had previously been envisaged [17]. Some existing works were enlarged: the copper refinery at Port Kembla, which began operations in 1907, was extended and wire manufacturing commenced nearby. In other instances new industries made an appearance, sometimes with the Commonwealth Government providing both pressure and assistance. The production of zinc at Risdon (near Hobart) and motor bodies at Adelaide (and elsewhere) began in 1917, and calcium carbide was made at Electrona (south of Hobart) in 1918. But it is also appropriate to note here that not all progress made at this time was permanent: thus, shipbuilding yards, expanded during the war, had little work between 1924 and 1939.

Secondly, the war showed the government the strategic dangers and difficulties of relying on overseas supplies, and the restriction of imports allowed manufacturers to glimpse the scope for expansion if imports were also controlled in peacetime. Thus, when the Commonwealth Government introduced new tariffs in 1920/21 virtually all opposition to protection had disappeared. In 1921 the Tariff Board was established, and the Industries Preservation Act was passed to provide against 'dumping'.

Australian manufacturing in the inter-war period has been discussed in detail elsewhere [18] and need be mentioned here only briefly but with an emphasis on location. Now firmly protected by tariffs and aided by overseas capital and knowledge, industrial development occurred in three different but intimately linked directions. Firstly, there was a further growth of the ferrous and non-ferrous metal producing and associated processing industries. Secondly, there was further growth in the textile industry. An expansion of the existing woollen textile section was mainly responsible for the growth, but there was also the development of sections new to Australia such as the manufacture of cotton goods, hosiery, and knitted products. Thirdly, there was a very important build-up of new industries making motor cars, domestic appliances, electric motors, wireless sets, rubber goods, and chemicals. The motor industry, for example, expanded output from a few hundred bodies a year at the end of the First World War to nearly 90,000 in 1926/27 and this was accompanied by the growth of a rubber tyre industry. These new industries placed additional demands on the old and promoted further growth in the metal, timber, textile, rubber, paint, and chemical industries. Between 1918 and 1924 the production of electric power doubled, it doubled again by 1930 and yet again by 1939; before the First World War the consumption of electricity was about 60 kWh per head of population but this had risen to 640 kWh per head before the Second World War. At first much of the demand for domestic and industrial electrical

apparatus and appliances was satisfied by imports but local products began to replace these towards the end of the 1920s.

After reaching a peak of 452,000 in 1926/27 the level of factory employment remained stationary for two years and then fell with the onset of the depression to a trough of 337,000 in 1931/32. Not all industries were equally affected and some, like hosiery and knitted goods, electrical appliances, and woollens even increased their workforces [19]. Total employment had almost returned to the 1926/27 level by 1934/35, and from then until 1938/39 the number of factory workers increased at an annual average rate of 5·9 per cent—that is considerably faster than the rate of increase (3·4 per cent) between 1919/20 and 1926/27 (Fig. 4).

The growth of these newer industries had a major impact on the geography of manufacturing in Australia. In the 1900s the proportion of the population in each State engaged in manufacturing was, with the exception of Victoria, more or less similar as can be seen from Table 4. The newer industries tended to con-

Table 4 *Number of Factory Workers per Thousand Population*

State	1906	1913	1920	1939
New South Wales	51.5	66.5	70.9	83.7
Victoria	69.6	85.2	90.3	107.6
Queensland	45.0	64.9	56.4	53.7
S. Australia	53.4	65.8	61.1	73.0
W. Australia	49.6	55.1	48.2	50.2
Tasmania	47.5	49.9	48.8	58.3
Australia	56.0	70.2	71.4	81.6

Source: Year Book of the Commonwealth of Australia.

centrate in New South Wales and Victoria for here were the main sources of labour, capital, markets, and raw and partly processed materials. Between 1913 and 1926/27 these two States accounted for most of the workers starting in some industries, for example, 96 per cent of the new workers in engineering, founding, and ironworking; 85 per cent in brass and copper; 91 per cent in wireworking; and 86 per cent in stoves and grates. They were also attractive to the older industries, and absorbed 97 per cent of the new textile workers, and 79 per cent of those entering the printing and paper making

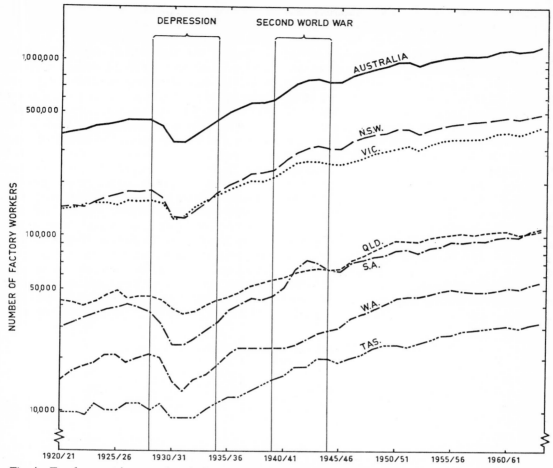

Fig. 4—Employment in secondary industry 1920/21 to 1960/61 (ratio graph)

industry. New South Wales alone accounted for 51 per cent of the extra factory employment during this period and Victoria for another 33 per cent.

In addition, there were some significant developments in two other States. In Tasmania cheap hydro-electric power became available from the Waddamana station in 1916 and almost immediately zinc and calcium carbide plants commenced operations [20]. Research during the 1920s and 1930s into the use of local timbers led to the establishment of a mill for fine papers at Burnie in 1936 and another for newsprint at Boyer in 1941. Cheap power, climate, and the availability of suitable water (as well as supplies of raw materials) also attracted other firms. Cadbury, Fry, Pascall

Pty. Ltd. (confectionery) was established at Hobart in 1922, and Kelsall and Kemp (Tasmania) Ltd. (woollens) and Patons and Baldwins (Australia) Ltd. (knitting wools) at Launceston in 1923.

In South Australia two coach-building firms turned their attention to motor car body building. One of these, Holden and Frost, became Holden's Motor Body Builders in 1920 and General Motors-Holden's Ltd. in 1931. It increased output from two motor bodies in 1917 to 36,200 in 1926 and employed between 3000 and 3500 in the years 1926 to 1929 with up to 4300 in peak periods [21]. The other firm, T. J. Richards & Son, was eventually taken over by the Chrysler Corporation. The chance seized by these two firms and the stimulus to factories supplying materials and parts became the main foundation for South Australia's industrial progress. In the mid-1930s the South Australian Government started a deliberate programme to attract industry, one of its first successes being to persuade I.C.I.A.N.Z. Ltd. to set up an alkali plant at Osborne which began operations in 1940 [22].

In Queensland and Western Australia a smaller proportion of the population was engaged in manufacturing in 1920 than in 1913. During the war years, factory employment in Western Australia declined from 18,800 in 1914 to 13,350 in 1917 and it did not rise above the pre-war level until 1921. Both States found it difficult to attract the newer kinds of manufacturing. To a certain extent Western Australia benefited from its distance from the eastern States as manufacturing employment during the 1920s and 1930s grew relatively quickly compared with most of the other States (Table 5), and more quickly

economic fluctuations. An impression of the special nature of Queensland's manufacturing can be gained from Table 13.

During the latter part of the nineteenth century there was, as noted already, a distinct trend for manufacturing activities to concentrate in the capital cities. This trend persisted in the twentieth century, and in several industries, such as flour milling and brewing, the number of factories operating outside the metropolitan areas continued to diminish as can be seen from Figs. 1 and 2. At the same time, the newer industries, developing during the inter-war years, tended to congregate in the capital cities—particularly Sydney and Melbourne. There were, of course, some exceptions. Apart from the growth of manufacturing in Newcastle and Port Kembla, which will be discussed later, a few country towns were picked out as sites for large manufacturing plants. Thus, woollen mills were set up at Goulburn, Orange, Albury, Wangaratta,

Table 5 *Factory Employment and Population 1919-20 to 1938-39*
(000's)

State	Factory Employment			Population		
	1919-20	*1938-39*	*Average Annual Increase (%)*	*1919-20*	*1938-39*	*Average Annual Increase (%)*
New South Wales	144	229	2.5	2092	2765	1.5
Victoria	137	202	2.1	1528	1886	1.1
Queensland	41	54	1.5	751	1018	1.6
S. Australia	29	43	2.1	491	598	1.0
W. Australia	15	23	2.2	331	467	1.8
Tasmania	10	14	1.7	213	242	0.7
Six States	376	565	2.2	5406	6976	1.4

Source: *Year Book of the Commonwealth of Australia.*

than its population. In contrast, Queensland's factory employment grew more slowly than that of any other State and more slowly than its rate of population increase. This was partly because Queensland had to contend with competition from the more industrialized States in the south, and partly because a considerable proportion of its factory employees was in primary processing industries that not only varied in activity seasonally but were also particularly susceptible to climatic and

Daylesford, Mount Gambier, and Albany; cement works at Kandos and Berrima; meatworks at Bourke, Ballarat, and Bendigo; and fruit and vegetable canning works at Shepparton, Kyabram, Mooroopna, and Bathurst. Particularly important, too, was the selection of Whyalla in South Australia as the site for the first blast furnace to be erected outside New South Wales.

The only State for which adequate statistical data are available from which to trace these geographical changes in detail is New South Wales. From 1901 to 1921/22 factory employment in that State increased by 82,800 of whom 83 per cent found jobs in the metropolitan area. From 1922/23 (when regional data became available) to 1938/39, the State's factory workforce increased by 79,500 and of these 84·6 per cent were in the Cumberland Statistical Division (which includes Sydney). During the first four decades of the century Sydney metropolitan area steadily increased both its share of Australia's factory workforce and its share of that in New South Wales (Table 6). Much of the factory workforce out-

Table 6 *Factory Employment in Sydney Metropolitan Area 1901 to 1938-39* (a)

| Year | Proportion in Sydney Metropolitan Area of Factory Workforce in: | |
	Australia	New South Wales
1901	21.6	63.6
1913	25.5	71.6
1919-20	28.6	75.0
1926-27	30.3	74.8
1938-39	32.5	79.3

(a) The metropolitan area as defined by the N.S.W. Government Statistician at these dates.
Sources: Statistical Register N.S.W. and *Production Bulletins.*

side the Cumberland Statistical Division was concentrated either in the Hunter and Manning Statistical Division (which absorbed 7·6 per cent of the State's increase between 1922/23 and 1938/39), or in the South Coast Statistical Division (which absorbed 6·6 per cent). The

Newcastle area accounted for much of the factory employment in the Hunter and Manning Division where, apart from the development of the steel works itself, there was a growth of 'parasitic' plants dependent on the steel works and making such products as wire netting, railway equipment, tubes, pipes, and steel hawsers. The iron and steel works at Lithgow was older, smaller, and less mechanized than the works at Newcastle and its inland site was disadvantageous both from the point of view of obtaining raw materials and also for distributing products. Accordingly, a new iron and steel works was erected at Port Kembla (the blast furnace being 'blown-in' in August 1928) and the Lithgow works was gradually closed down. In Fig. 5 the very rapid increase in factory employment in the South Coast Division after 1930 is largely attributable to the growth and development of these works and ancillary plants in the Port Kembla-Wollongong area. Outside the Cumberland, Hunter and Manning, and South Coast Divisions the factory workforce in the rest of New South Wales increased between 1922/23 and 1938/39 by only 1300.

(c) 1939 to 1964

The immediate effect of the Second World War was to give further stimulus to manufacturing both because of the demand for munitions and also because goods previously imported were in short supply. Between 1939 and 1943 the number of government factories producing ammunition, explosives, ordnance, and small

Table 7 *Construction and Disposal of Government Munitions Factories*

| State | Wartime Construction Factory Area (acres) | Postwar Disposal | | |
		Area Leased or Sold (sq. ft.)	Factories Disposed of (No.)	Number of Firms
New South Wales	6,972	3,245,500	23	128
Victoria	4,266	996,300	20	20
Queensland	455	1,364,300	18	88
S. Australia	5,397	1,789,100	9	24
W. Australia	140	395,200	3	19
Tasmania	133	409,500	7	14
Total	17,363	8,199,900	80	293

Source: Department of Post-War Reconstruction, (1949) *Wartime Factories with a Peacetime Future: The Story of Decentralisation.*

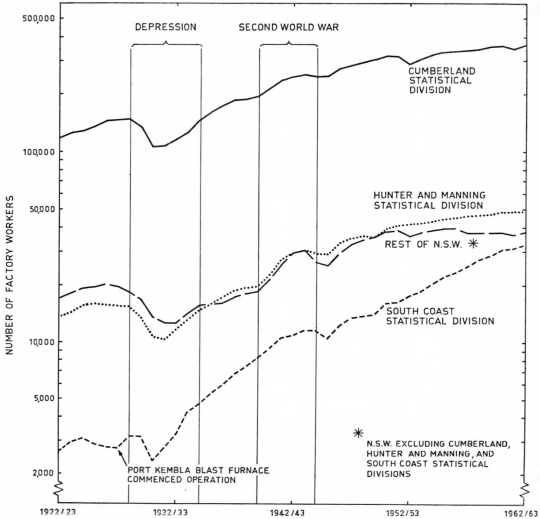

Fig. 5—Employment in secondary industry in main statistical divisions of New South Wales 1922/23 to 1962/63 (ratio graph)

arms increased from four to forty-six. In addition, thirty-two food dehydration plants, four grain (power) alcohol plants, and several warehouses were built, as well as over 200 annexes to existing State-owned or private factories [23]. The total increase in the factory workforce between mid-1939 and mid-1943 was 194,000 (about 34 per cent) of whom about 80,000 were employed in munitions factories and annexes. These developments were not only significant in that they enabled war production to be expanded rapidly but they also had two important and long-term effects on industrial location. Firstly, a significant proportion of these wartime government munitions factories were built in South Australia for considerations of defence strategy, and this helps to explain the sharp rise in factory employment in that State between 1940 and 1943 which is very noticeable in Fig. 4. Moreover, South Australia benefited more than any other State, relative to the size of its secondary industry, when some of the buildings were leased or sold to commercial undertakings after the war (Table 7).

Table 8 Employment and Other Data by Industry Groups

Industry Group	Employment			Females as Proportion of Total – 1962-63 (%)	Postwar Immigrants as Proportion of Total – 1961 (%)	Value of Production	
	1948-49	1962-63	Annual Rate of Increase (+) or Decrease (–)			1948-49 ($ mill.)	1962-63 ($ mill.)
Motor vehicles, parts and spares	62.0	134.9	+5.7	9	33	69.0	451.2
Machinery and engineering	84.0	126.2	+3.0	10	27	107.4	471.6
Food processing	100.1	113.0	+0.9	29	19	145.4	509.4
Clothing	106.9	94.3	–1.2	76	34	93.4	230.6
Textiles	68.5	74.9	+0.6	56	33	77.4	243.0
Electrical and electronic equipment	39.2	72.3	+4.5	29	30	44.8	256.2
Other transport equipment	69.4	64.2	–0.7	3	21	72.4	176.4
Iron and steel	30.6	62.5	+5.2	6	32	47.0	324.2
Wood products	50.8	56.7	+0.8	6	16	58.8	189.4
Printing and publishing	34.8	50.7	+2.7	24	14	46.2	213.4
Miscellaneous products	41.0	44.6	+0.6	34	26	45.0	151.4
Cement, clay, and glass products	31.9	44.2	+2.4	8	30	40.2	204.2
Chemicals	31.7	42.5	+2.1	24	21	61.4	315.8
Other metal products	30.5	39.5	+1.9	19	27	34.8	150.0
Non-ferrous metals	17.7	25.6	+2.7	13	25	46.6	129.2
Paper and paper products	15.5	24.9	+3.4	31	21	24.0	135.4
Furniture	20.0	21.8	+0.6	21	21	21.8	70.0
Rubber products	11.8	18.9	+3.4	21	30	15.4	82.6
Beverages	13.0	13.7	+0.4	12	17	26.6	87.8
Plastics products	5.5	11.8	+5.5	39	33	7.0	48.4
Petroleum refining	1.6	5.0	+8.5	7	36	5.8	95.6
Tobacco	5.2	4.7	–0.3	50	22	7.6	40.4
Leather tanning	5.4	4.2	–2.1	9	26	7.8	16.2
Total	877.1	1151.1	+2.0	24	26	1105.8	4592.4

Source: Commonwealth of Australia, Report of the Committee of Economic Enquiry, Vol. I, 8.70 – 8.76.
Industry groups are special ones prepared for the Enquiry—see details Vol. II, G.117—G.121.

Secondly, many of these wartime factories were in country towns (Fig. 15) and this gave an immediate post-war stimulus to decentralization —a subject considered in more detail in the penultimate section of this chapter.

The wartime demand for munitions and fighting vehicles had caused manufacturers to learn new skills and adopt new techniques which were then applicable to peacetime production. At first post-war expansion was restricted by shortages of imported plant, machinery, raw materials, power, fuel, and labour. Consumer demand was stimulated early in the 1950s by the high export earnings resulting from the Korean war and thereafter by such factors as the expansion of hire purchase finance and the high level of employment. The effect of recessions in 1952/53 and in 1961/62 can be seen in Fig. 4.

Two other influences were of special importance after the war. Firstly, post-war immigration policy resulted in additional demand for manufactured products. Immigrants arriving between 1947 and 1961 and their Australian-born children were responsible for about half the total increase in Australia's population in that period [24]. At the same time, immigrants helped to fill a deficiency in the age structure (caused by the drastic effect of the depression on the birthrate) and they accounted for 80 per cent of the increase in the male labour force between 1947 and 1961. At this latter date 26 per cent of the factory workers were post-war immigrants (Table 8). Secondly, overseas investment played an important part in industrial expansion. Although exact information is not available, one estimate is that approximately two-thirds of direct overseas investment is in manufacturing, and about one-third of the

capital in Australian manufacturing companies may be directly owned overseas [25].

Since the Second World War some industries, such as petroleum refining, and the manufacture of plastic products, iron and steel, motor vehicles, and electrical equipment, have expanded their workforces rapidly while others, such as leather tanning, clothing, tobacco, and beverages, have reduced employment (although this may be the result of greater productivity in some cases rather than a falling-off in output). From Table 8 it can be seen that food processing and clothing, the leading employment groups in 1948/49, have been displaced by motor vehicles, parts and repairs, and machinery and engineering. Employment and output in these industry groups did not, of course, rise (or in some cases fall) steadily throughout this period and Fig. 6 gives an impression of the fluctuations in activity in seven representative groups. The majority of industries were affected by the recessions of 1952/53 and 1961/62 but activity in the electrical equipment industry, for example, tended to oscillate more markedly than most of the others, whereas the iron and steel industry was hardly affected at all. It can be seen, too, that the long-term trends in the petroleum refining and leather tanning industries are in marked contrast. The major industry groups are, of course, composed of many sub-industries; thus Fig. 7 shows that although the output of the total food processing industry moved steadily upwards some of its component sub-industries grew more slowly (cereals and food processing), or more quickly (fruit and vegetable preserving), and that the years of increased output in some sub-industries were years of decreased output in others.

Table 9 *Manufacturing and Population in Australian States 1963-64* (a)

| | Proportions of Australian Total | | | | | | Actual Total (000's) |
	N.S.W.	Vic.	Qld.	S.A.	W.A.	Tas.	
Total population	37.0	28.1	14.2	9.3	7.1	3.3	11,250
Total labour force (b)	37.9	28.7	13.9	8.9	6.6	3.1	4,225
Factory workforce	40.3	34.2	9.1	9.2	4.6	2.6	1,210
Value of production	43.0	33.2	8.4	8.1	4.4	2.9	$A5,269,546
Factories	39.9	29.6	10.0	9.8	7.8	2.9	59

(a) The A.C.T. and N.T. together have 1.3% of the population but only 0.3% of the factory workers.
(b) As at census of population 30 June, 1961.

FACTORY OUTPUT 1949/50–1962/63
SAMPLE INDUSTRY GROUPS
(INDEX BASE 1955/56 = 100)

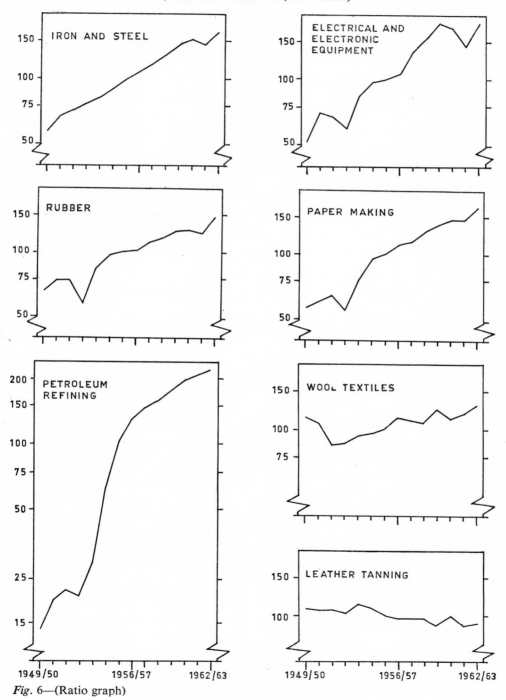

Fig. 6—(Ratio graph)

FACTORY OUTPUT 1949/50–1962/63
FOOD INDUSTRIES
(INDEX BASE 1955/56 = 100)

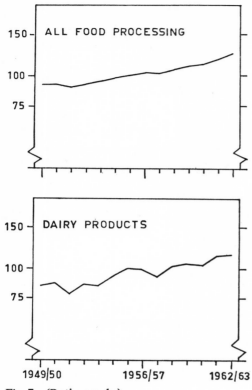

Fig. 7—(Ratio graphs)

The proportion of the total employment in each industry group made up by females is also shown in Table 8. Over half the females are employed in three industries—clothing, textiles, and food processing. The noxious or heavy industries employ, as might be expected, relatively few females. In fact, one measure of the heaviness of an industry is the ratio of female to male operatives. This ratio is 1:17 in the case of iron and steel and 1:0·32 in the clothing industry.

The Location of Manufacturing

This section of the chapter investigates the distribution of manufacturing between States, Statistical Divisions, and towns but, because it is discussed elsewhere in this book, no space has been devoted to the arrangement of manufacturing activity within urban areas.

Distribution Between States

The present distribution of manufacturing between States is set out in summary form in Table 9. It is obvious that New South Wales and Victoria, with three-quarters of the factory workforce, stand head and shoulders above the other States. Moreover, within these two States factory employment is relatively more important than in the others although, as Fig. 8 shows, factory workers form nearly as important a proportion of the total workforce of South Australia. In Fig. 8 the width of the columns has been made proportional to each State's share of the Australian workforce so that the actual area shaded for each industry

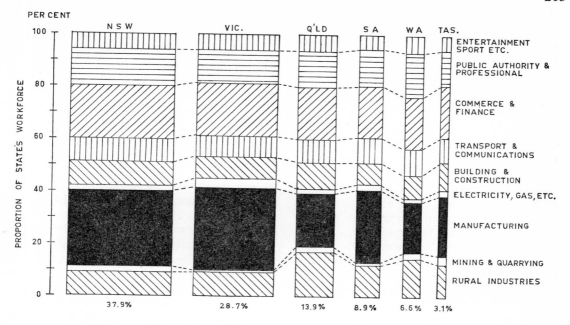

PER CENT

PROPORTION OF STATE'S WORKFORCE

ENTERTAINMENT SPORT ETC.

PUBLIC AUTHORITY & PROFESSIONAL

COMMERCE & FINANCE

TRANSPORT & COMMUNICATIONS

BUILDING & CONSTRUCTION

ELECTRICITY, GAS, ETC.

MANUFACTURING

MINING & QUARRYING

RURAL INDUSTRIES

WIDTH OF COLUMNS PROPORTIONAL TO STATE SHARE OF AUSTRALIAN WORKFORCE

Fig. 8—Main employment categories by States in 1961

represents the number of workers employed and can be compared not only within but also between the columns.

One of the problems about discussing the absolute or relative importance of manufacturing is to know what criteria to use. For example, the *number of persons employed* and the *value of production* are not interchangeable criteria in studies of distribution, e.g. one area might have a relatively low value of production but many employees, while another may have few employees but a high value of production. A technique that overcomes some of these difficulties is the calculation of MAGNITUDE and INTENSITY RATINGS [26]. Briefly, the ratings depend on fixed bases which are averages of the conditions found in the six States. Thus, the MAGNITUDE BASES (obtained by dividing the 1960/61 Australian total by six) are: (a) the number of factory workers—190,788; (b) salaries and wages paid—$A381,272,000; and (c) the value of production—$A723,268,000. The actual amount in a State is divided by this base; the three quotients are summed, divided by three, and multiplied by one thousand.

For example, the magnitude rating for New South Wales is calculated in the following way:

$$\frac{472,061}{190,788} + \frac{980,032,000}{381,272,000} + \frac{1,933,512,000}{723,268,000}$$

$$\left(\frac{2 \cdot 474 + 2 \cdot 570 + 2 \cdot 673}{3}\right) \times 1000 = 2572$$

The INTENSITY BASES, which are obtained from the Australian totals, are (a) the number of factory workers divided by total population—0·109; (b) the number of factory workers divided by the total labour force—0·271; and (c) the value of factory production per head of population—$A412·8. The actual ratio in each State is divided by this base, the three quotients are summed, divided by 3, and multiplied by 100.

Thus, the intensity rating for New South Wales is obtained as follows:

$$\frac{0 \cdot 120}{0 \cdot 109} + \frac{0 \cdot 294}{0 \cdot 271} + \frac{493 \cdot 6}{412 \cdot 8}$$

$$\left(\frac{1 \cdot 101 + 1 \cdot 085 + 1 \cdot 196}{3}\right) \times 100 = 113$$

Table 10 *Magnitude and Intensity Ratings—States*

State	Magnitude		Intensity	
	Rating 1960-61	*% Increase 1953-54 to 1960-61*	*Rating 1960-61*	*% Change 1953-54 to 1960-61*
New South Wales	2,572	20.2	113	+5.0
Victoria	2,002	16.1	119	−1.5
Queensland	501	4.1	61	−3.0
S. Australia	504	13.8	92	−3.3
W. Australia	256	8.3	64	−4.4
Tasmania	163	23.3	83	+9.2

In effect the magnitude rating is a way of indicating the amount of industrial activity in an area. In Table 10 it can be seen that the magnitude rating for Victoria (2002) is 3·97 times that of South Australia (504)—thus it takes into account that Victoria has 3·71 times the number of factory workers in South Australia but its value of production is 4·10 times as great. The intensity rating gives an indication of the importance of manufacturing in a State's economy by considering the relationship of factory activity, population, and the total labour force. On this basis there is a very great difference between the importance of manufacturing in Victoria and New South Wales, on the one hand, and Queensland and Western Australia, on the other. For example, Queensland has only 19·6 per cent of its workforce in secondary industry (compared with 32·1 per cent in Victoria), and a value of factory production per head of population of $A223 (compared with $A486 in Victoria).

It is useful also to compare magnitude and intensity ratings over time. Individual factory criteria may differ considerably in the amount, rate, and direction of change. For example, in Western Australia between 1953/54 and 1960/61 the factory workforce increased by 5·8 per cent, wages and salaries (after correction for changes in the value of money) by 1·3 per cent, and value of factory production (after correction) by 17·6 per cent. These differences are taken into account by calculating ratings in the manner described. Table 10 shows the percentage change between 1953/54 and 1960/61 (labour force statistics are available only for census years); the 1953/54 fixed bases were used for both years and the 1960/61 raw data were corrected for changes in the value of money by means of production and price

indices. These percentage changes show that not only is Tasmania's factory activity growing at a greater rate than that of the other States but its intensity rating also showed the greatest increase during this seven year period.

So far the discussion has been concerned with manufacturing as a whole but it is now necessary to consider the distribution of the various kinds of manufacturing between the States [27]. It is inadequate to describe the distribution of industries by quoting actual figures or percentages. For the most part this would simply emphasize the importance of New South Wales and Victoria. More useful is the LOCATION QUOTIENT—a device which takes some account of the size of a region measured here by its total labour force. It is calculated by dividing the percentage of the Australian workforce in an industry in a particular State by the percentage of the total labour force. Thus, if a State has 20 per cent of the workforce employed in an industry and 10 per cent of the total labour force, the location quotient for that industry would be 2·00. Each State in which an industry has a quotient of more than 1·00 has more than its proportionate share of those workers, similarly, a quotient of less than 1·00 indicates a less than proportionate share.

A summary of the location quotients for 142 industries in six States is set out in Table 11. This indicates that there is a fundamental difference between the industrial development of New South Wales and Victoria and that of the other States. New South Wales and Victoria have only fourteen and twenty-six industries, respectively, in which there is more than twice or less than half as much employment as might be expected on the basis of the distribution of the working population.

In New South Wales the industries which

Table 11 *Summary of Location Quotient Analysis by States*

State	Number of Industries Out of 142 With Quotients:		
	Greater Than 2.00	0.50-2.00	Less Than 0.50
New South Wales	6	128	8
Victoria	14	116	12
Queensland	6	69	67
S. Australia	13	77	52
W. Australia	6	71	65
Tasmania	13	42	87

had a location quotient greater than 2·00 (on the basis of 1961 data) include iron and steel, aluminium and alloys, incandescent lamps, and telephone equipment; in Victoria they include aircraft and parts, bolts and screws, knitted goods and hosiery, boots and shoes, carpets, explosives, and malting; in Queensland they include meat freezing, sugar milling, margarine, plywood, and saddlery; in South Australia they include refining of non-ferrous metals, iron and steel pipe making, munitions, refrigerators, motor vehicles, fish canning, fruit and vegetable drying, distilling, winemaking, and coopering; in Western Australia they include petroleum and products, wool scouring, sawmilling, chemical fertilizers, and minting; and in Tasmania they include cement, refining of non-ferrous metals, aluminium smelting, textile fibre making and dyeing, fish canning, confectionery, jam and vegetable preserving and drying, sawmilling, fibreboard, and pulp, paper, and paper board. It is also interesting to consider the kinds of industries in which States are deficient. Queensland, South Australia, Western Austra-

lia, and Tasmania tend to be deficient in many branches of the metal working, chemical (except fertilizers), textile, clothing, and appliance industries. The relative lack of some of the main female employing industries, such as textiles, clothing, plastics, and light assembly work, is reflected in the much smaller proportion of female labour in the factory workforce of these States. No matter which of the criteria in Table 12 is examined it shows that much less use is made of female labour in these States compared with New South Wales and Victoria.

The location quotients can be graphed to give a visual impression of the distribution of employment in an industry and Fig. 9 contrasts some industries that have distributions similar to that of the total workforce (graphs A to D) with others that tend to be concentrated in a few of the States. The width of the columns in each graph has been made proportional to each State's share of the total labour force; thus the norm for each State is 1·00 and this is indicated by a horizontal line drawn across each graph at this point. In each graph if some States have columns rising above unity there must be other columns with an exactly similar area left uncovered below unity. For each State the area shown in black on a graph is proportional to the size of the workforce. Each of the graphs represents a different number of workers so that, in effect, the scales are different and the graphs cannot be directly compared.

Location quotients are simple to calculate and can be used not only for employment but also with other data such as the value of production. In addition, income, area, value of production, population, employment in another industry, and so forth, can each be used as the

Table 12. *Employment of Females 1961*

State	Percentage of:			
	Females in Workforce	Females in Manufacturing	Total Female Workforce in Manufacturing	Females in Total Factory Labour Force
New South Wales	21.1	5.4	25.6	22.8
Victoria	22.2	6.8	30.7	26.1
Queensland	18.0	2.5	13.9	16.7
S. Australia	18.6	3.6	19.4	16.8
W. Australia	17.5	2.0	11.3	14.0
Tasmania	17.2	3.0	17.8	17.8

Source: Census of population 1961.

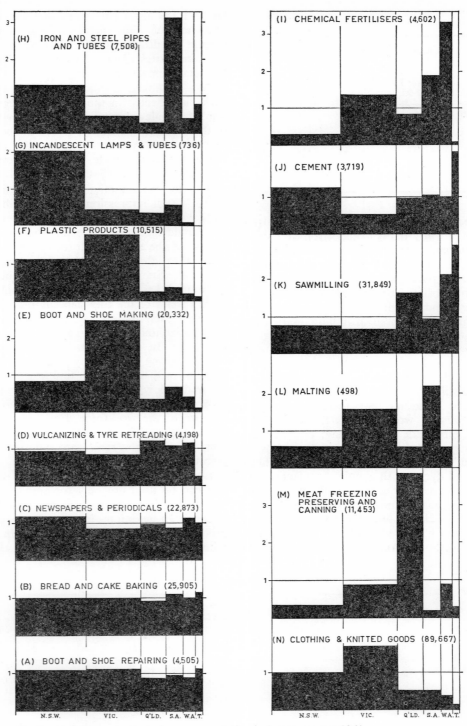

Fig. 9—Location quotients for representative industry groups 1961

Table 13 *Proportion of Factory Employment in Categories of Industry*

Category	N.S.W.	Vic.	Qld.	S.A.	W.A.	Tas.	Aust.
1938-39 Processing	8	9	35	14	16	38	12
Market orientated	28	20	27	32	36	28	26
Other	64	71	38	54	48	34	62
1947-48 Processing	9	10	31	15	16	34	13
Market orientated	31	24	33	28	38	25	29
Other	60	66	36	57	46	41	58
1961-62 Processing	7	8	28	12	16	28	11
Market orientated	31	25	34	29	38	21	29
Other	62	67	38	59	46	51	60

denominator to help show up the characteristics of an industry's distribution. Location quotients are, of course, a very elementary research tool and must be used with discretion. For example, for a particular industry two areas may each have a location quotient of 1·00, but the first area may be consuming little of the product locally and have an important export trade while the other may be consuming all that it produces and importing more to make up a deficiency. Apart from differences in demand brought about by areal variations in taste and expendable income, there may also be differences in production techniques with a low quotient for employment in an industry in a particular area resulting from higher productivity. Despite all these shortcomings, however, the location quotient is a useful device in the preliminary stages of research. Thus, the high location quotient for employment in petroleum refining in Western Australia (2·8) draws attention to the bunkering trade at Fremantle, and the low quotient for brick making in Queensland and Tasmania (0·54 in both States) to the high proportion of dwellings in those parts of Australia built of materials other than bricks.

There are several quotients, coefficients, and indices that can be used to examine various aspects of the areal distribution of manufacturing such as the COEFFICIENT OF LOCALIZATION, the COEFFICIENT OF GEOGRAPHICAL ASSOCIATION and the COEFFICIENT OF REDISTRIBUTION [28]. Others examine the number of industries and diversity of manufacturing in an area such as the INDEX OF ECONOMIC DIVERSIFICATION and the REFINED INDEX OF INDUSTRIAL DIVERSIFICATION [29]. It is also possible to group industries in various ways. For example, employment in the industries

listed in the *Secondary Industries Bulletin* can be divided into the categories: *processing* (those associated with primary production such as sawmills and meatworks), *market orientated* (those that are usually close to the market because of bulk, perishability, or time such as newspapers, printing, and bread baking), and *others*. The allocation of some industries into categories of this kind has to depend on judgments made on the basis of the calculation of some of the coefficients and indices listed above, and assumes that industries are more homogeneous than they are in practice. Nevertheless, the results, set out in Table 13, indicate that there are considerable differences between the States. Many of these measures of the distribution and 'mix' of industries are enhanced in value if they can be examined over a period. It would seem from Table 13, for instance, that the processing industries in Queensland and Tasmania are gradually becoming relatively less important.

Distribution Between Statistical Divisions

Some data on manufacturing activities are available for 60 divisions of Australia (including the Australian Capital Territory and Northern Territory). These divisions vary greatly in size and population and in the nature of their economies so that it is useful not only to consider the amount of manufacturing but also its significance in terms of the population and labour force. The magnitude and intensity ratings (obtained in the way shown above) have been mapped for each division in Figs. 10a and 10b. These maps emphasize the way in which manufacturing is concentrated in the southeast, southwest and northeast peripheries of the continent and how it shades off in significance

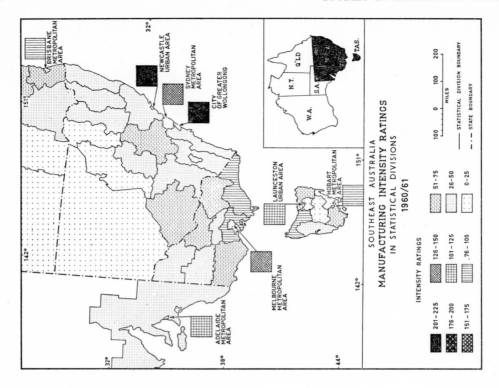

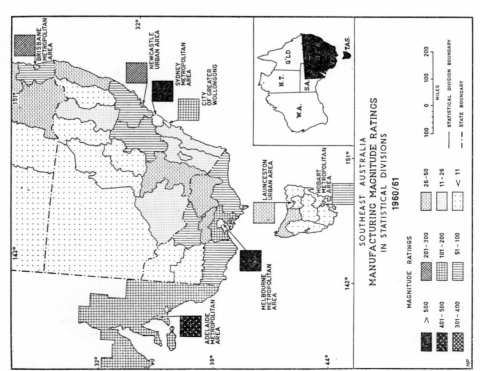

Fig. 10a

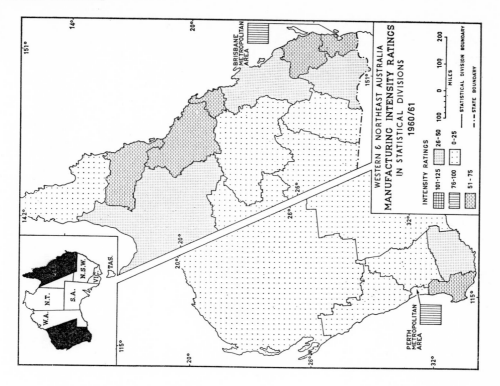

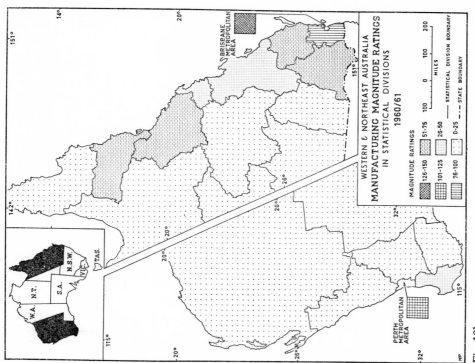

Fig. 10b

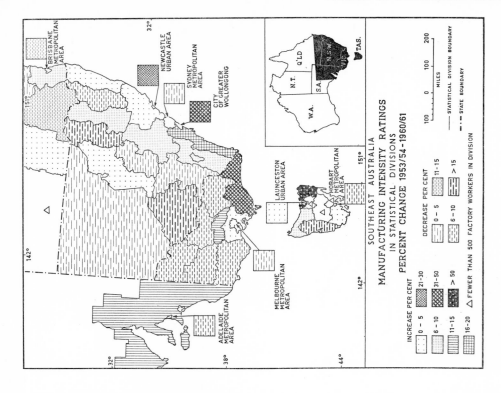

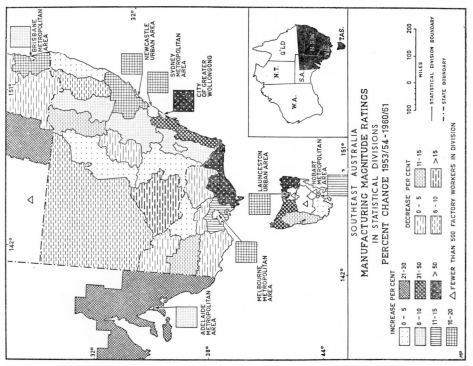

Fig. 11a

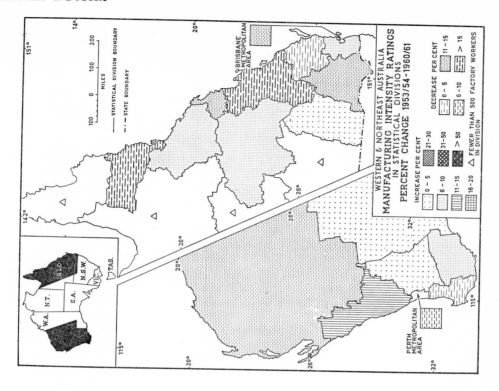

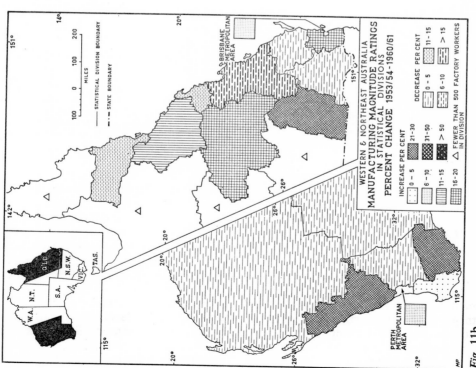

Fig. 11b

away from the coast. The six capital cities together account for 74·3 per cent of Australia's factory activity (measured as the sum of their magnitude ratings compared with the rating for Australia). Only eight other statistical divisions have a magnitude rating greater than 50—namely, in decreasing order of importance, Newcastle Urban Area, Greater Wollongong, Central (Vic.), Gippsland (Vic.), Western (Vic.), Northern (Vic.), Moreton (Qld.), and Central Tableland (N.S.W.), and these together account for a further 12·9 per cent of the manufacturing activity.

The changes over time shown in Figs. 11a and 11b are in some respects more interesting. Regrettably, data are not available before 1953/54 on an adequate basis to make comparisons possible over a longer time-span. In many divisions of the country there was a decrease in both the intensity and magnitude

lutely and, in terms of the local economy, relatively more important such as Gippsland (mainly the Latrobe Valley), and the northwest and northeast of Tasmania.

Distribution Between Urban Places

Most manufacturing is carried on in towns, and Fig. 12 shows the location of all towns which had at least 250 factory workers in 1962/63. One of the problems in compiling a map of this kind is that data for the smaller towns are not shown separately in the factory statistics of all States (because of the non-disclosure rule and different systems of local government). The forty-one urban places named on the map—those with 1000 or more factory workers—accounted for 90·0 per cent of Australia's factory workforce while the others shown but not named accounted for only an additional 3·4 per cent. This map and Table 14 together

Table 14 *Factory Employment in Towns 1962-63*

State	Proportion of Factory Workers in:			
	Metropolitan Area (a)	*Towns With More Than 1000 Factory Workers* (b)	*5 Towns With Most Factory Workers* (b)	*Metropolitan Area and 10 Towns With Most Factory Workers*
New South Wales	75.7	16.5	14.5	91.7
Victoria	81.5	10.8	9.3	92.5
Queensland	59.6	15.7	14.2	79.4
South Australia	80.4	6.5	8.0	91.3
Western Australia	80.9	none	6.2	90.2
Tasmania	36.4	43.8	46.8	88.7

(a)   The metropolitan areas used are as follows: Sydney is the Cumberland Statistical Division; Melbourne is the Metropolitan Statistical Division; Brisbane is the Metropolitan Statistical Division plus City of Ipswich; Adelaide is the Metropolitan Statistical Division plus Elizabeth, Salisbury, and Tea Tree Gully; Perth is the Metropolitan and Swan Statistical Divisions; Hobart is the Metropolitan Statistical Division.
(b)   Excluding the metropolitan area.

ratings. In the Riverina division, for example, during this seven year period the number of people in factory employment and the total workforce both declined absolutely as did (after correction) the value of salaries and wages paid and the value of production, whereas the total population increased. All the metropolitan area divisions increased in magnitude but decreased in intensity because the growth in factory activity failed to keep pace with the growth of the population and the labour force. These maps draw attention to those parts of Australia where manufacturing is quickly becoming abso-

indicate the differences between the States. At one extreme is Western Australia with no industrial towns of much consequence outside Perth, and at the other extreme is Tasmania where there are four towns, each with more than 1000 factory workers, that together have a greater proportion of the State total than the Hobart Metropolitan Area.

The metropolitan areas play a very significant role in Australian manufacturing. A detailed analysis of unpublished data from the 1961 census of population, summarized in Table 15, shows that at least three-quarters of

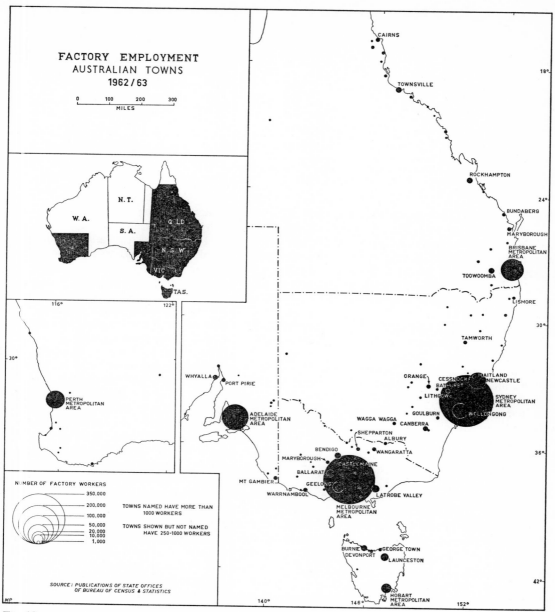

Fig. 12

the employees in 86 out of 142 manufacturing industries are located in the five mainland capital cities. The industries not having the greater part of their workforces in the capital cities are those associated with primary production such as fish preserving, milk processing, winemaking, and sawmilling; some of the metal

working industries such as steel smelting, the refining of non-ferrous metals, and coke ovens; and some miscellaneous industries such as incandescent lamp and munitions making.

The calculation of location quotients points up the difference between Sydney and Melbourne and the other three mainland capital

Table 15 *Concentration of Manufacturing in Mainland Capitals*

Industries With Stated Per Cent of Employment in Five Mainland Capitals	Number of Industries	Total Employment in Australia		Total Employment in Five Mainland Capitals	
		Persons	*%*	*Persons*	*%*
More than 90	42	173,600	17.0	162,000	93.4
80–90	36	323,300	31.6	275,600	85.3
75–80	8	44,100	4.3	34,000	77.3
50–75	39	344,800	33.7	219,800	63.8
Less than 50	17	140,400	13.4	25,400	17.9
Total	142	1,026,200	100.0	716,800	70.0

Source: Derived from unpublished census of population data. The analysis excludes 'other' codes in which 114,200 persons were employed. The capital cities are metropolitan areas as defined for the 1961 census of population.

cities which, as Table 16 shows, each have at least 48 industries with location quotients of less than 0·50. Brisbane, Adelaide, and Perth tend to be 'deficient' in employment in such industries as metal products (cutlery, small tools, nuts and bolts); electrical goods (telephone and telegraph equipment, electric cable); textile products (wool, cotton, and synthetic fibres, textile dyeing, carpets); clothing (nearly all forms of outer and under clothing); chemicals (cosmetics, glue, soap); and a wide range of miscellaneous industries (sports goods, toys, buttons, and so forth). This and other evidence suggests that Brisbane and Perth, in particular, have narrower industrial bases than the other mainland capital cities which may act as a deterrent to new manufacturing wishing to set up where a wide range of partly or wholly fabricated materials, parts, and equipment is available.

Apart from the mainland metropolitan areas there were 415 urban places in Australia with more than 1000 population in 1961. Of these only three (Newcastle Urban Area with 2·8 per

Table 16 *Summary of Location Quotient Analysis— Mainland Capitals* (a)

Capital	Number of Industries Out of 142 With Quotients:		
	Greater Than 2.00	*0.50-2.00*	*Less Than 0.50*
Sydney	30	93	19
Melbourne	28	97	17
Brisbane	13	81	48
Adelaide	20	74	48
Perth	11	74	57

(a) As defined for the 1961 census of population.

cent, Greater Wollongong with 2·5 per cent, and Geelong Urban Area with 1·3 per cent) had more than 1 per cent of Australia's factory workforce. Metal working and transport equipment accounted for about 80 per cent of the factory workforce of both Newcastle and Wollongong (compared with about 40 per cent in Sydney and Melbourne), whereas metal working, transport equipment, and textiles each had about 20 per cent of Geelong's workforce.

The other towns in Australia can be divided from a manufacturing point of view into five groups. Firstly, there are urban places such as Hobart, Launceston and Ballarat where a number of industries have developed but none of them employ more than 10 per cent of the total workforce. Secondly, there are urban places which have several industries but one (or, occasionally, two) of them employs a large proportion (over 20 per cent) of the total workforce; this is the case in Whyalla (metal working and shipbuilding), Wangaratta (textiles), and Burnie (paper making). Thirdly, several towns have virtually only one industrial activity— sometimes only one factory—such as the cement works at Portland and Kandos (N.S.W.). Fourthly, there are towns, often quite small, which have manufacturing activities common to other towns in the region and this applies to towns in the dairying areas in Victoria, the wineries in South Australia, the sawmills in the southwest of Western Australia, and the sugar milling towns of Queensland. Fifthly, there are urban places, such as Canberra, which have little factory activity beyond that required to serve the day to day needs of the community (such as bread baking, builders' woodwork, and printing).

There is a tendency in the literature to

classify towns on a single function basis (such as manufacturing towns, transport towns, and so forth). It is fairly evident however that the functions of a town are not as simple as this approach would suggest. Smith has used workforce data from the 1954 census of population to examine the functions of 422 towns in Australia [30]. He suggests that there seem to be three groups of manufacturing towns. The first group of fifty towns can be termed manufacturing towns proper (such as Newcastle, Wollongong, Geelong, Ballarat, Port Pirie, Whyalla, Bundaberg and Burnie) and consists mainly of centres of heavy industry, primary processing industries and textile manufacturing. A second group of seventeen towns (which includes the metropolitan areas and country centres (such as Launceston, Orange, and Toowoomba) have, in addition to manufacturing activities, commercial and administrative functions. The third group of eleven towns (including Byron Bay, Daylesford, and Bacchus Marsh) display neither an additional specialization in commercial and administration nor consistent underspecialization in other categories.

Inherent in this classification is the fact that the proportion of the labour force engaged in manufacturing activities varies considerably between towns. At one extreme are places such as Whyalla where 56·0 per cent of the workforce is engaged in manufacturing, Greater Wollongong (46 per cent), Burnie (42 per cent), and Geelong (41 per cent). But at the other extreme are places like Canberra, Broken Hill, Kalgoorlie, Mount Isa, Armidale, and Darwin where less than 10 per cent of the labour force finds employment in factories.

There is scope for a good deal of research into manufacturing in Australian towns, both global studies such as the one by Smith reported above, and detailed examinations of the industrial structure of individual towns [31]. There are difficulties about data. Secondary industry census information cannot be published in very great geographical detail because of the non-disclosure rule (no information can be released that could be attributed to a particular firm). Moreover, many enterprises keep accounts for the whole of their activities rather than for the individual parts; thus, a certain amount of estimating has to be done by the statistician to allocate the total value of production of a firm between the towns in which it has factories. Another source of data, the census of population, refers only to place of residence and it is possible to be misled about the economic activities in a town if due weight is not given to such considerations as commuting [32]. Moreover, serious errors may be made if it is not realized that towns defined separately for census purposes may in fact be functionally related. For analysis of functions, therefore, Elizabeth, Salisbury, Tea Tree Gully, Morphett Vale, and Noarlunga must be regarded as part of Adelaide; Penrith and Campbelltown as part of Sydney; Redcliffe and Ipswich as part of Brisbane; Wodonga as part of Albury; Queanbeyan as part of Canberra; and Mackay North as part of Mackay [33].

The Location Pattern Examined

The points of origin and consumption of most substances are separated so that each manufacturing firm has to make a decision about where to locate its factory. One main approach to a theory of industrial location has tended to emphasize the cost aspects of a firm's decision. Weber [34], for example, stressed transport and labour costs and the effect of agglomerating and deglomerating factors on costs, and he assumed competitive pricing and a given market. Hoover [35] also emphasized costs, although in a more realistic and penetrating framework, but did not consider to any great extent the influence of demand. A second main approach to the theory of industrial location stems from the work of Fetter [36] and Hotelling [37] who assumed that buyers are scattered over an area and that delivered price varies with location. The demand factor was no longer taken as given but was regarded as a variable governed by the location of competitors. This second approach emphasizes that a firm may be willing to locate away from the least cost location in order to place a wider market area under its control and therefore recognizes that the most profitable location for a firm need not necessarily be the one at which costs are minimized [38].

It is necessary to dwell, for a moment, on the nature of a firm. The actual manufacturing pro-

1

cess is only one of the functions that have to be undertaken; others include design and research, warehousing, advertising, selling, and distribution. For a small firm it may be necessary for all these functions to be undertaken under the one roof—the showroom and the administrative office may in fact be one and the same. In such cases the 'packet of functions', as Haig neatly termed it [39], cannot easily be split because of difficulties of control and coordination. The location required for the 'packet' may have to be something of a compromise between, say, the ideal location for the showroom and the ideal location for the factory itself. A larger firm, however, may be able to divide up the 'packet' and physically separate the various functions: in a simple situation the showroom and the office may be in the Central Business District of a city while the factory operates at an outer suburban location or in a country town. Sometimes, too, the factory operations themselves can be split up. A simple example is the way that footwear and clothing firms are able if necessary to carry out certain stages in workrooms away from the main factory. Some factory operations, particularly of the process type defined at the beginning of the chapter, show considerable economies of scale and it is not desirable on economic (and often technical) grounds to divide production between several small units each located in respect of a particular market. But for some kinds of manufacturing there are no such restrictions or they are much less important. Thus, a canister-making firm may, fairly conveniently, break its manufacturing operations into several units some of which can be located in the fruit-growing districts and others can be set up in the metropolitan areas. While the Australian Consolidated Industries group has a bottle making plant in each State and the Colonial Sugar Refining Co. Ltd. has a refinery in each of the mainland capital cities, other firms try to achieve the same object by allowing their products (such as venetian blinds and soft drinks) to be made by franchised manufacturers.

It becomes obvious that a great many reservations of detail have to be made when discussing industrial location in the space available here. At first a firm may be small, weak, and uncertain about the future and have to locate where it can obtain external economies by renting space, drawing upon commercial and industrial services (such as accountants and electroplaters) in relatively small lots as and when they are needed. As the firm matures it may be able to bring more of these services under its own roof and within its direct control. The firm then has less need of a nursery atmosphere and reaches a point at which it is capable of a more self-contained existence elsewhere [40]. Or again, the firm may change its 'mix' of products or need to alter methods as the product evolves (e.g. from adding a body to an imported chassis to assembling a complete car) and these changes may affect locational requirements. The firm may become more capital-intensive or more labour-intensive, or the demands for the various materials may change not only in amount but relative to each other. One of the best examples of the locational impact of changing technology is the iron and steel industry. Before the First World War in Australia, seven tons of coal were required for every two tons of steel as compared with three tons of iron ore; by the outbreak of the Second World War fuel technology had changed so that the quantity of coal required per unit of steel product differed little from the quantity of iron ore needed. The locational effect of technological development is not, of course, confined to the manufacturing processes. Changes to transport techniques may affect a firm's material supplies (such as the development of glass-lined tankers for the transport of milk from farm to factory), or its product distribution (such as refrigerated road transport for frozen foods).

The conditions of demand and supply may change over time. For example, a small firm may set up in a country town to make pumps for a fairly confined market. The product may, in time, meet a need over the whole of a State or in several States. In terms of the original market the locational decision may have been correct, but in terms of the market that later develops the location may not be the most profitable one. Conditions of supply may also change, e.g. decisions to alter the level of a tariff or to pay a bounty may suddenly make local or imported sources of materials more, or less, attractive to other manufacturers. Sometimes a firm knows that supplies are likely to change and tries to take account of this locationally, e.g. a canning firm may try to locate where it can process fish for one part of the year and fruit and vegetables for the other.

Probably few firms are operating at their most profitable location although this is a concept which, in the light of the changes taking place more or less continuously, is somewhat unreal except in relation to a particular point in time. Locational theorists would argue that, in the long run, only optimally sited firms would survive because the less well sited firms would be unable to compete. In fact, however, many distortions affect the operation of the economic system. There may be no optimally sited firms in the industry, or if there is one such firm, gross inefficiency may make it only as profitable as a firm badly located but highly efficient in other respects. Then there are various ways in which the full effects of competition may be minimized such as by restrictive trade practices—sometimes euphemistically called 'orderly marketing'. The protection of local industry by tariffs on competing imports may suppress the economic signals and penalties of poor locations. Indeed the Tariff Board sometimes takes into account the extra costs that have to be borne by some producers because of their locations. In a report on woollen yarns the Board notes that 'most of those Australian mills in decentralized areas have an additional disadvantage in the form of higher costs of services and transport than their capital city counterparts' [41].

Even when firms recognize that they are badly located, geographical inertia may cause the period of adjustment to be a very long one especially if a great deal of capital has been invested in buildings and immobile plant. Firms tend to try to overcome the problem by expedients which may mean the investment of even more capital at the existing location. The longer that this continues the more reluctant the firm becomes to make a move and, in any case, the less financially able it is to do so. Locational adjustment tends to be a slow process and it is not until industries are examined over a long period, such as in Figs. 1, 2, and 3, that such changes become obvious.

Two other ways in which deviations from optimum location may arise must be mentioned. Australia is only one of many possible countries in which a large international manufacturing organization could set up a plant. In terms of present conditions Australia may not be the most profitable alternative. But the firm may be willing to accept a lower return on capital for the time being in the expectation of gaining greater returns in the long run. One of the circumstances that influenced Fibremakers Ltd. (then British Nylon Spinners (Australia) Pty. Ltd.) to set up in Australia was that it held patents that were due to expire in 1961. By commencing operations in Melbourne in January 1958 this firm not only became the first in this field in Australia but also gained a few years in which to consolidate its position before local competition also protected by tariffs could take place. There is, therefore, in the location of some factories an element of gamesmanship—an attempt to calculate the likely decisions of existing or new firms so as to make decisions now with future competitive situations in mind. It is perhaps the desire of firms to establish a foothold for the future that has enabled South Australia and Western Australia to attract two motor tyre factories each since 1962. These decisions illustrate that considerations of future developments outside the control of the firms affect not only locational choice as between nations but also as between States and as between regions within a State.

The second way in which deviations from an optimum location may arise is through personal tastes and preferences. So far, for convenience, 'the firm' has been referred to as though *it* was capable of exercising judgment. Decisions are of course made by individuals who may allow judgments to be coloured by personal considerations. A well-known example from overseas is the piano factory located on the River Medway in Kent because the owner was fond of sailing. Another kind of influence is a feeling of attachment or loyalty to a particular State or city, e.g. the founder of Fletcher Jones and Staff Pty. Ltd. stated that he set up a factory in Warrnambool (Vic.) because he had 'faith' in that town. Not least in importance can be the opinions of the wives of senior management who might argue that rather than live in a depressing country town it is better to be less well off but socially prominent in Vaucluse or Toorak. The importance of these somewhat nebulous influences must not be over-stressed but they undoubtedly play a more important role than some writers on industrial location would care to admit. It is often difficult for research workers in this field to penetrate the public relations facade and uncover these more human and personal influences on location.

It will be clear that the location of manufacturing in a country is neither simple nor static. The total pattern is made up of many distributions superimposed on each other. Some industries have coincidental distributions (e.g. bread baking and aerated water making) not because there is any contact between them but because both are serving essentially the same market. Sometimes there is an indirect relationship: in towns or areas where the predominant industries are heavy or dirty and unsuitable for females (such as mining and steelmaking) female-employing industries, particularly clothing and textiles, sometimes develop. Then there are various kinds of industrial linkage. Perhaps the most obvious case in Australia is the petrochemical complex at Altona (Melbourne) where a group of half a dozen plants technically and, to some extent, financially interrelated have congregated on a site of about 500 acres. Firms may be associated with others because they provide materials used during production (lubricating oils), packaging materials (cartons, crates, canisters), or services (electroplating, typesetting), or because they use waste products, such as the manufacture of pet foods from the offal of other food industries. Consider, for example, the hundreds of different sizes and shapes of cartons and containers in which goods are packed; these are not items that can be bought 'off the shelf' but have to be designed to meet individual needs and tastes. Much liaison has to take place, therefore, between the firm making the goods and the firm producing the packaging.

The influences on the location of manufacturing in Australia have been considered elsewhere [42] recently so that the commentary here can be rather more succinct. The discussion so far in this chapter will have made it clear that the influences on location differ between industries and between firms in the same industry. Obviously, therefore, the list that follows must be regarded as no more than examples of the kinds of considerations that impinge on firms.

Transport

Transport plays a particularly important role in Australia. It has been estimated that about one-fifth of the economy's productive activity is spent in carrying goods and people [43]. Coastal shipping plays a minor role in the total domestic transport task (about 5 per cent of the ton miles) but it is particularly important for bulk cargoes such as bauxite, alumina, ironstone, petroleum, lead-zinc ores, and sugar. Recent developments such as the use of standard-size containers and the employment of drive-on-drive-off ferries between Tasmania and the mainland may encourage more manufacturers to use this form of transport. Rail transport (performing about 18 per cent of the ton miles) is divided into six State systems and Commonwealth-owned lines. Not only are there difficulties caused by breaks of gauge at some of the State borders but each State charges a tapering rate that makes long hauls cheaper per ton mile than short ones. Although a measure of agreement has been reached between the States, goods passing over a State border may be liable to the sum of two tapering rates rather than one long one over the whole distance. Moreover, the freight rates tend to encourage raw materials to move towards the coast, and manufactured goods to move from the coast inland. The rates charged vary considerably between the States: the freight rate on a truckload of cement moved one hundred miles ranges from $3.30 to $5.98 per ton, depending on which State railway system is being used. But the actual rates paid in any particular case depend on whether a firm is eligible for concessions and subsidies that are offered by most of the States. The Victorian Railways alone grant freight concessions that are said to cost $2,500,000 a year and, in addition, a country manufacturer may apply for a freight subsidy from the State's Decentralization Fund. Road transport (performing about 75 per cent of the ton miles) is restrained in New South Wales and Queensland by means of a ton-mile tax; in other States each transport operation is separately examined and granted a licence only if rail services are shown to be unable to do the particular task adequately. The details of the legislation vary between the States, and are changed from time to time.

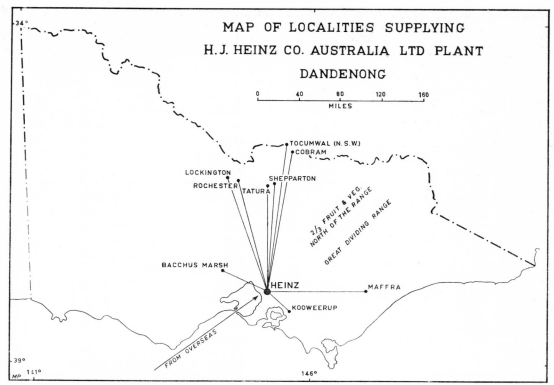

Fig. 13—(From the evidence of Mr H. G. Dennet, Deputy Managing Director of Heinz to Distribution of Population Committee in Victoria, *Evidence*, 5 December 1961)

Thus, in Victoria a person operating an 'approved decentralized industry' (that is, with some exceptions, an enterprise operating more than fifty miles from Melbourne) has been able since 1963 to obtain a licence to operate road vehicles to carry raw materials and products [44]. Interstate road services are not subject to this legislation because Section 92 of the Constitution Act, 1900, declares that intercourse between the States 'shall be absolutely free'.

The importance of transfer costs (that is transport costs plus the costs of storage and inventory keeping, packaging, insurance, and interest on capital tied up in the form of products being transported) differs considerably between industries. The nature of the demand on the transport industry also varies—some industries require a large volume of goods to be shifted though not necessarily very rapidly, whereas others require small lots to be moved frequently and quickly. For the most part manufacturers rely on existing transport facili-

ties but a few firms, such as The Broken Hill Proprietary Co. Ltd. and the Colonial Sugar Refining Co. Ltd., have a sufficiently large transport task to make it worthwhile for them to operate their own ships and, in the former case, aircraft. In some industries, such as pharmaceuticals, it is not so much the actual transport costs that are significant but those of packing and insurance for transport. The importance of transfer costs to a firm can vary over time, e.g. the Lithgow ironworks was not only affected by the working out of accessible raw materials but also by the setting up of a competitor at a much more favourable site (Newcastle) from a transport point of view. Within this general category of transport costs must be included expenditure on communications whether in the form of executives' travelling expenses, or payments for telephone calls or teleprinter services. Obviously considerable expense can be incurred if a firm has, for example, a branch factory in a country town.

Attention must be drawn to two ways in which the general pattern of location in Australia has been affected by transport considerations. Firstly, much of the heavy industry is located on the coast, often with its own wharves and shipping facilities and this is the case with iron and steel making (except for the charcoal furnace at Wundowie east of Perth), alumina and aluminium processing, much of the other non-ferrous metal processing, petroleum refining, and many of the plants making industrial chemicals. Secondly, the metropolitan areas are particularly attractive for many kinds of manufacturing because the transport routes in each State focus on this node. Not only is the collection of raw materials from various parts of the State facilitated but so is the distribution of finished products. For example, H. J. Heinz Co. Australia Ltd., located at Dandenong (Melbourne), draws supplies from the areas shown in Fig. 13, and the nodal position allows the firm to vary more easily its sources of supply according to demand and the quality, quantity, and seasonality of the produce available.

Materials

Generally, if there is a loss of bulk or weight during processing, industries are attracted towards the source of the materials. Thus, other things being equal, pulp and paper mills tend to be located near forests because they require three tons of logs for every one ton of pulp. (However, other factors may prevent such a simple relationship developing in particular cases, e.g. the case of aluminium manufacturing which is treated on pp. 233 to 236.) Sometimes the association of manufacturing plants and the source of materials is based on the need for rapid processing as is the case with fish and fruit canning, vegetable freezing, and the manufacture of dairy products. The influence of loss of weight and time can both be important. In sugar milling three-quarters of the sugar cane consists of water and the cane has to be milled within about thirty-six hours of cutting. In several instances some initial processing is done near the raw material source. At Broken Hill the concentrating process means that for every three tons of silver-lead-zinc ore mined, only one ton need be railed to Port Pirie or Cockle Creek. At the other extreme there are

manufacturing processes that add bulk (bread baking), or weight (aerated waters) to the materials, or which make products that are more fragile (furniture) or perishable (ice cream) than the materials, and these industries tend to be attracted towards the market.

The relationship of a firm to its materials is by no means constant. Mineral deposits may be worked out, or a resource destroyed (such as forests by fire), or a land use may change (see Fig. 1 in relation to flour mill location). Manufacturers sometimes try to safeguard their material supplies by integrating backwards into farming, fishing, mining, or forestry or into the manufacture of partly-processed materials upon which they are dependent. A steel mill may own coal mines, a fish cannery may control a fishing fleet, a food manufacturer may operate a canister-making plant, or a paper mill may use surplus process water to irrigate land for growing flax needed in the manufacture of fine papers.

Fuel and Power

For many manufacturing industries fuel and power requirements are of minor importance, where for instance more fuel or energy may be consumed in heating and lighting the factory than is used in driving machinery. But there are some industries where fuel and power considerations may be of critical importance, such as in the manufacture of aluminium, zinc, and calcium carbide. Prices of fuel and power vary considerably between States, depending partly on costs of production and partly on commercial and government policies. Furthermore, over a period the relative costs of energy from different sources can change. Thus, the cost of bulk power in Tasmania, due to inflation and the development of more expensive hydroelectric power projects, has risen eight times since 1920 while the cost of coal in eastern Australia has risen only four times because of modernization and improved mining practice. One direct effect of this was the erection of a coke-fired blast furnace to treat about one-fifth of the Broken Hill zinc and lead concentrate at Cockle Creek (Newcastle) whereas previously the zinc concentrate was treated at Risdon (Tasmania) and processed into zinc by an electrolytic process. Similarly, it has become feasible in some areas to use coal as a source of energy for the aluminium industry rather than hydro-electric power (see pp. 233 to 236).

The availability of power and fuel, and therefore the range of locational choice, can also change over time. It has been suggested that if the Tasmanian grid had been more extensive during the First World War when the Risdon zinc plant was set up, Burnie on the north coast might have been selected instead because it had an adequate harbour, was at the terminus of the Emu Bay Railway, and was 200 miles nearer the mainland [45]. Locational adjustments may result from the discovery of new power sources (atomic reactors), and the development of new fuel transportation and energy transmission techniques such as the long-distance transmission of electrical energy, gas, or oil, and the pumping of coal and other materials (as a slurry or in capsules) through pipelines.

Labour

Labour in Australia is fairly homogeneous in quality, character, and outlook, unlike some countries where there are marked differences in educational standards, cost, ability, and union attitudes between regions. However, there are some variations. South Australian wages, after taking into account both the basic wage and margins, tend to be lower than in other States by as much as $2 a week for an adult male. For the motor vehicle manufacturing firms in Adelaide this factor may help to offset the extra costs of distributing vehicles from a location not centrally placed with respect to the main markets. Furthermore, in the light of the large proportion of immigrants in some industries (see Table 8) it is significant that, in 1961, 69 per cent of the overseas born population lived in metropolitan areas compared with 54 per cent of those born in Australia. Another difference is in the employment of females as has already been shown by the data in Table 12. Factors of this kind may affect the cost, skill, and availability of the female labour needed for a particular factory. It should be noted, too, that labour and capital inputs may be substituted over a period of time, and also that the ratio of female to male labour may change as a result of changing costs (increases or decreases in differentials for male and female labour), or changing needs (due to changes in technology or the nature of the product).

Markets

This is a very broad term that covers many different situations. Firstly, some industries deal direct with the public because they are located in relation to the distribution of the population they serve, and therefore tend to be composed of many small units. Several are, in fact, virtually service industries (tyre retreading, laundries and dye works, and the repairing of motor vehicles, shoes and watches) which, as suggested at the beginning of the chapter, can scarcely be thought of as manufacturing. Other industries are close to the market because they are bulk- or weight-adding or make materials more susceptible to breakage or damage, because they need close contact with the market (tailoring, printing) or because they are particularly susceptible to sudden changes in demand or fashions (umbrellas, dress-making). Secondly, some manufacturers sell their finished goods to other firms. These firms may simply pass them on to the public without further processing (such as pre-packed grocery items delivered to the bulk-warehouses of grocery chains), may use them as an aid to business (accounting machines in offices), may incorporate them in other products (such as spark plugs and tubes and tyres for motor vehicle assembly works), or may use them as packaging (drums and crates). Thirdly, some products are only partly manufactured and are sold to other firms for further processing. Thus, raw aluminium is sold by the producers to processors who are mainly located in Sydney and Melbourne [46] and the steel works at Newcastle and Wollongong-Port Kembla supply ancillary industries nearby with raw materials including not only steel in various stages of processing but also coke and chemicals.

It must be borne in mind that for any particular line of goods 'the market' is made up really of many different markets depending on the price, quality, and characteristics of the products and the income, tastes, and preferences of the users. Thus, the market for motor vehicles is divided into fairly distinct segments, three of which can be represented by the purchasers of Rolls-Royces, Holdens-Falcons, and

Minis. Sometimes, these markets have distinct geographical variations as shown, for example, by the differences in the per capita consumption of beer, wine, spirits, and rum in the various States. Markets are, of course, subject to change and sometimes they gradually disappear as did the market for leather for motor vehicle upholstery (because of competition from newly developed materials), or grow up or expand overnight as did the market for canisters at Shepparton when Campbell Soups (Aust.) Pty. Ltd. decided to locate there.

Government

Government activities are an important influence on manufacturing in Australia. The Commonwealth Government determines the level of tariff protection to be granted to industries [47] and provides bounties and subsidies for shipbuilders and manufacturers of tractors, sulphuric acid, continuous acetate yarn and acetate flake. The gradual change in the attitude towards tariff protection was indicated earlier (pp. 196 to 212). Now the importance of the tariff can be seen from the fact that 60 per cent of the total Australian factory workforce are in industries making import competing goods and the average tariff is about 30 per cent *ad valorem*. The Commonwealth owns only a few factories (mainly engaged in making goods for the armed services) and makes little attempt to control industrial location except in the Northern Territory (which it controls) where bauxite leases have been granted subject to a commitment to build an alumina plant nearby. The main way in which the Commonwealth has influenced location is by selling and leasing ex-wartime munitions factories—this has already been mentioned and will be discussed again later.

The State Governments are concerned with two aspects of industrial location. Firstly, they are each endeavouring to foster the development of secondary industry within their own border, and this leads to policies conceived in a spirit of competition rather than of co-operation [48]. Secondly, all the mainland States are attempting to influence the location of manufacturing within their own border—this is discussed in more detail later.

The interest by State and local governments in secondary industry means that financial and practical assistance and inducements are made available to manufacturers. The State may provide harbour facilities, construct roads or railways, build houses, give long-term mineral leases, make guarantees about markets, provide cheap electricity, give subsidies on the transport of raw materials and finished products, and so forth. Dozens of Acts have been passed in State Parliaments setting out details of agreements between the State and a particular firm in such industries as iron and steel, aluminium, chemicals, oil refining, and pulp and paper making. Usually these agreements between governments and firms have been concerned with such matters as the supply of water, electricity, and steam; the construction, improvement, and maintenance of road and railway facilities; the disposal of effluent; the use of fresh and sea water and the sinking of bores; the provision of wharf and navigational facilities as well as channels and swinging basins; the payment of harbour and wharfage dues and mineral and forestry royalties; the construction of houses; and the provision and appropriate zoning of industrial land. The agreements set out, sometimes in very great detail, the dates by which services will be operating and who will meet the cost of providing and maintaining them. Thus the agreements with pulp and paper firms discuss such matters as the amount of timber to be supplied from State forests and the types of trees, the protection of the water rights of graziers and other users, the prevention of fires, erosion, damage to fences, and river pollution, and one agreement even makes it clear that the company is responsible 'for any failure to close gates'. Apart from Acts of Parliaments, which usually concern only basic, capital-intensive industries, many other arrangements are made to assist industry through other State agencies such as the Housing and Electricity Commissions and the Department of Railways.

While some firms are given assistance by the State Governments they may also have to accept certain conditions that limit their range of locational choice. Thus, many of the agreements specify that mineral leases are granted on condition that all or some of the processing and manufacturing operations are carried out in the State concerned. Thus, three firms (Broken Hill Proprietary Co. Ltd., Hamersley Iron Pty. Ltd., and Mt. Newman Iron Ore Co.) have signed agreements with the Western Australian Government each undertaking to establish an integrated iron and steel works in the State before the end of the century. Further examples are given on pp. 233 to 236 of this chapter.

Climate and Water

Climate can affect the location of manufacturing in a number of ways. It influences the production of primary produce (dairying, sugar growing, etc.); it may facilitate manufacturing (the production and processing of solar evaporated salt); or add to the difficulties of manufacturing and distribution (such as high temperatures and the making and distribution of chocolate biscuits). Climate may necessitate special types of building (to keep dust out of factories making photographic films, pharmaceuticals, and some kinds of moulded products). The general effects of climate impinge on all manufacturing and may in some cases influence locational decisions. Labour productivity can be affected by extremes of heat or cold; there may be extra maintenance costs on buildings brought about by expansion and contraction due to sudden changes of temperature; machinery may deteriorate more rapidly in hot, humid climates; and extra plant to cool or heat the factory may be required or it may have to be used for a greater part of each year.

Very large quantities of process water are required by some industries—the manufacture of ascorbic acid requires nearly 900 gallons per lb. of product, viscose rayon requires 175 gallons, and lactose 100 gallons. Water is an important influence in any country but, clearly, in a dry continent like Australia this consideration is especially significant. Mere quantity of water may not be as important as the reliability of supply, its chemical composition, or cleanliness. The disposal of water and of other effluent may also be important because of the dangers of pollution.

Other Factors

It is possible to mention briefly only a few of the other considerations that may affect location:

Historical factors. Examples have been given of firms located at some time in the past when different locational influences were operative (e.g. Holden and Frost at Adelaide).

Services of all kinds may be required. Some are fairly obvious such as those of banks, finance companies, and government departments but others, such as the availability of security patrols or fire fighting units, may also be needed in some cases.

Industrial services such as machinery repair and maintenance firms, and trucking companies may be important as well as the ability to hire occasionally and at short notice equipment such as cranes or a facility such as refrigerated warehouse space.

Safety may be an overriding consideration in the siting of a factory making, for example, fireworks, or explosives.

The availability of land and buildings is obviously of very great importance but it is not discussed here because of the more detailed examination given to it elsewhere in this book. But the point must be made that many firms try to acquire 50, 100, or 200 acre blocks on flat land so that they can build single-storey factories and still have room for later expansion; clearly blocks of this size are becoming increasingly difficult to obtain in the larger Australian cities and the locational decision of a firm may hinge round a problem of this kind. Thus, when a reasoned recommendation to acquire a block of land at Ballarat was being considered by the Board of Fibremakers Ltd., a 90-acre site at Bayswater (Melbourne) became available and was selected instead. Some kinds of manufacturing have special site requirements, e.g. oil refineries need large sites near deep water which is free from tides or strong winds [49].

An Example of a Locational Problem: Aluminium

Some of the points made in the previous section of the chapter can be illustrated by a brief consideration of the siting of the aluminium manufacturing industry in Australia [50].

Bauxite contains about from 30 to 65 per cent alumina, and the large deposits are found in tropical and sub-tropical regions such as northern Australia, Malaysia, India, Africa, South America, and Jamaica. There are three distinct phases in the production of aluminium from bauxite:

1. *Bauxite Mining* is usually fairly easy because the deposits are near the surface and open-cut methods can be employed. The bauxite is then screened or beneficiated. At a remote location like Weipa on Cape York Peninsula a port and township has to be built. Gardner indicates that in such an environment distillate for mobile plant would be required at the rate of 2·6 lb. per ton of bauxite, and diesel fuel for a power station (to drive conveyors, screening plant, and provide energy for the township) at the rate of 1·7 lb. per ton. For a production of 3,000,000 tons of bauxite ore, therefore, 35,000 tons of distillate and 23,000 tons of diesel fuel would have to be transported into the area.

2. *Conversion of the Bauxite into Alumina* is done by separating the sodium aluminate from the iron oxide and silica and treating this to form alumina. This is a pure granular substance which is a stable compound that can be stored and transported. Gardner lists the raw materials and energy requirements for one ton of alumina as being:

     2·00 tons bauxite
     0·16 tons caustic soda (50 per cent solution)
     0·05 tons lime
     0·40 tons fuel oil (or equivalent)
     4·50 tons (about 1000 gallons) water
     250 kWh of electrical energy.

3. *Smelting of Alumina into Aluminium* is essentially an electrolytic process. According to Gardner the materials required for one ton of aluminium are:

     2·00 tons alumina
     0·50 tons petroleum coke
     0·25 tons pitch
     0·10 tons cryolite
     0·04 tons fluorspar and sulphur
     0·10 tons fuel oil
     18,000 to 22,000 kWh of electrical energy.

Several locational possibilities emerge: (a) all operations could be carried out at the bauxite field; (b) the alumina plant could be located at the bauxite field and the smelter somewhere else; (c) the alumina plant and smelter could be together but away from the bauxite field; and (d) the mining operations, the alumina plant, and the smelter could all be at different locations. Gardner notes that the ideal solution would be to have a bauxite deposit beside a source of low cost energy at a coastal location, but in practice this combination is unlikely because large bauxite deposits occur in tropical regions whereas most low cost electrical energy originates from snowfed hydro-electric schemes in temperate areas. The problem becomes one, therefore, of examining the costs of alternative siting arrangements taking into account also such considerations as the cost and availability of labour, and the location of markets (local and/or overseas). Large supplies of energy, it must be emphasized, are required only at the third stage when the alumina is converted into aluminium. Gardner notes that the incremental costs of transporting alumina over longer distances is comparatively not very great, particularly when the alumina is being transported in bulk sea carriers on a regular cycle:

For example, the incremental freight rate might be, say, 0.25 pence per ton mile, in which case the freight per ton of alumina over an additional 1000 miles would be 250 pence which represents about 500 pence per ton of metal. At the rate of 18,000 kWh per ton of metal, this is equivalent to roughly 0.23 pence per kWh on the energy cost. This means that, other things being equal, it would be economic to haul alumina an additional 1000 miles to a power source where electricity is 0.03 pence per kWh lower in cost [51].

So far in Australia five separate sets of decisions have been made, and others are at present under consideration, about the location of aluminium plants.

1. In 1944 an agreement was reached between the Commonwealth and Tasmanian Governments to establish an aluminium industry in that State [52]. At that time there were no suitable supplies of bauxite available locally and this material had to be imported mainly from Indonesia, Malaysia, and India. Thus, the solution was to locate the smelter on a coastal site in Tasmania where power could be supplied from the Trevallyn power station twenty-five miles away. There was no reason to locate the alumina plant away from the smelter. This Bell Bay plant did not come into operation until 1955, and in 1961 the Commonwealth

Government sold the works, operated on its behalf by the Australian Aluminium Production Commission, to Comalco Industries Pty. Ltd. During 1962 the Bell Bay refinery began to use bauxite from Weipa, and the alumina thus produced was fed to the nearby smelter. Early in 1967 the smelter began to receive additional supplies of alumina from the new refinery at Gladstone. The capacity of the smelter is being increased to 72,000 tons a year by the end of 1967.

2. In 1961 Alcoa of Australia Pty. Ltd. made an agreement with the Western Australian Government to erect an alumina plant at Kwinana (south of Perth) in return for the tenure of bauxite leases in the Darling Ranges and other assistance from the Government including the construction by the State of a twenty-eight mile railway from the deposits to the refinery on the coast [53]. The plant originally had a capacity of 310,000 tons and began operations in November 1963. In 1966 it was announced that the capacity would be expanded to 550,000 tons by the end of 1968. Alcoa obtains supplies of oil by pipe from the B.P. Refinery (Kwinana) Ltd. about three miles to the south, uses natural depressions for the red sludge effluent of iron oxide and silica; and has its own wharf from which to make bulk shipments of alumina. The alumina is shipped in 10,000 ton bulk carriers operated by the Australian National Line to the smelter of 40,000 tons capacity on Point Henry, on the eastern outskirts of Geelong. For the time being electricity from the State grid is being used but a brown coal power station is being erected by Alcoa at Anglesea twenty-five miles away. One of the reasons given for the selection of the Point Henry site was that there are greater reserves of fuel there as compared with possible sites in Western Australia, and another was that there are a considerable number of aluminium processing firms in Melbourne. The possibility that Alcoa may erect a smelter near its Kwinana refinery within ten to twelve years has been indicated by an exchange of letters between the company and the Western Australian Government.

3. In exchange for bauxite mining leases at Weipa Comalco Industries Pty. Ltd. promised the Queensland Government in 1957 that it would 'establish within the State . . . a plant for the production of alumina in commercial quantities' [54]. The range of possible sites was restricted to Queensland and after examination of coastal sites from Townsville to Brisbane, the site at Gladstone was selected. This involves a bauxite haul by sea of 1130 miles from Weipa but Gladstone has the advantages of being within 100 miles of several low-cost coalfields, and being an established though small (7200 population in 1961) town with harbour facilities. The capacity of the plant, which came into operation in March 1967, is 600,000 tons of alumina a year; it will require annually about 1,200,000 tons of bauxite, 230,000 tons of coal, 80,000 tons of fuel oil, and 150,000,000 kWh of electric power. The Gladstone plant also provides a good example of a situation in which a number of firms have combined in a single project to obtain mutually the benefits of economies of scale. Associated with Comalco (which is owned equally by Kaiser Aluminum & Chemical Corporation and Conzinc Riotinto of Australia Ltd.) are Alcan Aluminium of Canada and the Péchiney Compagnie de Produits Chimiques et Electrométallurgiques of France. No sooner had the Gladstone refinery commenced operations than it was announced that further extensions would be made to bring capacity up to 900,000 tons a year.

By mid-1967 Comalco had not finally announced its decision about the location of the aluminium smelter. The firm had investigated possible energy sources at Weipa, Papua, Blair Athol (Queensland), and examined the economics and feasibility of using thermal power sources in Victoria or New South Wales, atomic power, fuel cells, tidal power, acyclic generators, and magneto-hydrodynamic generation, but all these sources were considered to be unsuitable or too expensive. An examination was made of the possibility of using hydro-electric power in New Zealand from a new station in the Manapouri area, and it is expected that Comalco will establish an international smelter at Bluff in the South Island of New Zealand. In the meantime part of Comalco's share of the alumina output of the Gladstone refinery will be shipped to Bell Bay for smelting.

4. In September 1965 the Minister for Territories announced that the Special Mineral Lease No. 1 at Gove in the Northern Territory had been granted to Nabalco Pty. Ltd. (of which Swiss Aluminium and the Colonial Sugar Refining Co. Ltd. are the chief among nine shareholders). This company has undertaken, as part of the lease conditions, to construct an alumina plant with an annual capacity of not less than 500,000 tons at Gove by 1971. The completed alumina plant, plus associated mining, wharf and township facilities, is expected to cost $100,000,000; this project will provide employment for about 800 people and will support a township of 3000. It can be seen that this locational decision, presumably largely controlled by the lease conditions, differs from the three others previously discussed in that the alumina plant is to be erected at the bauxite deposit. Moreover, 'Nabalco will also examine the report on the economic feasibility of aluminium smelting in the Northern Territory, and will build a smelter if an adequate supply of continuous low-cost electricity is available' [55].

5. In December 1965 Alcan Australia Ltd. (formerly Australuco) announced plans to build a smelter in the Newcastle-Port Stephens area of New South Wales, but in July 1966 the planned location was changed to Kurri Kurri about twenty-five miles west of Newcastle. The smelter will have an initial capacity of 40,000 tons a year and will use part of its parent company's (Alcan Aluminium of Canada) quota of 120,000 tons of alumina from the Gladstone plant. Power will be supplied from the N.S.W. grid (at an undisclosed rate per therm) presumably from thermal stations near Newcastle. The plant is expected to commence operations in 1969.

6. Several locational decisions still have to be made or, as at mid-1967 announced: (a) as mentioned above Nabalco has to decide where to build a smelter; (b) the Péchiney Cie of France has to decide where its share of the output from the Gladstone works is to be smelted; and (c) Comalco has to announce definitely whether it is to proceed with a smelter in New Zealand. It will be interesting to see whether these companies decide to build smelters in Australia or whether they elect to send the alumina to smelters elsewhere in the world.

Decentralization

No discussion of the geography of manufacturing in Australia would be complete without some consideration of decentralization. The term is sometimes used to mean the reduction of the industrial dominance of New South Wales and Victoria by the development of manufacturing in the four other States. More commonly, however, it is used to mean the reduction of the industrial dominance of the metropolitan areas by the growth of manufacturing in other parts of each State [56].

Interstate Decentralization

Reference has been made to the fact that each State is attempting to develop industrially and that there is active competition between them to attract new enterprises. Each State has attempted to obtain a fully rounded portfolio of industrial activities including an iron and steel works, an oil refinery, a petrochemical complex, motor manufacturing plants, and so forth. States that lack a particular major industry are very hopeful: 'the possibility of the eventual establishment of an iron and steel industry in Queensland has not flagged during the year' is a typical sentiment [57].

This competition for manufacturing seems to be one important reason why each of the States has about the same share of Australia's factory production now as it did before the Second World War (Fig. 14). Between mid-1939 and mid-1964 the Australian factory workforce grew from 565,000 to 1,210,000 but this increase was divided more or less proportionately between the States, none of which have been forging ahead industrially at the expense of the others. Furthermore, the proportion of each State's workforce engaged in manufacturing changed little between the censuses of 1947 and 1961.

Intrastate Decentralization

It is not intended here to argue the pros and cons of decentralization because this has been done elsewhere in more detail [58]. For several decades concern has been felt about the ever-increasing concentration of population and economic activities in the metropolitan areas. It was resolved at a Premiers' Conference in August 1945 that the State and Commonwealth

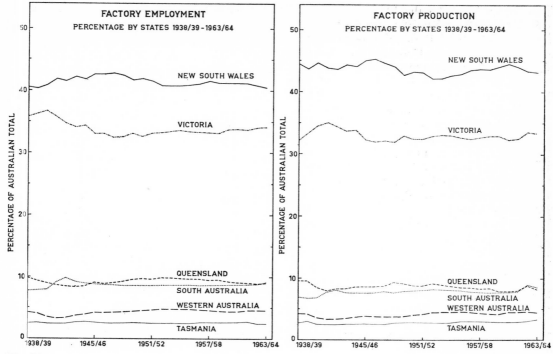

Fig. 14

would act together to carry out the decentralization of secondary industry. The Commonwealth at first co-operated by selling and leasing wartime munitions factories and warehouses with a total area of 8,200,000 square feet (see Table 7) to private enterprise. Many of these factories were in country towns (Fig. 15), and at a time when there were shortages of building materials, ready-made premises, even if away from the metropolitan areas, were a persuasive influence on location. The Commonwealth has done little else to assist decentralization specifically, although its financial contributions to road, rail, irrigation and other major schemes, its subsidies to farming, mining, and oil search, and even the development of Canberra (now the largest inland town in Australia), have all contributed towards decentralization in a general way.

Decentralization as such has been left in the hands of the State Governments. Tasmania has few formal policies designed to achieve a spread of industry because of all the States (see Table 17) it has the smallest proportion of its

manufacturing activities in the capital city. In Western Australia, too, there are few formal policies and, because the new trade in iron ore may result in seven new towns being built, such policies may not be needed for some time. In the four other States, particularly in New South Wales and Victoria, considerable time, effort, and finance are being devoted to the promotion of decentralization. The exact arrangements vary between States [59] but the general aim is to reduce the locational disadvantages of a country location by granting concessions and subsidies on freight, on power and water, and on establishment costs; and to assist by providing houses and other facilities, by helping towards the costs of training workers, and by providing grants or loans at low rates of interest. Thus, contributions have been made to help meet the cost of building railway sidings, the cost of telephone calls to the metropolitan area, and the cost of the installation of a water filtration plant at a cotton mill.

The proportion of each State's population, factory employment, and net value of produc-

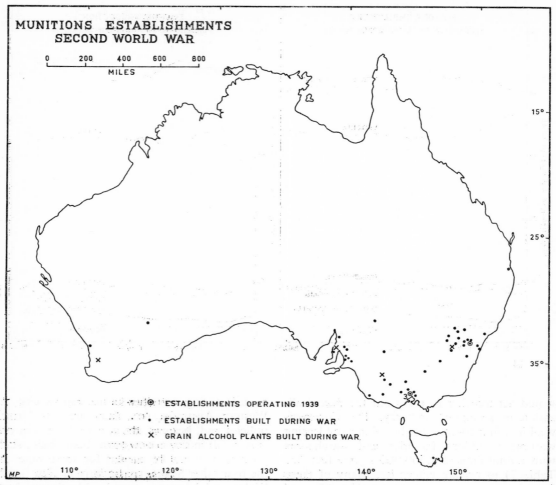

MUNITIONS ESTABLISHMENTS
SECOND WORLD WAR

0   200   400   600   800
MILES

⊚ ESTABLISHMENTS OPERATING 1939
• ESTABLISHMENTS BUILT DURING WAR
× GRAIN ALCOHOL PLANTS BUILT DURING WAR

Fig. 15

tion in the metropolitan area is shown in Table 17 for three post-war years. Between 1947 and 1963 the metropolitan area of each State increased its share of the population. Over the period population in the capital cities grew more rapidly than factory employment so that the number of factory workers per thousand population in the metropolitan areas decreased (in Sydney, for example, from 161 to 151, and in Melbourne from 170 to 161), whereas in the 'rest of' each State it increased (from 58 to 71 in the 'rest of' New South Wales and from 61 to 70 in the 'rest of' Victoria).

These long-term changes mask the real significance of what occurred. Most of the growth

of population and factory employment outside the metropolitan areas took place immediately after the Second World War. There was a general falling off in growth rates after 1954 but there was a particularly marked fall in the rates for the 'rest of' each State with the exception of South Australia and Tasmania. Thus, the average annual rate (per cent) of increase of factory employment in the 'rest of' New South Wales was 3·9 between mid-1947 and mid-1954 but only 2·0 per cent between mid-1954 and mid-1963. The corresponding figures for Victoria are 4·9 and 1·7 per cent; for Queensland 4·4 and 0·4 per cent; for South Australia (1950 to 1954, and 1954 to 1963)

Table 17 *Per Cent of State Total in Metropolitan Area* (a)

State	Year (b)	Population	Manufacturing	
			Employment	Value of Production
N.S.W. (Sydney)	1947	56.6	78.3	76.7
	1954	56.3	75.7	76.4
	1963	58.4	75.7	72.2
Victoria (Melbourne)	1947	62.9	83.1	83.2
	1954	62.2	81.0	79.7
	1963	65.6	81.5	80.7
Queensland (Brisbane)	1947	40.3	57.8	55.4
	1954	42.4	58.2	60.0
	1963	44.7	59.6	59.7
S. Australia (c) (Adelaide)	1950	60.4	83.5	83.6
	1954	61.6	83.2	81.1(?)
	1963	64.5	80.4	81.1
W. Australia (Perth)	1947	60.3	77.7	78.0
	1954	61.7	79.9	79.2
	1963	65.3	80.9	80.9
Tasmania (c) (Hobart)	1950	39.2	40.2	38.2
	1954	41.0	41.0	39.2
	1963	33.6	36.6	33.3

(a) The metropolitan areas used are as follows. Sydney is the Cumberland Statistical Division; Melbourne figures have been adjusted to 1963 boundaries of the Melbourne Statistical Division; Brisbane is the Metropolitan Statistical Division adjusted to 1963 boundaries plus Ipswich; Adelaide is the Metropolitan Statistical Division plus Elizabeth, Salisbury, and Tea Tree Gully; Perth is the Metropolitan and Swan Statistical Divisions; and Hobart is the Metropolitan Statistical Division.

(b) Population figures are census results in 1947 and 1954, and official estimates for mid-1963. Factory statistics are for the year ending 30 June.

(c) Manufacturing statistics for the Adelaide and Hobart Metropolitan Areas are not available prior to 1949-50.

5·2 and 4·1 per cent; for Western Australia 3·4 and 0·8 per cent; and for Tasmania (1950 to 1954 and 1954 to 1963) 0·5 and 3·4 per cent. After 1954 in New South Wales the non-metropolitan factory employment increased more rapidly than that in the metropolitan area but this was almost entirely due to the rapid industrial growth of Newcastle Urban Area and, more especially, of Greater Wollongong. If these two urban areas are discounted from the 'rest of' New South Wales and Geelong Urban Area from the 'rest of' Victoria, factory employment elsewhere in these States between mid-1954 and mid-1963 grew at 0·3 and 1·9 per cent respectively compared with metropolitan rates of, respectively, 1·8 and 2·1 per cent.

Comparisons of growth rates tend to conceal the small number of workers involved (Table 18). Leaving aside Tasmania, the factory labour force outside the State capitals, Newcastle, Wollongong, and Geelong increased by 41,278 between mid-1947 and mid-1954 (about 4·1 per cent per annum), but it increased between mid-1954 and mid-1963 by only 18,787 (1·2 per cent per annum). Outside Sydney, Newcastle and Wollongong the 'rest of' New South Wales gained only 1729 new factory workers in the nine years after 1954, and in the same period, the parts of Victoria outside Melbourne and Geelong gained 8752. One of the most interesting features shown in Table 18 is the increase of over 6000 in the 'rest of' South Australia between mid-1954 and mid-1963. Much of this increase took place in such towns as Whyalla and Mount Gambier [60].

This analysis suggests that the mainland State Governments (with the possible exception of South Australia) have not been particularly successful in their efforts to bring about an upsurge of manufacturing activity away from the metropolitan areas. The figures for Newcastle and Wollongong and for Geelong have

Table 18 *Actual Increase of Factory Workers 1947 to 1954 and 1954 to 1963* (a)

		State	Metropolitan	Other	Rest of State
N.S.W.	1947-54	58,260	35,099	10,307(b)	12,854
	1954-63	72,561	53,135	17,697(b)	1,729
Victoria	1947-54	65,520	47,426	4,619(c)	13,475
	1954-63	65,879	55,337	1,790(c)	8,752
Queensland	1947-54	25,902	15,290	—	10,612
	1954-63	6,604	5,294	—	1,310
S. Australia	1950-54(d)	6,905	4,551	—	2,354
	1954-63	19,762	13,457	—	6,305
W. Australia	1947-54	13,653	11,670	—	1,983
	1954-63	5,976	5,285	—	691
Tasmania	1950-54(e)	1,083	867	—	216
	1954-63	6,166	1,144	—	5,022

(a) In New South Wales and Queensland the figures are on the basis of average employed during the period of operation whereas in the other States they are on the basis of average employed during the year. Statistics are for year ending 30 June. Metropolitan areas are those defined in note (a) to Table 17.

(b) Newcastle Urban Area and Greater Wollongong.

(c) Geelong Urban Area (including the aluminium works on Point Henry).

(d) Manufacturing statistics for the Adelaide Metropolitan Area are not available prior to 1949-50. Total increase in South Australia 1947-54 was 14,792.

(e) Manufacturing statistics for the Hobart Metropolitan Area are not available prior to 1949-50. Total increase in Tasmania 1947-54 was 4,652.

been shown separately in Table 18 because whether or not increases in these towns should be regarded as decentralization depends on a point of view.

Five main reasons for the lack of success of decentralization as a policy can be suggested:

Firstly, a State Government is unwilling to force a possible investor to a country location if there is any danger that another State may then seem more attractive to the entrepreneur.

Secondly, the financial and other help provided by the State Governments does not overcome many of the difficulties and diseconomies of operating away from the main manufacturing centres. A few of these problems are: the costs, which can be substantial, of holding extra stocks of raw materials and products, containers, and spares; the lack of specialist services such as repair firms; the lack of a large, experienced, and skilled labour pool; the increased difficulties of drawing materials from a wide range of sources (see Fig. 13); and the increased difficulties of keeping in touch with markets, business associates, research organizations, government departments, and financial

and legal institutions. Moreover, small or new firms that lack finance and certainty about the future may be able to obtain external economies by locating at a large centre where there is already a complex of specialist commercial and industrial services.

Thirdly, the subsidies and other forms of assistance have been spread thinly over a wide area and between many kinds of secondary industry. The point is also made by the Committee of Economic Enquiry:

. . . we can see nothing to commend, and much that is against, the establishment of numerous small industries in numbers of small country towns. However, we think there is a case for accelerating the growth of a limited number of non-metropolitan centres that have already, as a result of natural advantages, achieved some degree of development. Such centres with only a moderate degree of capital expenditure and encouragement to industry, could soon reach the take-off point, that is the point after which further development would be natural and self-sustaining [61].

Clearly there are political difficulties in choosing in each State a limited number of centres and getting politicians to agree that investment should be directed to these.

Fourthly, the State Governments have not set an example by decentralizing sections of their own departments.

Fifthly, the Commonwealth Government has not assisted the States by instituting regional differences in company tax, payroll tax, sales tax or, except in limited cases (northern Australia and southwestern Tasmania), income tax. Nor has the Commonwealth Government attempted to reduce the costs of some essential items in country areas. The only action of this kind has been the subsidy scheme for petrol started in 1965 which is designed to bring country prices within about 9 per cent of metropolitan prices.

Conclusion

It was suggested early in the chapter that the general outline of the geography of manufacturing in Australia had appeared by the end of the nineteenth century. It has, of course, been modified in detail since then by the setting up of industries using hydro-electric power in Tasmania, the growth of food processing industries in the irrigation areas, the development of industries based on minerals sometimes in remote parts of the continent, and the use of ex-munitions factories to promote the development of textiles and other forms of manufacturing in country towns.

But it is hard to see any signs of fundamental changes taking place to the present geographical pattern. As Fig. 14 shows, the States appear to be retaining more or less the relative positions that they had achieved by 1939 and none of them seem to be forging ahead or (except possibly Queensland) dropping seriously behind. There is little indication that the methods used so far to promote decentralization are succeeding or are likely to succeed in the future. A growing body of opinion is suggesting that efforts to achieve decentralization should be directed towards stimulating the growth of a few chosen towns that would become development centres. Even if such a policy were to be adopted now it would be many years before such towns could begin to affect significantly the distribution of population and industry within a State.

Yet within this generally stable pattern of location there is a constant process of adjustment and re-adjustment taking place. Sometimes this involves changes of location as is illustrated by the way in which the flour milling and brewing industries adapted themselves locationally in the face of changing markets and production and transportation technology (Figs. 1 and 2). At other times a firm may stay where it is but adapt itself locationally by other means, such as by substituting inputs or adopting new technology. Not only are the locational influences themselves in a constant state of change (caused, for example, by decisions of government, actions of other firms, and changing technology) but the requirements of a firm change, e.g. as it grows and matures it may have less need for external economies as it achieves economies of scale. The geography of manufacturing should not be regarded as a static but as a dynamic subject.

REFERENCES

1. Factory output and factory production are different concepts. The value of output is the gross value of goods manufactured. The *value of production* is the value added to materials by the process of manufacture; it is calculated by deducting from the value of output the value (at the factory) of the materials used, containers and packing, and power, light, and fuel.

2. For an account of manufacturing in Sydney at this time see WALSH, G. P. (1962) The English Colony in New South Wales: A.D. 1803. *New Zealand Geographer*, *18*, 149–169; and *idem*, (1963) The Geography of Manufacturing in Sydney, 1788–1851. *Business Archives and History*, *3*, 20–52.

3. BUTLIN, N. G. (1959) Colonial Socialism in Australia, 1860–1900, in AITKIN, H. G. J. *The State and Economic Growth*. New York, 26–78.

4. SINCLAIR, W. A. (1955) The Tariff and Manufacturing Employment in Victoria,

1860–1900. *Economic Record, 31*, 100–104.

5. BUTLIN, N. G. (1962) *Australian Domestic Product, Investment and Foreign Borrowing 1861–1938/39*. Cambridge, 12.

6. BUTLIN, N. G. (1964) *Investment in Australian Economic Development 1861–1900*. Cambridge, 203–4.

7. SINCLAIR, W. A. (1956) *Economic Recovery in Victoria 1894–1899*. Canberra.

8. BUTLIN, [3], 72.

9. LYNE, C. (1882) *The Industries of New South Wales*. Sydney, 80.

10. Several changes in definition and coverage of factory statistics occurred during this period but these would not have greatly affected the relative position.

11. COGHLAN, T. A. (1896) *Wealth and Progress of New South Wales 1894*. Sydney, 531–2.

12. HUGHES, H. (1964) *The Australian Iron and Steel Industry 1848–1962*. Melbourne, 35.

13. COGHLAN, T. A. (1900) *A Statistical Account of the Seven Colonies of Australasia 1899–1900*. Sydney, 597.

14. GOODE, J. (c. 1959) Australian Early Car Manufacturers, *Bulletin Business Archives Council of Australia, 1*, No. 6 (undated), 50–9.

15. HUGHES, H. (1964) Federalism and Industrial Development in Australia. *Australian Journal of Politics and History, 10*, 323.

16. For a detailed discussion see FORSTER, C. (1953) Australian Manufacturing and the War of 1914–18. *Economic Record, 29*, 211–30.

17. For an account of the Newcastle works and their expansion, see HUGHES [12], 63–79.

18. FORSTER, C. (1964) *Industrial Development in Australia 1920–1930*. Canberra; MELLOR, D. P. (1958) *The Role of Science and Industry*. Canberra, (Chapter 1: 'Between the Wars'); & WINDETT, N. M. (1933) *Australia as Producer and Trader 1920–1932*. London.

19. MAULDON, F. R. E. & POLGLAZE, J. (1935) Australian Manufacturing in the Depression. *Economic Record, 11*, Supplement, 139–48.

20. The Waddamana power station had been commenced by the zinc firm, the Hydro-Electric Power and Metallurgical Company, but lacking adequate financial resources it sold the partly completed station to the Tasmanian Government who brought it into operation.

21. Data from FORSTER [18], 39.

22. MITCHELL, T. J. (1962) J. W. Wainwright: The Industrialisation of South Australia

1935–40. *Australian Journal of Politics and History, 8*, 27–40.

23. An annexe was, in effect, a government works run by a private concern which acted as operating contractor for the Commonwealth Government. Data about wartime factories is contained in MELLOR [18], esp. 27–56 & 673–706; DEPARTMENT OF POST-WAR RECONSTRUCTION. (1949) *Wartime Factories With a Peacetime Future: The Story of Industrial Decentralisation*; and KENLEY, W. J. (1953) *The Effect of War on Secondary Industry*. Unpublished M.Com. thesis, University of Melbourne.

24. BORRIE, W. D. & SPENCER, G. (1965) *Australia's Population Structure and Growth*. Melbourne, 17.

25. COMMONWEALTH OF AUSTRALIA. (1965) *Report of the Committee of Economic Enquiry*. 2. J. 32.

26. THOMPSON, J. H. (1955) A New Method for Measuring Manufacturing. *Annals Association American Geographers, 45*, 416–36.

27. Throughout this analysis unpublished data derived from the 1961 census of population has been used because it is available by individual industry codes in considerable geographical detail.

28. See a discussion of these in ISARD, W. (1960) *Methods of Regional Analysis: An Introduction to Regional Science*. Cambridge, Mass., 249 ff.

29. RAPKIN, C., WINNICK, L. & BLANK, D. M. (1953) *Housing Market Analysis: A Study of Theory and Methods*. New York, 88–90; & RODGERS, A. (1957) Some Aspects of Industrial Diversification in the United States, *Economic Geography, 33*, 16–30; see also some worked examples in LINGE, G. J. R. (1961) Some Measures of the Distribution of Manufacturing Applied to New Zealand. *New Zealand Geographer, 17*, 195–208.

30. SMITH, R. H. T. (1965) The Functions of Australian Towns. *Tijdschrift voor Economische en Sociale Geografie, 56*, 81–92.

31. For a list of references to work on Australian towns, see LINGE, G. J. R. (1960) Recent Literature on Manufacturing in Australia. *New Zealand Geographer, 16*, esp. 207–8.

32. HOLMES, J. H. (1965) The Suburbanization of Cessnock Coalfield Towns: 1954–1964. *Austr. Geographical Studies, 3*, 105–28.

33. For a more detailed discussion of these problems, see LINGE, G. J. R. (1965) *The Delimitation of Urban Boundaries: A Report*

to the Commonwealth Statistician. Canberra. To the examples in the text many more, of course, can be added. See also, LINGE, G. J. R. (1966) Urban boundaries for Census and Statistical Purposes. *Australian Planning Institute Journal*, 4, 193–200.

34. WEBER, A. (1909) *Uber den Standort der Industrien*. Tübingen. Translated as FRIEDRICH, C. J. (1929) *Alfred Weber's Theory of the Location of Industries*. Chicago.

35. HOOVER, E. M. (1948) *The Location of Economic Activity*. New York.

36. FETTER, F. A. (1924) The Economic Law of Market Areas. *Quarterly Journal of Economics*, 38, 520–9.

37. HOTELLING, H. (1929) Stability in Competition. *Economic Journal*, 39, 41–57.

38. A summary of some of the leading theories of location and a list of references is contained in GREENHUT, M. L. (1956) *Plant Location in Theory and in Practise*. University of North Carolina Press.

39. HAIG, R. M. (1925–26) Towards An Understanding of the Metropolis. *Quarterly Journal of Economics*, 40, 417 ff.

40. The kinds of factors involved are discussed more fully in LINGE, G. J. R. (1963) The Diffusion of Manufacturing in Auckland, New Zealand. *Econ.Geog.*, 39, 23–39.

41. *Tariff Board's Report on General Textile Reference, Interim Report on Yarns, Woollen or Containing Wool*, Mar. 26, 1962, 13.

42. LINGE, G. J. R. (1963) The Location of Manufacturing in Australia, in HUNTER, A. (ed.) *The Economics of Australian Industry*. Melbourne. 18–64.

43. HIRST, R. R. The Transport Industry, in HUNTER, A. (ed.) [42], 65–111. See also RIMMER, P. J. (1967) *Coastal Shipping*, No. 3 in Industry In Australia Series, Longmans, Melbourne.

44. Commercial Goods Vehicles (Decentralized Industries) Act, 1963, *Vict.Acts of Parl.*, 1963, 567–9. At June 30, 1965, there were 348 firms approved as decentralized industries: a list can be seen in *Vict.Parl.Debates*, Dec. 7, 1965, 2346–52.

45. GIBLIN, E. M. (1965) The Siting of Industries in Relation to Natural Resources. Paper read to Section H, A.N.Z.A.A.S. Conference, Hobart.

46. DUNCAN, C. (1961) The Aluminium Industry in Australia. *Geog.Review*, 51, 40.

47. CORDEN, W. M. The Tariff, in HUNTER, A. (ed.) [42], 174–214; and for a list of Tariff Board Reports and Tariff Board Annual Reports see LINGE, G. J. R. (1964) *Index of Australian Tariff Reports 1901–1961*. Canberra.

48. For a discussion of the nature and consequences of competition between the States see LINGE, G. J. R. (1967) Governments and the Location of Secondary Industry in Australia. *Econ.Geog.*, 43, 43–63.

49. DALE, M. B. (1959) The Location of Oil Refineries in Australia. *New Zealand Geographer*, 15, 160–72; & GRIFFIN, T. L. C. (1965) An Example of Oil Refinery Location: Port Stanvac. *Austr.Geog.*, 9, 307–9.

50. This account draws on GARDNER, G. E. (1965) Siting of Industries in Relation to Natural Resources. Paper read to section H, A.N.Z.A.A.S. Conference, Hobart. See also DOWIE, R. F. *Aluminium*, No. 4, in Industry In Australia Series, Longmans, Melbourne.

51. *Ibid.*, 8.

52. Aluminium Industry Agreement Act 1944. *Tasmanian Statutes 1826–1959*, Vol. 1, 94–100.

53. Alumina Refinery Agreement Act, 1961. *Statutes of Western Australia 1961*, Vol. 1, 7–40; & Kwinana-Mundiyong-Jarrahdale Railway Act, *ibid.*, 351–3.

54. The Commonwealth Aluminium Corporation Pty Limited Agreement Act of 1957, *Queensland Statutes, 1957–58*, 618–70.

55. MINISTER FOR TERRITORIES, (1965) *Parl. Debates (House of Representatives)*, Sept. 15, 1965, 924–5.

56. Decentralization is also used in the sense of political decentralization, e.g. New State Movements, etc. The use of decentralization to mean the growth of manufacturing in the outer suburbs of the metropolitan areas is confusing. It is probably better to use diffusion to mean the tendency for manufacturing (and other economic activities) to become more widely spread through a metropolitan area, and decentralization to mean the process whereby the productive capacity of firms already established in the inner zone is partly or wholly shifted to the outer zone (and hence is one of the ways in which diffusion occurs).

57. Report of the Director of Secondary Industries, (1961–62) *Queensland Parl.Papers*, 1961–62, 823.

58. See NEUTZE, G. M. (1965) *Economic Policy and the Size of Cities*. Canberra; GOUGH, M. et al., (1964) *Queensland Industrial Enigma*. Melbourne; ANON. (1963) Decentralization Dialogue. *Current Affairs Bull.*, 31, No. 8, Mar. 4.

59. For details, see paper noted in [48].

60. The entries in Table 17 for the increases in metropolitan and 'rest of State' factory employment in South Australia are partly estimated on the basis of unpublished factory statistics provided by the Bureau of Census and Statistics, the results of the 1954 and 1961 population censuses, and data relating to factory employment by local government areas since 1959–60 published in the *Quarterly Abstract of South Australian Statistics*. Between 1959–60 and 1962–63 factory employment in South Australia outside the Metropolitan and Central Statistical Divisions increased by 2,509 persons, or about 5.7 per cent per annum. For another view see HEFFORD, R. K. (1965) Decentralization in South Australia: A Review. *Austr. Geog.Studies*, 3, 79–96.

61. COMMONWEALTH OF AUSTRALIA, (1965) *Report of the Committee of Economic Enquiry*, 1, paragraph 8, 247.

Capital City
Development in Australia

M. I. LOGAN

Introduction

The continuing growth of the large city in most parts of the Western world is an outcome of important structural changes in the nations' economies. A decline in the rural workforce and a rising number in manufacturing activities have long been recognized as important indicators of economic development [1]. There are two reasons for these shifts. Firstly, in advanced Western societies the rate of increase in the demand for food is less than the rate of increase in per capita income, while at the same time the rate of increase in demand for manufactured goods is greater than the rate of increase in per capita income. This means that an increasing percentage of labour, and of other factors of production, is devoted to the production of secondary goods as per capita incomes grow. Secondly, technical progress in farming has been such that despite the fall in percentage of the total labour force employed in the rural sector there has been an increase in output. The result of these processes has been a depopulation of rural areas and the absorption of workers in the town-based activities of manufacturing and tertiary industries.

An important feature of technical changes involving the substitution of capital for labour is that they occur unevenly among regions [2]. It is common, for example, for rural population egress to be greatest from areas of relatively high incomes. The cheapening of transport increases the concentration of economic activities at nodal points in the transport networks. Regional differences, therefore, tend to be accentuated as economic development proceeds. Large cities, arising from continuing specialization and interdependence among economic activities, become the most advanced regions where the economic system tends to work best. They develop as organizational nodes and exert tremendous power over the economy as a whole [3].

Processes similar to those which have led to the concentration of population and economic activities in metropolitan cities have affected the arrangement of land uses inside the cities. Here, the transport net has contributed to a concentration of activities in or near the Central Business District (C.B.D.), the most accessible point in the city. Because of restricted space in the C.B.D., vertical development occurs, but, even so, some activities are forced to move out. In general, space tends to be allocated to the individual or firm capable of paying most for it [4]. Technical changes which at the national level led to further concentration, at the city level have freed establishments from central locations and have encouraged a decentralizing or deconcentrating movement. The relocation of establishments and the absorption of new growth in the suburbs have established changing patterns of land use and of inter-firm linkages in the cities.

Australia, with its concentration of population and economic activities in the metropolitan cities, conforms to a recognized pattern. In some respects this concentration has taken on peculiar forms. The capital cities are centres of major importance in each state and a multiple-nucleated pattern of development, focussing on the six widely-spaced metropolitan cities, has arisen [5]. Each city has been built on a port which has heightened the concentration in the C.B.D. Most of the post-war growths in population, retailing and manufacturing have been absorbed in low-density suburbs sprawling away from the city centres [6].

The purpose of this chapter is to examine the impact of economic processes on capital city development at three levels: on the growth of the Australian cities, on the distribution of retailing and manufacturing in the cities, and on the development of suburban manufacturing areas in one of the cities. Emphasis is placed on empirical data drawn from the Sydney metropolitan area.

HISTORICAL GROWTH OF CITIES

The dominance of capital cities in Australia's political and economic life began with the colonial period when the pattern of dependence on overseas countries for commodities and markets was established. Initial European penetration into Australia was through six port towns each to develop subsequently into a node of internal transport nets and a capital city of a sovereign State. All were closely linked to Great Britain.

As the original aim of settlement in New South Wales and Tasmania was to provide an effective penal system, the development of other towns was not considered immediately necessary by the British Government. Moreover, the concentration of colonial administration and of various trade services at a few points was an accepted method of colonization in the eighteenth century. The port towns received convicts and goods from Great Britain and later primary products were sent through them to Great Britain. For some years there was a strong dependence on Great Britain for food supplies, despite the hazardous crossing and the abundance of land in the early settlements.

The early dependence on Great Britain contrasted with the position in the U.S.A. where the early settler was self-sufficient to a considerable degree, partly explained by the difference of time at which the two countries were settled [7]. Settlement in Australia, occurring a century later than that in the U.S.A., was a part of the sudden growth associated with industrialization in Europe. Colonies were appendages of the European economy and effort was directed to the production of those commodities which could not be produced as cheaply, or of such quality, in the parent country. The early Australian settlers were conditioned therefore to a commercial attitude which was further developed in a country where land, although abundant, was never very suitable for intensive farming. In addition, labour has almost always been a scarce resource in rural Australia, tending to promote relatively high wages. Settlers could afford high prices for food and there was no stimulus to farming of the subsistence-type.

Entrepreneurs in Great Britain, the main suppliers of capital, largely decided the forms of investment to be pursued in the colony. The initial emphasis was on wool production in a suitable physical environment, with a small supply of rural labour and with strong orientation to markets in the expanding industries of Great Britain. Costs of production were generally low and Australia's favourable position in the wool industry ensured a fairly rapid spread of settlement inland, rather than along the coastal plains. The better watered littorals were not occupied until much later, when technical changes in agriculture made the dairying industry economically feasible. This important point helps to account for the radial transport pattern that developed, instead of a linear system linking each capital city node.

The spread of commercial sheep farming consolidated the importance of the port cities in the first half of the nineteenth century. Strong links were maintained for supplies of food and other commodities in addition to the sale and export of wool. The establishment in the capital cities of wool stores, exporters, agents, and of other business undertakings associated with the pastoral industry, such as some large department-store trading, dates from this period. The shipping facilities of the cities also developed. Not only did the cities grow with the internal trade organization but they reflected changes in overseas marketing conditions.

Since dependence on overseas markets and the willingness of early settlers to travel long distances for basic supplies did not foster the growth of other large towns, a well-developed urban hierarchy is absent from Australia. In particular, there is a national lack of medium-sized towns in the range of 50,000 to 200,000 population. Victoria has no town between 100,000 and 500,000, and New South Wales none between 50,000 and 100,000 (Table 1). Despite the concentration of population and of towns in the southeastern corner of the continent, there is an absence here of main regional centres (Fig. 1). At least three State capitals have combined the role of regional centre with port and capital city functions. Perth and Adelaide are centres of restricted productive areas, and Melbourne the centre of a State which is small in total area. The great distances between the cities, their separation in some instances by land of poor productivity, the existence of State boundaries, and the concentration of governmental instrumentalities within them have all helped to identify the State with the city.

parts of Europe, and also in the U.S.A. where the formation of many towns occurred long before the advent of the railway. Moreover, the highly centralized nature of each State-owned transport system, designed to funnel the State produce through its capital city has contributed to the dominance of the six metropolitan cities.

Throughout most of the nineteenth century, then, growth was affected by a combination of abundant but generally poorly endowed land, scarce labour, European capital, and great distance from a market over which the producer had little control. In the second half of the century, agricultural expansion into new areas was closely associated with the development of railway facilities. These were essential prerequisites to growth in countries where population was small in comparison to land area. After railway expansion in the U.S.A., however, tremendous private investment resulted in increased specialization and the rise of centres

Table 1 *Distribution of Towns by Size Groups, 1961*

State	1,000,000 and over	500,000 to 1,000,000	100,000 to 500,000	50,000 to 100,000	25,000 to 50,000	15,000 to 25,000	10,000 to 15,000	Under 10,000	Total
N.S.W.	1	—	2	—	5	10	7	132	157
Victoria	1	—	—	2	2	1	3	90	99
Qld.	—	1	—	2	3	4	2	67	79
S.A.	—	1	—	—	—	2	2	41	46
W.A.	—	—	1	—	—	1	3	28	33
Tasmania	—	—	1	1	—	—	2	16	20
N.T.	—	—	—	—	—	—	1	2	3
A.C.T.	—	—	—	1	—	—	—	—	1
Total	2	2	4	6	10	18	20	376	438

Source: Commonwealth Bureau of Census and Statistics, (1961) *Commonwealth Census.* Canberra

It has been argued that conditions for the establishment of small towns were much less favourable at the time of maximum population expansion in the nineteenth century than they had been at a comparable stage of development in Europe. Population growth in inland New South Wales, and Victoria in particular, coincided with rail and road construction, so that the growth of towns post-dated technical changes in transport. This circumstance could have prevented the growth of strong community interest arising from a long period of relative isolation. A reverse situation applied in most

of regional growth [9]. Since investment in Australia was never as high as it was in the U.S.A. and since the natural resource endowment was much poorer, little internal specialization developed; the capital city remained the main centre of economic growth. Campbell [10] appears to have approached a cognate conclusion when he states:

Australia and New Zealand are probably unique as regards the relative absence of marked regional divergences in agricultural progress. The precise reasons why this has happened have never been adequately explored . . .

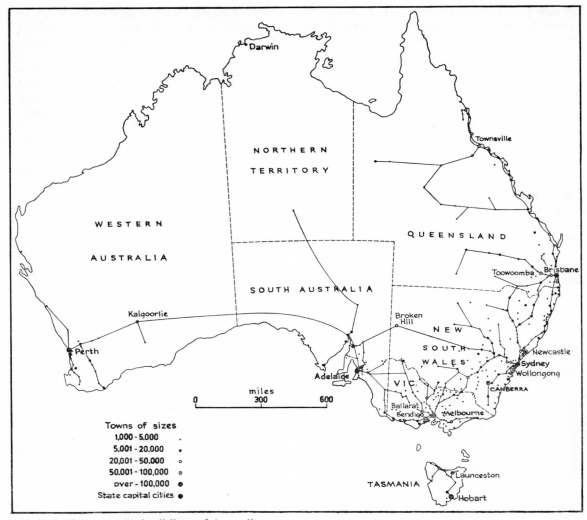

Fig. 1—Major towns and rail lines of Australia

The orientation of Australian production to overseas markets fostered high living standards and high technological development. Rostow argues that the take-off into manufacturing was delayed

not by political, social and cultural obstacles but by the high levels of welfare that could be achieved by exploiting land and natural resources [*11*].

The economy could continue to grow in per capita output using agricultural innovations developed elsewhere, but this form of growth in itself would eventually become a stimulus to some form of industrialization. Rostow [*12*] fixes the Australian take-off as occurring somewhere between the mid-1930s and mid-1950s. The main stimulus came from an increased value placed by world markets on Australian primary products, leading to an increase in production of these commodities and a rise in real incomes. The demand for manufactured goods within Australia therefore increased rapidly, and imports of these goods were permitted by the high level of primary exports. Some local industrialization was promoted by the great distances from supplying countries with distance acting as a form of protection, but major developments were responses to blockages in the inflow of manufactured goods. The imposition of tariff barriers on manufactured goods, either for revenue or protection, stimulated manufacturing growth, as did the cutting of trade routes in World Wars I and II.

Rostow appears to base his brief discussion of the Australian situation largely on Brian Fitzpatrick's interpretation of Australian economic history in the second half of the nineteenth century [13]. This interpretation has recently been seriously questioned by N. G. Butlin [14], in view of that writer's estimates of Australian national product and capital formation in the period.

According to Butlin, whose work has important implications for Australian geographers, the usual notion is that the decline of the gold workings left the pastoral industry as the basis of the Australian economy. It is generally assumed that manufacturing grew very slowly and was unimportant. Butlin argues, however, the period 1861 to 1890 experienced rapid economic growth on account of growing population and fast-rising stock of capital equipment. Capital was concentrated mainly in residential building, pastoral equipment, railways, and local authority works. Butlin stresses that economic leadership was not so much in primary industry but in manufacturing and the building industry. Manufacturing's share of the net national product rose from less than 5 per cent in 1861 to 12½ to 15 per cent in 1881. This fact can be interpreted to mean that Australian economic development during the period in question is a story of urbanization as well as one of the pastoral industry. It would seem, therefore, that in Australia the period prior to Federation had already experienced

considerable economic growth. According to Butlin, that period recorded a population growth higher than those of U.S.A., Canada, Germany and Britain. His research throws doubt on the widespread tendency to talk of an industrial revolution in Australia dating from the end of the 1930s, and to see the urban sector as a mere appendage of the pastoral industry.

The wider implications of his findings are indicated by Reitsma [15]:

If Butlin's picture of the earlier development in Australia is correct, one would be inclined to ask whether Rostow's take-off had already begun in Australia before the turn of the century.

There is a strong suggestion that manufacturing was already well established, and already stimulating city growth in Australia, prior to Federation. This does not deny that the most spectacular growth in manufacturing has occurred over the past forty years, proceeding at an accelerated rate since 1945. Manufacturing is now responsible for some 30 per cent of the gross value of all Australian production, and the proportion of the workforce engaged in manufacturing is higher than in the U.S.A. The growth in the relative position of the manufacturing sector and the relative decline in numbers in primary production are clearly shown in Table 2. In addition, rising real incomes have been associated with the development of an extensive range of tertiary services, which are almost as highly concentrated in the capital cities as are manufacturing industries.

As outlined on p. 245 the changes in distribution noted in Table 2 between manufacturing and primary industries can be attributed to structural changes in the nation's economies. These changes have led to shifts in the propor-

Table 2 *Changes in Distribution of Australian Workforce*

Industry Group	Distribution of Workforce (%)				
	1921	1933	1947	1954	1961
Primary production	22.2	20.5	15.5	13.3	11.1
Mining	2.9	2.4	1.7	1.6	1.3
Manufacturing	19.0	17.8	26.0	22.7	27.7
Building & power	11.6	12.4	7.3	10.8	20.0
Transport, commerce & govt. services	32.8	32.4	42.2	45.6	38.2
Others	11.5	14.5	7.3	1.0	2.1

Source: Bureau of Census and Statistics, *Commonwealth Census, 1921 to 1961.* Canberra.

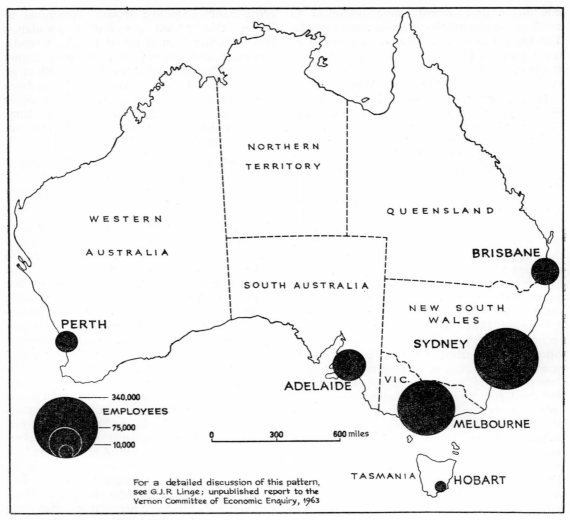

Fig. 2—The distribution of manufacturing employees by capital cities

tions of total population living in the capital cities. At the 1891 Census 36 per cent of Australia's population lived in the six capitals. From this time on there has been a steady increase in the percentage of the nation's population living in these cities—to 47 per cent in 1933, 51 per cent in 1947, 53 per cent in 1954 and 56 per cent in 1961. Capital city population growth has been caused, in part, by a movement of people away from rural areas and country towns.

However, the small towns have not always lost population; in the 1947 to 1954 intercensal period, for example, towns with populations ranging from 2000 to 5000 increased by 27 per cent, compared to an 18 per cent growth in capital cities [16]. The absence of medium-sized cities has meant that almost all population movement away from the country areas is to the capital city in each State. The only secondary towns of importance on the mainland — Newcastle, Wollongong, Geelong, Latrobe Valley—are located near Sydney and Melbourne, thereby reinforcing the concentration. A clearly defined spatial structure has evolved in Australia. Each capital city is the centre of a growth matrix [17], especially attractive to manufacturing because of its nodality, and the huge market concentration and external economies which it offers (Fig. 2). External economies are advantages a firm may gain through a growth in the industry, or the industrial area or city in which it is located. Examples include accessibility to a skilled labour supply, to sub-contract firms, and to other specialists such as carriers, printers, insurance and banking companies [53].

Australian cities are therefore points of enormous concentration of political and economic power (Table 3). In very few advanced countries is the dominance of a few centres so clearly marked as in Australia.

Table 3 *Concentration in Australian Capital Cities*

City	State	City's Share of State's Activities (%)		
		Population 1961	Retailing 1957	Manufacturing Jobs 1960
Sydney	N.S.W.	56	57	73
Melbourne	Vic.	65	66	80
Brisbane	Qld.	41	41	53
Adelaide	S.A.	61	67	80
Perth	W.A.	57	65	68
Hobart	Tas.	33	40	32

Sources: Commonwealth Census, 1961; Commonwealth Census of Retail Est. 1957; N.S.W. Statistical Register, 1960.

INTERNAL STRUCTURE OF CITIES

Models of city structure such as concentric ring and sector models have relevance to all Australian cities at particular points in time, but in this essay the main concern is with dynamic aspects of the cities. While technical changes arising from the process of economic development have furthered concentration at the national level, they have led to a loosening of the concentrations in the central areas of cities [18].

Manufacturing activities, for example, have moved from locations near the centrally located wharves and rail terminals as reliance on imports has diminished and as road transport is used more widely. Demand for more space where one-floor plants are desirable has also led, in many cases, to factory relocation. Similarly retailing growth has been associated with a marked decline in the proportion of sales occurring in the C.B.D.'s. Technical changes in the retail industry, amounting to what has been called a merchandising revolution, have given rise to a completely new type of shopping centre in the suburbs.

A new multiple-nucleated form of city is developing in Australia. In this form the city is arranged around a number of centres (for shopping and cultural activities) of roughly equal size, in contrast to the city where a single centre exists. (Los Angeles is probably the best example of a multiple-nucleated city.)

The development of the multiple-nucleated form can be explained to some extent by the off-centre location of some C.B.D.'s, by town planning processes and by inadequate public transport services. Despite its unfavourable location in some respects, however, the Australian C.B.D. continues as a node of major importance in the city [19]. It remains an organizational and administrative centre for commercial and governmental activities, although there has been a relative decline in its retailing and manufacturing functions. In its changing role, the C.B.D. provides an example of the way land uses adjust to new locational attributes of particular areas as the city grows. The suburbs, in which new growth occurs, also demonstrate the succession of land uses.

Retailing

The distribution of retail sales in a city may be discussed broadly in terms of Central Place Theory. This theory suggests that shopping centres of equal size and function tend to be distributed in a pattern which parallels that of urban population and that over time an hierarchical arrangement of centres evolves [20].

The location of centres depends on a number of other variables also which make the theory applicable in broad sense only. For example locality depends on accessibility patterns and frictions of distance which are related to the highly complex structure of movement and connections in a city and the resulting distribution pattern is closely related to the arterial road network. Also the urban population is unevenly spread and varies in income characteristics and in purchasing power.

Over time, the city builds up an hierarchical pattern of shopping centres which tend to acquire two distinctive shapes or forms, called nucleated and string-street conformations. Nucleated shopping centres cater more for nearby residents and, in Australian cities, are usually arranged around transport nodes such as railway stations and bus terminals. String-street centres are commonly elongated along arterial roads, and, while they do serve nearby residents, a high proportion of their sales is to commuters passing through the centre on their way to and from work.

The distribution of retailing and the form of shopping centres in a city are both highly dynamic. The purpose of the ensuing section is to discuss some of the variables contributing to the changing character of retailing in Australian cities. The suburbanization of retail sales can clearly be related to the high rate of suburban growth in population in the post-war years [21], and to difficulties in gaining access to the C.B.D.'s. Institutional factors such as Government intervention and the activities of large firms have also been of great importance, but have rarely been studied systematically [22]. Many of the present characteristics of the C.B.D. shopping districts derive from the activities of the giant retailing firms. The suburbanization of C.B.D. department stores likewise affects the viability, growth or decline

of particular suburban centres. Post-1957 retailing in Australia has seen the advent of the 'planned regional' type shopping centre, usually built distant from existing centres and planned as a unit to meet the needs of people shopping by car.

Areal Changes

The capital cities' share of their respective State's total retail sales is greater than their share of population. This 'over-concentration' is explained by the extensive trade area of each capital city, extending usually to the boundaries of the State in which it is situated [23]. The location of these cities at sea-port nodes in radial transport networks makes them the most accessible points inside their States so they offer specialized *high-order* goods and services such as specialist medical services, high class clothing and jewellery shops requiring a large tributary area (in terms of purchasing power) [24]. As well, they provide for city-dwellers all the *lower-order* goods such as food and clothing offered by smaller centres. It is likely also that at least some of the capital cities act as regional centres serving nearby rural inhabitants for their everyday needs [25].

The most significant areal change in retailing has been a large growth in the proportion of retail sales in the outer suburban areas and a corresponding decline in the proportion of sales in the C.B.D.'s of the larger Australian cities (Figs. 3, 4, 5). This is in keeping with trends in large cities in the U.S.A. [26]. The central area of Melbourne, for example, accounted for 34·1 per cent of Melbourne's retail sales in 1956, but by 1961, it accounted for only 27·0 per cent; in the case of Sydney, corresponding percentages were 39·6 and 30·1. Fifty-three per cent of Adelaide's retail sales took place in its central area in 1956 compared with 48·9 per cent in 1961. The higher percentages in this case are explained by the much smaller size of the city and the relative ease of access to the central area from all parts of Adelaide.

The suburbanization or decentralization process has not proceeded uniformly in all suburbs, as shown in Figure 6. The largest upward shifts in retail sales in Sydney from 1956 to 1961 took place in the local government areas of Bankstown (from 3·1 per cent to

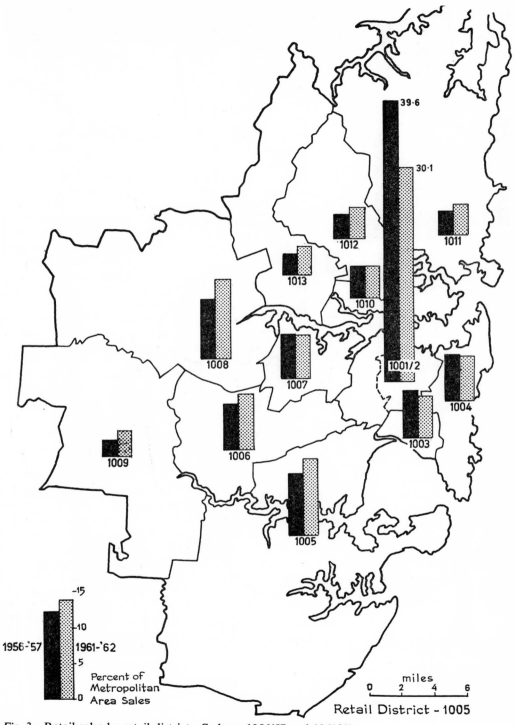

Fig. 3—Retail sales by retail districts, Sydney, 1956/57 and 1961/62

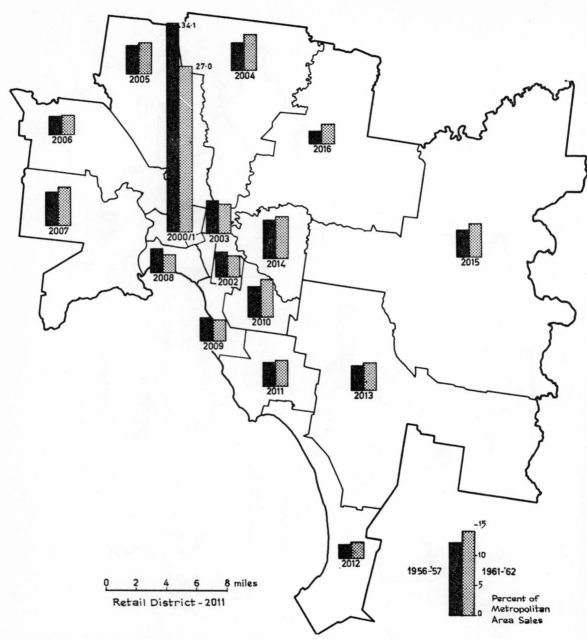

Fig. 4—Retail sales by retail districts, Melbourne, 1956/57 and 1961/62

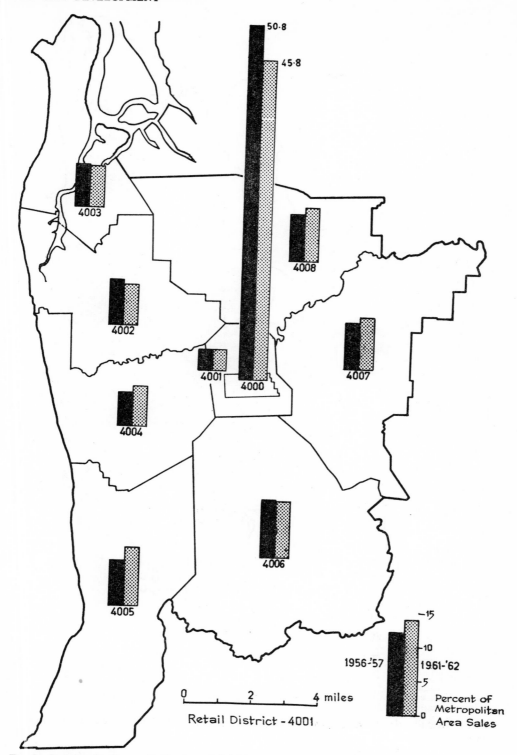

Fig. 5—Retail sales by retail districts, Adelaide, 1956/57 and 1961/62

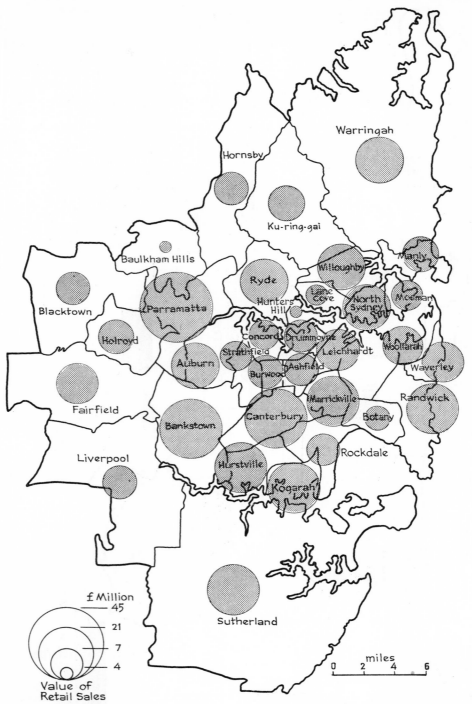

Fig. 6—Retail sales by local government areas (excluding the City of Sydney) Sydney, 1961/62

4·5 per cent), Sutherland (from 1·9 per cent to 3·3 per cent), Blacktown (from 0·5 per cent to 1·4 per cent) and in Warringah (from 1·7 per cent to 2·7 per cent. Each of these areas has experienced major population growth as well. In Melbourne and Adelaide there has been a more uniform increase in retailing activity in the suburbs than in Sydney, where the suburbanization process has been accelerated in certain areas by the development of completely new planned shopping centres. While these new centres are not peculiar to Sydney, they have had a much greater impact on this city [27].

The suburbanization process is related to differences in the types of goods being sold in the suburbs and in the central areas. In locating, retailers are very sensitive to demand considerations; hence the close areal association of population and retailing. Certain goods, such as groceries, require a small population because purchases are made frequently, while other goods, such as clothing and jewellery are purchased much less frequently and establishments selling them are less ubiquitous.

It follows logically from these elementary principles that the central areas, the most accessible points in cities, contain most of the *higher order*, comparison goods, i.e. higher order goods for which people compare prices. The suburban shopping centres, serving a more local population, contain establishments selling mainly *lower order*, convenience goods, i.e. lower order goods which are purchased frequently. Such a distribution is shown in Figs. 7, 8, 9. At the 1961 retail census, for example, the central area of Sydney accounted for only 11 per cent of the metropolitan area's grocery sales, but 51·5 per cent of the men's clothing sales. In Melbourne differences are more marked with the central area having only 6·7 per cent of the grocery sales and 55·1 per cent of the men's clothing sales. Adelaide with 24·3 per cent of the grocery sales and 84·3 per cent of the men's clothing sales in the central area shows how the continuing accessibility of that city's C.B.D. has retarded the growth of suburban secondary nodes.

Structural Changes

Major technical and economic changes in the last two decades have also contributed to the emergence of new distribution patterns in retailing. These changes have been associated with marked rises in personal incomes and expenditure, and in the nation's productivity as a whole. One important aspect of rising incomes is an increasing rate of car ownership, making suburban dwellers more mobile and less dependent on public transport systems. At the present time in Australia there is one car or station wagon for every 4·6 persons [28]. Given the present rate of increase in the number of cars of 200,000 per year, by 1970 the car: population ratio for Australia is likely to be 1:3·6 persons. More widespread ownership of cars has the general effect of increasing the volume of shopping at suburban centres, especially at those providing parking facilities and has been a major force contributing to the growth of the new planned shopping centres. Whereas small shopping centres and even isolated stores were once typical of suburban areas, the trend now is toward large concentrated centres attempting to duplicate at least some of the qualities of the C.B.D. shopping areas which offer a wide range of both convenience and comparison goods.

Aggregation has proceeded also at the firm level where widespread mergers and takeovers have produced great economic concentration especially in department stores and chain stores.

A department store traditionally offers a wide variety of goods under one roof and sells these goods throughout the metropolitan area. For these reasons they are located usually at the most accessible points, near transport terminals and at peak pedestrian points in the C.B.D. Strong inter-firm competition, the declining accessibility of some C.B.D's and a growing use of the car for shopping have encouraged, however, a movement to suburban centres of some department stores. Competition, firm strategy, changing market areas and managerial qualities have led to the closing of some stores and to the growth of others.

At the national level the two department store giants are Myers and David Jones [29]. In Melbourne, Myers is clearly dominant and has recently established in Sydney with the acquisition of a department store. It is also active in Adelaide but here meets competition from David Jones and John Martin. David

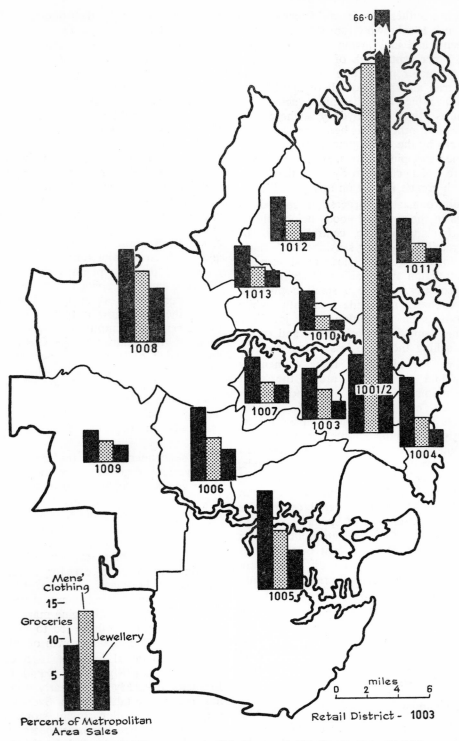

Fig. 7—Retail sales of different commodities by retail districts, Sydney, 1961/62

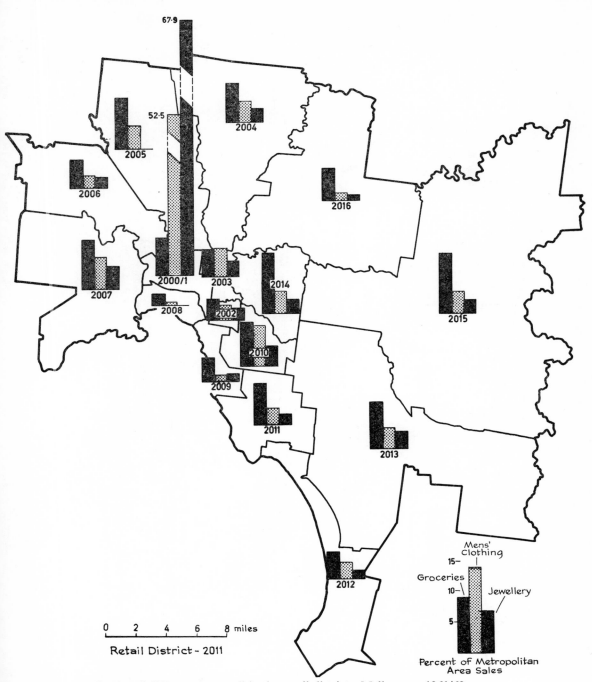

Fig. 8—Retail sales of different commodities by retail districts, Melbourne, 1961/62

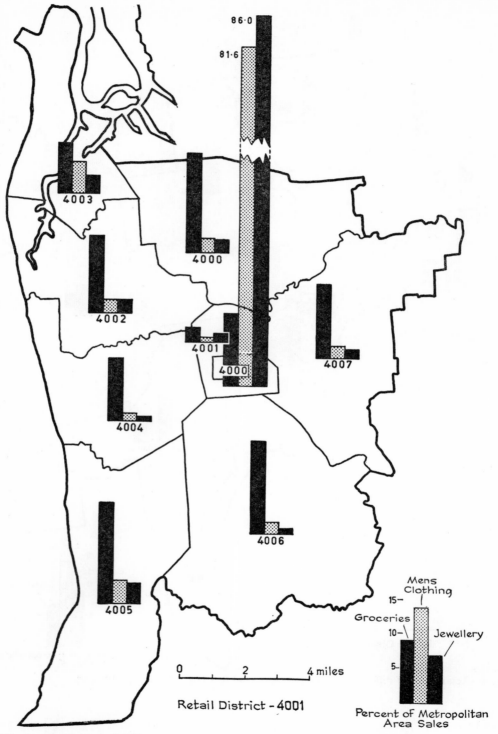

Fig. 9—Retail sales of different commodities by retail districts, Adelaide, 1961/62

Jones is Sydney's largest city retailer with three C.B.D. outlets and three in the suburbs at Brookvale, Bankstown and Parramatta. Interstate, the expansion of David Jones has been rapid. Perth was 'invaded' in 1954 with the acquisition of Bon Marche and Foy and Gibson. In Brisbane the group absorbed Finney Isles and T. C. Beirne. In Adelaide it acquired, and rebuilt the old-established firm of Charles Birks. There are also branches in Newcastle, Wollongong, Townsville and Mackay. The obvious omission in the David Jones network is Melbourne, where the Myer group is most important in retailing in both the C.B.D. and the suburbs.

Some department stores have exploited the strategy of regional development by establishing stores in the C.B.D. and in carefully selected suburban nodes. The best example is Grace Bros. in Sydney, which first set up in the suburbs more than twenty years ago when it became obvious that its inner city department store at Broadway was, in some respects, mislocated. Suburban sites were carefully selected at key locations, Bondi Junction, Chatswood, Parramatta and Wiley Park (Roselands). The firm claims that 90 per cent of Sydney's population now lives within 20 minutes' driving time of at least one Grace Bros. store. There is no doubt that exceptional managerial skill has contributed to the success of Grace Brothers' strategies. Some other department stores in Sydney have been forced to close premises when confronted with similar problems.

Economic concentration has developed in chain stores as well as in department stores. Chain stores, dealing mainly in convenience and variety goods, depend on a huge turnover and, therefore, operate through many outlets. They aim, also, at tapping impulse buying through a wide display of goods and by locating near high volumes of pedestrian traffic. Two chains, Woolworths and Coles, have greatly expanded their activities in the post-war years [30]. Woolworths commenced in 1928 and today have over 700 outlets throughout Australia, many acquired through takeovers of firms such as B.C.C., Flemings and McIlraths. Coles began in the same year and now have about 600 outlets. Much of the success of the variety chain stores can be related to their entry into food marketing. Conversion to self-service (supermarket operations) has increased the amount of store selling space and has eliminated costly credit, order-taking and delivery from the grocery field. By virtue of their strength in marketing large department stores and chain stores have been able to achieve economies in two other ways. Both have engaged in backward vertical integration by incorporating manufacturing activities, and department stores have engaged in forward vertical integration through establishing their own hire purchase companies.

Giant firms have important effects on the distribution of retailing in the cities. Each outlet in itself becomes a node of pedestrian and car movement and therefore affects the trade area and viability of the shopping centre as a whole. Higher volume of sales may reflect themselves, however, in higher rentals generally, which can force some retailers to relocate. As much department store and chain store activity has occurred in new planned shopping centres, some old suburban centres have experienced a relative decline.

Some of the differences among the cities can also be traced to department store activity. In Sydney, for example, strong competition among such large firms as David Jones, Myers, Grace Brothers and Mark Foys, has contributed to the rapid suburbanization of department stores. In Melbourne, on the other hand, the strength of Myers has tended to hold department store activity in the C.B.D. The internal geography of the central area is also affected by the concentration of economic power. In Melbourne retailing is remarkably highly concentrated in a small area bounded by Flinders Street Railway Station and Myers in Bourke Street. In Adelaide the location of the three department stores of Myers, John Martin and David Jones alongside each other in Rundle Street, provides an outstanding shopping node.

Shopping Centres

Associated with the shift of retailing to the suburbs has been the growth of the planned shopping centre. While such centres have been widespread in the U.S.A. for many years [31], the first centre in Australia was built at Top Ryde, Sydney in 1957. Since that date another 40 planned centres have been built in Sydney,

Table 4 *Largest Planned Shopping Centres in Sydney*

Centre	Cost of Centre ($m)	Site Size (acres)	Gross Floor Area (sq. ft.)	No. of Stores	Major Tenant
Roselands, Wiley Park	12	37	1,134,000	98	Grace Bros.
Warringah Mall, Brookvale	12	40	290,000	53	David Jones
Miranda Fair, Miranda	6.50	16	240,000	18	Farmers
Seven Hills	3	16	90,000	30	Woolworths
Hurstville	3	3.5	205,000	40	Coles
Top Ryde	2.50	16	144,000	69	Grace Bros.
Compass Centre, Bankstown	2	2	40,000	42	—
Westfield Park, Eastwood	2	2.5	72,000	18	Mark Foys
Bankstown Square	17	26	431,000	132	David Jones

Sources: National Cash Register Co., (1965) *Shopping Centres—Australia*, Sydney (Multilithed).
Bankstown Square News Bureau.

some free-standing and some within existing shopping centres. Their distribution is shown in Fig. 10 and some of their characteristics summarized in Table 4. The Australian centres have followed the pattern of their American counterparts, except in size where the U.S. centres are much larger. Each centre is planned as a unit, owned by one company which selects tenants, and provides extensive parking space for customers' cars. Smaller centres, called neighbourhood and community centres, have been built to serve people living nearby with convenience goods, but it is the new regional centres that have had most effect on the geography of retailing in our cities. They provide both convenience and comparison goods and operate on the basis of drawing on a population of over 100,000 living within 15 minutes' driving time of the centre. In Australia these centres have usually been built around a department store, which with a variety store is the first tenant and helps to assure the success of the centre. Melbourne's largest centre at Chadstone has not only been constructed around a department store but the centre is owned by that store. The large centres of Miranda Fair and Roselands in Sydney are also both owned by department store retailers.

An example of a planned regional shopping centre is the Warringah Mall, one of the largest completed centres, situated at Brookvale along Sydney's northern coastline. Built at a cost of $5,000,000, Warringah Mall has an estimated population of 135,000 people living within 15 minutes' driving time. The development company acquired a site of 40 acres, most of it inside land zoned originally for manufacturing, and constructed a centre of 290,000 square feet in total size. Parking space was provided for 2500 cars. There are 53 shops, but the three major tenants, a department store, a variety store and a chain grocer take up over three-fourths of the total floor space.

The movement of retailing into new centres located in the suburbs has had some serious effects on retailers in the C.B.D. As traffic congestion increases and as the cities sprawl outwards away from the centre, there is reluctance by shoppers to visit the C.B.D. Some department stores have met this problem by establishing branch-stores in the suburbs closer to their market although some marginally located firms have met disaster.

Retailers in Sydney's C.B.D. have always been dependent on shoppers brought to the city by train. Up to 1926 Railway Square at

Table 5 *Changing Function of Uptown Sydney*

Firm	Year of Closure	Former Use	New Use of Site
R. H. Gordon	1960	Furniture retailing	Storage Depot
Bon Marche	1961	General merchandising	Technical Education
Sydney Snow	1961	General merchandising	Variety store
Morley Johnson	1964	Furniture retailing	Bank
Bebarfalds	1965	General merchandising	Variety store
Marcus Clark	1965	General merchandising	Technical Education

Source: Railway Square Without Marcus Clark's, *Sydney M. Herald*, July 15, 1965.

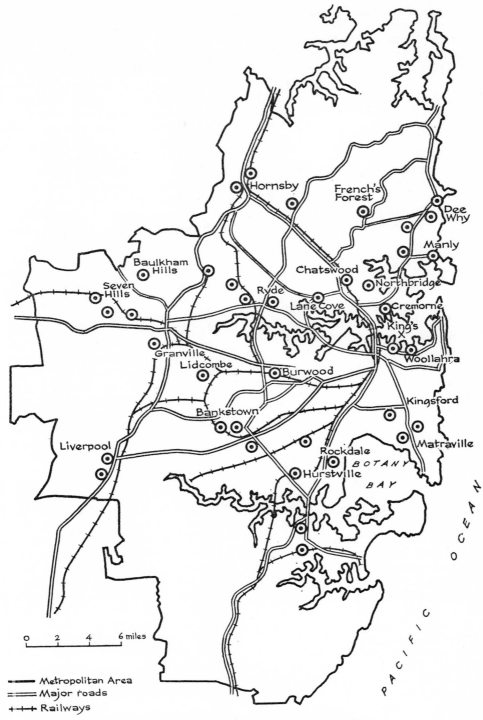

Fig. 10—The distribution of planned shopping centres, Sydney, 1964

the southern end of the C.B.D. was the place where most train travellers entered the city and a number of large retailers established around this point (see Fig. 11). The completion of the underground railway system in the central area by 1932, however, initiated the decline of Railway Square and the southern end of the C.B.D. This process of decline was heightened by the completion of the underground rail network with the construction of the St. James-Circular Quay-Wynyard link in 1954, and by the general loss of sales to the suburbs. Large retailers located in the southern end of the city who have been forced to close in the last five years are listed in Table 5. Unimproved Capital Values of land, well above market values, limit the opportunities for the redevelopment of sites formerly occupied by retailers.

Manufacturing

The manufacturer is primarily concerned with the cost relationships between inputs. He may substitute rent outlays for transport outlays, or may incur additional rent outlays to acquire more revenue, or may substitute among raw material inputs. In these ways, he has a highly complex set of linkages likely to affect the location of his firm. Traditional industrial location analysis (notably by Weber) has largely ignored the fact that the optimum location points might be the same for several firms. The neglect of inter-firm competition for land is a weakness in industrial location theory, especially in city situations where space is greatly limited. It is here general urban land use theory is more useful. This theory suggests firstly that each firm will seek to occupy the minimum transport cost point, where, because of transport savings, they can afford higher rents. Firms that can pay the most will appropriate the accessible sites—other firms being forced away. Secondly, a firm forced away will continue to substitute transport units for rent payments until the rent imposed on it (by competition from others) is equal to or less than the rent it can actually afford. Substitution of this kind underlies the removal of firms from high rent inner areas to low rent peripheral suburbs. Because of their common ties with certain establishments providing raw materials to numerous industries or with railway ter-

minals for deliveries, manufacturing firms may be arranged around a number of nodes inside the city.

One of the great advantages of a city location for a manufacturer is the external economies to be had from access to ancillary services, to a skilled labour supply, to technical and research organizations and so on, although these economies are not consistent throughout the city. It is also likely that the entrepreneur's approach to location will vary with the size and capital reserves of the firm and with his personal background. In Australian cities, institutional factors, mainly as expressed through the zoning of land and the attitudes of local government bodies to industry, have had important effects on the distribution of manufacturing.

The following sections of this essay examine the arrangement of industry in the Australian cities, with emphasis on the Sydney metropolitan area, and in two manufacturing areas in Sydney. The areas have been selected as representative of some important trends in manufacturing in Sydney. Brookvale is a small pocket of industry remote from the central area, developed in the last decade through the replacement of agricultural land use. Alexandria is the oldest industrial area, close to the C.B.D., wharves and railway terminals and occupied mainly by large-scale heavy industry.

City Distribution Patterns

With the exception of Adelaide and Perth, Australian cities have port and main internal transport nodes coinciding with the central areas. Manufacturing is most concentrated in these inner city areas, which were developed intensively by industry prior to the end of World War II. Industry up to this time was more dependent on direct access to primary raw materials obtained from within the country and overseas, and factory locations near rail heads and the port were therefore advantageous. While technological change has freed many firms from such centrally located sites, the inner areas are still the most suitable location for firms requiring waterfrontages or requiring quick and easy access to the C.B.D., as in the food and clothing industries. A force still holding firms here is the pattern set by the intra-city

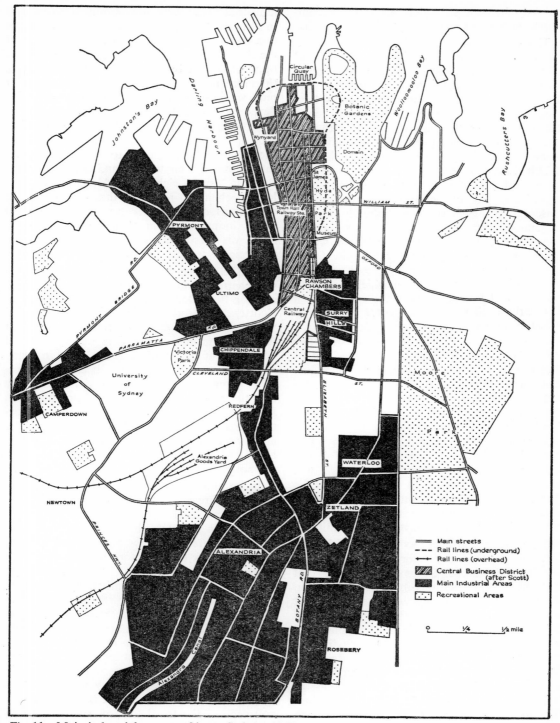

Fig. 11—Main industrial centres of inner Sydney, 1965

transport networks, which are almost completely lacking cross-connections in every city.

The area most heavily built-out by manufacturing in Sydney lay in the suburbs of Alexandria and Waterloo, some four miles south of the C.B.D. towards Botany Bay (Fig. 11). Much of this land was initially low-lying and swampy. The city had grown around and beyond it to the east, west and southwest, leaving a large unoccupied tract of land close to the C.B.D. [34]. After being reclaimed, some of this land was acquired for Mascot Aerodrome and the remainder was quickly absorbed by industry. At an earlier stage, the Botany-Mascot area further south had already become the site of certain noxious industries and of some with heavy demands for fresh water. Sands around Botany Bay provided an excellent source of water for wool scouring works and tanneries, many of which remain to the present day. But it was in the area between this early outlier and the centre that major industrial growth was to occur.

Alexandria-Waterloo was one of the few places in Sydney where factories were established on land subdivided especially for industrial purposes as opposed to replacing other buildings. As the huge daily labour influx came through the city transport terminals, Alexandria-Waterloo in one sense came to constitute an extension of the central area (see Fig. 11). Throughout the entire post-war period it has been an area of manufacturing decline. It was intensively built-out when proximity to the inner city was essential and when manufacturers were prepared to operate in multi-storeyed buildings to achieve this proximity.

No detailed statistical records exist of factory distribution in Sydney prior to 1952, but the Cumberland Planning Scheme report states that there were 1750 factories in the city centre in 1948 [35]. Field surveys conducted at that time show a great mixture of land uses, notably industrial and residential, in most of the inner suburbs. Balmain, Leichhardt, Marrickville and Redfern among others contained factories which, invading living areas, had occupied sites in the old residential subdivisions. Many of these factories disappeared after the introduction in 1951 of zoning regulations which restricted further industrial development in the inner suburbs. Factories located outside zoned

industrial areas were not permitted to expand in size. In the boom conditions of the 1950s this was so serious an imposition that many of the firms affected either moved to the suburbs or went out of business. The small factory is therefore not so typical of inner Sydney as it once was. Important extensions of industry also developed along the waterfront. Sites here were essential to firms importing heavy raw materials such as sugar and timber. The harbour foreshores were also attractive to early housing and the result was a mixture of land uses in Rozelle, Balmain and Leichhardt. Although technological changes involving the substitution of road transport for water transport have freed many industries from their waterfront sites, high disinvestment costs frequently make relocation uneconomic [36].

In Melbourne, too, most manufacturing is still centrally situated in the old inner suburbs such as Port Melbourne, South Melbourne and Footscray close to the port and main railhead where there were extensive tracts of land, not used by housing, at the time when industrial development began [37]. Adelaide is in many respects a unique city. It has been more carefully planned than any other Australian city and the central area is distant from the port. For these reasons manufacturing is less important in Adelaide's central area; much of the early industry developed around Port Adelaide and along the road connecting the centre with the port [38].

In addition to these inner zones which are generally areas of decline in manufacturing employment, each city has pockets of manufacturing in the suburbs (Figs. 12, 13, 14). These are areas of new growth and contain firms entering the city for the first time and those which have relocated from central areas. For these reasons the suburban areas contain more firms in national growth industries than do the older areas. Thus in Sydney the manufacture of electrical consumer goods is heavily localized in the suburbs in contrast to the clothing and textile industries which are more centrally located. This pattern becomes more complex, however, by changes within the industry, irrespective of whether it is expanding or not, such as the trend towards standardization in the clothing industry encouraging an important decentralization movement.

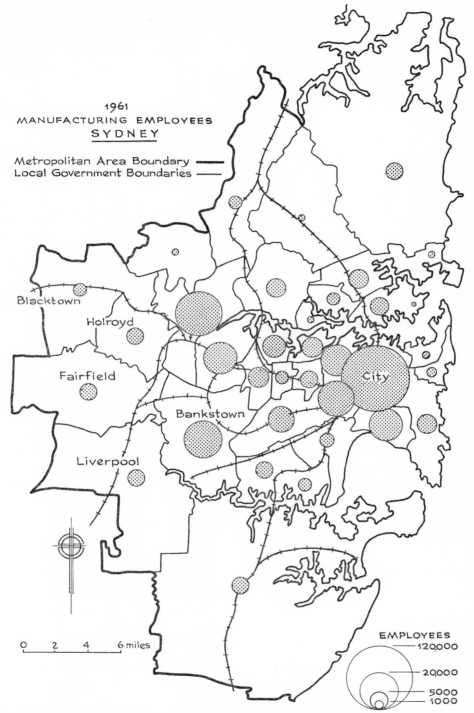

1961
MANUFACTURING EMPLOYEES
SYDNEY

Metropolitan Area Boundary ——
Local Government Boundaries ——

Blacktown
Holroyd
Fairfield
Bankstown
Liverpool
City

0   2   4   6 miles

EMPLOYEES
——120,000
——20,000
——5000
——1000

Fig. 12—The distribution of manufacturing employees by local government areas,
Sydney, 1961

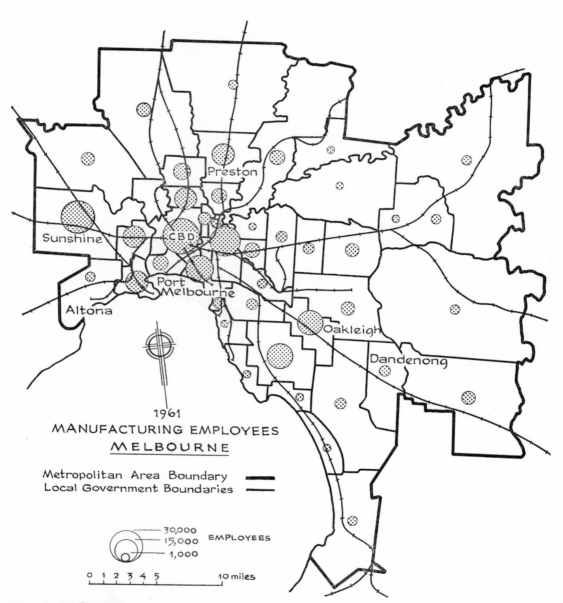

Fig. 13—The distribution of manufacturing employees by local government areas, Melbourne, 1961

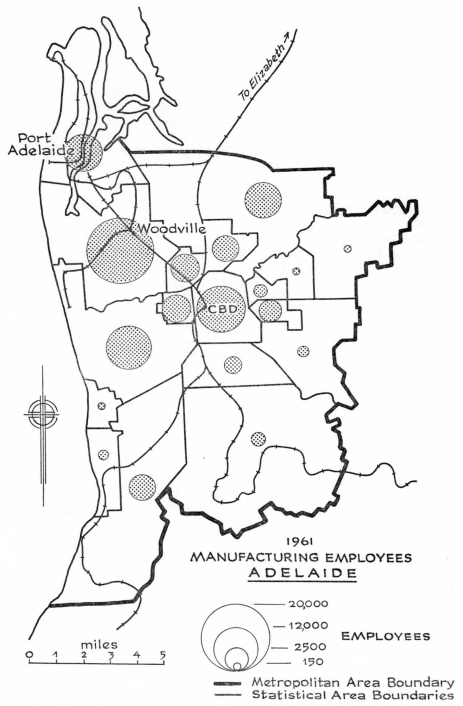

Fig. 14—The distribution of manufacturing employees by local government areas, Adelaide, 1961

In order to find sites of the size required in the expanding post-war economy many manufacturers were forced to 'leap-frog' an intensively developed ring of residential build-up abutting the C.B.D. and the old industrial areas. This can be illustrated in the case of Sydney where post World War II manufacturing quickly built out former market gardening and poultry farming areas in Bankstown, Auburn and Rydalmere. The southwestern sector of the Cumberland Plain has continued to attract manufacturing, as well as population, and now forms a second industrial complex in Sydney [39]. The rugged topography on the northern side of the Harbour and transport difficulties from the centre have retarded industrial development here. As most residential growth in Melbourne has occurred to the north, east and southeast, large tracts of industrial land could be obtained close to the C.B.D. on the western side [40]. Important cross-city movements of manufacturing workers were thereby generated, and, more recently, firms have sought out sites on the eastern side, broadly following the pattern of population growth. In particular the southeastern sector following the Prince's Highway connecting Melbourne with the Latrobe Valley, the main source of electricity, coal and gas, has attracted many engineering firms. In Adelaide most newly established firms have gone to Port Adelaide, Hendon, Woodville and other suburbs to the north and northwest of the city. The Adelaide metropolitan plan anticipates further growth occurring in this direction [41].

The Sydney Pattern of Industry

During the past twenty years the Sydney metropolitan area has consistently held around 75 per cent of the manufacturing employees in New South Wales. In 1940 the city had 79 per cent of the State's industrial employment, 63 per cent of the factories and 75 per cent of the total value of factory production. By 1960 it still had 63 per cent of the factories, 74 per cent of total production, and 73 per cent of the industrial jobs. A similar pattern of concentration characterizes individual industry classes (Table 6). In absolute terms, Class 4 (industrial metals and machines) is the most important group and Sydney has always provided more

than 70 per cent of the State's employment in this industry. Traditional processing industries, Classes 1, 9 and 10, are under-represented. Only in the clothing and food-drink-tobacco groups has Sydney's share declined significantly. Despite this decline, the clothing industry remains highly concentrated in Sydney. A highly diverse industrial profile characterizes the metropolis: the metal and engineering industries are most important, but the paper, rubber, chemical and clothing industries are also heavily concentrated. Not only do the 15,000 factories in the metropolitan area range widely through industry groups, but they also vary greatly in size. The workforce per factory, 23, is very small but some very large firms rise well above the average. Some 650 factories employ workforces of more than 100 each.

Table 6 *Sydney's Share of N.S.W.'s Industrial Employment*

Industry Group	1940 (%)	1950 (%)	1960 (%)
Non-metalliferous mine and quarry products	42	44	53
Bricks, pottery, glass, etc.	79	77	80
Chemicals, paints, oils, etc.	92	89	85
Industrial metals, machines, etc.	71	73	70
Precious metals, jewellery, etc.	99	94	93
Textiles	87	75	81
Skins and leather	94	94	97
Clothing	96	81	82
Food, drink, tobacco	74	68	65
Sawmills, joineries	52	43	48
Furniture	95	88	90
Paper, printing	90	89	89
Rubber	94	91	90
Musical instruments	100	98	83
Miscellaneous products	66	97	92
Heat, light, power	60	63	52
Total	79	75	74

Source: Commonwealth Bureau of Census and Statistics, *Factories in Local Government Areas*, Sydney, 1940, 1950, 1960 (duplicated).

Areal Distribution

Fig. 12 shows the distribution of manufacturing employees by workplace for local government areas in 1961. The inner area of concentration comprising the local government areas of the City of Sydney, Leichhardt, Marrickville and Botany already existed at the end of World War II. From 1953 onwards there has been a

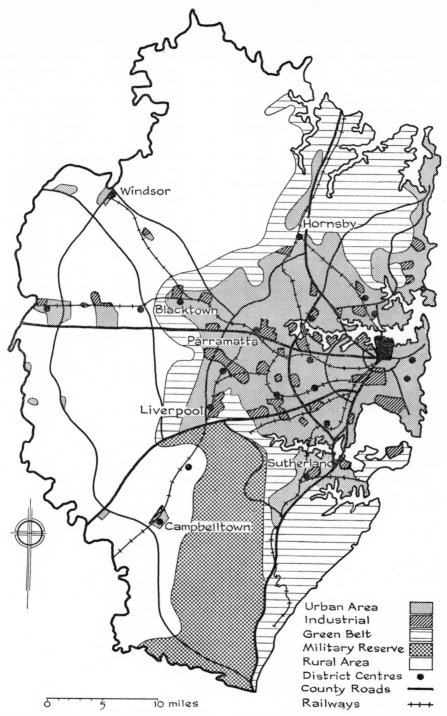

Windsor

Hornsby

Blacktown

Parramatta

Liverpool

Sutherland

Campbelltown

Urban Area
Industrial
Green Belt
Military Reserve
Rural Area
District Centres   ●
County Roads   —
Railways   +++

0   5   10 miles

Fig. 15—Generalized outline of the County of Cumberland Plan, 1964

steady shift of manufacturing firms from this area, for example, the City of Sydney's share of Sydney's industrial jobs fell from 45 per cent in 1954 to 34·5 per cent in 1961. A secondary area of concentration has developed in the outer western suburbs centring on Bankstown, Parramatta and Auburn. These two areas of concentration provide in combination more than 70 per cent of the industrial employment in the metropolitan area. As the city expands in area manufacturing firms are forced to locate in suburbs distant from the C.B.D. Because manufacturers are sensitive to, and try to avoid the costs associated with overcoming this distance, manufacturing as expressed by employment, has grown much less rapidly than population.

Technical change, while enabling a reduction in production costs per unit through the introduction of new techniques, generally increases the space needs of manufacturing industries. Because of the high price of industrial land, technical change can be an important decentralizing force. The larger site may also enable an increase in the scale of operation and the dependence on other firms will decrease as more stages of manufacture are able to be handled economically by the one firm. A firm with a small scale of operation has to depend on other firms and is forced to locate in the midst of a well established industrial district.

The direction of post-war manufacturing growth in the suburbs has been largely determined by physical planning controls, which have operated in Sydney with varying degrees of effectiveness from 1951 onwards. An authority responsible for planning the future development of the County of Cumberland was established in 1945. The Cumberland County Council's planning scheme became law in 1951. A main object of the scheme which is shown in broad outline in Fig. 15 was to consolidate the then existing pattern of land use and to facilitate natural growth processes. For example, pockets of land in the suburbs were zoned for future industrial development on the periphery of the residential areas. With space for industry in the inner areas restricted, these suburban industrial zones encouraged the suburbanization of manufacturing.

A second object of the Cumberland Planning Scheme was to produce in the suburbs a number of district centres which would serve as commercial and cultural nodes secondary to the C.B.D. Here in essence was an application of the multiple-nuclei model. While this second object has not been fully achieved by reason of lack of executive power on the part of the planning authority, substantial suburbanization of retail sales has arisen from the development of so-called 'regional' shopping centres and the revitalization of some existing centres. A green belt established to control the outward growth of the city has proved ineffective. It has been gradually encroached on, pressure being exerted both by private individuals and by public authorities.

The main principles of the Cumberland Planning Scheme in regard to secondary industry were [43]:

1. Close relationship between place of work and residence, to be achieved by a dispersal from the inner area of population and employment.

2. Establishment of suburban industrial zones in convenient relation to a transport system communicating direct with the city: this, on account of linkages within industry.

3. Liberal choice of employment for individual workers to best be achieved by a circumferential transport system.

4. An average density of about thirty industrial employees per acre of industrial land was considered desirable; since many inner areas were overcrowded, extensive relocation and suburban development were essential for its achievement.

5. Development in the suburbs of urban communities self-contained in shopping, education and culture with local industrial areas capable of functioning efficiently as independent units.

These principles foreshadow some of the problems which beset planners in the next ten years. The strong linkages between industry and the city centre and the need for a continuing radial road pattern do not altogether match the idea of self-contained suburban communities and a circumferential transport system. In actuality, the city centre has continued dominant: little integrated suburban development has occurred. To help achieve the Plan's aims, the planning authority zoned land

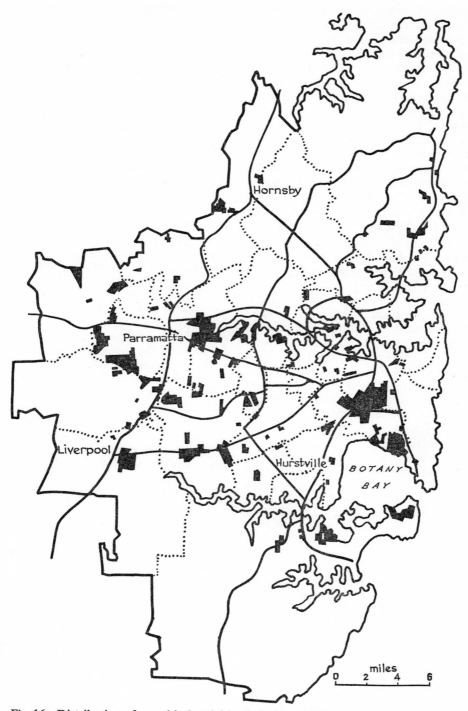

Fig. 16—Distribution of zoned industrial land, Sydney, 1964

throughout the County for industrial usage. The areas zoned for industry are shown in Fig. 16. The industrial zones largely followed the formerly existing pattern in the extensively built-out part of the metropolitan area. In locating zoned areas in the outer ring of suburbs where very little industry existed, the planners were powerfully influencing the future development of the metropolis. There is little evidence of how judgments were made, but no serious study appears to have been undertaken either of existing industry or of the likely implications of extensive industrial development in the outer suburbs. The general policy was to zone for industry land unsuitable for other uses or land currently used by agriculturalists.

Additional forms of government intervention add further complexities. Within the framework of the Cumberland Plan, local councils within the county are required to prepare local planning schemes. In general these councils observed the original plan but some deliberately discourage industry by delaying approval to development applications from industrialists. Furthermore numerous non-conforming industries exist and their factories, lying outside the zoned industrial areas, were not until recently allowed to expand beyond their existing site. A separate State Government department, the New South Wales Division of Industrial Development, is responsible for advice on the placement of industry. Insofar as this department carries out the policy of decentralization to which the New South Wales Government is committed, it is mainly concerned with industry outside the metropolitan area.

Localization of Specific Industries

Two important industrial complexes—the inner city and the outer western suburbs—have already been recognized in Sydney. The industrial composition of the two complexes, as shown in Table 7, reveals certain locational tendencies within industry groups. In the City of Sydney there is an important concentration in the paper and printing, clothing and food-drink groups while in Leichhardt, the processing of heavy chemicals and the manufacture of furniture are most important. In Marrickville the textile industry and in Botany the skin and leather industry are outstanding. The outer western area of largely new growth has a highly diverse industrial profile, except that the industrial metal industry is strongly represented in all three outer local government areas, particularly in Bankstown. The importance of metal processing in the more recently established industrial areas of the western suburbs reflects the high national growth rate in this industry. Because of its industrial profile the Bankstown-Auburn-Parramatta area has a very high growth potential, compared with the inner areas which have a greater share of the national slow-growth industries.

From 1940 to 1960, Sydney's total industrial employment increased by 88 per cent, from 189,000 to 357,000. Table 8 shows the absolute and relative changes in employment in industry groups for this period and for the period 1954 to 1960. In 1940 to 1960 the industrial metal and machines class experienced the greatest increase, with 161 per cent, and in 1954 to 1960 maintained a rapid rate of growth. In contrast, the clothing industry, traditionally the industry of second importance in Sydney, experienced an increase of but 22 per cent. A low rate of growth also characterized the textiles, skins and leather and food-drink-tobacco classes over both periods. From 1954 to 1960 employment in textiles has decreased by 5 per cent, and employment in clothing has increased no more than by 0·3 per cent, during a time when total industrial employment increased by 16·3 per cent. The chemical, paint, oils class is in direct contrast. During the past six years, employment in this class has increased much faster than the metropolitan average for all industry, and the class now takes fifth place to classes 4, 8, 9 and 12 in industrial employment in Sydney.

The tendency for the rapidly growing industries to be more widely distributed in the outer suburbs than in the inner area is important in Sydney's manufacturing growth. Specialization of industry within local government areas can be measured in terms of local location quotients [44] calculated along similar lines to Sargent Florence's original quotients. The location quotients measure the degree to which a particular industry is concentrated in a local government area, compared with the extent to which all industry is concentrated in that area.

Table 7 Percentage Distributions of Employment in Sydney's Leading Industries, 1960

Local Government Area	Bricks, Pottery	Chemicals, Paints	Indl. Metals	Textiles	Skins, Leather	Clothing	Food, Drink	Sawmills, Joinery	Furniture	Paper, Printing	All Manufacturing
Inner Area											
City of Sydney	42.7	24.6	34.3	34.5	34.1	54.5	40.5	35.5	34.0	66.4	38.6
Leichhardt	0.5	12.6	5.6	2.2	2.6	4.0	4.1	9.3	10.5	2.0	5.5
Marrickville	10.4	4.2	5.9	20.4	5.6	4.0	5.7	4.3	8.9	1.6	6.0
Botany	1.8	10.8	5.8	2.4	38.4	0.9	4.6	3.4	4.2	1.4	4.8
Total	55.4	51.5	51.6	59.5	80.7	63.4	54.9	48.5	57.6	71.4	54.9
Outer Western Area											
Bankstown	2.2	6.2	8.7	1.3	0	2.5	0.7	5.9	8.7	1.1	5.6
Auburn	5.2	2.9	6.1	7.7	0.2	1.2	6.1	5.4	1.4	2.2	5.0
Parramatta	4.6	2.7	5.2	4.1	1.2	3.7	3.1	4.5	2.6	2.1	5.3
Total	12.0	16.8	20.0	13.1	1.4	7.4	9.9	15.8	12.7	5.4	15.9
Total Two Areas	67.4	68.3	71.6	72.6	82.1	70.8	64.8	64.3	70.3	76.8	70.8

Source: Commonwealth Bureau of Census and Statistics, (1960) *Factories in Local Government Areas*. Sydney (duplicated).

Table 8 *Change in Employment in Industry Classes in Sydney 1940 to 1960*

Industry	Absolute Changes		Relative Changes (%)		Ranking	
	1939-40 to 1959-60	1953-54 to 1959-60	1939-40 to 1959-60	1953-54 to 1959-60	1939-40	1959-60
Non-metalliferous quarry products	2,816	1,306	149	38	14	13
Bricks, pottery, etc.	3,557	1,207	54	13	7	9
Chemicals, paints, etc.	11,621	4,604	143	30	6	5
Industrial metals, etc.	100,083	34,092	161	26	1	1
Precious metals	1,228	87	136	4	15	15
Textiles	4,082	−979	27	−5	5	6
Skins, leather	760	220	15	3	10	12
Clothing	6,903	142	22	0.3	2	2
Food, drink, etc.	5,564	511	25	2	3	3
Sawmills, joinery	4,598	1,217	85	14	8	8
Furniture	3,318	1,636	60	23	9	10
Paper, printing, etc.	11,355	5,745	72	27	4	4
Rubber	3,779	952	111	15	12	11
Musical instruments	294	−581	147	−50	16	16
Miscellaneous	6,462	2,151	154	25	11	7
Heat, light, power	1,704	−645	89	−15	13	14
Total	168,124	50,225	88	16		

Sources: Commonwealth Bureau of Census and Statistics, (1940) *Statistical Register for N.S.W.* Sydney. *Factories in Local Government Areas.* Sydney, 1961 (duplicated).

The measure can be modified into a local location quotient by using the total for the Sydney metropolitan area as a base for comparison instead of the national total of industrial workers. Following Florence's use of these quotients, an industry with a quotient above unity indicates that the area has more than its 'expected' share of that industry. A high quotient does not imply a concentration of a particular industry, but simply that the industry is distinctive to the area. McGovern has suggested a modification of Florence's work through classifying industries as 'important' and 'distinctive' [45]. For this study, important industries are defined as those with more than the average number of employees for local government areas outside the City of Sydney. A distinctive industry is an important one with a location quotient of 2 or more. On this basis the industries listed in Table 9 are distinctive in particular local government areas. In many cases apparent specialization can be explained by the presence of a single factory, as with the textile industry in Holroyd and Baulkham Hills and the skin and leather industry at Lane Cove. The areas listed in the table have developed little in the way of those industrial complexes which exist in some older English cities.

Industry groups are so defined that an extremely wide range of activities is included in each hence an area can be rated high for specialization, but still be quite diversified in industrial structure. Certain distinct groupings

Table 9 *Distinctive Industries in Local Government Areas*

Industry Group	Local Government Area
Mine and quarry products	Bankstown, Concord, Fairfield, Parramatta
Bricks, pottery, glass	Drummoyne, Holroyd, Willoughby, Blacktown, Warringah
Chemicals, paints, oils	Botany, Concord, Lane Cove, Leichhardt
Textiles	Holroyd, Marrickville, Baulkham Hills
Skins, leather	Botany, Lane Cove, Willoughby
Clothing	Kogarah, Marrickville, Waverley, Woollahra
Food, drink, tobacco	Concord, Randwick
Sawmills, joinery	Holroyd, Warringah
Furniture	Drummoyne, Hurstville, Rockdale
Paper, printing	Burwood, Randwick
Rubber	Bankstown, Drummoyne, Parramatta
Musical Instruments	Ashfield, Leichhardt, Willoughby

Source: Calculations based on Commonwealth Bureau of Census and Statistics (1961), *Factories in Local Government Areas.* Sydney (duplicated).

of industry recognizable in the table are confirmed by field checks—notably the clothing industry in the inner suburbs of Waverley and Woollahra, sawmilling and joinery in the expanding areas of Holroyd and Warringah, and textile manufacture in Marrickville.

A local coefficient of localization can be derived for industry groups within the metropolitan area. It compares the percentage distribution for single industries in individual local government areas with the area's percentage of all manufacturing. The limits are 0 and 1; if the particular industry is distributed in exactly the same manner as all industry the coefficient will be 0; if the industry is concentrated in one area, the coefficient will approach unity [46]. Table 10 lists the coefficients of localization for Sydney's industries. The outstanding feature is the very low value of each industry group, indicating a general lack of localization.

Two industrial areas will now be examined in detail to show the processes by which industrial growth occurs, and the variables influencing locational decisions. One area, in Warringah, has been occupied by industry in the last decade, while the other, Alexandria-Waterloo,

is one of the oldest industrial areas in Sydney. The former is an area of growth and the latter, an area of decline in manufacturing. The areas therefore contain firms of different ages and sizes, confronted with different kinds of problems.

Table 10 *Coefficients of Localization for Sydney's Industries, 1960-61*

Industry Group	Localization Coefficient
Non-metalliferous mine & quarry products	0.499
Bricks, pottery, glass, etc.	0.225
Chemicals, paints, oils	0.318
Industrial metals & machines	0.104
Precious metals, jewellery, etc.	0.310
Textiles	0.276
Skins, leather	0.379
Clothing	0.242
Food, drink, tobacco	0.159
Sawmills, joineries	0.129
Furniture	0.216
Paper, printing	0.354
Rubber	0.572
Musical instruments	0.561
Heat, light, power	0.665

Source: Calculations based on Commonwealth Bureau of Census and Statistics (1961), *Factories in Local Government Areas.* Sydney (duplicated).

SUBURBAN MANUFACTURING IN WARRINGAH

The outer western suburbs, including Bankstown, have absorbed most of Sydney's post-war industrial growth, mainly by reason of the extensive zoning for industry of land topographically suitable, and of their accessibility to the central area and the metropolitan market. The continuing importance in location of transport nodes has promoted a pattern of sectoral growth, especially in the heavy metal processing and assembly industries. But significant clusterings of industry have emerged on the northern shore, despite its difficult topography and distance from suppliers, where some pockets of agricultural land amid residential areas were zoned for industry under the Cumberland Planning Scheme. The most isolated of these pockets, Brookvale in the Warringah peninsula, is studied as an example of a suburban manufacturing area.

Urban Spread in Manly-Warringah

The simple concentric zonal and sectoral models of city structure are substantially modified in Sydney by physical considerations [47]. The western and southwestern sectors of the city were flat and open enough for factory building, whereas the more rugged northern part attracted high-class housing. Separated from the main settlement by the harbour, the northern shore was developed late in the city's history.

Superimposed on the modified concentric pattern is a transport system, which does not spread uniformly through the metropolitan area. Transport arteries, becoming channels of least resistance, increase the accessibility of activities located near them. This circumstance is especially important in areas of difficult topography. The Warringah peninsula has not been penetrated by rail transport, its development being moulded by arterial roads and vehicular traffic on a terrain of dissected plateaus and coastal plains. The main line of access runs along the narrow coastal littoral from Manly, which is linked to the C.B.D. by a ferry service. This network terminates at Palm Beach (Fig. 17), making the Warringah sector the only one lacking a through road.

Recent growth within cities generally tends increasingly towards multiple nucleation. Moreover residential growth in the outermost rings has not been uniform; instead linear patterns have developed along arterial roads. In the recent period of rapid growth, new housing settlements have been developed beyond the existing built-up areas, and breakpoints in transport such as railway stations have frequently acted as nuclei for new communities. The spread of residential land uses around these nuclei has tended to be limited by easy walking distance, so that a pattern has been formed of nucleated communities separated by areas of open space. When low density urban sprawl has encompassed such communities many have lost their identity, but the Cumberland Plan has aimed at a return to community consciousness through the implementation of its district centre concept.

A series of communities, separated by open space and farming, emerged along the coastal strip from Manly to Palm Beach. But here a railway had no influence and the discontinuity of distribution can be explained largely in terms of physical geography. As settlement spread from the Manly node, along the coast, its location was affected by the alternation of valley lowlands with eroding headlands. Small streams drain between pairs of headlands into lagoons which are dammed or partially dammed by spits. Each valley is the logical site of a suburban community—Harbord, Brookvale, Curl Curl, Dee Why, Collaroy, Narrabeen, Mona Vale, Newport, Bilgola and Avalon. Development spread from the Manly core which, from 1854 onwards, was directly linked to the C.B.D. by ferry. Orientation to Manly was further strengthened by a steam tram service, which operated from 1903 onwards, from Manly to Manly Lagoon some five miles to the north [48]. In 1910 the service was extended to Brookvale, in 1912 to

Collaroy Beach, and in 1913 to Narrabeen. But from 1913 onwards patronage of the steam trams and the accompanying orientation to Manly both diminished; while new routes opened in 1924 across the Spit Bridge and across the plateau via Roseville Bridge subsequently came into vigorous use. In 1939 the tramway network within Warringah was discontinued.

It is in the post-war era that spectacular growth has occurred throughout the peninsula. At the 1911 census there were but 2823 people in the Warringah Shire. By 1933, there were 16,054 and at the end of the war in 1947 there were 33,176. During each of the two post-war intercensal periods, 1947 to 1954 and 1954 to 1961, the population has doubled. This growth has initiated important processes: not only has settlement tended to invade the interfluvial spurs and the open spaces between communities tending towards a general merging, but it has spread into the plateau. Important replacement of land uses has occurred, open space being taken by housing, and agricultural land by industry. A changing pattern of land uses has been encouraged in Warringah by the zoning of land under the Cumberland Planning Scheme and local planning scheme.

Unlike most other communities, Brookvale's development has been based on the opportunities it offered for agriculture rather than as a centre for commuting to the C.B.D. It attracted market gardeners, mainly Italians and Yugoslavs who fostered development of a self-contained community. Close family and national ties have resisted to some extent that erosion of community enclaves, which inevitably accompanies urban sprawl. Mainly because farming had persisted there into the 1950s keeping considerable areas open, Brookvale was selected in the Cumberland Planning Scheme as the main area for industrial zoning in Warringah. Within a period of ten years agriculture has been almost completely replaced by industry despite the certain remoteness of the area from the C.B.D. and other parts of the city. Not only is it in a narrow peninsula some thirty miles from the expanding markets of the western suburbs, but also it is cut off from the C.B.D. by two harbours; the three bridges, two of which must be used in a given crossing, are

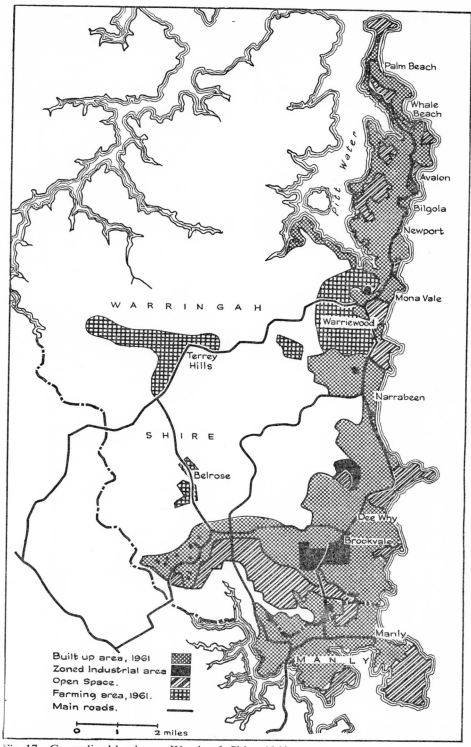

Fig. 17—Generalized land uses, Warringah Shire, 1964

congested with traffic. As a counter to high transport costs, Brookvale factories could limit themselves mainly to serving the Warringah market or could take advantage of low land values if these obtained. As a preliminary to examining the industrial composition of Brookvale and market areas served by firms, it is necessary to analyse the changes in land uses and land values.

The Process of Change

Most land in Brookvale was owned by first- or second-generation Italians and Yugoslavs, with Italians always the more numerous and increasing so with passage of time. As they have built up capital, Yugoslavs have tended to move away from Brookvale to the more prosperous Warriewood farming area further north. Italians and Yugoslavs alike came originally from closely-knit homeland communities—the Italians from a few villages in Calabria and the Yugoslavs from villages on the Adriatic. Almost all were pre-war immigrants who, initially settling elsewhere, came to Brookvale from about 1930 onwards.

Most of the Yugoslav migrants moved from Broken Hill where they had worked in the mines, raising money to bring their families from Europe. Seeking security, they entered farming either at Mildura—in vine growing— or at Cabramatta, Fairfield, Brookvale and Warriewood in the Sydney area. The wealthier families mostly went to Warriewood where glass house cultivation required most capital; the poorer went to Brookvale.

Before World War II Italians were in a minority among the Brookvale market gardeners, but the post-war influx of migrants has reversed the position. Italians in Brookvale have adapted to changing land uses by diversifying their economic activities—running owner-operated grocery and food stores, selling cars, or, more recently, erecting factories for rental on former gardens. Many Italian families supply female workers, especially for the clothing industry.

Government agencies first penetrated the predominantly agricultural communities and five acres were acquired for a bus depot, ten acres for the Department of Technical Education, two acres for a park, and 32 acres for

Warringah Golf Course. It was land use zoning, however, that brought the most spectacular changes. Except for five very small machine shops, and for the Brookvale brickworks which exploited local shale lenses in the Hawkesbury Series, there was no secondary industry in Brookvale in 1954. Within the next decade some seventy factories were established.

Warringah Shire is one of the three local government areas in the County of Cumberland to have a prescribed plan, but this is essentially identical with the original Cumberland County Council proposal. The Cumberland Planning Scheme report [49], drawing attention to the absence of industry in Warringah and to the huge daily exodus of manufacturing workers, pointed out that the provision for industry in this area was hampered by scattered housing in the few areas suitable otherwise for manufacturing development. It claimed that the geographical isolation of the district favoured such industrial development. From the manufacturer's viewpoint this claim is questionable, but it nevertheless formed the basis on which some 400 acres of land in Warringah were zoned for industry in four main areas (Fig. 17). The potential capacity of employment was assessed as in Table 11.

Table 11 *Major Industrial Zonings in Warringah*

Zone	Area Acres	Employment Capacity
Brookvale east of Pittwater Rd.	135	4,050
Brookvale west of Pittwater Rd.	120	3,600
Dee Why West	170	5,100
Manly Vale	2	60
Total	427	12,810

Source: Warringah Shire Council, 1956 *Planning Scheme*, Civic Survey, Ordinance **106**.

The estimated employment capacity is reckoned from the Cumberland plan's ideal ratio of 30 manufacturing employees per acre of land. Under the local scheme, Warringah Council amalgamated the County A and B class industries on the grounds that the line of demarcation between them was very fine. The areas zoned for industry were provided with water, gas and electricity services, but lacked sewerage until 1961. Most industrial growth in the shire has taken place in Brookvale, where the eastern and western sections of the industrial zone (divided by Pittwater Road) were occupied at the same time (Fig. 18).

Dee Why West about four miles to the north occupies another valley of predominantly market gardening uses. It is less accessible than Brookvale, being more isolated from the main housing areas and poorly provided with roads. Although its industrial growth has been slow, some large firms have recently acquired land there. It seems likely that Dee Why West will be developed by big firms as land in Brookvale becomes scarce and expensive.

Land Values

By 1963 the replacement process in Brookvale was almost completed; a few isolated pockets of farming remained, along Old Pittwater Road. Each of these has acquired a semi-derelict appearance. The owners have deferred selling in expectation of further increases in land values. If the yearly increase in the market value of land is greater than the total of Council rates and government land tax, it is clearly in the interests of the farmer not to sell his land. But most farmers have taken the first big offers made, considering land values to have reached their probable peak at the relevant times.

Unimproved Land Values in Brookvale doubled between 1957 and 1961. The market value per acre of land in Brookvale is at least equal to and is often higher than the value of industrial land in more accessible parts of the metropolitan area. Residential blocks of 66 by 165 feet in the Brookvale industrial zone have an Unimproved Capital Value (1961 valuation) of from $8600 to $11,000 while one-acre lots west of Pittwater Road are valued at some $12,000 [50]. But these valuations are well below market prices; for example, a manufacturer in March 1963 paid $30,000 for one acre, an investment company bought two acres from a Yugoslav market gardener for $30,000 in August 1962, and sold the property, still unimproved, to a manufacturing firm for $56,000 in August 1963.

The smallness of the Brookvale industrial area and its intensity of development make land values highly responsive to individual purchases

of large holdings. This circumstance is well illustrated by recent transactions involving the Warringah Mall regional shopping centre where the total holding is 40 acres (Fig. 18). In 1960 an English firm, in association with an Australian firm, began buying land for the development of a regional shopping centre in the Brookvale industrial area. Purchases were made before the group applied to Warringah Council for re-zoning for commercial use. Taking account of the size of the area concerned, and its location in the heart of the main industrial area, the Council rejected the application. The group subsequently appealed to the Minister for Local Government who reversed the Council's decision. Land values then rose very quickly, with strong repercussions on industrial development. For example, one half-acre lot adjoining Warringah Mall, but still zoned for industrial use, was offered for sale in 1963 at $30,000. Local real estate agents believe that industrial land values in Brookvale are inflated on account of the Warringah Mall but that these values will fall within a short period.

The highest values per unit area apply in the east of the Brookvale district. Subdivisional boundaries along Old Pittwater Road originally ran at right angles to the road up the steeply rising slope. Glasshouse and field cropping were alike confined to the gently sloping lower portions of the allotments, between the 50 foot and 80 foot contours. Industry, with land requirements not dissimilar to those of urban agriculture has maintained the same pattern of occupancy. Because only the lower one-third of the allotments is usable by industry and because even here levelling is necessary, the price of land per unit of useful area becomes very high. To the east of Pittwater Road, in contrast, the topography is very gentle and land was subdivided for residential development on a grid pattern, leading to a more intensive industrial development.

The price paid for a parcel of industrial land is not always a function of its size. Sometimes a vendor can sell a half-acre site almost as dear as the price of one acre, or even two acres, of similar land nearby. The marginal return from additions over the half-acre can be very small. Small operators often look for land irrespective of size, and search the land market for a parcel of land at the prices they can afford. They tend

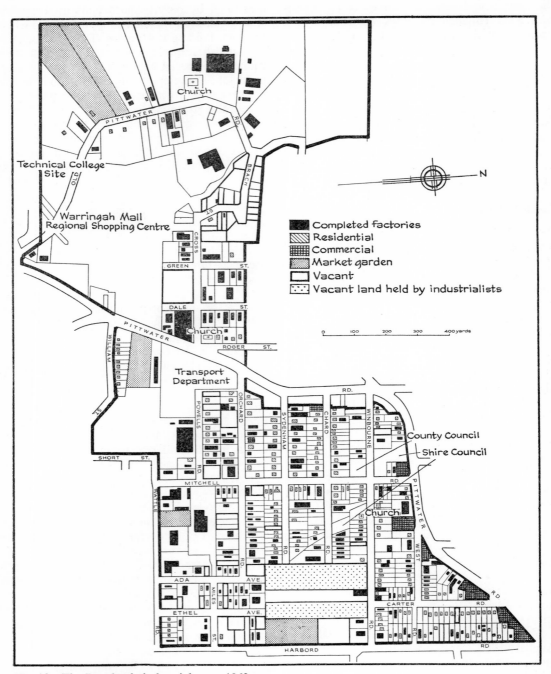

Fig. 18—The Brookvale industrial area, 1963

solely to consider price, whereas large manufacturers are concerned both with size and with price per unit area. Whereas variations in price within a particular industrial area usually allow the small manufacturer to find land, the large manufacturer is often forced to move elsewhere in order to obtain the space he requires. In Brookvale, the strongest demand up to 1961 was for small blocks of land, encouraging subdivision of former market gardens. Recently however demand for larger holdings has grown. The absence of such holdings in Brookvale will almost inevitably further the development of Dee Why West by large firms.

Among the industrial districts in Sydney, Brookvale offers the greatest proportion of its factories for rent. This has been an important factor contributing to the area's growth and it reflects in the main investment by former market gardeners. Some Italian ex-farmers have invested capital obtained from the sale of part of their holding. Rentals for factory space are surprisingly high, ranging among the firms interviewed from $1.50 to $1.00 per square foot, compared with $1.25 per square foot in Surry Hills abutting the C.B.D. Investment in speculative factory building, with these rent levels operating, is very profitable especially if

it involves no initial outlay on land. The greater supply of rented floor space, compared with Bankstown, reflects the uncertainty of manufacturers about the suitability of Brookvale as a location. Not only does renting allow a small manufacturer to minimize locational risk, but it also permits him to use all his capital in production, greatly increasing his freedom and mobility during the first few years of operation.

Brookvale's Industrial Structure

The remoteness of Brookvale has not been reflected in low land values or a low rate of consumption of industrial land. On the contrary, land values there are higher than those in other industrial areas at similar distances from the C.B.D. This fact suggests that industrialists here would be likely to concentrate on serving markets, protected by distance, of Warringah and nearby areas. To explore this possibility, the entire area was mapped in the field and interviews were sought with all industrialists in 1963. The ensuing discussion is based on data obtained from interviews with 47 firms.

Local market industries have small importance in Brookvale. While some firms such as bakeries, builders' suppliers and small work-

Table 12 *Brookvale—Industrial Composition*

Classification	Number of Firms	Number of Employees	Floor Space (sq. ft.)	Site Size (acres)
Durable				
Furniture	1	30	10,500	0.5
Foundry products	1	8	7,000	0.75
Fabricated metal—				
Equipment manufacturing	3	104	45,000	4
Machine shop services	7	54	31,000	3.25
Steel fabrication	5	85	159,000	9
Aluminium fabrication	3	52	37,500	2.25
Machinery manufacturing	1	12	10,000	0.5
Electrical machinery manufacturing—				
Electrical consumer goods	3	166	75,000	11.5
Electrical components	2	35	12,500	0.75
Non-Durable				
Industrial chemicals	2	60	30,000	20
Cosmetics	4	140	12,100	10.5
Paints, varnishes	3	27	25,000	4
Clothing	4	305	105,600	5
Photographic equipment	1	400	50,000	7.5
Plastics, fibreglass	6	33	17,300	3.75
Printing, etc.	1	20	20,000	2

Source: Personal interviews with factory managements.

shops distribute mainly within the bounds of Warringah, these are essentially ubiquitous rather than localized undertakings, typical of most suburban industrial areas. Indeed, there is little evidence that industry is organized along these lines in the city as a whole. Internal economies of scale are so great that bigger plants can afford to distribute goods over greater distances and can provide better services than can the small local firms. With a few notable exceptions industries in Brookvale serve outside markets. One noteworthy exception is the processing of fibreglass surfboards, where manufacturers exploit the market potential of nearby beaches. Twelve factories in Harbord-Brookvale-Dee Why make custom-built boards, sold directly from the factory. The area is now recognized throughout Australia as a surfboard centre.

Of the 47 firms interviewed, most were in the non-durable manufacturing group, producing consumer goods as distinct from producer goods. Especially prominent are the plastics, fibreglass, cosmetics and clothing industries (Table 12). Their prominence suggests that Brookvale offers specific locational advantages. None of these industries has expanded greatly in recent years at the national level, and the clothing industry has experienced occasions of decline. Their prominence in Brookvale produces an industrial structure contrasting with that of leading manufacturing suburbs such as Bankstown, which is characterized by a high proportion of national growth industries and especially by the fabricated metal industry. Only 295 out of a total of the 1531 employees of the firms interviewed in Brookvale came into the fabricated metal category. Brookvale lies far from the main steel fabricating complexes in Alexandria and Bankstown-Auburn, and steel fabricating requires bulky inputs and outputs; it was accordingly most unlikely that Brookvale would engage deeply in fabricating. Sub-contractors for fabricating are scarce, and engineering supply shops completely absent. Metal fabricators in Brookvale must obtain most sub-contracting and all supply from Alexandria or from elsewhere on the southern side of the C.B.D.

Most firms in Brookvale produce goods to which much value is added during processing. Distribution costs will therefore be low in

relation to total value. The fibreglass industry and its developed forms of surfboard and boat-building exemplify such firms. Indeed fibreglass manufacturing in Sydney began largely in association with small-boat building, which originally concentrated in the Warringah peninsula where beaches are extensive and tourism was vigorous. As the fibreglass goods market expanded, firms diversified their products. Very little capital or skill are required in fibreglass manufacture, but the products are expensive. Custom-built surfboards are sold for around $90 each; selling at the factory eliminates transport costs. If the products are bulky, as are some of the hardware items produced by British Fibre Glass, the firm charges a delivery fee.

The cosmetics industry well illustrates the relation of high value product with low delivery cost. Four firms, including two which are of international importance in this industry, have established factories in Brookvale taking count of the clean air and the reserve of women workers. Raw materials are non-bulky and, for the most part, imported on a monthly programme. Outputs are also non-bulky and very highly priced. The manufacture of photographic equipment is in a similar position to that of cosmetics. One firm, Australia's largest manufacturer of projectors and other photographic equipment, produces for an international market; its transport costs comprise but two per cent of total production costs. Undertakings of these kinds impart a distinct uniformity to industry in Brookvale.

There is also some uniformity in firm size, which is small by metropolitan standards. The average size of a factory in Brookvale is 14,500 square feet. Only seven of the 47 firms interviewed have floor spaces of more than 20,000 square feet or employ more than 50 workers. Heavy industries, in particular, have not been attracted to Brookvale. Overseas firms which have entered the area reflect the tendencies of local firms. Only seven such firms have entered Brookvale. All operate on a very small scale (Table 13). Brookvale's industrial structure is typified by small firms in lighter industries not oriented to local markets but integrated in a city-wide pattern of distribution. It is important to discover whether purely economic or non-economic variables explain these circumstances.

Table 13 *Overseas Based Firms in Brookvale*

Country of Origin	Date of Entry	Product	Site Size (acres)	Floor Space (sq. ft.)	Number Employed
U.K.	1959	Cosmetics	7	36,000	86
U.S.A.	1963	Heavy chemicals	13	10,000	20
U.K.	1958	Soaps	2	10,000	36
U.K. (S. Africa)	1958	Cosmetics	1½	5,600	17
U.K.	1961	Light shades	Rented factory	4,000	6
U.K.	1956	Chemical engineering equipment	11	130,000	30
U.K.	1958	Spray equipment	1	7,000	13

Source: Personal interviews with factory managements.

Reasons For Location Decisions

Personal Considerations

The chief reason given by the managements of almost all firms for the choice of their present sites was a personal liking for the Warringah area and the need to live close to their factory. There is no doubt that this has affected factory location. The concentration of managers' houses either in Warringah or along the north shore rail line which has ready road access across the Hornsby plateau is outstanding. Personal considerations have been as important for overseas as for local firms.

Among the small firms of local origin, purely personal motives have been even more effective in locational decision. Nearness of residence to factory can amount for the small manufacturer to an important revenue increasing factor permitting the manager to work long hours and in his weekends. Eight of the Brookvale factories interviewed originated in backyards within a few miles of their present sites (Fig. 19). To these and similar enterprises along the northern railway line the industrial zoning of land in Brookvale was welcome. None considered moving to other areas, provided that land could be obtained in Brookvale.

It would be dangerous to deduce from this discussion that a dominant causal relationship exists between the residence of management and factory location. Admittedly, the managements of many local firms are deeply involved in local activities and were aware of the area's economic disadvantages prior to establishing their factories, but personal motives have not attracted a wide range of industries to Brookvale, and economic selection has been ruthless. For instance at least three very large firms

have been forced in the past decade to sell their Brookvale factories, one clothing company sold to another firm in the same industry, while a paint manufacturer and a brewery sold to manufacturers in other types of industry. The two latter firms experienced difficulties from the isolation of Brookvale from the C.B.D. and the metropolitan market.

Personal motives therefore have been important within an economic framework. It is possible to envisage the entry of firms ranging widely in size and product because their managements wanted to live there. Within a short time however the economic system has selected the firms which could successfully operate from the location. In order to overcome economic difficulties in a Brookvale location, considerable entrepreneurial skill has been required in entering new markets, diversifying production and in overcoming distance costs.

External Linkages

The virtual absence of heavy metal processing industries in Brookvale is especially significant. Firms in these industries are localized on the southern side of the harbour where all steel suppliers except one are located. A location in Brookvale would place a producer of bulky and heavy steel products at a comparative disadvantage on account of transport costs. The steel industry needs access to rail sidings both for inward and outward traffic. Brookvale is separated from the nearest rail line by seven miles of congested roads with some steep grades. The area can offer only some of those external economies or inter-firm linkage which are offered by the well-established industrial districts of Alexandria-Waterloo and Bankstown. Although seven small machine shops

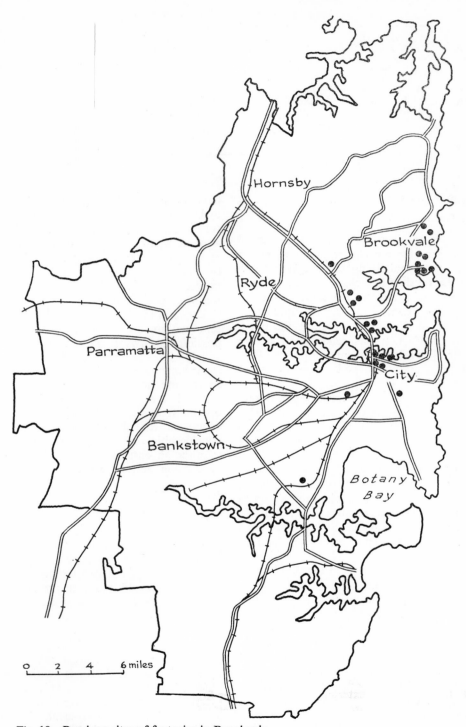

Fig. 19—Previous sites of factories in Brookvale

offer sub-contract services, their range is severely restricted by the unwillingness of small-scale manufacturers to invest in expensive equipment that would not be in constant use. The sub-contractor in Brookvale has reacted to small demand for his services by placing much importance on proprietary lines. These are considered essential for secure profits in the long term.

Predominance of light industries does not however mean that Brookvale firms are oriented to the Warringah consumer market (Table 14). Only two of the 47 managements interviewed estimated that more than 30 per cent of their total market was in Warringah. Eight firms distribute quite costly products to an interstate market, but the interstate sales total no more than 40 per cent of their total sales. Brookvale manufacturers as a group serve the metropolitan market, and in this respect, have fewer locational ties to consider than have manufacturers serving a number of market areas.

Table 14 *Market Areas Other Than Sydney Served by Brookvale Factories*

Product of Firm	Floor Space (sq. ft.)	Number Employed
Firms With More Than 30% Output Distributed in Warringah		
Welding services	5,000	11
Paints	5,000	6
Firms With More Than 40% Output Distributed Interstate		
Cosmetics	36,000	86
Soaps	10,000	30
Photographic equipment	100,000	600
Light fittings	4,000	6
Clothing	5,600	35
Garage doors	26,000	28
Spray equipment	7,000	13
Radios, etc.	50,000	120
Firms Distributing to an Overseas Market		
Photographic equipment	100,000	600
Radios, etc.	50,000	120
Cosmetics	5,600	86

Source: Personal interviews with factory managements.

Figs. 20 and 21 show the distribution of supply sources and distribution points for Brookvale factories. Linkages with the C.B.D. and central manufacturing areas are outstanding. Three other areas are important for material inputs—the Parramatta Road-Auburn-Bankstown complex, a small clustering of industry at St. Leonards and Crows Nest on the north shore, and the I.C.I. oil refining complex on the shores of Botany Bay. The Botany area is particularly prominent in supplying materials used in the plastics, lacquer, and fibreglass industries. A chemical plant at Balmain is another node from which five Brookvale users of fibreglass regularly obtain materials. Sixteen factories import raw or semi-processed materials, a high figure which reflects the specialized nature of manufacturing production in the area. Two international cosmetic and soap firms import almost all their materials, and although these are of high value, they are non-bulky. Surfboard manufacturers import chemicals from U.S.A., claiming that locally-produced components do not produce good quality foam.

Almost 30 per cent of Brookvale's factories produce commodities that are distributed to other manufacturers. Because of the relative unimportance of manufacturing on the northern side of the harbour, the markets for producer goods are in Alexandria and in the manufacturing agglomerations to the south and west. Manufacturers in the clothing and cosmetics industries distribute through centrally located wholesalers. The end-result is a cluster of distribution points between the wholesale area of the C.B.D. and Botany. The remaining firms distribute consumer goods to most of the retailing centres throughout the city. The distance from Brookvale to the market centres served presents serious problems to manufacturers.

On the grounds of distance to suppliers and markets, Brookvale is a poor location. It is one of the least accessible areas in Sydney for the manufacture and distribution of consumer or producer goods. Clearly, high returns from production can alone serve to offset the costs of overcoming distance and the very high land rentals. Although the actual road distance from Brookvale to the city centre is no greater than that from Bankstown, there are disadvantages additional to distance. The Brookvale area is much less self-contained industrially than Bankstown, and probably less than many other industrial districts, especially in respect of steel manufacture. Firms in Brookvale wanting heat treatment have to send their goods to Leichhardt, the nearest plating works are at

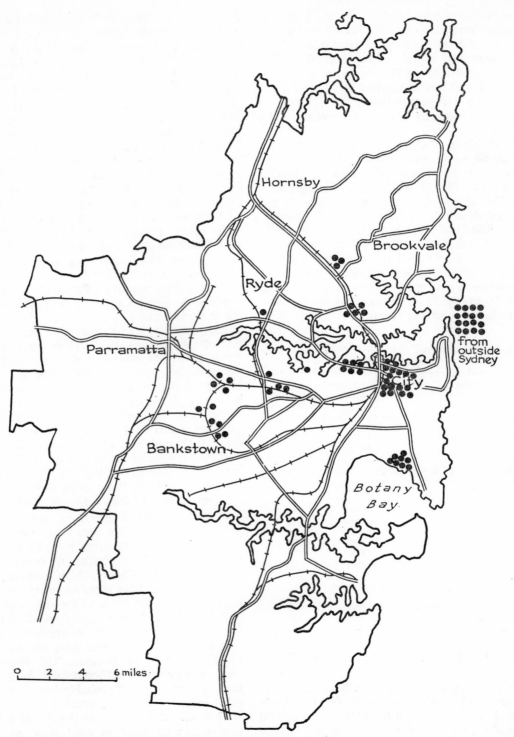

Fig. 20—Points from which Brookvale factories obtain supplies

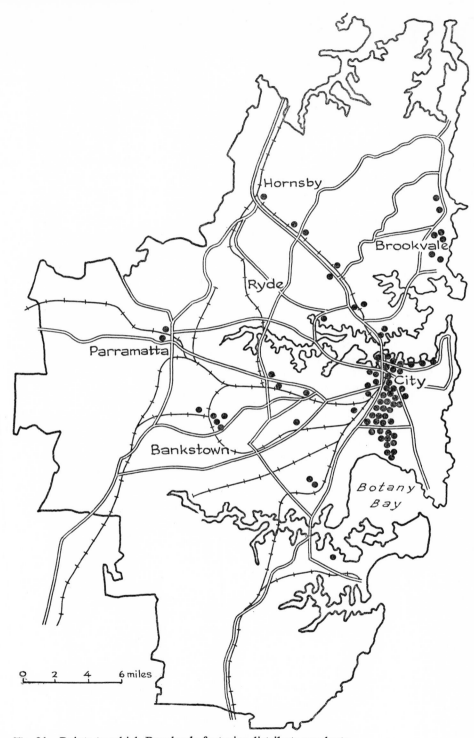

Fig. 21—Points to which Brookvale factories distribute products

Crows Nest and Camperdown, and most industrial printing is done in the C.B.D. The absence of such services generates much external movement from the area to other parts of the city.

As Warringah, developing primarily as a dormitory area for the C.B.D., has no rail system, heavy vehicular traffic runs on the arterial roads used by industry. The two main outlet roads both cross an arm of Sydney Harbour, by narrow bridges which further retard the flow of traffic. The transport problem is aggravated by the small volume of output of most Brookvale factories so that deliveries have to be made with half-loaded vehicles.

Distance problems have been met and overcome by manufacturers in a number of ways. Most firms commenced by maintaining their own delivery vehicles, but manufacturers are tending strongly to share deliveries and to use common carriers. A taxi truck is shared by an electrical component manufacturer with several manufacturers nearby. Two carriers operate a daily service from Palm Beach to the city, calling by at most manufacturers in Brookvale. Other firms have been forced to restrict deliveries in order to ensure a full load for the vehicle. Another firm, a glue manufacturer, has reduced from daily to weekly delivery and some firms now levy a delivery fee on bulky commodities.

The distance factor has had effects also on the supply side. Until 1955 Brookvale was outside the free delivery area of Sydney suppliers, but the growth of industry prompted most suppliers to include the area in their free runs. Although most materials can be obtained now at the metropolitan price, Brookvale manufacturers still suffer from infrequency and irregularity of delivery, and from a restricted range of suppliers. Whereas firms in Bankstown were approached for steel orders by almost all merchants each week, a single firm supplied more than 60 per cent of the steel purchased in Brookvale. The area is very costly for a steel merchant to serve. Only when a single supplier has a large share of the market does delivery to Brookvale become economic. Dependence on one supplier places Brookvale firms in the position that steel fabricators always try to avoid. In the paint industry, deliveries of cans to Warringah from suppliers are made fort-

nightly, instead of daily as to Bankstown. In furniture manufacturing too, the main suppliers of cabinet timbers are located at Annandale, Leichhardt and Auburn, delivering only twice per week to Brookvale in contrast to daily on the southern side of the harbour.

Internal Linkages

Not only does the relative isolation of Brookvale lead to difficulties in the supply of raw materials, it also presents problems for the supply of processing services. These problems are aggravated by the smallness of the Brookvale area, which unlike larger manufacturing areas supports a wide range of small service firms. The larger manufacturers in Brookvale have met this problem in one of two ways. Either they have made use of sub-contractors scattered throughout the metropolitan area or they have incorporated a large range of services, at great capital cost, within their own plants.

Despite their smallness, therefore, firms in Brookvale display little interdependence. The six sub-contract firms claim that, so small is the local demand for their services, they are forced to obtain work from other parts of the city and to produce proprietary lines of their own. Larger manufacturers claim that the range of services offered by sub-contract firms in Brookvale is so inadequate that they are forced to go outside the area. Compared with establishments in other areas, Brookvale machine shops do not have great variety of equipment. But the Brookvale sub-contractor probably concentrates rather on quality of workmanship and on meeting regular orders than on operating on a weekly basis. One of the forces preventing investment in specialized equipment is that firms installing plant cannot obtain sufficient orders to sustain regular operation.

The Labour Supply

The distance of Brookvale from the C.B.D. and its inaccessibility to parts of the city other than the C.B.D. have created a labour force seeking local employment. In a 1952 survey of rate payers, Warringah Shire Council discovered that 45 per cent worked in the City of Sydney, 15 per cent in other suburbs south of the harbour, 31 per cent in Manly-Warringah and 9 per cent in other suburbs north of the harbour [51]. At this time there were only 1900 job opportunities for manufacturing workers within the shire. A main aim of the Cumberland and local planning schemes in the zoning of Brookvale for industry was to provide more local employment. At the 1954 and 1961 censuses, Warringah had but a little of its total workforce in manufacturing while Kuringgai municipality with 22 per cent had a smaller fraction. There was, however, an important daily exodus of manufacturing workers. There are also large numbers of married women recorded in the census in the category of domestic duties, who become manufacturing workers as soon as local employment is offered. Especially is this so with Italian women living in and near Brookvale. Because of language difficulties and home ties these are unwilling to travel long distances to work. Preliminary results of a study by the State Planning Authority indicate that the journey to work by industrial employees in Warringah is considerably shorter than that in other municipalities.

The availability of female labour was an important locational consideration for many firms; three of the earliest firms to enter Brookvale were in the clothing industry. The clothing industry is especially sensitive to labour supply, but is also sensitive to closeness to subcontract firms and to downtown retail stores. Standardized production in the industry has released many clothing firms from sites near the C.B.D. Clothing factories in the suburbs can increase in size, incorporating activities formerly performed by sub-contract firms. The four clothing factories in Brookvale are relatively large, and produce non-fashion standardized goods (Table 15).

In selecting sites the managements aimed at proximity to a section of the living areas that had not been tapped by competitors. The first firm to enter located on the southern extremity of the industrial area next to the Harbord residential area, and a late entrant, on the western side of Pittwater Road away from other clothing firms. A major problem in the clothing industry is to maintain production and labour force at uniformly high levels. The market for clothing is notoriously unstable with quickly changing tastes and fashions and fluctuations are passed on to the manufacturer. As labour is the main cost component, the manufacturer usually meets fluctuations by temporarily dismissing some employees or by offering part-time work. Because he has trained the women dismissed, it is in his interests to re-employ them when market conditions improve. Married women, especially Italians, do not object to working under these conditions; they in their turn often choose to work for a short period and then to leave voluntarily. In these conditions accessibility to a relatively skilled labour supply is an important external economy to the clothing manufacturer.

The industry worked well while there were but two factories in the area. In fact the managements kept each other informed of their dismissals and tried to assist each other in obtaining labour. But the presence of four large manufacturers means competition for labour. Faced with great difficulties in getting labour back after it has been dismissed, the management of one firm has been forced to keep up production and to store the finished garments. It has tended to depart from fashion lines, which it is pointless to store.

A number of industries have made use of the supply of married women willing to work in factories. So-called 'outdoor work' is common in the clothing industry, where housewives work on some aspect of garment-making

Table 15 *Clothing Factories in Brookvale*

Date of Entry	Product	Site Size acres	Floor Space sq. ft.	Number Employed	Previous Site
1952	Underwear	2	50,000	110	New
1950	Women's dresses	1	20,000	90	North Sydney
1961	Children's wear	2	30,000	80	Manly
1954	Socks	2	5,600	35	New

Source: Personal interviews with factory managements.

at home. Payment is made on a contract basis, involving the firm in no overhead costs. Manufacturers agree that production is cheaper under these conditions although they probably mean that standards deteriorate. At least two firms in the electrical appliance industry have also used the home services of married women.

Conclusions

The Brookvale industrial area has developed out of the overall manufacturing growth in post-war Sydney and the impact of physical planning controls. The establishment and consolidation of manufacturing here has been at the expense of agricultural land use. On first impression, the remoteness of Brookvale from the C.B.D. and from other industrial areas suggests it is unsuitable for manufacturing. But land values are high and land has been rapidly acquired by industrialists. The market area

served by firms in the area is not restricted to Warringah; a number of firms sell to an international market. An important distinguishing characteristic, however, is the large number of firms which produce high-value products; that is to say, the high amount of value added in processing offsets some of the locational disadvantages of the area. These disadvantages arise from the infrequent and irregular deliveries of material inputs from other firms on the southern side of the harbour. Because of the comparative smallness of the area and of its firms there has been little generation of internal linkages and manufacturers are dependent on firms located outside Brookvale for various sub-contracting services. Some large firms have been forced to close down their plant in Brookvale and there is evidence therefore of a tight form of plant selection being imposed by the economic system on manufacturers.

MANUFACTURING IN ALEXANDRIA-WATERLOO

The suburbs of Alexandria and Waterloo, located four miles south of the C.B.D., contain the oldest, largest, and most intensively developed industrial district in Sydney (Fig. 11). This district records significant industrial emigration, contrasting with the Brookvale industrial district, which has undergone invasions by new factories, many relocating from the central area. A further point of contrast is that the establishment of industry in Alexandria-Waterloo preceded physical planning in Sydney. Whereas the implementation of planning schemes largely determined the location and extent of industrial areas in the outer suburbs, planning in central Sydney did little more than consolidate an existing pattern.

Alexandria and Waterloo have long been attractive to industry. The sparseness of housing on the poorly drained sandy soils, stretching from Redfern Hill to Botany Bay, left this area free for factory development from about 1850 onwards. For this reason it could be anticipated that these suburbs would contain highly diverse industries and firms, arising from the impact of locational forces changing as the city grew.

The geographical position of Alexandria in the metropolis changed from a peripheral one in the early 1800s to a highly central one in the early 1900s and to a cul-de-sac location as the city sprawled westwards in recent years. Manufacturing is being replaced by other land uses as the qualities offered by the area to economic activities have changed. Decline in the number of factories and employees is currently related to the replacement of industry by transport and warehousing—non-industrial land uses which are permitted in zoned industrial areas. Table 16 shows the changes in numbers of factories and employees, and in the value of wages and salaries paid in the City of Sydney, the local government area which includes Alexandria-Waterloo. The amount of change is roughly equal in the three measures. The inner industrial areas still contain the largest factories in the metropolitan area. Relocation of factories from this area represents response mainly to congestion, to high land values, and to shortage of space. Insofar as most of the relocating firms have moved from Alexandria-Waterloo, this area is at the other end of the

Table 16 *Manufacturing in the City of Sydney*

Year	Factories		Employees		Wages, Salaries		Employees per Factory	
	Number	% of Metro- politan Area	Number	% of Metro- politan Area	$A000	% of Metro- politan Area	City of Sydney	Metro- politan Area
1954	4,935	38	136,210	45	196,800	44	27	23
1961	4,441	29	122,145	34	248,776	34	27	23
1963	4,337	28	115,883	32	245,578	32	26	23

Source: Commonwealth Bureau of Census and Statistics, *Factories in Local Government Areas*, Sydney, 1954, 1961, 1963.

spectrum to Brookvale in a locational sense. The replacement process has not been confined to recent years, but has operated in several ways for a long time.

The Changing Locational Pattern

The availability of fresh water supplies was a critical factor in early settlement in Sydney. The Lachlan Swamps, two miles southeast of the original colony, provided an important source of domestic water. In 1813 they also provided a location for one of the earliest established factories, Hutchinson's and Lord's Mill, which made cloth and pottery. This year introduced a period when manufacturing was located with reference to supplies of water for power and processing. Up to 1823 the present Alexandria-Waterloo area was Crown land, but in that year two grants of 1400 acres and 185 acres, were made to William Hutchinson and John Campbell respectively [52]. Within six years both initial grants were acquired by members of the Cooper family. The combined estate was divided into the Waterloo and Lachlan Estates (Fig. 22). Mills for woolwashing and scouring continued to be established, especially in the northernmost (Waterloo) section of the estate, while some market gardening developed along the mudflats of Shea's Creek in Alexandria. The Lachlan and Waterloo Estates were not subdivided until 1853, by which time the expanding city, by-passing Waterloo and Alexandria, had spread into Mascot and Botany. This 'leap-frog' process left vacant in Alexandria and Waterloo a large tract of low-lying poorly drained land which subsequently underwent intensive development by industry.

After 1853 the Estates were subdivided for limited housing development, but the freehold remained with the Cooper family. Much property in the two suburbs is still held in the name of the estate of the late Sir William Cooper. The original property boundaries of the Lachlan and Waterloo Estates are clearly discernible on present-day land use maps of the city. They coincide with sharp divisions between residential and manufacturing activities. In the second half of the nineteenth century the area continued to offer industry a good water supply and relative isolation, promoting clusterings of noxious industries—wool scours, tanneries, tallow and soap works. Many of these industries, still using local groundwater, remain in the area today.

By the turn of the century the locational attributes of Alexandria and Waterloo had changed. Shea's Creek and its swamps had been drained by the construction in 1890 of a canal designed originally for shipping traffic from Botany Bay, but never used for this purpose. Gas mains and a town water supply were provided to attract manufacturers. The large expanse of level land and the sandy soils greatly favoured factory construction. The area was close to the C.B.D., the port facilities and to the major railway goods terminal at Alexandria. Its proximity to the focus of radial transport routes gave it access to a city-wide supply of labour. Whereas the earliest manufacturing had been attracted by the area's isolation, industry from 1900 onwards began to exploit the great advantage of centrality. Few cities elsewhere had so large an open tract of level land close to the C.B.D., at the very time when heavy industry was beginning to grow. World

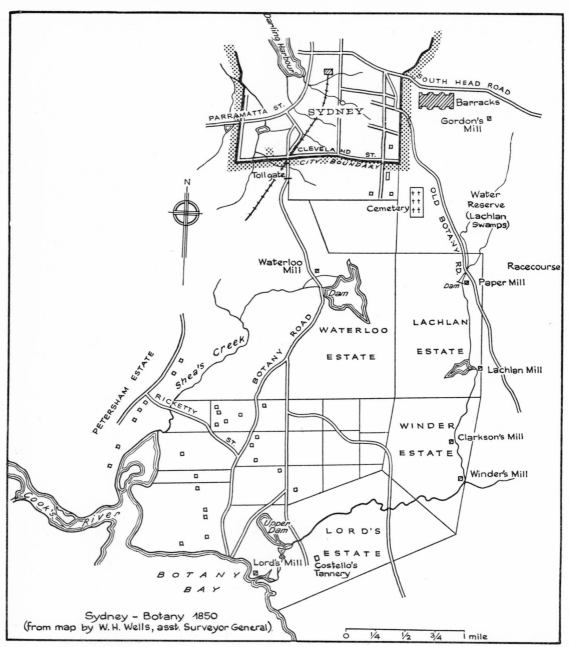

Fig. 22—Waterloo and Lachlan estates, 1850

War I provided a major stimulus to the development of heavy industry in Australia, many manufacturing plants then being established in Alexandria and Waterloo. At this time Alexandria recorded a high proportion of national growth industries. Emphasis continued in subsequent years to fall on heavy metal fabrication but an increasingly diversified industrial structure tended to evolve, bringing its attendant external economies. Until the early 1950s this remained the one industrial area in the city offering so great a range of locational qualities.

After World War II began the exodus of industrialists from Alexandria to the suburbs. In order to meet the increased demand for manufactured goods, and to take advantage of advances in production techniques, most manufacturers needed additional space. Many firms secured additional space by relocating in the industrial areas newly established by the Cumberland Planning Scheme, by which the Alexandria industrial area was little, if at all affected. But other firms remained, because of high disinvestment costs. Expansion became possible in Alexandria because of space freed by relocating firms.

Although the rate of out-movement by manufacturers has been constant during the post-war period, three important stages can be discerned in the processes of replacement and expansion. From 1945 to 1950 existing holdings were consolidated by large firms who acquired adjacent factories or terrace houses. In the ensuing period, 1951 to 1955, land values were low, at about 15/- per square foot.

Numbers of firms were able to afford scattered additional sites. Established firms buying additional space during this period were generally those in the heavy industries (metals and glass) which already had large investments in the area in plant and equipment. In association with the relocation of firms, purchases by established large firms promoted industrial uniformity. Re-adjustment has been furthered during the last decade by a noticeable influx of lighter industries, wholesalers and transport firms. As demand for space has continued, land values have risen greatly. New firms are replacing older firms in those heavier industries where multi-storey expansion is uneconomic and where open storage space is required.

The 'invasion' of new types of firms is suggested by a study of applications for development in Alexandria and Waterloo made between 1960 and 1963 (Table 17). The proportion of applications from heavy industry fell from 22 per cent in 1960 to 9 per cent in 1963. Of particular interest is the recent 'invasion' of wholesalers-with-stocks, separate storage firms, and national transport firms. All of these have close relations with the C.B.D. They are prepared to pay high land prices for accessibility. Under these circumstances they can easily outbid heavy manufacturers for space. Wholesaling and storage can operate on more than one storey and can thus achieve high returns per unit area of land. Some of the in-coming firms have themselves relocated from high value sites in the C.B.D. By selling premises there, they have capitalized on the gain in land values, and have been enabled to

Table 17 *Applications for Development in Alexandria Received by Sydney City Council 1960 to 1963*

	1960	1961	1962	1963	Totals
Number from heavy industry	7	—	8	10	25
Number from light industry	15	—	28	44	87
Number from wholesale and storage activities	5	5	11	16	37
Number from transport activities	5	2	9	9	25
Number from other activities (banks, hotels, etc.)	—	2	12	14	28
Number for parking, office facilities, etc.	—	—	12	14	26
Total Number of Applications	32	9	80	107	228

Source: Development Application Registers, Sydney City Council.

Note: Main heavy industries include heavy metal and steel fabrication, engineering, chemicals and equipment manufacture. Main light industries include food, printing, packaging, shoe, small goods and jewellery manufacture.

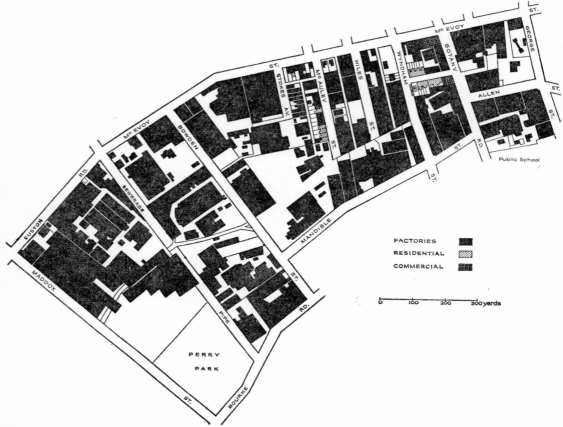

Fig. 23—The Alexandria case study area, 1963

buy larger areas in Alexandria. This process compares precisely with the movement of heavy industry from Alexandria to Bankstown.

Land Values

The rise in land values in the Alexandria and Waterloo industrial area can be explained largely in terms of the process of invasion and succession. Throughout the zoned industrial area, unimproved land values range from $60,000 to $90,000 per acre—remarkably high values for industrial land. The recorded rate of increase in value in Alexandria is moreover very great.

Unimproved Values have been increasing and now constitute the larger part of total Improved Values. Old buildings in this early-established industrial area are deteriorating rapidly and the value of an industrial site now lies rather in location than in buildings, a fact which can hold firms to existing sites. Although rates and taxes in Alexandria and Waterloo are very high, firms which have long been in the area acquired their land cheaply in the first place. To build new factories of comparable size would cost much more than the present differences between unimproved and improved values. Some managers feel that so long as buildings have not reached the limit of their physical lives they should continue in use, especially as Unimproved Values continue to rise. Unimproved Values doubled between 1955 and 1963, showing an increase of approximately $8000 per acre per year. Although Government land tax and Council rates are high, the capital appreciation on one acre of land is still almost three times as great as the outgoings. A firm should, but rarely does, consider the return it could get from investing this capital gain in some form of production. These are the highly complex problems of actuality, far more significant than the superficial questions of congestion with which entrepreneurs have to grapple.

Transfers of vacant land are rare. When they occur, they demonstrate the willingness and ability of certain types of activity to pay very high prices. Market prices tend to be highest when a purchaser already owns adjoining buildings. The number of transport firms in the area has increased rapidly. The services which these firms offer are more diversified than those of suburban carriers and include not only pick-up and delivery work for C.B.D. retailers, but also haulage of all kinds of materials to other capital cities. Closeness to the C.B.D. and to large-scale manufacturers is therefore important to these transport firms. A part of the service they offer usually includes the provision of space required by retailers for storage of overseas shipments.

Industrial Composition

The case study area selected within Alexandria (Fig. 23) has an industrial composition not dissimilar to that revealed for the entire area by detailed field survey. The fabricated metal industry has always been concentrated in Alexandria and Waterloo throughout its history. Its dominance in the study area is shown in Table 18. Twenty of the 50 firms interviewed were in metal fabrication. This industry, accounting for 30 per cent of the manufacturing workers, is characterized here, as at Brookvale, by small plants. The other major group in the area is the electrical machinery industry, which is dominated by one firm, the sole supplier of telephonic equipment to the Federal Government. Servicing industries, providing important external economies to other manufacturers are well represented. Printing and packaging among others, typify intensively-developed, mature industrial areas. Shoe, food and furniture manufacturing are typically central area activities, tied to C.B.D. retailing and to sites accessible to the metropolitan area. As population and retailing have expanded increasingly in the suburbs, pressures to decentralize exert themselves on manufacturing activities oriented to retail outlets.

Table 18 *Alexandria-Waterloo Industrial Composition*

Product	Number of Firms	Number of Employees	Floor Space (sq. ft.)
Durable			
Furniture	1	62	25,000
Joinery	1	50	20,900
Glass	1	583	384,000
Builders' supplies	1	330	76,000
Fabricated metal			
Steel equipment manufacturing	9	990	408,600
Machine shop services	5	109	37,401
Other steel fabrication	4	274	184,390
Non-ferrous fabrication	1	20	6,000
Machine manufacturing	1	30	8,336
Electrical machinery			
Electrical consumer goods	3	1,915	149,831
Industrial electrical equipment	1	12	3,000
Electrical services	2	48	23,667
Non-Durable			
Textiles	1	14	11,958
Cardboard containers	1	160	27,315
Wrapping services	1	14	3,000
Car servicing	1	35	25,523
Printing	2	114	54,720
Shoe manufacturing	1	50	2,850
Food manufacturing	2	120	130,635
Tallow manufacturing	1	16	2,800
Carrying, Storage	10	673	572,210

Source: Personal interviews with firm managements.

The transport and storage function, in which over 20 per cent of the firms are engaged is most important. Providing facilities for manufacturers in Alexandria, this function is complementary to manufacturing. Inasmuch as transport and storage firms serve a C.B.D. market, however, they compete with manufacturers for sites. As more manufacturing firms move to other parts of the city, transport functions become increasingly significant, both absolutely and relatively; competition between the two activities increases with time.

Uniformly high Unimproved Land Values, of about two dollars per square foot, result in heavy land taxes and rates. Industrialists in Alexandria are therefore under strong pressure to use their sites intensively. The site area/employee ratio and building investment on sites both tend to run high. The study area comprises 36 acres with an average density of 109 employees per acre, a figure much higher than corresponding values for industrial areas in the outer suburbs. The high density contrasts also with the ratio of 30 employees per acre thought suitable in the County Planning Scheme. Intensity of site usage, obvious throughout the area in multi-storeyed buildings and extensive site cover, may be measured by amount of investment per unit of site area. The ratio of Improved Capital Value to Unimproved Capital Value in the study area averages 2:1, reaching the very high figure of 17:1 in the case of one multi-storey firm. The absence of firms employing assembly-line techniques is probably the most distinctive feature of the industrial structure of the study area. The basis of economic selection has been intensity of site exploitation or revenue per unit area, rather than the product.

Locational Ties

The main locational attributes of Alexandria-Waterloo are closeness to transport terminals and the C.B.D., and the external economies that have developed with the passage of time. A case study area close to the transport and C.B.D. nodes was chosen, on the assumption that economic forces have been most selective here. The area, in Fig. 23, is approximately three miles south of the C.B.D. and the major wharf areas, two blocks south of the Alexandria goods station, two miles north of Sydney's airport and one mile from Prince's Highway.

An important contrast between the case study area on the one hand and Brookvale on the other made itself evident during interviews with manufacturers. The greater age of the Alexandria industrial area required more emphasis on discovering reasons for persistence there, than on original location decisions. The study revealed that the major reasons for the area's continuing importance were firstly the external economies available, the most important of which are accessibility to metropolitan-wide labour supply and low transport costs, and secondly the high costs of disinvestment.

External Economies [53]

Transport Costs. Among the attractions to industrialists of Alexandria are the low transport costs made possible by the area's central location. This benefit applies both to transport

of materials for processing and to movement of finished goods to markets. It is related to the proximity of main interstate rail and shipping terminals. A furniture manufacturer, for instance, through a location close to the timber wharves achieves savings in the delivery of imported timber. Two large-scale food processors chose locations in Alexandria because of the access to deliverers of primary products from rural areas in New South Wales and Victoria. Both firms distribute processed goods daily to wholesalers and retailers throughout the metropolitan area. As the pattern of retailing distribution has been dispersed away from the C.B.D. costs of distribution have increased. Both firms are considering relocating.

Alexandria-Waterloo provides a large market for producer goods and services, especially in the heavy metal industry. It also has access to the suburban producer market. Links among the two case study areas soon became apparent, especially in the metal industries. Alexandria functions as a supply and service area for outer suburban industries. By locating in a central position in the producer-market area small firms can ensure low costs of delivery.

Alexandria has lost some of the centrality it once offered to distributors of consumer goods. As the consumer market has become decentralized, it has also become dispersed. Rapid growth of new shopping centres in the suburbs has made it difficult for manufacturers to select centrally-located sites. Faced with this problem some manufacturers have decided to remain in Alexandria, where transport costs to the C.B.D. market are lowest and where location is in a general sense central to the main areas of suburban growth.

Accessibility to Labour. An important external economy is access to a skilled labour supply. Alexandria's position close to the C.B.D. places it within easy reach of employees who travel by public transport. Some firms requiring a skilled labour force were attracted to Alexandria on this account. But interviews suggest that Alexandria-Waterloo no longer offers to manufacturers the locational attribute of access to labour to the extent that it once did. Shortage of labour in the 1950s was a major stimulus to the relocation of certain firms. Shortages of labour have arisen from the increasing job opportunities and settlement of the workforce in the suburbs and from the inadequate system of public transport. The absence from Alexandria of off-street parking areas and the presence of highly congested narrow streets, do not accord with the growing tendency for workers to drive to work.

Proximity of other Manufacturers. Many manufacturing firms gain substantial economies from relations with other manufacturers nearby. They are especially important in the steel fabrication industry, where they alone enable some small manufacturers to stay in business. By reasons of proximity to a number of steel merchants, for example, a manufacturer can purchase raw materials at short notice, and can minimize stock holding. Not only does this mean that the manufacturer needs less space for storage but it increases his working capital. He has been freed from investment in raw material stock and from the need to provide additional space, from each of which there is no direct return.

Sub-Contracting Services. External economies can also be gained by a firm through locating in an industrial area where sub-contract services have developed. Examples of such services in the study area are job printing, wrapping services, patternmaking, toolmaking, engineering services and carrying and transport services. All these usually can be provided more cheaply by specialist firms. A manufacturer requiring these services cannot afford to provide them himself. Interdependence among firms which results from this form of specialization characterizes a highly-developed industrial complex.

Storage Services. Transport and storage firms are dominant in the industrial composition of the study area. Most of them developed in complement to manufacturers and retailers alike. They do not merely provide delivery services, but commonly store goods for the customer firms until the goods are required. They provide an important source of external economies to firms with insufficient capital or space to provide their own storage facilities. Although little manufacturing space is available for rental in Alexandria-Waterloo, abundant and cheap storage space is in fact available. Manufacturers tend to take advantage of this fact by extending their production into storage space. Some storage firms provide specialized facilities such as cold stores, which customer firms cannot afford to incorporate within their own plant.

The Costs of Disinvestment

The relocation of firms to the suburbs has usually involved changing factor combinations with increased capital invested in plant and equipment. Land taxes are lower and holdings are usually larger in the outer areas, but transport costs frequently increase on relocation. Movement of plants has been stimulated not only by the need for space, but also by changing technical conditions within an industry—by the need to install new equipment and to adopt new techniques of production. High unimproved land values have encouraged firms to capitalize on their inner city holdings and to invest in production at a new site. Many firms in Alexandria have experienced these pressures, but have been prevented from relocating by the tremendously high costs of disinvesting.

Disinvestment costs in Alexandria take several forms. These include the simple costs of acquiring new land and capital, interest, and transport costs of erecting a new factory and of transferring equipment. More significant however is the actual loss of much equipment in certain types of industry. Brick furnaces, for example, cannot be broken down and re-assembled. Because of the considerable age of factory buildings in the inner area, plants have been slow to sell and a wait of up to two years is common. A relocating firm is faced with a high rate of interest on the capital invested on its old site and also with the loss of the interest which could have been gained if this capital had been invested in production. Buildings in Alexandria have little value. The cost of replacing them there or elsewhere would be great. Some firms, therefore, argue that as long as the buildings are physically usable they should remain in use at their present sites.

REFERENCES

1. FISHER, A. G. B. (1935) *The Clash of Progress and Security.* Macmillan, London; CLARK, C. (1940) *The Conditions of Economic Progress.* Macmillan, London.

2. SCHULTZ, T. W. (1953) *The Economic Organisation of Agriculture.* McGraw-Hill, New York; PERLOF, H. S. *et al.* (1960) *Regions Resources and Economic Growth.* Hopkins, Baltimore.

3. LAMPARD, E. (1955) The History of Cities in the Economically Advanced Areas. *Econ. Dev.and Cul.Change, 3,* 81–136; FRIEDMANN, J. R. (1956) Locational Aspects of Economic Development. *Land Econ., 32,* 213–227.

4. GARRISON, W. L. *et al.,* (1959) *Studies of Highway Development and Geographic Change.* University of Washington Press, Seattle.

5. RUTHERFORD, J. (1963) Metropolitan Sydney and Economic Growth in Western Communities, in *Readings in Urban Growth.* Dept. of Geography, University of Sydney; and Geographical Society of N.S.W.

6. DEPARTMENT OF NATIONAL DEVELOPMENT, (1964) Population Changes in Capital Cities. *Atlas of Australian Resources.* Canberra.

7. ANDREWS, J. (1964) *Australia's Resources and their Utilisation.* Dept. of Adult Education, University of Sydney, Sydney.

8. ROBINSON, K. W. (1962) Processes and Patterns of Urbanisation in Australia and New Zealand. *N.Z.Geog., 18,* 32–49.

9. NORTH, D. C. (1955) Location Theory and Regional Economic Growth. *Journ.of Pol. Econ., 63,* 243–258.

10. CAMPBELL, K. O. Rural Population Movement in Relation to Economic Development. *Proceedings Tenth International Conference of Agri. Economists.*

11. ROSTOW, W. W. (1960) *The Process of Economic Growth.* Clarendon Press, Oxford.

12. ROSTOW, W. W. (1961) *The Stages of Economic Growth.* University Press, Cambridge.

13. FITZPATRICK, B. (1949) *The British Empire in Australia 1834–1939.* University Press, Melbourne.

14. BUTLIN, N. G. (1964) *Investment in Australian Economic Development.* University Press, Cambridge.

15. REITSMA, A. J. (1960) *Trade Protection in Australia.* University of Queensland Press, Brisbane.

16. RYAN, B. (1964) A Paradigm of Country Town Development in New South Wales. *Austr.Journ.of Social.Issues, 2,* 2–19.

17. FRIEDMANN, J. R. (1963) Regional Economic Policy for Developing Areas. *Reg.Sci.Assoc. Papers, 11,* 41–62.

18. LOGAN, M. I. (1963) The Pattern of Industrial Growth in Metropolitan Sydney; BEED, T. W. Retail Centralisation and Decentralisation in Sydney, in *Readings in Urban Growth.* Dept. of Geography, University of Sydney; and Geographical Society of N.S.W., Sydney.

19. SCOTT, P. (1959) The Australian C.B.D. *Econ.Geog., 35,* 290–314.

20. GARRISON, W. L. (1959) *Studies of Highway Development and Geographic Change,* ch. 3. University of Washington Press, Seattle.

21. LOGAN, M. I. (1962) Population Changes in the Sydney Metropolitan Area. *Geography, 97,* 475–478; DEPT. OF NATIONAL DEVELOPMENT, (1964) Population Changes in Australian Cities. *Atlas of Australian Resources.* Canberra.

22. An exception is BEED, T. W. (1964) *The Growth of Suburban Retailing in Sydney.* Unpub. Ph.D. thesis, University of Sydney.

23. The most rigorous study relating to state boundaries in Australia is SMITH, R. H. T. (1962) *Commodity Movements in Southern New South Wales.* Aust. National University, Canberra. See also WOOLMINGTON, E. R. (1965) Metropolitan Gravitation in Northern New South Wales. *Austr.Geogr., 9,* 359–376.

24. BERRY, B. & PRED, A. (1961) *Central Place Studies.* Regional Science Research Institute, Philadelphia.

25. TOWN PLANNING COMMITTEE (1962) *Report on the Metropolitan Area of Adelaide.* Govt. of South Australia, Adelaide.

26. See, for example REEDER, L. G. (1952) Central Areas of Chicago. A Re-Examination of the Process of Decentralisation. *Land Econ., 28,* 369–373.

27. NATIONAL CASH REGISTER CO. (1965) *Shopping Centres–Australia* (multilithed). Sydney.

28. *Ibid.,* 4.

29. THE AUSTRALIAN, (1965) *The Great Spread to the Suburbs.*

30. ANON., (1963) The Merchandising Revolution. *Current Affairs Bull., 31.* University of Sydney, Sydney.

31. MCKEEVER, J. ROSS (1963) *Shopping Centres Re-Studied*. Urban Land Institute, Washington.

32. DUNN, E. S. (1954) *The Location of Agricultural Production*. University of Florida Press, Gainesville.

33. ISARD, W. (1956) *Location and Space Economy*. Wiley, Cambridge, Mass.

34. See Map, *Sydney–Botany 1850* drawn by Wells, W.H. Asst. Surveyor-General. Mitchell Library, Sydney.

35. CUMBERLAND COUNTY COUNCIL, *Planning Scheme Report, 90*. Cumberland County Council, Sydney.

36. *Ibid., 91–92*.

37. BORRIE, E. F. (1954) *Melbourne Metropolitan Planning Scheme 1954*. Melbourne and Metropolitan Board of Works, Melbourne.

38. TOWN PLANNING COMMITTEE, (1962) *Report on the Metropolitan Area of Adelaide*. Govt. of South Australia, Adelaide.

39. LOGAN, M. I. (1963) Industrial Location in the Sydney Region. *Austr.Plan.Instit.Journ.*, 2, 155–160.

40. *Melbourne Metropolitan Planning Scheme*, ch. 3.

41. *Report on the Metropolitan Area of Adelaide*, ch. 12.

42. LOGAN, M. I. (1964) Manufacturing Decentralisation in the Sydney Metropolitan Area. *Econ.Geog.*, 40, 151–162.

43. *Cumberland Planning Scheme Report*, ch. 10.

44. HALL, P. G. (1962) *The Industries of London Since 1861*. Hutchinson University Library, London.

45. MCGOVERN, P. D. (1961) Industrial Development in the Vancouver Area. *Econ.Geog.*, 37, 189–206.

46. For a discussion of these and other measures see ISARD, W. (1960) *Methods of Regional Analysis*. Wiley, Cambridge, Mass.

47. RUTHERFORD, J. (1963) Metropolitan Sydney and Economic Growth in Western Communities, in *Readings in Urban Growth*. Dept. of Geography, University of Sydney; and Geographical Society of N.S.W.

48. WARRINGAH SHIRE COUNCIL, *Planning Scheme 1956 Report Ordinance, 106*, (duplicated) 17.

49. *Cumberland Planning Scheme Report*. 101.

50. WARRINGAH SHIRE COUNCIL, (1964) *Valuation Records*.

51. WARRINGAH SHIRE COUNCIL, *Planning Scheme 1956 Report Ordinance, 106*, 34.

52. See WATERLOO MUNICIPAL COUNCIL, (1921) *Waterloo 1860–1920 Jubilee Free Industrial Exhibition*. Brooks, Sydney; WATERLOO MUNICIPAL COUNCIL (1944) *Alexandria—The Birmingham of Australia 1868–1943*. W. C. Penfold, Sydney.

53. For an excellent discussion of the role of external economies see CHINITZ, B. *Freight and the Metropolis, Part 2*. Harvard University Press, Cambridge, Mass.

Methods in Australian
Trade and Transportation Studies

R. G. GOLLEDGE

Introduction

Transportation is the process whereby people and things are moved through space. The geography of transportation includes more than merely an answer to the question, What moves? Equally important are questions relating to the why and how of movement. To find reasons for the movement of people and things between places, geographers have examined a complex of variables. In the search for order and regularity in movement, they have investigated factors that influence interaction, the structure of transport networks, theories of transport cost, rate-charging practices, transport competition, and theories of migration and trade. While many of the relevant concepts have been developed in other fields—especially in economics, physics and sociology—the geographer can use them to help solve his own problems, and in particular to explain the patterns, distributions, and movements of people and things in space.

Transportation can be viewed as *a process designed to pass through space, by means of a path, to integrate points of potential interaction.* Reduced to its basic elements, transportation consists of a ROUTE, or series of interconnected points and lines, and a PROCESS, or medium whereby people and things are moved through space. Paths can be interpreted in terms of the geometrical relations of their points and lines, and processes in terms of the characteristics of the major elements that comprise a modern transportation system.

Transportation Routes

In considering the paths and processes of transportation in connection with the movement of people and things, the geographer can be likened to the physicist who studies the movement of particles through space and time. For the physicist, particles exist individually or conjointly in space. Movements are identified by examining differences in the locations of given particles at given time periods. Paths are the geometric patterns traced by the particles as they move through space. Processes are forces, such as gravitation and natural or artificial currents, which induce movements.

Within the framework of human experience, movements are the spatial shifts of humans and commodities resulting from specialized production, variations in demand and supply, and unequal distributions of resources; paths are the available routes over which traffic may flow; and processes are the means of transportation existing within a given society.

Between any two locations, be they those of particles, humans, or resources, an infinite number of paths exists. In the context of human transportation, the potential number of paths is reduced by considerations of accessibility and cost. Some paths are rigidly defined in space; others are more flexible, with particular origins and destinations given, but with less strictly defined routes. Either situation deals with a geometry of human relations. A particular example of the translation of transport routes into geometric terms is introduced below.

The Process of Transportation

Five major elements appear in a modern, comprehensive transportation system:

1. Shipping lanes, inland or coastal.
2. Railroads.
3. Roads.
4. Airlines.
5. Pipelines.

Table 1 *Per Cent Ton and Passenger-miles in Australia*

Form of Transport	1951-52		1954-55		1958-59	
	Freight	*Pass.*	*Freight*	*Pass.*	*Freight*	*Pass.*
Road	32.30	67.32	27.50	69.46	29.13	77.88
Rail (incl. trams)	27.40	29.38	23.32	27.03	21.38	19.07
Water	40.20	0.76	49.07	0.73	49.41	0.41
Air	0.10	2.54	0.11	2.78	0.08	2.64
Pipe	0.00	0.00	0.00	0.00	0.00	0.00

Source: Estimates compiled by the *Depts. of Shipping & Transport,* 1960.

Each of these elements is available to some extent in Australia, although pipelines and shipping on inland waterways do not play a major role (Table 1).

Routes and processes together provide the elements of a transportation system. By bridging the gaps between spatially separated producers and consumers, transportation permits interaction and exchange.

The Bases of Interaction

Interaction does not occur indiscriminately. It is mainly an outcome of regional differences in production and consumption, and of the availability and cost of transportation. Demand and supply conditions represent the forces of potential attraction, and barriers of cost and distance are referred to as the FRICTIONS OF DISTANCE.

The attractions and frictions of movement represent what E. L. Ullman calls the BASES OF INTERACTION. These can be summarized as *complementarity, transferability,* and *intervening opportunity.* For example, if there is a demand for a product in one area, a supply of that product in another area, and a means of interaction is available between the two areas, then the areas are said to be complementary. Such a situation is a direct result of the territorial specialization of production common in present economic structures. A world in which every area was completely self-sufficient in all respects would have no need for movements of this type.

Assuming specific complementarity to exist, movements will take place only if the friction of distance is not excessive. This depends on the transferability of the product. If a product proves too costly, or too difficult to move, the potential consumer will attempt to substitute for that product either by producing it himself, by consuming an alternative good, or by seeking an alternative source of supply. Adopting the latter course of action means substituting a different area of production for the original source, or finding an intervening opportunity which can supply the goods at a price which the consumers are willing to bear.

This new producer is usually closer and presumably cheaper than the original, and is said to intervene between the original producer and the consumer. Thus, even if perfect complementarity exists between two areas for a particular product, interaction may not take place if there are alternative products, or alternative and less costly sources of supply.

To answer questions about the means of interaction, form of transportation, paths followed, potential supply and demand, and character, direction, and volume of movement, the transportation geographer must draw on a wide range of hypotheses, laws, and theories. Where laws and theories do not exist, he must seek and analyse empirical evidence in the hope of finding regularities or specific answers to these problems.

The Structure of Routes and the Australian Transportation Network

An understanding of the nature of a transportation network of an area leads towards an understanding of economic, social, and political linkages within that area. The density of the network, the magnitude of the connections between individual centres, and definition of the paths over which people, goods and ideas may flow, give striking insights into the way a region or country functions.

For the most part, analysts have concentrated on the individual routes rather than on whole systems. Typical studies examine the arguments for selecting one path rather than

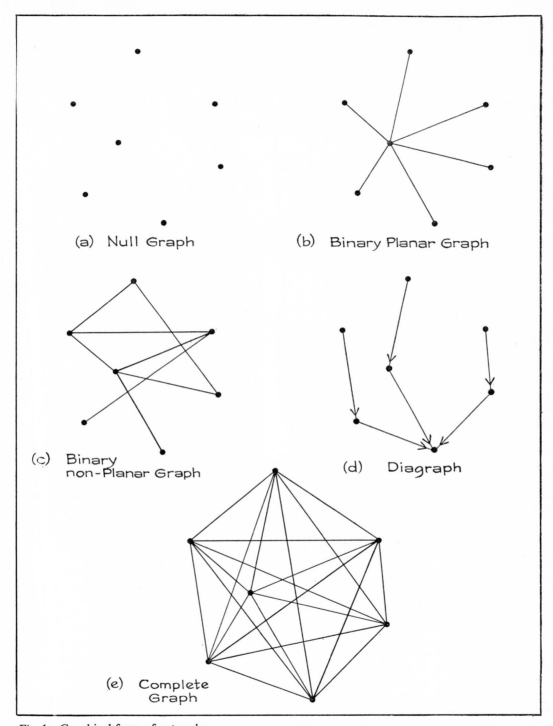

(a) Null Graph   (b) Binary Planar Graph

(c) Binary
     non-Planar Graph   (d) Diagraph

(e) Complete
     Graph

Fig. 1—Graphical form of networks

another for individual modes of transportation. This approach examines measures of the distance covered by the route, the gradients overcome, costs involved in construction, and isolation of the individual and group pressures which influence the selection of routes.

An alternative approach is to concentrate on the network—to attempt to find expressions of the length, connectivity, and circuity of networks in such a way that valid comparisons can be made at any level. This means the translation of network features into their graphical and geometrical characteristics.

Consider for instance a rail network. Basically this consists of a series of points which mark origins, intersections, and terminals, and of lines connecting these points, each line representing an existing railroad route. This

collection of points and lines essentially is a graph, susceptible to analysis by the mathematics of graph theory.

By definition, a graph consists of a number of points or vertices and a number of line segments or edges. It can take a number of forms, including those shown in Fig. 1. The applicability of this sample of graphs to transport networks is at once obvious. A binary graph emphasizes the focussing of the system on one centre, permitting inferences about the interrelationships of phenomena at the vertices. The diagraph illustrates how traffic fed into a system is drained toward a focus. The complete graph, exemplifying a comprehensive network, is quite distinct from the individual accumulation of routes in the other graphs. The following discussion will examine some statistics derivable

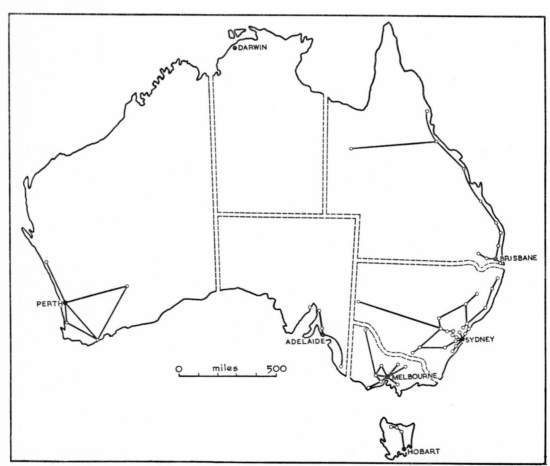

Fig. 2—Graphical interpretation of State rail networks linking cities over 10,000 people

from graphs, and will show how various measures can be used to describe and compare the structures of existing transportation systems in Australia.

The State Networks

As a preliminary, take a grossly simplified graph of the rail network of each State, excluding linkages between towns whose populations in 1961 were less than 10,000 persons, and including only direct links. Directions of connection become generalized, and separated from physical routeways. Generalization is not however a limitation, for values can be allocated to each edge that will account for actual distances between vertices.

The graphs in Fig. 2 are simple binary planar graphs which highlight the principal characteristics of each network. Queensland, Tasmania, and South Australia all show simple straight-line graphs with few multiple connections. Western Australia, New South Wales and Victoria on the other hand show more complex networks with several centres prominent. Each of these examples illustrates various stages of the formation of a graph tree, a connected graph with no circuits. This condition implies that there is a unique arc connecting any pair of vertices. The simplest tree has a single edge, as in the Tasmanian network. A more complicated tree is found in the northern New South Wales network.

An alternative way of examining the networks as defined would be to allocate magnitudes to each edge. Either the edges themselves can be scaled proportionately in length to the distances they cover (Fig. 3a) or the graphs can be generalized and distances be accounted for by allocating a magnitude value to each edge (Fig. 3b).

The next step is to reduce the graphs into ratios and arithmetic expressions so that comparisons can be made between State systems. Design can permit individual elements of each system to be examined, e.g. definition of focal points, degree of connectivity of the system, and extent of interstate connections.

Perhaps the simplest arithmetic process applicable to the graphs so far derived is the assessment of nodality and centrality of vertices. The number of edges connected to a

vertex gives a ranking. The highest-ranking vertex in each system is the focal point of that system (Table 2). This table is derived only for New South Wales. It represents a dichotomous classification with a dot representing no direct connection and one (1) representing a direct connection. The following characteristics appear:

1. Sydney is the principal focus of the State system with five direct route-connections to surrounding centres;

2. Cessnock, Broken Hill, Lismore, Albury, Shellharbour, Armidale, and Windsor, each with a score of 1, are the extremities of the total network as defined.

As the number of vertices increases, a more accurate description of the relative foci and extremities of the total system is obtained. The example is sufficient to show how the technique could be applied in more detail.

Other relevant measures of network graphs that can be used in comparing transportation systems are ratios described as ALPHA, BETA and ETA indices, and graphical characteristics such as the cyclomatic number of a graph and the diameter of a graph.

The simplest index relevant to this discussion is the BETA INDEX, a ratio between the number of edges and vertices of a network:

$$\text{Beta} = \frac{e}{v}$$

where e = number of edges
v = number of vertices.

This index expresses the connectivity of a graph. As the number of connections (edges) increases, then the value of the index increases, indicating the complexity of the network. In terms of this index, Western Australia has the greatest proportionate connectivity and South Australia the least (Table 3).

The ETA INDEX relates some measure of the entire network to the number of routes in the network.

$$\text{Eta} = \frac{M}{e}$$

where M = total network mileage
e = number of edges.

Table 2 *Connectivity of New South Wales Network*

	S	N	W	C	P	BH	BM	M	WW	G	T	O	L	C	A	B	G	L	D	SH	A	WWE	WI	TA
Sydney	|	1	1	·	1	·	·	·	·	·	·	·	·	·	·	·	·	·	·	·	·	1	1	·
Newcastle	1	|	·	·	·	·	·	1	·	·	·	·	·	·	·	·	·	·	·	·	·	1	·	1
Wollongong	1	·	|	·	·	·	·	·	·	·	·	·	·	1	·	·	·	·	·	1	·	·	·	·
Cessnock	·	·	·	|	·	·	·	1	·	·	·	·	·	·	·	·	·	·	·	·	·	·	·	·
Penrith	1	·	·	·	|	·	1	·	·	·	·	·	·	·	·	·	·	·	·	·	·	·	·	·
Broken Hill	·	·	·	·	·	|	·	·	·	·	·	·	·	·	·	1	·	·	·	·	·	·	·	·
Blue Mts.	·	·	·	·	1	·	|	·	·	·	·	1	·	·	·	·	·	1	·	·	·	·	·	·
Maitland	·	1	·	1	·	·	·	|	·	·	1	·	·	·	·	·	·	·	·	·	·	·	·	1
Wagga Wagga	·	·	·	·	·	·	·	·	|	1	·	1	·	·	1	·	·	·	·	·	·	·	·	·
Goulburn	·	·	·	·	·	·	·	·	1	|	·	·	·	1	·	·	·	·	·	·	·	·	·	·
Tamworth	·	·	·	·	·	·	·	1	·	·	|	·	·	·	·	·	·	·	·	·	1	·	·	1
Orange	·	·	·	·	·	·	1	·	1	·	·	|	·	·	·	1	·	1	1	·	·	·	·	·
Lismore	·	·	·	·	·	·	·	·	·	·	·	·	|	·	·	·	1	·	·	·	·	·	·	·
Campbelltown	·	·	1	·	·	·	·	·	·	1	·	·	·	|	·	·	·	·	·	1	·	·	·	·
Albury	·	·	·	·	·	·	·	·	1	·	·	1	·	·	|	·	·	·	·	·	·	·	·	·
Bathurst	·	·	·	·	·	1	·	·	·	·	·	1	·	·	·	|	·	1	·	·	·	·	·	·
Grafton	·	·	·	·	·	·	·	·	·	·	·	1	1	·	·	·	|	·	·	·	1	·	·	·
Lithgow	·	·	·	·	·	·	1	·	·	·	·	1	·	·	·	1	·	|	·	·	·	·	·	·
Dubbo	·	·	·	·	·	·	·	·	·	·	·	1	·	·	·	·	·	·	|	·	·	·	·	·
Shellharbour	·	·	1	·	·	·	·	·	·	·	·	·	·	1	·	·	·	·	·	|	·	·	·	·
Armidale	·	·	·	·	·	·	·	·	·	·	1	·	·	·	·	·	1	·	·	·	|	·	·	·
Woy-Woy—Ettalong	1	1	·	·	·	·	·	·	·	·	·	·	·	·	·	·	·	·	·	·	·	|	·	·
Windsor	1	·	·	·	1	·	·	·	·	·	·	·	·	·	·	·	·	·	·	·	·	·	|	·
Taree	·	1	·	·	·	·	·	1	·	·	1	·	·	·	·	·	·	·	·	·	·	·	·	|
Total	5	2	2	1	2	1	2	4	3	2	3	4	1	2	1	2	2	2	1	1	1	2	1	2

Source: Derived from *Atlas of Australian Resources*—map on railways.

Note: 1 indicates a direct link. · indicates no direct link. A direct link is simply a link between two of the given centres, that does not pass through another centre before the link is completed.

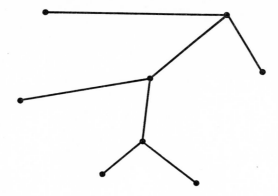

a.   edges proportional to distance : 1"= 50miles

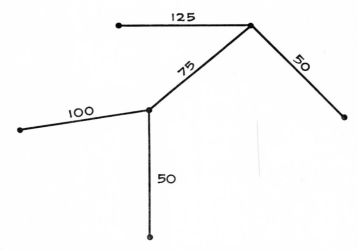

b.   magnitudes proportional to distance

Fig. 3—Alternative forms of network presentation: (a) proportionately
scaled binary graph (b) binary graph, with magnitudes proportionate to
distance

This gives the average edge length in miles, and provides additional information on the spacing of individual centres (Table 4).

This particular calculation relates number of edges defined, to the mileage of the entire State network. Perhaps a more realistic rela-tion would be the ratio between number of edges and total mileage of routes connecting the chosen centres. Any suitable measure can be chosen and substituted for the M-values in this example.

The third relevant network measure is the

CYCLOMATIC NUMBER, which expresses a relationship among edges, vertices, and non-connected subgraphs of a total network. It is defined as:

$$u = \text{CYCLOMATIC NUMBER} = (e-v)+p.$$

where e is the number of edges

v is the number of vertices, and

p is the number of non-connected subgraphs.

A non-connected subgraph is one not connected to the entire system. The rail line from Darwin to Birdum is the only non-connected subgraph in the total Australian transportation network. Each State has a minimum p — value of 1.

This index again expresses the degree to which a network is interconnected. Highly connected graphs have high cyclomatic numbers. It is especially useful when used as part of the fourth relevant index, the ALPHA INDEX:

$$\text{Alpha} = \frac{u}{\dfrac{v(v-1)}{2}-(v-1)} = \frac{(e-v)+p}{\dfrac{v(v-1)}{2}-(v-1)}$$

which assigns values between 0 and 1 to networks with varying degrees of connectivity. For complete graphs the Alpha index is unity. As the number of edges decreases, the value of this index falls. Disconnected graphs and graph trees have a zero index.

Multiplying the Alpha index by 100 gives the percentage of maximum connectivity represented by the present linkage. This index also can be modified by expanding the number of vertices used in each State network. It is doubtful, for instance, if the small number of vertices used in South Australia and Tasmania produce significant results in this index, although it nevertheless illustrates the tree-like nature of each network, and emphasizes the lack of interconnections among all vertices in each system (Table 5).

Other useful indices could be derived, relating volume of traffic to number of vertices or assessing diameter of a network and so on. Most such measures are described at length in elementary texts on graph theory.

The concepts of connectivity can be applied at all scales of operation and to all forms of transportation. The technique in question is eminently suitable for analysis of air routes and road routes. Linkages in the latter instance could be defined in terms of interstate, State, or local road connections.

Table 3 *Beta Index*

State	Edges (e)	Vertices (v)	$\frac{e}{v}$
N.S.W.	25	24	1.04
Vic.	10	9	1.11
W.A.	6	5	1.20
Qld.	11	12	0.91
S.A.	3	5	0.60
Tas.	3	4	0.75

Table 4 *Eta Index*

State	Total Route-Miles (M)	Edges (e)	Eta $\frac{M}{e}$
N.S.W.	6,303	25	252.0
Vic.	4,050	10	405.0
W.A.	4,577	6	762.8
Qld.	6,324	11	574.9
S.A.	3,836	3	1,278.7
Tas.	517	3	172.3

Table 5 *Alpha Value*

State	e	v	p	u	Alpha	Alpha × 100
N.S.W.	25	24	1	2	0.007	0.7%
Vic.	10	9	1	2	0.071	7.1%
Qld.	11	12	1	0	0.000	0.0%
W.A.	6	5	1	2	0.333	33.3%
S.A.	4	6	2	0	0.000	0.0%
Tas.	3	4	1	0	0.000	0.0%

The Boundary Problem

State control in Australia has played a vital part in shaping networks and modifying interstate movements, especially in rail transportation where transition from one State area to another has been emphasized by changes of rail gauge. Despite progress with gauge unification, the State rail systems are in general separate entities, independently developed and managed, with opportunity for continuous flow of people and commodities confined to one principal uniform-gauge link across borders.

Divergent State policies have encouraged the development of regional systems rather than a national railway. The Victorian system, for example, largely consists of feeder lines focussing on the ports of Melbourne and Geelong. Although the New South Wales system appears to have a higher degree of connectivity than others, three regional networks are recognizable, one tapping the North Coast, Northern Tablelands and Northwest Slopes and Plains, a central network stretching due west of Sydney as far as Broken Hill, and a southern network serving the South Coast, Southern Tablelands, and the Riverina. Individual lines in Queensland focus on nearby ports. Only Western Australia exhibits a reasonably compact and connected network, with no marked regional divisions except for the lone northern connection.

The effect of boundaries can, to some extent, be resolved by graphical methods. It would be possible to examine the total number of border towns, expressing the ratio of actual interstate connections to the potential number of connections, and finding a ratio, similar to the Beta index, which expresses which State is best connected to other States.

Structure of Freight Rates

As government instrumentalities, Australian railways have played a unique role in national development for the last century. Some lines served as instruments of government policy, providing transport services in sparsely populated areas, and providing concessional transportation to particular areas, in the general interests of national or sectional development. By virtue of the railway's early development under conditions of monopoly, freight rates and fare policies were broadly determined at the outset on the principle of what the traffic will bear.

But the development of alternate forms of transport has released the railway from much of its developmental role. Transport competition and annual deficits have encouraged closure of lightly-trafficked lines in remote regions, and have minimized the provision of under-cost services. Rating policies are being reorganized largely on the basis of cost-of-service, and rates have become less arbitrarily fixed.

Cost of movement is often the principal factor in deciding whether a movement will take place. Freight rates are implicitly determined by the interaction of forces of supply and demand. Only under exceptional circumstances will a national transporter carry goods below cost. In general, the demand for transportation is a derived demand, and the motive to move is generated usually by a desire to profit by increasing the price of goods. Such an increase is often only possible by changing the location of goods. A sender will not pay more than he considers the service worth, nor a shipper move a unit unless he gets a satisfactory return. The satisfaction derived depends on the nature of the transporter, i.e. whether he is a private individual motivated entirely by profit, or a corporation or government body measuring its rewards in terms of comprehensive action or developmental ideas.

The degree to which transport types can compete depends on their technical attributes and their cost structures. For all transport agencies, there are similar cost-components. As it is impossible to discuss the complete balance sheet of component-costs for different forms of transportation, only basic elements will be mentioned here.

Broadly speaking, costs of providing transportation can be divided into fixed (or terminal) costs, and variable (or line-haul) costs. Every carrier incurs some expense with the handling of freight at origins, destinations, and transhipment points. These terminal and way costs are the same for all shipments of a given size and type, irrespective of the length of haul. Line-haul or operating costs however vary with the length of haul. Since terminal costs are high relative to costs per mile of moving goods over the line, they make for relatively high rates on short hauls. As length of haul increases, the influence of terminal costs becomes progressively less important and net importance of line-haul costs increases. Unlike fixed costs, variable costs increase with every mile travelled, but total costs do not increase in proportion to distance. The incidence of fixed and variable costs depends on the form of transportation. For short hauls the cheapest form of

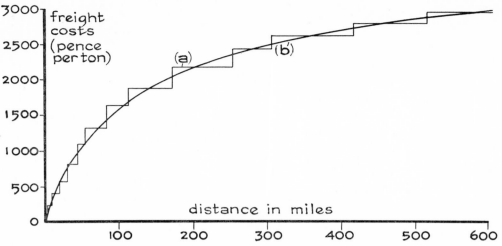

Fig. 4—Structure of freight rates

transportation has the lowest fixed costs per ton-mile. For long hauls, cheapest carriers are those with the lowest running costs.

A transportation process also contains cost relations that are distinguished by the spatial settings of the operations. The location of the system, directions and distances over which the process can move, and the quantity of output are all essential conditions governing movement behaviour.

Once a scale of operation has been decided, the cost of facilities appropriate to this scale is maintained for the life of the investment. This cost in the aggregate is constant, contrasting with expenses which vary with the volume of goods carried. If variable costs are proportional to business done, it follows from simple arithmetic that the average costs of a carrier decline as the volume of traffic grows.

Two main factors in determining freight rates are cost of service and value of service. These fix the two extremities of the range within which a rate is determined. The minimum charge equals the value of the service performed, the maximum charge is what the traffic will bear and still move. Within this range, freight rates are almost always closer to the lower than to the upper limit, on account of competition among carriers, anxiety that all available traffic should move, a desire to induce more traffic, and even a wish to give the user a fair deal.

If cost of service is the dominant factor, rates are determined by operating costs, traffic densities, and length of haul. In light-traffic areas, rates per mile are higher than in heavy-traffic areas. If what the traffic will bear is the basis, there is no logical procedure for allocating rates, the practice is simply to charge so as not to reduce business substantially. This leaves the way open for competitive concessions, subsidy of light by heavy traffic, or subsidy of low-value by high-value goods. It does not however follow that each commodity shipped must bear its full share of the costs of running the transport facility. Rates at less than out-of-pocket costs will occur only where it is desired to develop new areas for some purpose, or where it is desired to force competition out of business. The cost of service technique bulks large for a privately-owned service, where, if there is no profit, there is no operation.

Perhaps the most important factors in the geographical analysis of freight rates are the tapering effect over distance, the weight-bulk-loadability factor, and the grouping or classification procedures adopted by operators. Rates generally increase at a decreasing rate. Plotted continuously, they appear as a curve tapering to the right (Fig. 4). The principal reason for the initial steepness in the rate curve is the influence of constant terminal costs, whereas bulk-weight and distance are the prime factors in cost of movement, which influences the degree

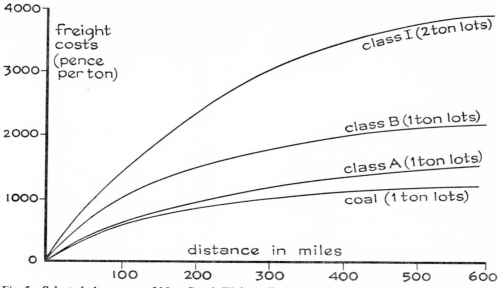

Fig. 5—Selected class rates of New South Wales railways

of tapering. Although many other factors, such as fragility, perishability, packing, liability for loss, and shape of processing, also affect rating, the factors cited are the most significant.

Classifications group articles into categories, simplifying the process of rate quotation. Each State in Australia has its own classification and rating system, and its own distance scales. These include comprehensive groupings into class rates; special rates (commodity rates) for low-value large-bulk goods; promotional rates, either subsidized by the Government to develop new areas or partly absorbed by transport companies to attract new trade; and concession rates which are price-discrimination for particular towns or particular companies. The last-named rates apply generally on a contract basis of set rates per truck regardless of goods carried. They may or may not cover the out-of-pocket costs of a trip.

Rating systems vary, depending on which criteria are used, or which State interests are at issue. Examples of cost-distance rates for specific commodities are shown in Fig. 5. Of especial interest are the different degrees of taper, the different mileage groupings, and the violent effects of crossing State borders. Principal additional costs include transhipment, storage, and checking (counting). In addition, interstate movements must contribute to the

terminal (constant) costs of both States, and incur the steeper part of the rate-curve costs in each State. A particularly dramatic illustration of this circumstance appears in Fig. 6. On the whole, however, Australian rates mix class and commodity rates, and also represent a compromise between cost of service and what the traffic will bear.

Users of transport are influenced not only by rates, but also by speed, convenience, reliability, costs of packaging and insuring goods, and by habitual preferences and idiosyncrasies. The charge is often critical, and can outweigh low speeds and inconvenience.

With transportation in Australia controlled by government authorities, rates appear to be based on value of service rather than on cost of service. If this were not so, there would be remarkably high rates on some developmental lines on which traffic has been at best ephemeral. Only by absorbing their operating costs into the general cost framework of the State systems can these lines cover their actual outlays.

Competition

Competition arises from variations in the cost of providing services, the nature of the service to be performed, suitability of an agency

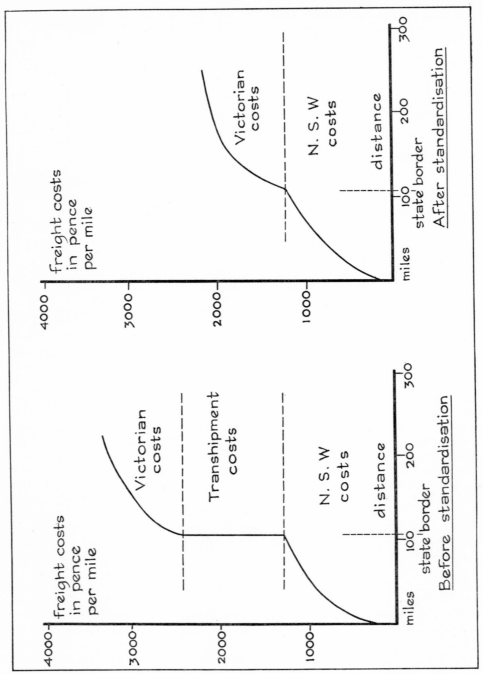

Fig. 6—Rates for trans-border movements

to perform the service, location of origin and destination, willingness and ability of the shipper to pay, knowledge of the opportunity of offering a service, and the relative efficiency of different carriers over various distances. Variations in the potentialities for movement by alternative forms of transportation give rise to a variety of competitive situations, the most common of which are competition between agencies along parallel routes, competition between alternative routes with common origins and destinations, market competition, competition of suppliers for a single market, and competition between substitute commodities.

Prior to the development of rail lines, long-distance carriage was carried out primarily by shipping, which in Australia meant coastal shipping, although paddle-wheel steamers on the Murray-Darling system also were important during parts of the nineteenth century. In the present century, road and air traffic complement rail and shipping.

The advent of a new form of transportation has a special impact on existing modes and on existing flows. New forms of transportation are initially selective in the types of traffic they carry, usurping from existing carriers the more highly-prized and more highly-priced goods. In Australia, interstate road transport has already secured a noticeable fraction of the valuable interstate trade in manufactures and in wool. Airlines concentrate on passenger service, but also carry mail and small-bulk high-value high-insurance goods. Further inroads by pipelines are being made into the potential of the railway as a bulk carrier. These developments illustrate the elasticity of demand for transport services.

Although transport competition is usually regarded as a process of substituting one type of carrier for another, complementarity is also possible. It is generally accepted, for instance, that a highly-developed rail structure will be accompanied by a highly-developed road structure. The various processes of transportation can thus be regarded both as complements and as substitutes. The competitive advantage of each form of transportation with respect to distance is illustrated in Fig. 7, which symbolizes the cost of operating different forms of transportation over increasing distances.

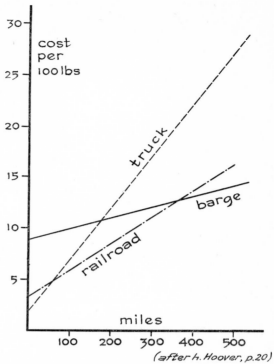

Fig. 7—Comparative advantages of selected transport processes

The principal advantage enjoyed by road transport is its terminal elasticity. Trucks can pick up and deliver at any desirable point that is accessible by road, removing the need for excessive handling and storage, decreasing time spent in shipment, and reducing the risk of breakage or pilfering. The terminal elasticity of road transport also reduces the need for any large investment in terminals. On account of their small payload capacity, road vehicles can operate economically in many areas where no rail service exists—where insufficient traffic is generated to warrant a spur line or scheduled trains.

The most obvious limitation of rail transport is its fixed tracks. Even at their densest, these cannot enmesh an area as finely as can road transport. To offset this disadvantage, railways build large, efficient, and centrally located terminals, complete with goods storage facilities. While a road transporter has confined load-space on his vehicle—which reduces his ability to move bulky goods or large quantities of goods quickly—railways are much less limited in this respect. Whereas road transport has the advantage of terminal elasticity, the railway has a comparable advantage of the lower costs associated with bulk loading and unloading, and—potentially at least—of subsidy under State ownership.

Though each type of transportation operates to some degree over the whole range of distances involved in movement, the inherent advantages of each type produce areas of maximum advantage where one form of transport will dominate. The factors of city dominance and of favourable terminals also enter here. Train schedules are often so devised that suburban stations are not disembarkation points except from local trains. Smaller stations can be envisaged as falling within the shadow of one larger terminal. The concept of traffic shadow can also be used in explaining the dominance of a particular airport or ocean harbour over nearby competitors, or in describing the area of dominance of a particular mode of transport. For example, the inherent advantage of the motor truck for short-distance haulage, and the Australian intrastate tax on trips of over 50 miles by motor trucks, effectively concentrate the power of this mode of transport to areas of 50 miles radius from its origins. Within the area of dominance of road transport, other forms of movement are relegated to minor positions, or lie in the shadow of road transport.

Flows In Southern New South Wales[1]

So far, this account has been concerned with manner of movement, with networks, costs, and competition among transport processes. Equally important, however, are the nature of things moved, and the reasons for movement. These matters will be discussed in the context of flows in southern New South Wales.

The inhabitants of this area have almost equal opportunity of allying themselves, in respect of trade, either with Sydney or with Melbourne. The area has a history of vigorous competition, which has produced two primary

---

[1]The ensuing discussion is based largely on R. H. T. Smith, *Commodity Movements in Southern New South Wales*: Canberra, Australian National University, 1962.

Table 6 *Commodity Components of the Intrastate Rail Goods Flow in Southern New South Wales 1959 to 1960*

Commodity Group	Tons	% of Total
Agricultural	54,851	38.50
Grain (a)	23,374	16.40
Wheat (b)	12,438	8.73
Wool	5,871	4.12
Fruit	4,190	2.94
Vegetables	3,927	2.76
Hay, etc.	3,574	2.51
Meat (b)	1,063	0.75
Butter	344	0.24
Milk, etc.	70	0.05
Products of Mines	13,228	9.28
Crude Ores	7,389	5.18
Coal, etc.	5,839	4.10
Timber	3,561	2.50
Manufactured Products	43,947	30.82
Superphosphate	14,658	10.28
Petroleum	13,887	9.74
Bulk loading (b)	8,031	5.63
Cement	5,736	4.02
Iron, etc.	833	0.58
Beer (c)	670	0.47
Sugar (c)	80	0.06
Less than carload lots	52	0.04
Identified	115,567	81.10
Unidentified	26,938	19.90
Total	142,525	100.00

(a) Includes all grain other than wheat, flour, stock-foods, etc.

(b) On New South Wales railways only.

(c) On Victorian border railways only.

Sources: Smith, Robert H. T. (1962) *Commodity Movements in Southern New South Wales*, Table 5, 82. Australian National University, Canberra.

A 29-day systematic random sample of New South Wales intrastate rail movements of goods on weekdays during 1959-60.

channels of movement and two actively competing forms of transport.

The principal products of southern New South Wales are agricultural and pastoral, the principal imports are manufactured or processed goods and fuels. A more precise statement of the components of movements in the area is presented in Table 6. Direction of these movements and their origins and destinations are just as important as volume. Volumes, directions, origins and destinations of movements define the pattern of regional specialization, show the direction of allegiance to a major market, and indicate local deficiencies which are reparable by exchange. As specific examples, fruits, wheat, manufactured iron and steel goods, and petroleum products will be examined.

Fruit flow is dominated by outward shipments from Griffith and Leeton. These shipments involve canned fruits and fresh citrus and stone fruits, supplemented by frozen and canned vegetables. Elsewhere, large quantities of potatoes move from the Crookwell district via Goulburn, while movements of apples and pears originate in the Batlow-Tumut areas in the south. Almost without exception, these goods move to the Sydney markets. Ultimate destinations are outside the southern region. Fruit and vegetables, while of local significance in the Murrumbidgee Irrigation Area, Crookwell, and Batlow districts, constitute little of total commodity movements in Southern New South Wales. It has been estimated that their combined totals constitute less than 5 per cent of total rail movements and less than 10 per cent of truck movements in the area.

Wheat movements can be divided into those for export and those for local consumption. Wheat production is concentrated in a belt approximately 150 miles wide extending northward from a base between Albury and Tocumwal. At the local level, wheat moves from farms to local silos or storage sheds, largely by road. Local needs are met by local processing. However, most of the total crop goes either to consuming points such as Sydney, or to ports. The direction of movement is again primarily toward Sydney. The wheat shipments lend themselves to bulk handling. Large volumes and bulk movements favour use of railways. Smith has estimated that wheat and other grains comprise 25 per cent of the total rail movements in the area. Virtually no wheat is carried by road on long trips, road transport being restricted to feeding bulk storage depots at sidings or at railheads.

The specialized nature of iron and steel manufacturing limits the possible locations at which processing of these materials can take place. Most of the iron and steel products needed in southern New South Wales are imported from Sydney, Newcastle, and Wollongong-Port Kembla. The directional flow of such goods contrasts with that of wheat, fruit, and vegetables.

Perhaps the most obvious feature of the movement of manufactured goods is that ultimate destinations are limited to the largest towns. This circumstance reveals a hierarchy of service in local areas. Typical products imported are structural steels, furniture, tools, automobile parts, household equipment, and farm machinery. Sellers both in New South Wales and in Victoria compete to provide these goods. Competition is expressed in terms of inflows by rail and road from eastern and southern directions.

Petroleum products on the other hand are extremely specialized. Their refining and manufacture are limited at present to areas with ready access to overseas supplies of crude oil. The intensely mechanized economy of southern New South Wales demands a large import of refined petroleum products. Motor fuel, diesel oils, and lubricating oils can all be moved in bulk. The pattern of distribution of the commodities is almost a mirror image of the pattern of wheat flows, with directions reversed. Petroleum products are railed to bulk depots in the area. Tax restrictions on the intrastate movement of road vehicles on journeys of more than 50 miles influence the scattering of bulk depots throughout the area, with each depot controlling a discrete area of 50-mile radius. The entire area is served by two-level delivery—rail delivery to bulk depots, and local road delivery to service stations and to individual consumers. Whereas wheat producers use road to feed rail bulk depots, petroleum product manufacturers use rail transport to supply local road distributors.

Like iron and steel and other manufactured products, refined petroleum products are imported into southern New South Wales both from Victoria and from eastern New South Wales. Almost all the imports from the latter area enter by rail, but those from Victoria enter by road also. Petroleum products constitute approximately 25 per cent of the total volume of goods entering the area from Victoria. Since interstate movements of these products are not limited by tax regulations to distances of less than 50 miles, Victorian distributors can range far, carrying from bulk depots just across the border. Then suppliers who range to Wagga Wagga, Young, and Hay, are also of major importance in towns south of the Murrumbidgee and dominate in border areas, about Corowa and Tocumwal.

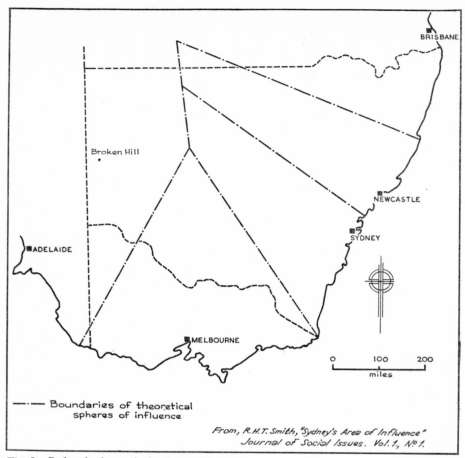

Fig. 8—Sydney's theoretical sphere of influence

Sydney's Sphere of Influence

Because of the present size of Sydney, its dominant historical role as the focus of activity in New South Wales, and the centralization of numerous State and private concerns in the city, many people would be prepared to claim that all New South Wales is tributary to Sydney. This implies that the boundaries of Sydney's sphere of influence coincide with the boundaries of the State.

Within New South Wales, Sydney's only major competitor for dominance over an extensive area is Newcastle. A simple diagrammatic representation of the areal extent of each city's sphere of influence can be derived, as in Fig. 8, when proximity is used as the major differentiating characteristic. The diagram clearly shows that large parts of New South Wales are nearer to other State capitals or to Newcastle than they are to Sydney. In terms of the distance criterion, much of northern New South Wales is nearer to Newcastle or to Brisbane than to Sydney, most of western New South Wales is nearer to Adelaide, and a large area of southern New South Wales is nearer to Melbourne. Only southeastern and central portions of the State are nearer to Sydney than to its competitors.

Direct distances are however of little practical significance, for most people and most goods move along strictly determined lines. The theoretical areas in Fig. 8 can be replaced by more restricted and more realistic distances, such as rail or road distances. As more often than not it is the time or monetary cost of traversing a distance rather than the physical mileage which is the significant factor in trip-making, the theoretical model can be refined by determining points where it costs less to go or send to Sydney than to other centres. The effect of using rail-freight cost as the deciding factor is considerably to expand the area tributary to Sydney, at the expense both of Melbourne in the south and of Newcastle in the north.

The reasons for this enlargement are two-fold. Boundary lines tied more specifically to rail routes reflect the extent to which an area is linked to a competing centre; and rate structures which differ between two States substantially increase the cost of transferring goods across a border. Even with standard gauge lines across both borders, separate State rate-structures produce results similar to the restriction imposed on movement by separate-gauge lines.

Table 7 *Sales of Greasy Wool from New South Wales 1958-59*

Selling Centre	Number of Bales
Brisbane	51,611
Sydney	1,149,824
Newcastle	359,624
Goulburn	55,051
Melbourne	226,067
Geelong	6,043
Albury	132,908
Adelaide	62,212
Total bales	2,023,340

The wool traffic provides an instructive example of the effect of transportation on spheres of influence. A desire to minimize transport costs accounts for Sydney's dominance in some areas of the State (Table 7). The most noteworthy deviations from dominance by Sydney occur along State borders in the Riverina, and in northern New South Wales where Sydney, Newcastle, and Brisbane compete. Perhaps the main reason for the vigorous competitive attraction of Newcastle is that all goods from northern New South Wales are channelled by rail or road through that town before making the extra 100 miles to Sydney. This circumstance gives Newcastle a decided cost advantage over Sydney for products moving to and from the north. The city is large enough to support such activities as wool sales,

it has a harbour suitable for overseas shipping, and provides a handy bulk storage depot for petroleum products. It can in consequence compete successfully with Sydney, limiting the northward extension of the major city's tributary area.

Both theoretical and empirical studies have isolated some of the possible ways that transportation factors affect the probable size and shape of areas tributary to any one city. However it can be argued that better measures of city dominance would be obtained by observing the movements of people. No treatment of transportation is complete therefore without some mention of the two main streams of human movements: migrations, and the journey-to-work.

Migration

The diversity of types of migration, as recorded by history, raises questions of regularity of movement, of the degree to which movements can be logically explained, and of the extent to which migrations generally include common elements.

Search for definite and regular patterns of movement has had mixed success. Investigations have suggested certain 'laws' of movement, and have isolated a number of principal factors by which movement is affected. Current migration theory, for instance, accepts the assumptions that individuals must be in communication, that the probability of migration is inversely proportional to the difficulty of reaching or communicating with a location, that migration is largely a result of socio-economic imbalance between areas, with migrants generally proceeding from less prosperous to (apparently) more prosperous areas, and that migrations occur by stages. Empirical evidence of migrations not only supports these basic assumptions, but produces the two important notions that human migration is not a unique event, and that migrations are non-random. Acceptance of these principles has encouraged the progress of migration theory from mere descriptive accounts of movement of people to and from political areas, to theoretical analysis of migration through the building of models. These models can be classified as deterministic models, where distributions are determined by economic or distance conditions (gravity and interactance models); as probabilistic models involving individual choice; or as diffusion models involving analysis of social conditions and movement through time.

A simple descriptive way of looking at migration, in terms of stimulus-response situations, is based on the idea that migrations are functions of a set of definable stimuli, and that responses vary with the intensity of occurrence of migration-stimulating conditions—an essentially causal relationship. This attempts to account for time-lags between stimulus and response, interpreting migration as a response to stimuli derived from frequent social and economic contacts. Migration here appears as a feedback process and is affected by changing local conditions. Other postulates are that migrations are not independent, and that probabilities can be defined to describe the chance that a movement started in one area will finish in another.

An alternative to this general descriptive interpretation of migration is the gravitational theory of human interaction, which proposes a method of measuring interaction between places. It assumes a closed system, drawing on the laws of physics which imply that the greater the number of molecules collected in a given space, the greater is the attractive force exerted there. The mathematical model representing the attraction exerted by a place on a person is usually expressed as:

$$M_{1j} = k(P_j)/(D_{1j})^n$$

where M_{1j} = migration to destination j from source i

P_j = population of destination j

D_{1j} = distance between source i and destination j (raised to some nth power)

k = a factor of proportionality.

This theory states that movement from area i to area j will vary directly with some function of the population of the destination, and inversely with some function of the distance between source and destination. The basic formula can be modified, e.g. by replacing population with job opportunities and by substituting intervening opportunities for distance as the friction coefficient.

If, as an example, it be assumed that Sydney is the only point of entry for German migrants settling in New South Wales, then the actual volume of such migrants living in any given area can be related to the theoretical values calculated from a gravitational formula. The following table shows the comparative rankings of 20 randomly selected local government areas according to both their actual and calculated (theoretical) values. The closeness of the two sets of rankings indicates the usefulness of the gravity model in explaining the dispersion of a migrant group in areas for which little actual information is available.

Table 8 *Comparison Between Actual and Theoretical Rankings of the Number of Migrants in Local Government Areas (a)*

Local Govt. Area.	Rank by Actual Number of German Migrants 1961	Rank by Theoretical Number of Migrants 1961
Bankstown	1	1
Newcastle	2	3
Sutherland	3	2
Orange	4	4
Tweed	5	7
Dubbo	6	6
Manning	7	5
Temora	8.5	12.5
Coonabarabran	8.5	9
Byron Bay	10.5	11
Uralla	10.5	14
Macleay	12.5	8
Tamarang	12.5	16
Inverell	14	10
Quirindi	15	15
Goodradigbee	16	12.5
Coolah	17	17
Ballina	18	19
Tintinbar	19	18
Bogan	20	20

(a) Not all the L.G.A.s receiving German migrants are included.

Source: Rankings in Col. 1 derived from information supplied by Australian Bureau of Immigration.

Journey to Work

This century has been a century of suburbanization, when the rapid growth of cities has increased the volume of intra-city movement to the point of severely overtaxing existing routeways. At the same time great strides have been made in transport technology and in traffic handling. In all large cities, and in many smaller ones, journey to work, however, is still the largest and most critical problem facing both individuals and planners.

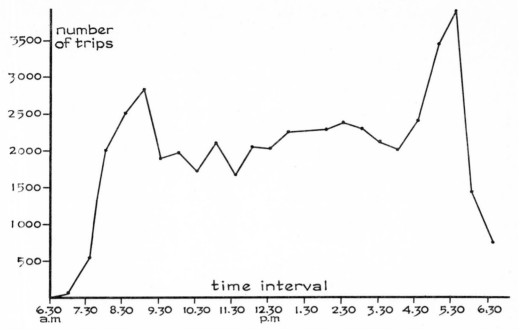

Fig. 9—Generalized time-pattern of daily trips in a city of about 200,000 people

Journey to work can be classified according to chronological criterion (duration of interbase movements), and chorological criteria (the spatial course of the trip, and its scope). Chronologically, this section deals only with daily movement. Within this limitation many forces operate in deciding the spatial aspects of the trips. For example, the apparent randomness of movement of individuals about a city reduces easily to a reasonably ordered pattern, when the aggregate of all moves is considered. The principal generators of traffic are employment, business, school, recreation, and trip home. The several movements, channelled into short time-periods, reflect the social values and economic conditions of a centre. Peaks of movement usually occur regularly in the mornings, at midday, and in the evenings, with a subsidiary peak about the end of the school period (Fig. 9). Most intra-city movements are channelled into routes that minimize the journey to work.

Various hypotheses have been explored, in attempts to explain patterns of daily movement, but no general theory has yet been produced. Variables regarded as significant generators of travel, and used in constructing indices express-

ing the dynamics of intra-city movement, include number of jobs available, distance of trip, size of Central Business District, and the like. One index of the kind in question is the COMMUTATION-INTENSITY RATIO, which is defined as the potential number of commuters generated in an area. This index is expressed by:

$$Cr = \frac{(No-Ni)}{Pe} \cdot 100$$

where Cr = commutation intensity rate
 No = number of out-commuters
 Ni = number of in-commuters
 Pe = total economically active persons in the area.

This index is of course purely descriptive, referring only to the proportion of endogenous or exogenous workers to the total workforce of an area. It classifies areas as having potential, or actual, inflows and outflows of commuters.

Despite the apparent irregularity of total movement, certain factors can be isolated. In most cities, the Central Business District (C.B.D.) is the principal single traffic generator, the proportion of total traffic to the

M

C.B.D. decreases as city size increases, and the attractiveness of the C.B.D. declines after a critical distance. Beyond this distance, diseconomies of travel and increased local job opportunities reduce the attraction of the centre.

Table 9 *Proportion of Daily Trips to Central Business Districts*

City	% Total Daily Trips to the C.B.D.	Population	
Christchurch (N.Z.)	39	217,300	(1959)
Washington, D.C.	25.2	1,109,860	(1948)
Melbourne	35.4	1,226,409	(1952)
Sydney	22.9	2,098,490	(1948)
Chicago	11.4	5,200,000	(1956)

Source: Golledge, R. G. (1963) Internal Traffic Patterns in Metropolitan Christchurch. (Unpubl. paper). Presented to Inst. Austr. Geog., Armidale, N.S.W.

Congestion and reduced travel-speed also limit the powers of attraction of the C.B.D. Alternative areas attract journeys in direct proportion to the job or business opportunities they offer. Regularities of journey to work are common to all of Australia. They are, of course, most noticeable in major cities.

International Trade

On an international scale, three major types of movement are commonly recognized. These are movements of people, of goods and services, and of money. Whereas international migrations can be largely explained within the framework of conventional migration theory, international trade and monetary exchanges, substantially different types of movements, have stimulated the development of theoretical frameworks quite distinct from those applicable to other types of movement.

With few exceptions, theories of international trade are fundamentally the same as those of domestic trade. International dealings are scarcely more complicated in principle than is local shopping. At the international level there are buyers and sellers, cash and charge accounts, local and external financing, and problems of delivery. One essential difference, however, is that activity in the international market is complicated by customs barriers, local laws, trade agreements, and political relations—all of which deliberately restrict the free flow of goods.

On international and domestic levels alike, goods are produced in the cheapest markets. But cheapness is a relative rather than an absolute concept, and must be interpreted as the cost of producing goods at home versus the cost of obtaining goods from abroad. This notion introduces the law of comparative advantage.

While a country may have many natural advantages with respect to production, resources, and capacity to move goods cheaply, it still tends primarily to develop industries wherein its superiority is greatest. A country exports those goods which are low in cost within its borders relative to the prices of the same goods abroad, and imports goods which would be high in price if they were domestically produced. This implies that a country will specialize in exporting goods for which it has the greatest comparative advantage, and will import goods for which its comparative disadvantage in production is greatest or its comparative advantage is least. In almost all cases, comparative advantage is measured in terms of price or cost. Costs of production can be substantially modified, however, by the numerous barriers inhibiting trade.

The imperfect coincidence between resources and markets, and the disequilibrium in the spatial distribution of resources, makes it axiomatic that some areas or countries are better off than others in some respect with regard to production potential. Such a situation results in specialization, both of production and of the factors of production—particularly land and labour. Australia, with a relative abundance of land suitable for agriculture and pasture, has specialized to a great extent in agricultural and pastoral activities, whereas the United Kingdom and Belgium, where land is much scarcer, have used their resources in a different way, particularly with respect to the training of labour for industrial activity.

So far, the algorithm for explaining trade incorporates two variables — comparative advantage, and the unequal distribution of resources. To round out the equation, it is necessary to examine the inverse relationship between trade and barriers to trade.

Obstacles to trade can be classified as those deliberately erected as part of national, state, or local policy; as those reflecting the inevitable difficulty of passing from one set of laws to another; and as those indicating the magnitude of environmental barriers. Barriers are deliberately erected in the form of customs or excise duties or of health regulations, or in accordance with national policies of development and growth. Such barriers may be primarily classified as absorbing barriers, where the commodity absorbs the additional expenses of entry and penetrates into the country to be sold at an increased price. Opposed to this type of barrier is the restrictive or prohibitive type, commonly taking the form of quotas and trade agreements, such as Australia's meat quota in the United Kingdom or the International Sugar Agreements. Prohibitive barriers, which are impenetrable, usually result from specific national policies. Australia's past restrictions on the export of mineral resources provides an example. Conditional prohibition occurs in health regulations and in controls on migration.

Environmental barriers are those most directly linked to the process of movement. Distance itself is of course a barrier. Two conditions must be met before movement will take place. People at one point must desire foreign-produced goods, and must be willing to pay the final delivered-to-customer costs of obtaining the goods—including production costs, transport costs, and any duties involved in crossing international borders.

The great distances separating Australia from most of its markets cause costs to loom large in the trade problem. Development of trade in meats and dairy produce has proved contingent on technological developments in refrigeration and in speed of movement. Specialization in shipping—particularly in oil tankers, ore and coal carriers, and perishable produce carriers—has stimulated the internal development of resources and has improved the trading ability of the Australian continent. Although of less importance in overseas trading, air transportation has also begun to carry high-value specialized cargo to and from Australia.

The sum effect of barriers is to constrain trade, so as to maximize developments and production programmes in individual countries,

without seriously disturbing the economic balance of other countries. While competition and discrimination exist in international trade, desires for advancement are conditioned somewhat by the need to maintain a reasonably stable international economy of which all trading nations form a part.

Volume, Direction, and Type of Australia's International Trade

At its present stage of development, Australia's total trade is not highly significant in the world trading pattern, although on a per capita basis Australia has consistently ranked high among the world's trading nations. It also ranks high with respect to trade in agricultural and pastoral products. Its comparative advantage is greatest in producing meat, wheat and wool, which have dominated production since the earliest days of settlement. Concentration on these, and the development of a profitable trade in them, have made possible the accumulation of capital and the release of the manpower resources necessary to diversify production. In the last three decades, this circumstance has produced a dramatic growth in manufacturing and service industries which are now developed sufficiently to command their own export markets.

The problem of accounting for variations in the volume of international trade appears somewhat more complicated than that of accounting for the volume of domestic traffic. Whereas domestic traffic lends itself to analysis by conventional gravity-type models which account for the search for equilibrium between forces of demand and supply, the variables influencing international movements are not so easily reduced to mass-distance relationships. It becomes exceedingly difficult to combine the effects of political, economic, and environmental forces into one simple equation. Perhaps the most complicating factors are the accurate definition of the strength of barriers, and the decision on whether population alone, or some characteristic of population, is the principal attracting element. In general, it seems reasonable to infer that a generalized algorithm for volume of international movements between countries has not yet been proposed.

Table 10 *Exports and Imports 1961-62—Countries of Origin or Consignment*

Country	Import Value ($A000)	% all Imports	Export Value ($A000)	% all Exports
United Kingdom	531,834	30.13	411,752	19.27
Canada	68,316	3.87	35,048	1.64
India	32,140	1.82	50,444	2.36
New Zealand	26,474	1.49	117,296	5.49
Arabian States	58,544	3.32	7,054	0.33
China (Mainland)	7,622	0.43	131,912	6.17
France	22,170	1.26	100,970	4.73
Germany	103,664	5.87	81,708	3.82
Indonesia	53,020	3.00	7,096	0.33
Japan	98,990	5.61	373,810	17.50
U.S.A.	348,160	19.72	217,982	10.20

Source: Commonwealth Bureau of Census and Statistics (1962-63) *Transport and Communication*, Canberra.

Table 11 *Exports and Imports 1960-61—Countries of Origin or Consignment*

Country	Import Value ($A000)	% all Imports	Export Value ($A000)	% all Exports
United Kingdom	681,062	31.38	400,130	21.54
New Zealand	33,930	1.56	123,780	6.66
Canada	91,328	4.21	34,054	1.83
India	45,414	2.09	27,772	1.50
Other Commonwealth Countries		8.11		10.86
Arabian States	71,034	3.27	7,524	0.41
France	33,444	1.54	102,144	5.50
Germany (W)	132,352	6.10	53,510	2.88
Japan	130,890	6.03	322,976	17.39
Indonesia	56,210	2.59	10,266	0.55
U.S.A.	434,082	20.00	144,942	7.80
Other Foreign Countries		13.23		22.16
Total	2,170,748		1,857,768	

Source: As for Table 10.

Direction of trade has been largely conditioned by historical and political ties. Australia, as a member of the British Empire and Commonwealth, has directed much of its trade toward the United Kingdom. In return for primary produce, the United Kingdom has provided industrial materials and manufactured products for developing the country. Economic ties between the two countries have however weakened as Australia has diversified its productive activities, altered its basic needs, and has aggressively sought new trading partners to foster its growth. The present trade pattern is still primarily oriented to Europe, but is supplemented by strong economic ties with the U.S.A. and Canada, and by an increasing frequency of interaction with Asian countries. A specific breakdown of the relative importance of the major nations trading with Australia can be seen in Tables 10 and 11.

The complementary nature of Australia's import and export trade is shown by the types of goods moving between the country and its trading partners (Tables 12 and 13). Wool, grains, and meats dominate exports, supporting the basic notion that Australia's small population and extensive land resources can best be employed in extensive use of land, efficient use of labour, and by extensive use of technological aids to production—in particular, mechanization of farming. The particular destinations of products vary, but most foodstuffs go to the U.K., Europe, and the U.S.A.—apart from a substantial movement of wheat to Communist China—while wool goes mainly to Japan, the U.K., the U.S.A., the U.S.S.R. and Europe. Australia imports machines and machinery, fuels, chemicals, and fertilizers. Its degree of dependence on foreign nations for such products is however declining substantially as its own industries mature. The geographical isolation of Australia has resulted in the overwhelming dominance of international shipping. The bulk of general cargo, and a good deal of processed products and even of wool, is carried by ships operating as passenger-cargo vessels, running to fairly regular schedules and restricting their calls to Sydney, Melbourne, and Fremantle. They attempt to minimize turn-round times, and are sometimes used as holiday cruise ships while waiting for cargoes to build up.

Table 12 *Principal Articles Exported 1960-62*

Article	Value 1960-61 ($A000)	Value 1961-62 ($A000)
Butter	39,302	47,074
Coal	15,364	27,222
Copper	20,006	16,508
Fruit (Fresh and Processed)	58,478	71,278
Gold	79,918	17,954
Grains and Cereals	300,314	383,148
Hides and Skins	54,388	64,294
Iron and Steel	55,022	86,304
Lead	31,742	36,872
Machines and Machinery	25,936	26,280
Meats	120,828	156,766
Ores and Concentrates	55,886	49,330
Petroleum and Shale Oils	43,386	44,726
Sugar (cane)	70,148	67,790
Wool (greasy)	668,884	745,062

Source: As for Table 10

Table 13 *Principal Articles (Commodities) Imported 1960-62*

	Value 1960-61 ($A000)	Value 1961-62 ($A000)
Aircraft and parts	27,612	24,348
Bags and sacks	26,766	20,760
Chemicals, drugs, fertilizers	113,634	116,312
Electric machinery and appliances	95,068	85,724
Iron and steel	116,870	40,806
Machines and machinery	334,100	275,676
Motor vehicles and parts	148,476	94,404
Cotton and linen piece goods	90,418	71,036
Other piece goods	25,398	37,582
Plastic materials	29,948	26,902
Rubber and rubber mfg.	47,290	35,544
Stationery and paper mfg.	25,030	38,764
Tea	25,648	25,828
Timber and logs	38,696	24,476
Tobacco	24,118	16,966
Oil and oil products	253,480	184,084

Source: As for Table 10.

Conclusions

The principal tenet of this chapter has been that transportation is a readily identifiable process which is subject to a range of economic, social, and political controls. Depending on the size of a country, its degree of development, and the attitudes of its people, different forms of the transportation process occur. Relatively advanced countries have at least five elements in their system of transportation: railways, roadways, shipping, air travel, and pipelines. Each element of transportation has its own route system. Some systems are complementary, others competitive. Regardless of this specific characteristic, networks are usually discrete entities which can be studied geographically and geometrically.

Geometrically speaking, each route or network is a combination of vertices and edges. Arithmetic characteristics of vertices and edges can be manipulated in numerous ways to form measures of networks—measures which form bases for comparative studies at local, national, or international levels.

The basic factors which decide movement from one location to another are economic. Specifically, these factors include the cost of providing a service, the added utility (value) that accrues from the movement, and the feasibility of favourable returns from movement. Movements fall into fairly regular patterns, directed to, or emanating from a principal nodal centre. Principles of transportation economics define market and supply areas for individual cities. The range of influence of any city is related directly to the attractive force it generates, and is related inversely to the frictions or barriers impeding the free flow of the force.

This latter concept applies to movements both of commodities and of people, and is being investigated with respect to the diffusion of ideas. Movement of people is in itself an extensive field of study, but regularities can be found, whether such movements are intracity, interstate, or international.

Although international movements are in many ways similar to domestic movements, complicating barriers and forces make this field a little more difficult to understand in terms solely of spatial variables or characteristics. Nevertheless, these barriers constitute additional elements in transportation, which must surely be included in any general treatment.

Perhaps the one feature that has not been stressed is the problem of *efficiency of movement*. Considering the complexity of modern transportation systems, the problem of choosing the most appropriate medium and path appears substantial. Minimum cost and least effort solutions can now be readily obtained using the techniques of linear programing or communication theory. More complex solutions require the use of network flow and queueing models. Such models are however, beyond the scope of this chapter.

The various factors sketched herein appear to be highly applicable to a study of transportation and trade in Australia. It is hoped that this discussion of them will encourage further exploration of this aspect of Australia's geography.

BIBLIOGRAPHY

1. ALEXANDER, J. W. (1963) *Economic Geography*. Prentice-Hall, New York.
2. ALEXANDER, J. W., BROWN, S. E. & DAHLBERG, R. E. (1958) Freight Rates: Selected Aspects of Uniform and Nodal Regions. *Econ.Geog., 34,* 1–18.
3. ALEXANDER, J. W. (1945) Freight Rates as a Geographic Factor in Illinois. *Econ.Geog., 20,* 25–30.
4. ANDERSON, T. R. (1955) Intermetropolitan Migration: A Comparison of the Hypotheses of Zipf and Stouffer. *Amer.Soc.Rev., 20,* 287–91.
5. AVONDO-BODINO, G. (1962) *Economic Applications of the Theory of Graphs*. Gordon & Breach, New York.
6. BERGE, C. (1962) *The Theory of Graphs and its Applications*. Translated by Alison Doig. Wiley, New York.
7. BRIGHT, M. L. & THOMAS, D. S. (1941) Interstate Migration and Intervening Opportunities. *Amer.Soc.Rev., 6,* 773–83.
8. BUNGE, W. (1962) Theoretical Geography. *Lund Studies in Geography, Ser. C., General and Mathematical Geography No. 1.*
9. CARROLL, J. R. & DOUGLAS, J. (1955) Spatial Interaction and the Urban-Metropolitan Regional Description. *Papers,Reg.Sci.Assoc., 1,* D1–D14.
10. CARROLL, J. R., DOUGLAS, J., BEVIS, J. R. & HOWARD, B. (1957) Predicting Local Travel in Urban Regions. *Papers,Reg.Sci.Assoc., 3,* 183–97.
11. CARRUTHERS, G. A. P. (1956) An Historical Review of the Gravity and Potential Concepts of Human Interaction. *Journ.Amer. Inst.Planners, 22,* 94–102.
12. CAVANOUGH, J. A. (1950) Formulation, Analysis and Testing of the Interactance Hypothesis. *Amer.Soc.Rev., 15,* 763–6.
13. CONVERSE, P. D. (1949) New Laws of Retail Gravitation. *The Journal of Marketing, 14,* 379–84.
14. DAGGETT, S. (1955) *Principles of Inland Transportation*. Harper & Bros., New York.
15. DODD, C. D. (1950) The Interactance Hypothesis. A Gravity Model Fitting Physical Masses and Human Groups. *Amer.Soc.Rev., 15,* 245–56.
16. FLEISHER, A. (1961) On Prediction and Urban Traffic. *Papers,Reg.Sci.Assoc., 7,* 43–50.
17. FULTON, M. & HOCK, L. C. (1959) Transportation Factors Affecting Locational Decisions. *Econ.Geog., 35,* 51–9.
18. GARRISON, W. L. (1960) Connectivity of the Interstate Highway System. *Papers,Reg.Sci. Assoc., 6,* 121–37.
19. GARRISON, W. L. (1960) Notes on the Simulation of Urban Growth and Development. *Canadian Assoc.Geog., Brit.Columbia Div., Occasional Papers, 1,* 1–11.
20. GARRISON, W. L., BERRY, B. J. L., MARBLE, D. F., NYSTUEN, J. D. & MORRILL, R. L. (1959) *Studies of Highway Development and Geographic Change*. University of Washington Press, Seattle, Washington.
21. GODLUND, S. (1951) Bus Services, Hinterlands, and the Location of Urban Settlements in Sweden. *Lund Studies in Human Geography, 3.*
22. GODLUND, S. (1956) Bus Services in Sweden. *Lund Stories in Human Geography, 17.*
23. GODLUND, S. (1956) The Function and Growth of Bus Traffic Within the Sphere of Urban Influence. *Lund Studies in Human Geography, 18.*
24. GOLLEDGE, R. G. (1961) Some Notes on the Effect of Road Competition on the Movement of Certain Commodities in Northern N.S.W. *Austr.Geog., 8,* 116–118.

25. GOLLEDGE, R. G. (1962) Comments on the Urban Pattern and Functional Role of Newcastle, Australia. *Tidjschrift Voor Econ. en Soc.Geographie, 53,* 72–8.

26. GOLLEDGE, R. G. (1962) Rail Gauge Standardisation in Australia. *N.Z.Geog., 18,* 236–8.

27. GOLLEDGE, R. G. (1963) A Geographical Interpretation of Newcastle's Rail Freight Traffic. *Econ.Geog., 39,* 60–73.

28. GOLLEDGE, R. G. (1963) Speculations on Commodity Flow and Market Areas in Northern N.S.W., in WARNER, R. F. (ed.) *New England Essays.* University of New England, Armidale.

29. GOLLEDGE, R. G., JOHNSTON, W. B., KING, L. J. & WILLIMAN, A. (1965) *Traffic in a New Zealand City.* Whitcombe & Tombs, Christchurch.

30. GOULD, P. R. & SMITH, R. H. T. (1960) Measuring the Relationship between Rail Shipments, Road Access, and Road Competition in Ghana and Australia. *Annals,Assoc.Amer. Geog., 50,* 322–3.

31. HAGERSTRAND, T. (1952) The Propagation of Innovation Waves. *Lund Studies in Human Geography, 4.*

32. HANNERBURG, D., HAGERSTRAND, T. & ODEVING, B. (1957) *Migration in Sweden: A Symposium.* Department of Geography, Lund Univ. C. W. K. Gleerup.

33. HOOVER, E. M. (1948) *The Location of Economic Activity.* McGraw-Hill, New York.

34. KANSKY, K. J. (1963) Structure of Transportation Networks. *Dept.Geog.Res.Paper, 48.* University of Chicago.

35. LOVGREN, E. (1957) Mutual Relations Between Migration Fields: A Circulation Analysis. *Lund Studies in Human Geography, 13,* 159–69.

36. LOCKLIN, P. D. (1954) *Economics of Transportation.* Richard D. Irwin, Homewood, 111.

37. LUKERMANN, F. & PORTER, P. W. (1960) Gravity and Potential Models in Economic Geography. *Annals,Assoc.Amer.Geog., 50,* 493–504.

38. MORRILL, R. L. (1963) The Development of the Spatial Distribution of Towns in Sweden: An Historical Approach. *Annals,Assoc. Amer.Geog., 53,* 1–14.

39. NYSTUEN, J. D. & DACEY, M. F. (1961) A Graph Theory Interpretation of Nodal Regions. *Papers,Reg.Sci.Assoc., 7,* 29–42.

40. OLSSON, G. (1965) Distance and Human Interaction. *Bibliography Series, Reg.Sci. Res.Inst.,Philadelphia, 2.*

41. ORE, O. (1963) *Graphs and Their Uses.* Random House, New York.

42. REILLY, W. J. (1931) *The Law of Retail Gravitation.* The Knickerbocker Press, New York.

43. SCHNEIDER, M. (1959) Gravity Models and Trip Distribution Theory. *Papers,Reg.Sci. Assoc., 5,* 51–6.

44. SMITH, R. H. T. (1962) *Commodity Flows in Southern New South Wales.* Australian National University, Canberra.

45. SMITH, R. H. T. (1961) Sydney's Area of Influence. *Austr.Journ.Soc.Issues, 1,* 2–11.

46. SMITH, R. H. T. (1961) Method in Commodity Flow Studies. *Austr.Geog., 8,* 73–7.

47. SMITH, R. H. T. (1963) Railway Commodity Movements Between N.S.W. and Victoria. *Austr.Geog., 9,* 88–96.

48. SMITH, R. H. T. (1964) Toward a Measure of Complementarity. *Econ.Geog., 40,* 1–8.

49. SMITH, R. H. T. (1963) Transport Competition in Australian Border Areas. *Econ. Geog., 39,* 1–13.

50. STEWART, C. T. (1960) Migration as a Function of Population and Distance. *Amer. Soc.Rev., 25,* 347–355.

51. STOUFFER, S. A. (1940) Intervening Opportunities: A Theory Relating Mobility and Distance. *Amer.Soc.Rev., 5,* 845–67.

52. STOUFFER, S. A. (1960) Intervening Opportunities and Competing Migrants. *Journ.of Reg.Sci., 2,* 1–26.

53. TAAFFE, E. J. (1956) Air Transportation and United States Urban Distribution. *Geog. Rev., 46,* 219–38.

54. TAAFFE, E. J. (1959) Trends in Airline Passenger Traffic: A Geographic Case Study. *Annals,Assoc.Amer.Geog., 49,* 393–408.

55. TAAFFE, E. J. (1962) The Urban Hierarchy: An Air Passenger Definition. *Econ.Geog., 38,* 1–14.

56. ULLMAN, E. L. (1957) *American Commodity Flow.* University of Washington Press, Washington, Seattle.

57. YOUNG, J. P. (1963) *The International Economy.* The Ronald Press, New York.

58. ZIPF, G. K. (1946) The P_1P_2/D Hypotheses: On the Intercity Movement of Persons. *Amer.Soc.Rev., 11,* 677–86.

Political Aspects

E. R. WOOLMINGTON

A. E. Moodie [1] considers that, for the purpose of analysis, the political geography of States may be subdivided into internal and external relationships. He does, however, point out these two sets of relationships are not, in any strict sense, capable of separation—they are too closely interdigitated in a world of increasing economic interdependence to be regarded as distinct elements.

Thus, of the two aspects of Australian political geography dealt with in this essay, one is clearly a problem of internal relationships, while the other, though also an internal problem, is one possessing external ramifications.

Australia has been called a nation with little history but with much historical geography. This is, of course, an overstatement; yet it contains a measure of truth. Australia is small in population, with some 12 million people, but large and mainly barren as to its land area of some 3 million square miles; it is geographically remote from its parent culture, but relatively close to areas occupied by overwhelmingly larger numbers of peoples of alien cultures. These circumstances have conditioned many of the events of Australian history, and, to the extent to which politics may be regarded as current events in history, they have conditioned also many of the events of Australian politics.

Much of the history of the Australian nation has been concerned with the physical occupation of the continent by man. Much of the nation's political organization has been concerned with the development of effective systems by which a small number of people might exercise control over so large an area. These aspects of the nation's history and politics fall undoubtedly into the realms of historical and political geography. In terms of Moodie's subdivision, such matters would appear to fall into the category of internal relationships. However, insofar as these relevant events have been associated with a determination to exclude alien neighbours, or at least to prevent these neighbours from assuming control, external relationships are also involved.

Two distinct aspects of Australian political geography have been selected for treatment, each closely concerned with the state of affairs outlined. The first aspect is undoubtedly a matter of the nation's internal relationships, and is concerned with a problem of spatial political organization arising out of the manner in which the continent was settled in earlier times.

AN INTERNAL ASPECT—NEW STATES WITHIN THE FEDERATION

The Commonwealth of Australia is a federation, comprising six full States and two Federal Territories. All are large in extent compared to size of population, and large fractions of the State populations are located in a few coastal cities, notably in the State capitals. Each of the original colonies comprised a port and its rural hinterland; the situation so established persisted after federation, and is still very far from disappearing.

The primary reasons for this situation relate to the circumstances of settlement; this latter was, in Australia, a product of the great age of European seagoing and the first settlements tended inevitably to be ports. So great were the land distances between one settlement and another that, for most of the first century of Australia's history, the primary links between settlements were those of sea—a factor reinforcing the development of ports. Overland settlement, proceeding slowly, did not fill the gaps between the port centres until the latter were already well established.

The period when Australia's white settlers were fanning into the interior fell almost entirely in the nineteenth century. By this time events of great significance had affected the parent culture. In particular, the industrial revolution and the development of urbanism and of city dominated economies.

At precisely the time when settlers in Australia were penetrating the inland, the drift to the cities had already achieved very considerable momentum in the parent countries. The rapid export overseas of Western technology and Western economic organization is well known. Its export to a country of white settlement, having a complementary economy and therefore close trading relationships with the parent culture, was rapid indeed. In consequence, the tendencies towards urban concentration were implanted in Australia during the very same period in which frontiers of settlement were advancing. This fact, at least as much as the aridity of much of the continent, was responsible for thin settlement of the interior whilst the coastal centres grew demographically fat.

This pattern of Australian occupance (concentration of the bulk of population in a handful of cities, connected by only the most tenuous membrane of rural settlement in the vast areas lying between them) provided the impetus towards the development of a federal system. During the first hundred years of Australian settlement the dominant theme was separatism and local self-government. Not until the occupance of the continent had been effectively completed and organized on this basis could nationalism set in.

The urge towards local self-government was an inevitable function of distance—distance from the United Kingdom, and distance between colonies. Independence both from Britain and from the original colonial govern-

ment in Sydney alike proved attractive. Thus the development of the pattern of colonies— which was subsequently to become the pattern of States within the Federation—was accomplished largely by a process of subdivision of the parent colony of New South Wales. When Captain Phillip was appointed the first Governor of New South Wales, the continent was still unknown and unoccupied except by aborigines. His empty empire extended from the east coast to the 135th meridian of longitude, encompassing an area of 1,584,380 square miles which now contains the whole of the States of Queensland, New South Wales, Victoria and Tasmania, with in addition a substantial portion of South Australia and the Northern Territory. The remainder of the continent was annexed and added to the Sydney's Governors' domain in 1829.

As exploration and settlement continued, so did subdivision. Tasmania (then Van Diemen's Land) was separated from New South Wales in 1825, Western Australia in 1831, South Australia in 1835, Victoria in 1850 and Queensland in 1859. A period of some 40-odd years of colonial autonomy then followed, before Australian nationalism had developed sufficiently to lead the colonies into federation in 1901.

The Act of Federation, though expressing the will of the inhabitants of the colonies to form a single nation occupying the entire continent, did not however terminate the urge towards separatism. The bases of separatism—great distances from centres of government and the isolation of dwellers in colonial hinterlands— were not altered by this political act. What were originally movements seeking the establishment of new colonies became movements seeking the establishment of new States within the new Federation. Indeed, the Federal constitution made provision for further subdivision by the creation of new States, although the terms were ambiguous and obscure as to possible machinery. Subdivision now became a matter involving States and Commonwealth alike. Its likelihood decreased as, with the development of an increasingly national economy, State powers waned. No new State has in fact been created, despite various new-state movements.

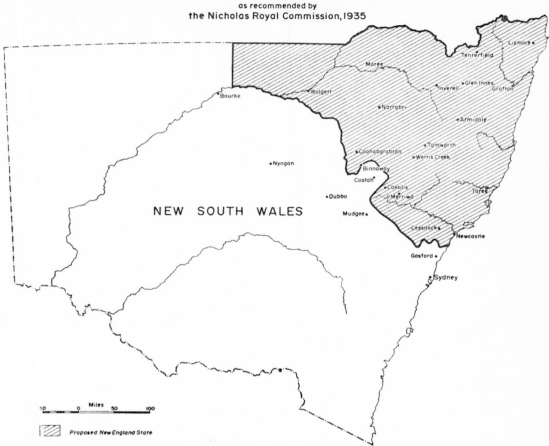

NEW ENGLAND STATE BOUNDARY
as recommended by
the Nicholas Royal Commission,1935

Fig. 1

Since 1901, new-state movements or similar separatist trends have been felt in north Queensland, central Queensland, northern New South Wales, south-eastern New South Wales, Gippsland in Victoria, and in the Riverina on both sides of the Victoria/New South Wales border. These movements have varied considerably in character and in their command of local support. By far the most vigorous and persistent has been that in northern New South Wales, which has become something of an ideological headquarters for new-statism throughout the Commonwealth.

The New England Movement

The separatist movement in northern New South Wales aspires to create a new State in a wedge of territory extending from Newcastle northward to the Queensland border and westward to the vicinity of Walgett (Fig. 1); the proposed name of New England is the regional name of the Northern Tablelands district. This movement has been supported intermittently since 1859, a year when certain inhabitants of the far northern districts of the residual colony of New South Wales, frustrated in their ambition to secede as a part of Queensland, immediately began agitating for the creation of a distinct colony. After Federation their movement became a New England New-State Movement.

Separatism prior to Federation, and separatism after it, prove however to be two somewhat different things. The increased difficulty of separating under Federation implies that a new State will only be created in response to persistent and compelling popular demand. Despite its long history, the New England New-State Movement does not appear to fulfil this condition. Instead of being pushed forward remorselessly by weight of popular support, the leaders of the Movement have often been hard pressed to whip up the semblance of widespread backing.

The fluctuation of popular support appears to have been mainly responsible for the unstable history of the Movement during this century. Persistence until the present day has depended upon the persistent enthusiasm of new-statists. These come chiefly from the grazing community, where separatism is something of a family tradition. They are reinforced by some members of the professional classes and especially by the country press. This combined group has kept the Movement alive in periods of popular apathy, and in face of indifference on the part of the Sydney Government.

Fluctuations in support suggest dependence on external factors. A brief review of the main cycles of the Movement's active life since 1900 will suffice to illustrate this suggestion. The post-federation life of the Movement began in 1915 after almost thirty years of near-dormancy. The stimulus was a dispute between the residents of the town of Grafton and the State Government over the cost of maintaining a steam ferry over the Clarence River. Growing local protests against alleged neglect by the Government culminated in the establishment of a Northern Separation Movement in the northern rivers district. But this particular outburst of new-statism did not survive the year, for public attention was diverted to the First World War.

The Movement revived shortly after the end of the war, when post-war expectations of progress, reform, and development, altered the climate of popular opinion. In addition, separation was urged by the northern press, and in particular by a Tamworth paper, the *Northern Daily Leader*. There was the inauguration of what may be termed the 'popular' period of the Movement's life, lasting from 1919 to 1925. Popular support

during this period is demonstrated by the rapid growth of new-state leagues throughout the north. By 1921, some 200 of these leagues had come into existence, being established in almost every town and village throughout the region.

The only practical consequence of the wave of agitation was the establishment by the New South Wales Government in December 1923 of the first Royal Commission of Enquiry into New States. But popular enthusiasm for the Movement had begun to wane, and most of the leagues had ceased to function even before the Commission was appointed. The Movement had already become dormant by the time that the Commission's report was tabled, in April 1925. And the Commission in any event found that a new State in the North was neither feasible nor desirable.

Agitation revived in the 1930s, again under the stimulus of external circumstances—this time, economic depression and the extreme financial policies of Lang's Labor Government in Sydney. The near-collapse of the rural economy provided the necessary background of discontent, for which the Government's fiscal policies provided a specific focus. New-state agitation was again widespread; but once again it did not long survive, lapsing after the dismissal of Premier Lang by the State Governor in May 1932. The main achievement of this particular agitation was the appointment of another Royal Commission on the new-states question, with terms of reference different from those of its predecessor. This time the Commission was required to report, not on the 'feasibility and desirability' of new States, but specifically on areas suitable for self-government. This time the Commission's report was favourable, in that it identified as being suitable for self-government as a State, an area closely resembling that proposed by the Movement. But by the time the report was tabled, in January 1935, new-state agitation had once again evaporated. Economic revival gradually removed conditions of rural hardship, and a promised referendum was not held.

The most recent popular outburst of new-state agitation took place between 1948 and 1953 under circumstances closely resembling those of the first post-war agitation. Preoccupation with post-war reconstruction, development, and decentralization, led once more to expectations of progress which were once again frustrated. It was natural that the notion of development through decentralization should revive interest in the new-state project. The first post-war New-State Convention, held in Armidale in 1948, was called essentially as a convention on decentralization. At this time the Movement gained considerable support from local government councils throughout the north, having approached them all with a request to conduct a referendum on the new-state question concurrently with the triennial local government elections of 1953. But the New South Wales Department of Local Government intervened to warn councils that such a procedure was beyond their powers. In the end, the referendum was conducted by 20 of the 83 local government areas within the proposed boundaries of the new State; and it proved inconclusive, even though hailed by the Movement as an outstanding victory. Nevertheless, of the votes actually cast, in no area did those favourable to a new State fall below 65 per cent, and the average 'yes' vote was 77 per cent. Although substantial numbers of people failed to vote in some areas, the Movement recorded considerable support at a time when enthusiasm was waning.

Perhaps for this reason, but more probably because in 1949 the Movement appointed a permanent paid secretariat to keep agitation going, the Movement did not after 1953 collapse as it had previously done; it has succeeded in keeping its cause before the public ever since.

Nature of the Movement

New-statism bears a clear family resemblance to separatist movements in the colonial era, stemming as it does from local desire to influence government, and from objection to government from a distance. These basic motivations appear in all analyses of grievance since 1900, even though the grievances themselves are usually quite specific, and although they vary from time to time according to alleged rural injustice inflicted by the city-dominated Government at Sydney. A new State has been offered as the solution to problems of population drift, and of the inadequate provision of railways, roads, water conservation projects, country-town water and sewerage works, and so forth. City-dominated legislature has been held responsible for railway freights which allegedly favour metropolitan interests, inhibit the growth of decentralized industry, and condemn the rural hinterland of New South Wales to the stagnant colonial function of primary production.

Notwithstanding the Movement's official dissociation from party politics, the rural and to some extent aristocratic interests that dominate it give a conservative flavour, and involve substantial although informal association with the Country Party. The creation of a new State in the north has been regarded as a safeguard against that left-wing extremism to which the city-dominated parliament of New South Wales has been called susceptible.

Thus, although the history of the Movement does not appear to be particularly impressive, its active life having been intermittent and its efforts not successful, its very survival for a century in a more or less consistent area is a matter of considerable significance, and constitutes *prima facie* evidence of the existence of a community of interest and of regional consciousness.

Areal Dimensions of New-State Sentiment [2]

Until April 1967 no vote on the new State of New England had ever been taken throughout the proposed area so that the real dimensions of new-state feeling were never known. However, the Movement had from time to time provided signs of areal identification. Admittedly the quality of these signs ranges considerably, and all are in varying degree unreliable. But each piece of evidence identifies a definite area of support for the Movement and, as Fig. 2 indicates, the coincidence of the several areas is impressive.

The earliest piece of evidence is provided by the distribution-pattern of new-state leagues. This evidence, relating particularly to the 1920s, discriminates precisely between that support and non-support for the Movement which has persisted to the 1960s. The leagues, committees, or branches, numerous and widespread in the 1920s, still occupy the same

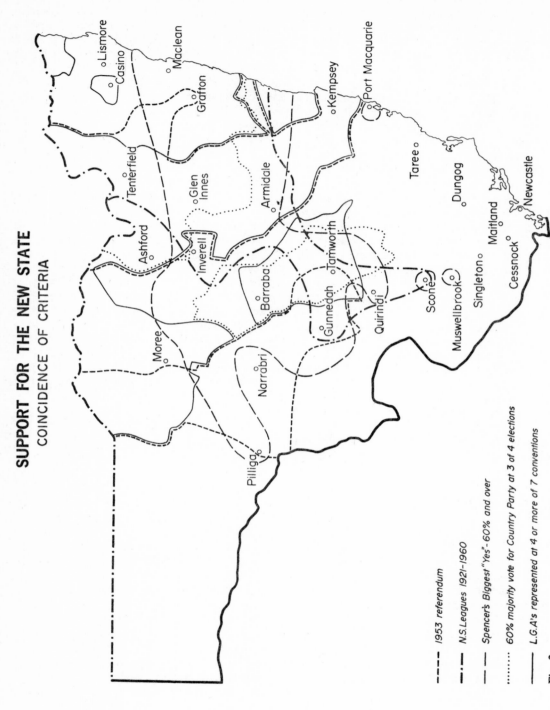

SUPPORT FOR THE NEW STATE
COINCIDENCE OF CRITERIA

--- 1953 referendum

-··- N.S. Leagues 1921-1960

— Spencer's Biggest "Yes" - 60% and over

······ 60% majority vote for Country Party at 3 of 4 elections

—— L.G.A's represented at 4 or more of 7 conventions

Fig. 2

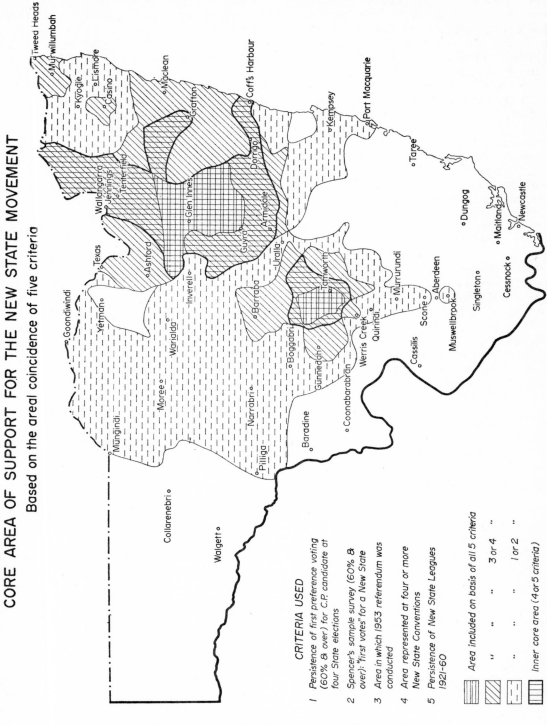

CORE AREA OF SUPPORT FOR THE NEW STATE MOVEMENT
Based on the areal coincidence of five criteria

CRITERIA USED

1 Persistence of first preference voting
  (60% & over) for C.P. candidate at
  four State elections

2 Spencer's sample survey (60% &
  over): "first votes" for a New State

3 Area in which 1953 referendum was
  conducted

4 Area represented at four or more
  New State Conventions

5 Persistence of New State Leagues
  1921-60

Area included on basis of all 5 criteria

  "   "   "   "   3 or 4   "

  "   "   "   "   1 or 2   "

Inner core area (4 or 5 criteria)

Fig. 3

general area as they did initially. Their persistence in localities within this area for almost half a century indicates the continuing existence in those places at least of a minority sufficiently enthusiastic to maintain agitation.

Further evidence is provided by the otherwise inconclusive referendum of 1953. The votes then recorded can be fairly regarded as constituting a large sample survey, and as identifying and locating support for the new-state project. As *all* the areas in which the referendum was conducted recorded such support, it leaves open to speculation the question of whether such support might in fact have been more widespread still. That question is not answerable, but the fact that the councils which did hold the referendum were defying the Department of Local Government suggests that support for the Movement in their areas may perhaps have been stronger than elsewhere. The areas concerned constitute two virtually consolidated blocks of territory, coinciding closely with the area occupied by new-state leagues.

Further evidence comes from local government participation in new-state conventions. Not all local councils in the north have been consistent supporters of the Movement. Frequent contact between Movement and councils has resulted from the preoccupations of both with local affairs. In the immediate post-war years this contact was particularly close, and numerous councils expressed their support by financial aid and by the sending of representatives to the various new-state conventions. The official records of these conventions during the period between 1948 and 1953 identify the councils represented. Among seven conventions, 21 of the 82 councils in the New England New-State area were represented at four or more, while another 13 were represented at three; another 20 councils were not represented at any. Many of the councils who sent representatives to a majority of the conventions were the same as these who conducted the referendum of 1953. It follows that the area identified on the basis of representation at four conventions bears distinct similarities to areas identified by the use of other criteria.

Voting patterns at State elections provide still further evidence of where support for the Movement lies. Circumstantial evidence suggests that support for the Australian Country Party coincides with support for the New England New-State Movement. The Country Party is the only political party which has voiced consistent sympathy for the Movement, and some leading Movement identities are also leading Country Party identities. In those areas where the 1953 referendum was held, there was a significantly high statistical correlation between 'yes' votes and voting for Country Party candidates at the simultaneous State election. In a nine year period embracing four triennial general State elections, areas manifesting a consistently high 60 per cent first preference-vote for Country Party candidates formed a consolidated block of territory which displayed remarkable coincidence with new-state support areas.

The latest attempt to delimit support for the Movement was undertaken in 1960, when a research student of Newcastle University College conducted a small sample survey of opinion on the new-state issue throughout the proposed New England New-State Area. Although the sample embraced less than 0·24 per cent of the total population of the area, the results of the survey bore a statistically valid resemblance to those of the 1953 referendum in those areas where the referendum was held; it can accordingly be regarded as valid for the entire area. The data from the survey provided two measures of support for the new-state project—a 'most favourable' one on the basis of first thoughts on the subject, and a 'least favourable' one on the basis of second thoughts after possible alternative methods of altering the constitutional status quo had been explained. The first-thoughts measure, resembling the indications of the 1953 referendum, is considered to provide an indication of spontaneous sympathy for the Movement. The distribution-pattern of such support, on the basis of a 60 per cent and over 'yes' vote in localities sampled, indicates a consolidated area resembling areas identified on other bases.

Core Area of Support for the Movement

Superimposition of the area identified by each of the five criteria selected permits the identification of a core area of support for the Movement (Fig. 3). The resulting composite map

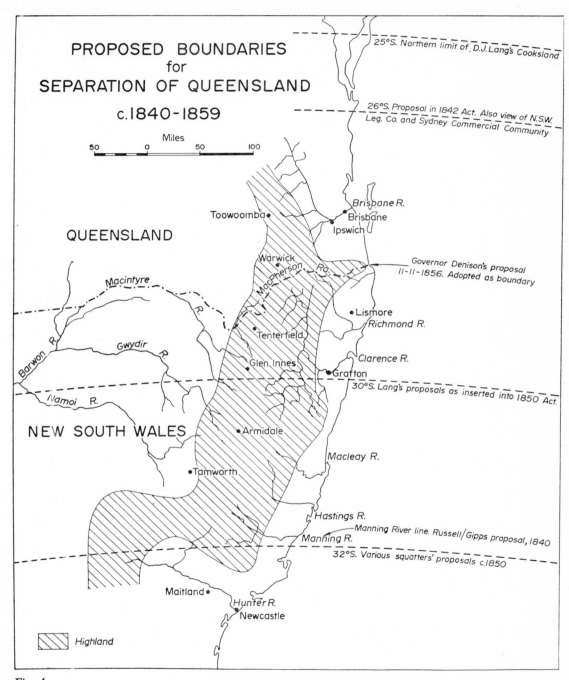

PROPOSED BOUNDARIES
for
SEPARATION OF QUEENSLAND
c.1840-1859

25°S. Northern limit of D.J.Lang's Cooksland

26°S. Proposal in 1842 Act. Also view of N.S.W.
Leg. Co. and Sydney Commercial Community

Miles

50   0   50   100

Brisbane R.
Brisbane
Toowoomba   Ipswich

QUEENSLAND

Warwick   Governor Denison's proposal
                11-11-1856. Adopted as boundary

Macintyre

Lismore
Richmond R.

Tenterfield

Barwon R.

Gwydir R.

Glen Innes   Clarence R.
                 Grafton

Namoi R.   30°S. Lang's proposals as inserted into 1850 Act.

NEW SOUTH WALES   Armidale

Macleay R.

Tamworth

Hastings R.
                Manning River line. Russell/Gipps proposal, 1840
                Manning R.
                32°S. Various squatters' proposals c.1850

Maitland
        Hunter R.
        Newcastle

Highland

Fig. 4

shows concentrations on the northern tablelands and in the Tamworth district. Intensities
reflect the degrees of confidence with which
any area may be regarded as supporting the
Movement. Areas of nil support occupy the
periphery of the New-State area, and include
the heavily-populated and industrialized Newcastle district and the entire Hunter Valley in
the far south.

The southern limits of support for the
Movement, as here established, extend no farther south than the most southerly limits ever
proposed as the boundary for the colony of
Queensland (Fig. 4), reinforcing the suggestion
that new-statism in northern New South Wales
was a direct consequence of denial of secession
to Queensland in 1859. Voting in the 1967
referendum broadly confirmed this demarcation, areas to the northward voting solidly for
a new State and areas southward voting solidly
against.

Reasons for the Persistence of New-Statism

Regional frustrations, arising from the character of much of northern New South Wales as a
marchland between the spheres of influence of
two major metropolitan centres, appear capable
of explaining the persistence of new-statism.

The town of Armidale, located close to the
midpoint of the main area of support for the
New State Movement—and incidentally the
Movement's headquarters—lies almost midway
between the metropolis of Sydney (350 miles)
and that of Brisbane (300 miles). Near the
southern extremity of the area, Tamworth, is
some 280 miles from Sydney. The most northerly main centre, Tenterfield, is located only
175 miles from Brisbane, whose influence is,
however, impeded by the intervention of the
Queensland/New South Wales border only 12
miles north of Tenterfield. The core area of
support is distinctly intermediate in location
between the two metropolitan centres of socio-
economic diffusion.

This fact is reflected in a number of adverse
circumstances—chronic demographic stagnation, reflected in outward migration; deprivation of some beneficial economic influences
emanating from Sydney and Brisbane; and
minimization of metropolitan socio-political
influences, such for instance as are expressed

in metropolitan newspapers. Local papers, of
course, with a localist viewpoint, make up for
this latter deficiency.

1. *Demographic Stagnation.* Within the proposed New-State area there are five statistical
divisions. Three of these—the North Coast, the
Northern Tablelands and the Northwestern
Slopes Divisions—occupy the core area of
support for the Movement, with the Northern
Tablelands in the centre. In New South Wales
as a whole the population more than doubled
(rising from 1,646,734 to 3,916,867) during
the period 1911 to 1961. Sydney was responsible for most of the growth. By contrast, the
Northern Tablelands Division in the period
1921 to 1961 recorded the lowest rate of
growth in the entire State, almost wholly on
account of loss by emigration. Some 94 per
cent of the Division's entire natural increase
was, in fact, lost. The two adjacent Divisions of
the core area suffered similarly. The North
Coast Division in 1947 to 1961 grew at but
7·6 per cent, even less than the 8·3 per cent for
the Tablelands. By contrast, Divisions on the
periphery of the New-State area—particularly
the Hunter and Manning Division (Newcastle
and its hinterland)—have experienced vigorous
population growth, natural increase being reinforced by immigration (Fig. 5).

2. *Economic Deprivation.* It is axiomatic
that the farther one is located from a metropolis, the more difficult and expensive it is to
benefit from metropolitan facilities. In a situation where a substantial proportion of the
economy is metropolitan-generated, increased
costs of metropolitan products amount to
economic deprivation. An expression of the
relative deprivation of New England in this
respect may be obtained from the application
of Reilly's Law of retail gravitation. In brief,
Reilly's Law states that, under normal conditions, two cities draw retail trade from a
smaller intermediate city ... in direct proportion to some power of the population of those
two larger cities, and in inverse proportion to
some power of the distance of each of the cities
from the smaller intermediate city. Although
concerned specifically with retail trade, the law
has obvious relevance for the whole general
field of metropolitan gravitation. The law may
be stated as a general formula:

$$\frac{B_a}{B_b} = \frac{P_a}{P_b} \times \frac{D_b}{D_a} \qquad (2)$$

where B_a and B_b are the proportions of retail trade attracted by cities A and B respectively, where $P_a:B_b$ equals the ratio of population for the two cities, and where $D_a:D_b$ equals the distance from cities A and B of any intermediate town under consideration.

Derivations of this formula make it possible to award Reilly gravitation-values for any centre. When this is done for all main centres in the New-State area (Fig. 6), it is found that the 'breaking point'—50 per cent gravitation to both Sydney and Brisbane—nearly bisects the core of support. This represents the theoretical line of least favourable position in respect of benefits of metropolitan influence. In reality, however, the Queensland/New South Wales border inhibits the natural extension of the influence of Brisbane into northern New South Wales, so that empirical tests of gravitation, based upon the flow of wholesale commodities into northern retail stores, on the flow of passengers by bus and rail from northern centres to Sydney and Brisbane respectively, and on the relative penetration of Sydney and Brisbane newspapers, locate the breaking point farther northward, and extend all Sydney gravitation values north of their theoretical positions. The implication is obvious. Not only does the core area of support tend to be located at the end of the line in respect of metropolitan influence, but also it is forcibly deprived of its natural proportion of association

PERCENTAGE INCREASE IN POPULATION
1921-1947

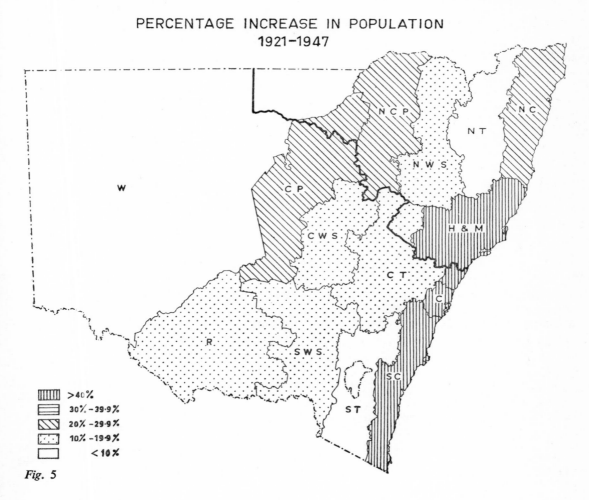

Fig. 5

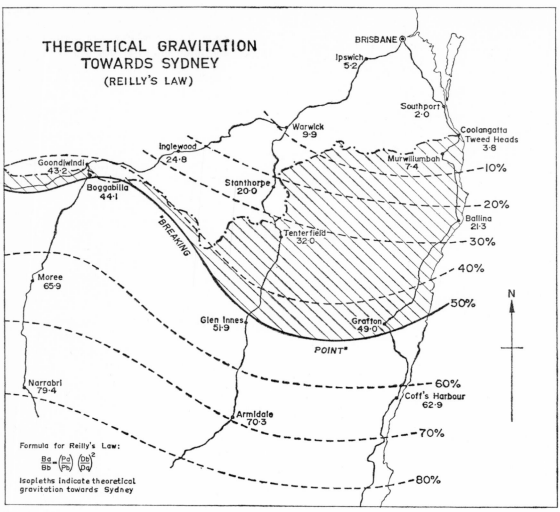

Fig. 6

with Brisbane, because of its location within New South Wales, and is compelled to substitute a measure of disadvantageous trade with Sydney.

3. *Localist Influence.* Fig. 7 shows the relative predominance over northern New South Wales of the metropolitan (either Sydney or Brisbane) and country presses. Penetration of Brisbane papers is confined to the far northern coastal districts, while that of the Sydney papers diminishes quite sharply northward of Newcastle. In an area which coincides remarkably with the core area of support for the New England New-State Movement, metropolitan

newspapers penetrate fewer than 25 per cent of homes. The influence of metropolitan newspapers is at a minimum throughout this region, where public opinion is largely localist opinion. Much of the local press in northern New South Wales is more or less sympathetic to the Movement; little is hostile. Regionalist and separatist views are kept before the eyes of the public.

Regionalism and the New-State Movement

Regions are still the basic units of study for many geographers. The proposed area of the New England New-State area has five clear

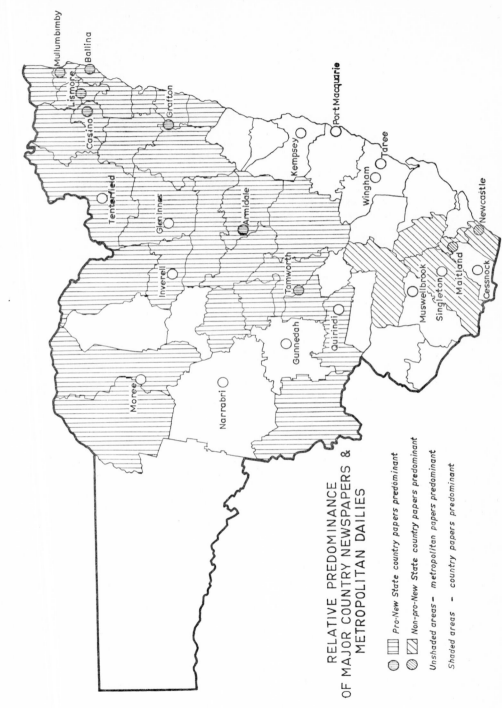

RELATIVE PREDOMINANCE
OF MAJOR COUNTRY NEWSPAPERS &
METROPOLITAN DAILIES

Pro-New State country papers predominant

Non-pro-New State country papers predominant

Unshaded areas — metropolitan papers predominant

Shaded areas — country papers predominant

Fig. 7

physiographic divisions: North Coast, Northern Tablelands, Northwestern Slopes, Northwestern Plains, and the Hunter River Valley in the south. Physiographic differences are reflected in differences in climate and in land use. On the basis of land use Robinson [3] has identified six distinct regions which lie wholly or partly within the New-State area; they range from regions of mixed farm economies with sub-tropical crops and/or dairying, through regions of mixed farming/grazing on the tablelands, to regions of wheat farming on the western slopes and grazing on the interior plains, and to the mature agricultural/industrial region of the Hunter Valley. On a somewhat different basis the New South Wales Regional Boundaries Committee, set up by the New South Wales Government in 1944 for the purpose of subdividing New South Wales into developmental units having 'a broad measure of . . . economic and social unity, and . . . community of interest', identified seven different regions, and parts of three others, within the New-State area.

The New-State area might perhaps be classed as a region on another level of the regional hierarchy. The area delimited by the 1935 Royal Commission contained a balance of rural and industrial entities and populations, such as would constitute a State with a balance of heterogeneity, both economic and political.

The Commission was much exercised by community of interest, but in seeking to achieve a balance of heterogeneity (for which Newcastle was essential) may well have prejudiced the requirements of 'community of interest'.

There can be no doubt that the New-State Movement is a regional movement. New-state traditions and sentiments exist in a clearly-defined area and for clear reasons. The area is the one omitted from Queensland, where socio-economic circumstances, calculated to preserve in the minds of local inhabitants a sense of frustration and neglect, have persisted for a long time. In a sense, new-statism here has carried into the twentieth century the frontier spirit—the urge of inhabitants of the hinterland to see that hinterland developed. The Movement is essentially a rural Movement, with its views unshared by dwellers in major cities—clearly, for example, unshared by the inhabitants of Newcastle and its immediate surroundings. Community of interest does not extend over the entire area of the proposed new State. The balance of heterogeneity advocated by the 1935 Royal Commission appears directly to militate against community of interest in the area proposed.

It seems highly unlikely at the present time that the New England New-State Movement, or any other comparable movement, will be able to succeed.

AN INTERNAL ASPECT WITH EXTERNAL RAMIFICATIONS
IMMIGRATION SINCE THE SECOND WORLD WAR

This second aspect is also clearly an internal aspect of Australia's political geography, relating particularly to problems of internal development. It does however already possess external ramification in terms, for example, of the origins of immigrants.

Since the end of the second world war, Australia has experienced a period of marked immigrant influx—an influx which, when inaugurated in 1947, constituted a revival of the immigration process after its virtual cessation during the economic depression years of the 1930s and during the war years that followed.

The incentive for the revival of wholesale

immigration was threefold. Firstly, near-invasion by the Japanese during the second world war provided a reminder of the vulnerability of underpopulated Australia. Secondly, the post-war world economic boom and the need for reconstruction at home stimulated a demand for labour that could not be satisfied by the existing population. Thirdly, the receding tide of war in Europe had left behind a vast labour pool of displaced persons unable to return to their native lands in eastern Europe, and had left behind also a general post-war pressure towards emigration elsewhere in Europe, including emigration from Britain.

In this setting, the Australian Government in 1947 set about the encouragement of fare-paying migrants; in addition, it instituted a wholesale programme of assisted migration, designed and administered specifically for the purpose of facilitating economic development.

Since that time, non-assisted and Government-assisted immigrants have alike contributed to Australia's substantial post-war economic development, but the general pattern of the contribution has been set by assisted immigrants, who have constituted a majority of the total influx, and who have been recruited specifically as workers in industry and in agriculture. The general pattern of post-war immigration was set by its first decade. It is with this period, up to approximately 1956, that this analysis is concerned.

Between January 1947 and December 1956, 1,133,683 persons arrived in Australia. Of these, 603,393 were assisted and 530,290 were unassisted immigrants. Net immigration (excess of 'permanent' arrivals over departures) amounted to 864,295 persons. Of those who departed during the period, relatively few had arrived in Australia as assisted immigrants; it can safely be estimated that such people accounted for more than 60 per cent of net immigration over the period.

Most of the countries of Europe have been represented in the post-war immigrant influx, particularly the countries of eastern, central, northwestern and southern Europe. A broad indication of the European regional balance in this immigrant influx, which involves a major departure from all previous patterns, is that immigrants from the British Isles have been in a minority throughout. However, proportions of British plus other western European groups —notably Dutch—have remained high. Of the rest, eastern Europeans predominated until 1951, whereafter Mediterraneans became the predominant immigrant group. The reasons for this development rest in the fact that the bulk

Table 1 *Number of Persons in Age-Groups in the Australian Population at the 1947 and 1954 Censuses, and Among Post-War Immigrants*

Age-group	1947(a)	1954	Increase 1947-54	Immigs.(b) at arrival	Immigs. at 1954
0-14	1,911,251	2,563,334	652,083	167,308	140,103
15-39	2,955,568	3,247,720	292,152	381,873	360,732
40-64	2,103,739	2,429,470	325,731	94,482	138,821
65+	608,800	746,006	137,206	7,033	11,040
Total	7,579,358	8,986,530	1,407,172	650,696	650,696

(a) Ages 'not stated' in 1947 census were distributed proportionately among age-groups.
(b) Excess of total arrivals over total departures.
Sources: 1947 and 1954 census vols.; and from *Demography Bulletins* Nos. 65-72.

Table 2 *Percentage Age-Distribution of New Arrivals in Australia Between January 1947 and June 1954, compared with the Australian Population at the 1947 and 1954 Censuses*

Age-group	Immigs. at arrival	Immigs. at 1954	Aust. Pop. at 1947	Aust. Pop. at 1954	Aust. Pop. at 1954 minus immigs.
0-14	25.7	21.5	25.2	28.5	29.1
15-39	58.7	55.5	39.0	36.2	34.6
40-64	14.5	21.3	27.8	27.0	27.5
65+	1.1	1.7	8.0	8.3	8.8
Total	100.0	100.0	100.0	100.0	100.0

Sources: Demography Bulletins Nos. 65-71.
  1947 census vol. 1, pt. 9.
  1954 Census Mimeograph No. 30.

of displaced persons left in Europe after the end of the war, and available for immigration, were the eastern Europeans, who had no wish to return to their countries of origin once the iron curtain had shut them off. Such displaced persons proved invaluable in certain sectors of the Australian economy, so that, when this pool of potential immigrants had dried up, Australia sought and secured increasing numbers of essentially comparable immigrants from the Mediterranean lands, notably from Italy and from Greece.

Influence on the Australian Population Structure

The economic contribution of these post-war immigrants to Australian development has been incomparable. It could well be argued that Australia's post-war 'industrial revolution' could not have gone forward without them. Some of the economic ramifications of this population influx are shown by its impact on certain aspects of Australia's population-structure. Between the censuses of June 1947 and of June 1954, the Australian population increased from 7,579,358 to 8,986,530—a gain of 1,407,172 people in seven years. The population gain from immigration during the same period amounted to 650,697 persons, or 46·2 per cent of the total gain. The great majority of the immigrants—upwards of 75 per cent—were people in the economically-productive age ranges between 15 and 64 years, this proportion being substantially greater than proportions in these age-ranges in Australia as a whole (see Tables 1 and 2). Because of this, immigration tended to mitigate somewhat the general increase during the 1947 to 1954 period in the proportions of persons in the 'dependent' age-groups in the total Australian population.

As elsewhere in the Western world, Australians' life-expectancy has increased considerably during the twentieth century, with the result that the proportion of the national population in the post-working age-range (65 years and over) increased steadily from 4·5 per cent total population in 1911 to 8·3 per cent in 1954. Between 1947 and 1954 alone, the proportion of these people increased from 8 per cent to 8·3 per cent. In addition, there occurred during the first post-war decade a marked increase in the proportion of youthful dependants in the 0 to 14 year age-range, from 25·2 per cent to 28·5 per cent of total population, as a result of the characteristic post-war increase in the birthrate.

Because of these developments, the proportion of total economically non-productive ages in the total population increased from 33·2 per cent to 36·8 per cent in the 1947 to 1954 intercensal period. This increase would have been substantially greater, had it not been offset by immigration—the immigrant population contained a markedly smaller proportion of elderly people (less than 1·7 per cent in 1954), and a somewhat smaller proportion of children (21·5 per cent in 1954). It has been estimated that without immigration total dependent ages in the population would have been 37·9 per cent.

In consequence of immigration, the Australian population-structure shifted both in terms of size and of age, providing a greater potential for economic productivity than would otherwise have been the case. Specific consideration of the economically productive age-group further illuminates this contention.

During the 1947 to 1954 intercensal period, the 15 to 64-year age-group increased from 5,059,307 to 5,677,190 persons, a gain of 617,883. Immigrant age-structure at June 1954 indicated that almost half a million people, or no less than 80·9 per cent of this gain, consisted of immigrants. Thus with immigration, the economically productive age-group increased by 12·2 per cent over that of 1947, but without immigration, this increase would have amounted but to 2·3 per cent. The root cause of the very low natural increase in the working-age population during this first post-war decade rests in the very low marriage and birthrates which prevailed during the depression years of the 1930s. It is not possible to calculate with any accuracy the number of births lost in those times, but a rough estimate based on intercensal trends during the twentieth century suggests a figure greater than 400,000. The effects of this loss have been felt in the scarcity of new recruits to the working-age groups from about 1945 onwards, when the first of the missing 400,000 should have reached 15 years of age.

Thus, between the 1947 and 1954 censuses, the number of young adults between the ages of 15 and 24, instead of increasing by 400,000-odd, actually fell from 1,202,048 to 1,191,937 —a decline of 10,111. This loss would have been more than ten times as great, had it not been for the 99,472 immigrant recruits to this age-range during that time. Moreover, the total estimated loss to the post-war working-age population of 400,000 was rather more than offset by the total immigrant working-age arrivals (499,553 people).

But that rectification of those deficiencies which resulted from the depression, and which would be occasioned by post-war immigration, was only short-term. The mean age of the half million-odd immigrants of working age was 34·5 years, whereas the mean age of the 400,000-odd recruits from natural increase would have been about 20 years. The immigrants will accordingly reach retiring age much earlier than would have done new recruits from natural increase, and the reproductive power of immigrants, reduced both by age and sex-structure which includes a marked male bias, will undoubtedly be considerably less, by the time they have finished their lives, than would have been that of the lost 400,000.

Immigration and the Industrial Workforce

Between 1947 and 1954, the Australian workforce (which is *not* the same as the population in the working-age ranges) increased from 3,196,431 to 3,702,022 persons—a gain of 505,591, or 15·8 per cent over 1947. All estimates of the immigrant contribution to this workforce increase place it in excess of 60 per cent.

During this period, the workforce engaged in all classes of industry, except that in primary production, expanded (Table 3). The decline in the primary production workforce is a consequence of increasing mechanization, which enabled productivity to expand with the employment of fewer actual workers. In terms of additional numbers employed, the greatest expansions occurred in manufacturing, commerce, and building, in that order. Relative to size at 1947, however, the most marked expansions occurred in building, communications, commerce, utilities (a category including the workforce in hydro-electricity and irrigation projects, and thus in some major developmental schemes) and finance, in that order. The expansion of the largest industrial category, manufacturing, was a relatively modest 25 per cent over its 1947 position, well below the expansion rate of other categories mentioned, although individual manufacturing industries such as rubber (up 61·1 per cent over 1947), building materials and mineral fuels (up 51·1 per cent), plastics (up 50·4 per cent),

Table 3 *Changes in the Australian Workforce During the 1947-1954 Intercensal Period*

Category	% of total w.f.		Changes 1947-54		% of total w.f. increase
	1947	1954	Numbers	% of 1947	
Primary production	16.7	13.3	− 4,743	− 1.0	—
Mining	1.8	1.7	+ 6,980	+12.8	1.0
Manufacturing	27.7	27.9	+205,207	+25.0	29.6
Utilities	1.8	2.0	+ 18,955	+34.7	2.8
Building	6.9	8.9	+123,619	+61.2	17.3
Transport	7.0	7.0	+ 48,993	+23.7	6.8
Communication	1.9	2.2	+ 22,758	+39.4	3.2
Finance	2.5	2.7	+ 24,933	+33.8	3.4
Commerce	14.3	15.9	+154,777	+36.6	21.9
Public authority	11.8	12.3	+ 98,038	+28.1	13.8
Amusement, etc.	7.6	6.1	+ 1,204	+ 0.5	0.2
Total	100.0	100.0	+700,721	+23.6	100.0
Other and 'not stated'			−195,130	−83.9	
Grand Total			+505,591	+15.8	

Sources: 1954 Census Mimeo. No. 48.
1947 Census Vol. 2, pt. 17.

chemicals (up 41·8 per cent), and all classes of engineering (up 33·6 per cent) greatly exceeded the average value.

It must be remembered, as is indicated particularly by primary production figures, that the size of the workforce engaged is but a crude indicator of actual production growth, for the differential role of mechanization or of automation is not considered, although its role must in some cases be an important one. However, to the extent to which workforce increases serve as indicators, there would appear to have been a broad element of balance in the critical first decade of Australia's post-war industrial expansion, in the sense that the most marked workforce increases occurred on one hand in fundamental industry, such as building, construction, and in industries manufacturing producer goods, and on the other hand in commerce and finance. The contribution of immigrants towards this balanced expansion is an important and perhaps unexpected one.

The greatest numbers of extra workers gained during the intercensal period went to manufacturing, commerce, and building, but the immigrant contribution to these industries was far from uniform. Instead, there were distinct sectors of industry in which immigrants tended especially to find employment, and others where immigrant penetration was substantially lacking. To a degree, this circumstance was a consequence of government policy, whereby immigrants, and particularly the Government assisted ones, were recruited with specific regard to the needs of expanding basic industry, and consequently tended to gravitate to such industries as iron and steel making, other metallurgical industries, building and construction, and so forth.

Various surveys conducted by the Commonwealth Department of Labour provide some measures of these kinds of tendencies. Two surveys conducted in 1954 and 1955, embracing a total of 613 firms employing altogether 183,258 workers throughout the Commonwealth, revealed high proportions of non-British immigrant workers in basic industries. For example, in such industrial categories as manufacture of building materials, iron and steel making, engineering and plastics, mining, transport, building and hospital domestics, non-

British immigrants accounted for 19·4 per cent of males and 12·6 per cent of females employed. As the concentration of non-British in Australia at the 1954 census was only 5·5 per cent of the total population, and the concentration of wage-earners of similar origin was only 9 per cent of all wage-earners, this specific industrial concentration is markedly above average. British immigrants, assisted or otherwise, do not manifest the same tendencies, but incline far more toward the employment tendencies of Australians. At the Port Kembla steel works, for instance, the British proportion of the total workforce amounted but to 5·6 per cent—a concentration below the average concentration of British in Australia as a whole (7·4 per cent), signifying a tendency for the British, like Australians, to avoid industries of this kind.

The bias of Europeans towards basic or dirty industry was in part a consequence of the contract system, under which assisted non-British immigrants were required to spend the first two years in Australia in specified employment—usually in basic industries. But behind this circumstance there operated the conditions of full employment prevailing in Australia. Native-born Australians tended to select, from the variety of opportunities open to them, the less unpleasant industries, thereby swelling the ranks of those employed in commerce and in the softer industries. Moreover, for many forms of white-collar jobs, fluency in the language is an important pre-requisite. Australians had a clear advantage in these fields over non-English speaking immigrants. In consequence, the expansion of the workforce in heavy and noxious industry was largely left to these people. British immigrants, speaking the same language as Australians, sharing the same cultural background, and generally coming to Australia under favourable circumstances, have tended to adopt Australian rather than European habits of employment.

From all this, it is evident that the immigrant contribution, and particularly the non-British immigrant contribution to the post-war industrial expansion of Australia has been critical. If the sizes of the working-age population and of the workforce have any significance, it is clear that immigration was essential if Australia were to maintain during the first post-war

decade a rate of economic expansion comparable to, let alone exceeding, that occurring under conditions of normal population increase. Furthermore, the influx of continental Europeans has materially assisted Australian workers in their search for better conditions, by enabling more of the latter to select the more comfortable—and perhaps the more profitable—occupations, more easily than would otherwise have been the case.

The price that Australia has had to pay for these benefits has been the creation of a problem of immigrant assimilation. The Australian public at large, like the Government, has given considerable attention to this and to related matters. Much concern was expressed about where immigrants were settling, whether they were in fact contributing to the development of Australia—a notion which in the minds of some people is synonymous with settlement in the rural hinterland regions—and whether they were tending to form alien communities. Various studies of the distribution of immigrants in Australia cast some light on these considerations.

A number of circumstances have governed the distribution of immigrant settlers in Australia, the major ones being the pre-existing pattern of population distribution, the attractive force of specific regions, and specific settlement tendencies manifested by various national migrant groups. In general, these are the circumstances primarily responsible for the broad outlines and the pattern of immigrant settlement that was discernible at the 1954 census.

The pre-existing pattern of population distribution reflects the adaptation of the total population to the environment under the given circumstances of the age. People have tended generally to locate where the environment offered advantage. Inevitably, therefore, immigrants, unless their socio-economic characteristics were vastly different from those of the indigenes, and unless they arrived in something approaching overwhelming numbers, might be expected to react to the environment in a fashion broadly similar to that of the indigenes as has in fact proved to be the case. Most immigrants have tended to locate in the major cities, in the largest concentrations of the pre-existing population, with few spreading through the hinterland areas. A high statistical correlation exists between the general distribution pattern of immigrants and that of Australians as a whole. This circumstance has been misunderstood by various critics of Australia's post-war immigration programmes, who have offered complaints that immigrants contribute relatively little to Australian development, but congregate instead where they can benefit from the amenities of the cities—a misunderstanding curiously comparable to one of the basic grievances of Australian separatists, such as have been discussed above. One interesting associated circumstance is that some evidence suggests that many of the immigrants settling in rural areas have in fact replaced Australians departing for the cities.

However, even though there is a high degree of general accord between the distribution pattern of immigrants and the distribution pattern of Australians in general, the accord is not perfect. Significant differences exist between the two patterns. A number of these differences may be explained in terms of the attractive force for immigrants of specific regions. Full understanding of the operation of this factor must depend on the understanding of certain characteristics of immigrants in general, and of immigrants to Australia in particular. A primary characteristic of immigrants anywhere is their initial mobility. They are not normally tied to any specific place within the recipient country by vested family, economic or social interests, as by contrast are members of the native-born population. Moreover, the possibly primary incentive of a newly-landed immigrant is an economic one—the desire for a job. Manifestly, therefore, in respect of the location he takes up the immigrant might be expected to respond more readily than the indigene to the simple motive of economic opportunity. In short, immigrants might be expected to settle in the greatest numbers where the job opportunities offer. This tendency is reinforced in Australia by the contract system, which has to a large degree governed the initial settlement of assisted non-British immigrants. In return for their assisted passages, many immigrants bind themselves to take employment as directed by the Australian Government for the first two years of their residence in Australia. They are directed

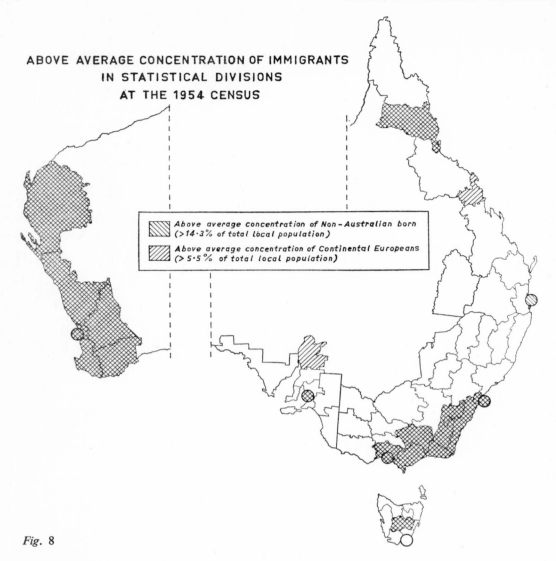

ABOVE AVERAGE CONCENTRATION OF IMMIGRANTS
IN STATISTICAL DIVISIONS
AT THE 1954 CENSUS

Above average concentration of Non-Australian born
(>14·3% of total local population)

Above average concentration of Continental Europeans
(>5·5% of total local population)

Fig. 8

into employment of national importance, such as developmental projects, and to those industries, such as the building trades and metallurgical industries, where the labour shortage (as a consequence both of the relatively unpleasant nature of the work or of the rate of expansion of the industry concerned) is the most acute.

The net result of these circumstances has been a pronounced tendency, some indication of which is given by Fig. 8, for immigrants to settle in greater-than-average concentrations in those locations where major developmental

works have been undertaken, or where economic expansion, and therefore employment opportunity, has been most pronounced.

One outstanding case in point has been the Illawarra region of New South Wales, where the markedly rapid expansion of the iron and steel industry at Port Kembla since the Second World War has produced in this and in associated industries a great number of employment opportunities, and has led to rapid urban growth on the Illawarra plain. This growth in turn has resulted in further development of employment opportunities in service industries.

Another instance is provided by the Southern Tablelands of New South Wales, where the Snowy Mountains water project (for hydro-electricity and for the further provision of irrigation waters in the Riverina) has involved major developmental works extending over a long period of time, and has involved heavy employment of immigrant labour. Immigrant concentration in these regions and in the Australian Capital Territory has been additionally reinforced by the development of the Federal capital, Canberra, which has again involved extensive construction work over a long period, with the inevitable extensive employment of immigrant labour.

Manifestly, it is also economic opportunity that has led to the pronounced tendency of immigrants to locate in the State capital cities. This handful of major cities represent the economic heart of Australia. They are the major industrial entities, and the areas of most rapid growth. The relative concentration of immigrants has been greater in the three southern mainland capitals of Melbourne, Adelaide, and Perth than it has in Sydney and Brisbane, suggesting that during the first post-war decade economic expansion was somewhat more rapid in the former group than in the latter. A further circumstance that accounts for some variations in immigrant settlement is what Rose refers to as the habitat preferences of specific national groups among the immigrants [4]. British immigrants, because of their linguistic and cultural affinities with Australians, and because of the absence of government direction, distributed themselves in a pattern closely resembling the Australian one. Other national groups displayed wide variations of pattern.

For example, northern and eastern Europeans (Germans, Latvians, Lithuanians and Ukrainians) tended to concentrate, at the 1954 census, in the industrial suburbs of the major cities, and also in such provincial industrial cities as Newcastle and Wollongong/Port Kembla. These people were for the most part the Displaced Persons who provided the bulk of the expanded industrial labour force during the earlier years of the post-war immigrant influx. Large numbers of them had been recruited as slave labourers in wartime German industry, and were therefore in a sense already trained to step into labouring jobs in Australian industry. Being for the most part the opposite of wealthy on arrival, they logically selected as districts of residence the industrial suburbs (including the slums) close to their employment, where accommodation was relatively cheap. Many of the Displaced Persons were single men—or at least unattached bachelors, widowers, or men who had lost track of their families or left them behind the iron curtain. Logical residences for such people were the residential hotels in the industrial suburbs. Fewer Mediterraneans were to be found in these locations by 1954, although subsequently, as the Displaced Persons pool of labour dried up, many Mediterraneans—notably Italians—were recruited for the same industrial purposes, and came to take up residence in similar locations. The exception to this was the Maltese, who as British subjects were very early given the opportunity of assisted migration; these were found in large numbers, in the locations referred to. Indeed, at the time, 75 per cent of the Maltese in Australia lived in the industrial suburbs of Sydney and Melbourne.

Another tendency discernible at the 1954 census was for the small numbers of Austrians, Hungarians, and Czechs then in Australia to be concentrated in the inner city area and in high-density residential suburbs. These people were not for the most part post-war immigrants, but were refugees from Europe during the 1930s. They were middle-aged to elderly people, many of them at least modestly affluent, who tended to become apartment dwellers in the more affluent or cosmopolitan areas—for example, the Kings Cross/Potts Point area of Sydney—of the major cities.

Also to be found in inner city areas were some concentrations of Greeks, Italians and Maltese, who were mainly proprietors of inner-city fruit shops, milk bars, and the like, or who were concerned with wholesale trading in foodstuffs and therefore had connections with the city markets.

Few national groups show tendencies toward concentration in country service centres: the most prominent in this respect are the Dutch and the Greeks. In Queensland, 37 per cent, and in New South Wales 25 per cent of all Greeks lived in 1954 in country towns, their location being connected with their pronounced tendency towards participation in certain areas of retail trading—particularly fruit and vegetables retailing, milk bar trade, and the fish-and-chip trade. Virtually every country centre in eastern Australia has a small Greek community, usually an extended family, which appears to dominate these aspects of trading.

In rural habitats, only the Dutch and the Italians display any pronounced tendencies to settle. The Italians here constitute the special case, particularly in Queensland in their association with sugar cane growing. Many rural Italians were pre-war immigrants; Italian immigration in Queensland was specifically concerned with provision of labour for the cane-fields, to which the migrants came in large numbers, and to which they have continued to come since the war. Thus, 60 per cent of Italians in Queensland live in rural areas; of these, nine-tenths are located in the Cairns Statistical Division.

From the foregoing discussion it would appear that, for the most part, tendencies toward the clustering of immigrant groups in any given locality constitute responses to special conditions prevailing in the circumstances under which they migrated, rather than any specific tendency generated by the group itself to cluster together in alien communities. The exception to this generalization is provided by immigrants from Mediterranean Europe— Italians, Greeks, and Maltese. The overseas migrations of these nationalities have, both in Australia and elsewhere, been identified as manifesting tendencies towards chain migration. This circumstance is associated with social customs and with settlement tendencies prevailing in some parts, particularly in rural parts, of Mediterranean Europe. Much rural settlement in Southern Italy, Greece and Malta occurs on the extended-family village basis— the majority of families in any one village being related to one another. Moreover, within the limited family, ties tend to be somewhat stronger than in their western European or Australian counterparts, so that a considerable amount of intra- and inter-family mutual aid is a recognized part of the social system. This fact has produced certain consequences when overseas migration occurs, manifesting itself in the migration chain whereby, over a period of time, a substantial proportion of an extended-family village will eventually locate itself at one spot in the recipient country, where family mutual aid continues, either in the form of provision of accommodation or of financial assistance in setting up in one of the favoured retail businesses. For this reason, Mediterranean communities have been found to develop in inner city regions, in country towns, and in the Queensland cane-fields. To this extent, the fears of those who aim at assimilation in the first generation may be seen to have some ground.

In direct contrast stand the settlement tendencies manifested by immigrants from the Netherlands. In the cities, these tend to locate in the outer (and newer) suburbs, in a fashion similar to that of the newly-adult or newly-married among the Australian community. This practice ensures more dispersion than would location in the inner city. The Dutch also locate in country towns and in rural areas, where they replace Australians who drift to the cities. In short, the Dutch community is dispersed. The reasons are not fully known, but some pointers exist. First, coming from a northwestern European community, the Dutch have a cultural background much more akin to that of Australians than is that of many other national immigrant groups. All Dutch are literate, most are fluent in English, and some arrive with modest capital. They are therefore able to locate much more readily according to Australian patterns than are many other groups. In addition, the Netherlands Government maintains emigration officers in Australia, and provides various other forms of assistance to assimilation, so that built-in tendencies and some specific pressures encourage the Dutch migrants to disappear into the Australian community—a somewhat contrary tendency to that manifested by the Mediterraneans.

Conclusion

This essay has dealt with a sample comprising two aspects of Australia's internal political geography. There are many other aspects not touched upon, some of them closely related. For example, the new-states problem can lead to consideration of a variety of other problems concerning the States within the federation, such as the effective role in the present age of State borders as barriers to intercourse between States, the extent to which States constitute real political entities, and so forth. In connection with immigrant settlement, far more needs to be known about the impact of different national groups upon many aspects of Australian society such as religion, electoral patterns, the growth and functions of the primate cities, the decentralization issue, and so forth. In addition, problems in external political geography, not touched upon in this essay, also exist, in connection with such matters as Australia's relations with Asia, fishing rights on Australia's continental shelf, Australia's presence in New Guinea, and many others.

It would be substantially true to say that, because political geography is a somewhat neglected field of research in Australia, many of these topics have simply not been investigated. There is room for many more research workers than are at present engaged in these fields.

REFERENCES

1. MOODIE, A. E. *The Geography Behind Politics.* Hutchinson University Library Series, *22*, London, 7 and 57.
2. A full discussion of this is to be found in WOOLMINGTON, E. R. (1966) *A spatial approach to the measurement of support for the separatist movement in northern New South Wales.* University of New England, Department of Geography Monograph Series, *2*, Armidale.
3. ROBINSON, V. L. (1960) *Australia, New Zealand and the South-west Pacific.* University of London Press, London.
4. ROSE, A. J. (1958) The Geographical Pattern of European Immigration in Australia. *Geographical Review, 48*, 510–527.

Index

N